CURRENT ASPECTS OF EXOBIOLOGY

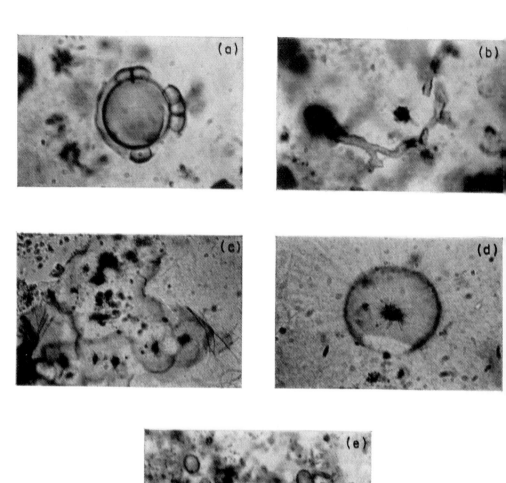

Photomicrographs of thin sections of Gunflint chert showing optical properties of organic structures in transmitted white light of 3200°K intensity (Fig. 5, Chapter III).

CURRENT ASPECTS OF EXOBIOLOGY

Edited by

G. MAMIKUNIAN
M. H. BRIGGS

Jet Propulsion Laboratory
Pasadena, California

SYMPOSIUM PUBLICATIONS DIVISION

PERGAMON PRESS

OXFORD · LONDON · EDINBURGH · NEW YORK

PARIS · FRANKFURT

Pergamon Press Ltd., Headington Hill Hall, Oxford
4 & 5 Fitzroy Square, London W.1

Pergamon Press (Scotland) Ltd., 2 & 3 Teviot Place, Edinburgh 1

Pergamon Press Inc., 122 East 55th St., New York 22, N.Y.

Pergamon Press GmbH, Kaiserstrasse 75, Frankfurt-am-Main

First edition 1965

Library of Congress Catalog Card No. 64–25625

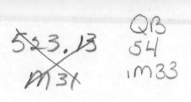

CONTENTS

PREFACE

"Why may not every one of these stars or suns have as great a retinue as our sun, of planets, with their moons, to wait upon them? . . . They must have their plants and animals, nay and their rational creatures too, and those as great admirers, and as diligent observers of the heavens as ourselves . . ."

CHRISTIAN HUYGENS

THERE is a large statistical probability that many presently undetectable planets exist throughout the universe which have environments capable of sustaining life. Harlow Shapley of Harvard concludes that perhaps one star in a million has a planet that meets all the necessary conditions. Since there are 10^{11} stars in our galaxy, this implies that there must be 100,000 planets in the Milky Way capable of supporting higher organisms. If one wishes to include the entire universe, consisting of perhaps 10^{22} stars, Shapley's estimate gives a total of 10^{16} habitable planets.

The probability that a certain percentage of these planets harbor life is also large. Abiogenic chemical synthesis and organic cosmochemical synthesis can occur whenever the conditions are favorable. Su-Shu Huang of the Princeton Institute of Advanced Study re-examined this question in great detail, concluding that 1 or 2% of all stars may at one time or another support intelligent life. Unfortunately, astronomical distances are so enormous that the probability of any two life forms making contact is exceedingly small. However, within a solar system such as our own, it seems likely that an intelligent life form would devise a means of bridging interplanetary space and examining other members of the system for the presence of life (at any stage of evolutionary development).

We are now in the initial stages of this kind of exploration. Presumably, manned expeditions to the planets will yield a maximum of information, but prior to such an undertaking, much valuable data can be obtained by the use of unmanned probes (fly-bys, orbiters, and landers). Before setting out on the search for extraterrestrial life, one must define life itself, the possible origins, the recognizable parameters, the measurable properties (be they chemical, physical, or biological), and the resolvable components of life; and, finally, one must be able to construct a reasonable and acceptable hypothesis for pre-life (abiotic synthesis of organic matter) and post-life (degradation of biogenic organic matter) characteristics and order. The living state represents a composite system in dynamic balance with its environment (thermodynamically, metabolically, and physically). It seems, then, that the question of the detection and acknowledgment of extraterrestrial life (as we study and comprehend terrestrial life) hinges on the degree of development of comparative planetary biochemistry and on our own understanding of the basic question concerning the dynamic state of terrestrial life and its origin. But the problem of the origin of terrestrial life still presents great difficulties, and even the most satisfactory form of review of the extensive and very stimulating literature would seem to be a purely formal approach, aimed only at the main question, "How did life originate?" It is therefore clear from the outset that the answer to the problem of extraterrestrial life must obtain its embryonic conception and development in terrestrial biological laboratories along terrestrial biochemical concepts.

Biology outside the terrestrial environment has been named "exobiology" by Professor Joshua Lederberg of Stanford University, while others prefer the term "cosmobiology" to denote the biology of the solar system, the galaxy, and even of extragalactic systems. Clearly, the search for extraterrestrial life forms is the most challenging of the scientific aspects of space exploration today, and probably will be for generations to follow. The investigation of the planets in the foreseeable future to obtain physical measurements and other scientific data is only a prelude to the development of a formula which will answer a few simple questions: Is extraterrestrial life possible? Does it prevail today in spite of the cosmological and geochemical processes that the planet has undergone and the fractionations which may still take place? Is it communicable to our level of intelligence? What correlations can be drawn, if any, with respect to our own origin and evolution?

Immediate difficulties become apparent in any method or approach, since life cannot be measured or defined in quantum-mechanical terms. The dynamic balance of life, including the phenomenon of reproduction, the stoichiometry of the organic constituent of the cell, and the disproportionation at its terminal stages, is still not completely elucidated. Our present knowledge suffers the lack of facts and theories available in the physical and mathematical sciences.

Life presents a great diversity of characteristics. It is constant but changing. It is simple in certain respects, yet complex in others. It flourishes but then degenerates. Life is continuous, but few of its biochemical constituents are preserved. How, then, can we abandon the parameters of terrestrial life that we have yet to comprehend and embark in search of an unknown extraterrestrial life? Or can we safely presume that the gross parameters of life are duplicated independently on other planets – and perhaps in our galaxy – giving rise to extraterrestrial life? Must this extraterrestrial life form be similar in its biochemical composition to our own? What are the probabilities that it is identical in its biochemical pathways, functions, and order? Having recognized extraterrestrial life, are we scientifically prepared to accept and understand its biochemistry and physiology? What might be its particular ecology? The answers to all of these questions must await the development of exobiology or cosmobiology to the level of a scientific discipline.

Like some other new branches of knowledge, exobiology has been created and formed at a junction, so to speak, of a number of scientific disciplines. Aside from the various biological sciences, it makes extensive use of the achievements of physics, chemistry, astronomy, geophysics, aerodynamics, radio-engineering, and many others. Therefore, the first characteristic of exobiology which distinguishes it appreciably from the biological disciplines created long ago is its inherent connection with other fields of natural and physical sciences; the second is its youth. This fact lends the unique quality of newness, which is the source of creative ideas, bold search, and methodical inventiveness for scientists devoting themselves to the problem of cosmobiology.

Despite its youth, exobiology has created and is continuing to create specific methods of investigation which are fundamentally different from routine laboratory or field biology methods. A striking example is the diversified use of biological radiotelemetering and the new approach to biological experiments accomplished automatically by specific instruments according to an assigned program.

It would be impossible to encompass all the areas of interest constituting the subject matter of exobiology in the present volume; however, the philosophy, scientific approach, and related research problems are covered. Most of the chapters were presented at a symposium, *Current Research in Exobiology,* held on February 26, 27, and 28, 1963, at the Jet Propulsion Laboratory. Papers presented by B. Nagy, E. Shneour, and R. Young at the Symposium and the scheduled paper of G. Kuiper were unfortunately not available for publication.

Selection of the chapters was the sole responsibility of the Editors. The contents of the chapters, with the exception of guiding suggestions, however, were left to the discretion of the individual authors.

The Editors would like to acknowledge their indebtedness to Dr. William Pickering and Dr. Frank Goddard of the Jet Propulsion Laboratory and to Dr. Freeman Quimby and Dr. Orr Reynolds of the Biosciences Program, Office of the National Aeronautics and Space Administration, Washington, D.C., for their interest in and support of the Symposium proceedings. We are grateful to Professor Melvin Calvin of the University of California, Berkeley, and Professor Edward Anders of the University of Chicago for their many helpful comments and suggestions in the course of the preparation of the manuscript. We would also like to express our appreciation to Dr. Robert Meghreblian, Dr. Hadley Ford, and our colleagues at the Jet Propulsion Laboratory for their constant encouragement and guidance in undertaking the Symposium.

Special thanks are due Mr. Irl Newlan and Mr. John Kempton of the Technical Information Section at JPL for their tireless efforts and patience in bringing the proceedings of the Symposium into a collected volume and to Mr. Thomas Moore and Mrs. Margaret Barry of the Library for their research on the references for the Bibliography.

Finally, we are deeply grateful to and appreciative of Mrs. Dorris Wallenbrock for her immense help in the preparation of the entire volume. Her constant efforts and willingness to guide the manuscript to fruition, even when it seemed hopeless at times, were a source of great inspiration and encouragement.

GREGG MAMIKUNIAN

Pasadena, California
June 1964

REFERENCES

THE scientific literature devoted to considerations of the existence of life on other planets and for the universe and to the origin of life is surprisingly large, and is scattered among a wide variety of books and journals in several languages. Most of this literature has been gathered together in the Bibliography presented at the end of this book. Also included is material on the physical and chemical nature of the planets that might be of relevance in assessing their suitability for supporting life and the stages of biopoesis.

The Bibliography is divided into four major sections, each covering one of the principal areas of interest. The sections, in turn, are subdivided into specific categories pertinent to each major topic. In the text, references to the Bibliography are indicated by the abbreviation *Ref.*, followed by the appropriate reference number.

In addition to the citations contained in the Bibliography, a list of references is presented at the end of each chapter. These lists cover literature specifically pertinent only to the respective chapters and not necessarily to the subject of exobiology in general and, in some instances, references omitted from the Bibliography for reasons of time or availability. In the text, these chapter-end references are indicated by superscript numbers.

INTRODUCTION: WHY EXOBIOLOGY?

J. R. VALLENTYNE

Department of Zoology
Cornell University
Ithaca, N. Y.

We need scarcely add that the contemplation in
natural science of a wider domain than the actual
leads to a far better understanding of the actual.

EDDINGTON, *The Nature of*
the Physical World

EXPERIMENT

AT the close of World War II, H. B. Phillips published a short essay, "On the Nature of Progress", in the *American Scientist,*[1] quite refreshing for its directness, wit, and common sense. In it, he related some past experiences in connection with a life-long habit of collecting ópinions on the future importance of certain current events. One of the first questions that he posed concerned the significance of automobiles, asked at a time when those objects were still referred to as horseless carriages. Though one might hopefully think that there would be a few souls in the universe with some intuition on the matter, the result was quite otherwise. He encountered only one person with any interest in the question at all, a professor of English who complained about the way people were pronouncing the word *automobile.*

As a result of this and similar experiences, Phillips soon began to wonder whether any real basis existed for predicting even the approximate significance of current events. "Here is the fundamental dilemma of civilization", he said, "Progress is the greatest thing there is; progress is going forward. Yet, there is serious doubt whether the way forward is known, and doubt whether beyond a very brief interval any forward direction is determinate."

But Phillips also noted that the problem was an old one; that it had been faced and solved by organisms in their evolution. The basis for progress in the evolutionary case had been through the production of new forms by mutation and recombination, both largely chance processes. He then went on to liken this to learning by trial and error—i.e. by experiment—asking how it was that Aristotle's works on government can be read today with profit, whereas his works on science are worthless in anything but an historical sense. He reasoned that the explanation did not lie in an inherently greater complexity of government on the one hand than matter on the other, but rather in the fact that experiments are much more easily carried out with matter than they are with governments. The key to finding the direction of progress lay in experiment.

The above remarks (as the author himself stressed) are so obvious that even the most casual reader must surely question their necessity here. But perhaps they are worth the repetition just because the point is so obvious that it is easily forgotten. In fact, it has been forgotten by most of those who have pronounced a verdict on exobiology.

Several scientific friends and colleagues, for example, have at one time or another stated in my presence that exobiology (space science in general, for that matter) is an utter waste of both time and money. The typical comment is: "Why go off into space when there are so many problems demanding solution here on Earth?" Simpson[2] has marshalled arguments for that point of view. At the opposite extreme lie some of the young optimists now passing through the universities who seem convinced that there is life on Mars and that we have only to go there to prove it.

The trouble with all this, of course, is that exobiology in particular and space science in general are costly ventures; and why should one spend large sums to obtain evidence that may not be worth the money spent? Is there a solution? If there is, it is surely not to avoid but rather to initiate experiments that will provide unequivocal answers to the questions asked. To adopt an attitude of no experiment would be to act like the manager of the small but thriving business concern who replied as follows when questioned about the need for research: "Why should we do research?... Times are good now.... We don't need research."

We must break with Phillips's logic now to consider just what the future significance of exobiology may be, at least insofar as one can approach the question at this time. Interest here is limited to the possible influence of exobiological discoveries on the science of biology, directly and indirectly, even though other results may be far more important in the long run.

POSSIBLE FINDINGS

Let us first consider several results that might be anticipated regarding the nature and occurrence of extraterrestrial living matter, assuming that samples of any extant or extinct extraterrestrial life can be studied *in situ* or transported to Earth in their natural states for detailed study.

Of all conceivable exobiological findings that could be anticipated, the most informative will undoubtedly pertain to the chemical composition of living matter, since they will focus attention most sharply on the fundamental nature and mechanisms of biological processes. The traditional biological topics of form, function, variation, and adaptation will undoubtedly benefit from the new knowledge, but the gain will be limited to an extension of currently held concepts for the most part. D'Arcy Thompson,[3] and before him Sir George Bell, for example, pointed out that the forms of organisms on Earth are very intimately related to the mass and dimensions of the Earth through the force of gravity. In this sense, exobiological studies along traditional lines may tell more of the nature of exobiological conditions than of any inherent properties of living matter.

The question considered here is whether conceivable exobiological results can be arranged in order of scientific importance. Within the context of the limitations outlined earlier, such an attempt will now be made, but only by considering possible results in a general sense.

1. The most significant result would be to find some type of *living matter radically different* from that of the Earth. One might cite under this category supposed organisms with a structure and metabolic machinery based on silicon rather than on carbon; or forms with an ammonia-based rather than a water-based machinery and metabolism. (One should note in the former case, however, that fully aerobic silicon metabolizers would be required to exhale quartz.)

These are not absurd possibilities; however, they cannot be discussed intelligently at the present time, since no such types of living matter have been found or constructed to date. The point is that if they were found, the discovery would generate many new concepts in the study of living matter.

2. The next most significant discovery would be a type of extraterrestrial *life almost identical* to that of the Earth in composition and function. One could even argue that such a finding would outweigh (1) in importance, providing an independent origin could be proved (e.g. on the basis of genetic code-unravelling techniques). Since current theory negates the possibility of such similarity among groups of independent origin (Ref. 1166), the scientific implications of such a discovery would be so immense as to cause an immediate collapse of most currently held concepts on the mechanism of biopoesis. But there would, of course, be nothing much to learn from the exobiological material that could not be learned equally well from Earth forms.

3. A third possibility would be the discovery of *organisms generally similar* to those of the Earth in composition and function *but differing* in several important details. This is usually considered to be the most probable type of extraterrestrial living matter, if any at all does exist.

In all cases, one would expect to find organisms with water as their most abundant molecule and with a carbon-based metabolism and machinery.

At the extreme end of this spectrum, one might consider organisms lacking polypeptides, with biocatalysts of a nonprotein nature; forms lacking nucleic acids, in which the genetic material might be composed of polymers of another sort; or perhaps organisms in which phosphorus is a nonessential element. Somewhat less drastic would be the discovery of organisms with proteins composed of D-amino acids or polysaccharides with only L-sugars but otherwise similar to Earth forms; or photoauto-trophs in which chlorophylls of any sort are lacking. At the lower end of the spectrum, one could consider organisms requiring "unusual" elements (e.g. helium, argon, chromium, or arsenic), or possessing "uncommon" attributes (e.g. utilization of low-wavelength ultraviolet light in photo-synthesis or with cellular receptors for radio waves or gamma-radiation).

When one comes right down to it, the main reasons why life generally similar to that on Earth is considered to be the most probable in the universe are: (a) one representative is known to occur and (b) so many chance phenomena were probably involved in the original evolution of that representative that the evolution of an exact duplicate elsewhere is unlikely.

But there are other compelling reasons beyond these. It is likely no accident, for example, that there is a closer resemblance between the elementary chemical composition (helium excluded) of organisms and galaxies than there is between that of organisms and the material in the Earth's crust with which they are in direct contact.[4] The sort of logic that eternally haunts one in this regard has been best expressed by Henderson (Ref. 1106) in his *Fitness of the Environment* (when read following George Wald's directions) and by Lotka (Ref. 1132). These authors rightly pointed out that the cosmic abundance of elements, the properties of water, and the chemistry of carbon compounds may go a long way toward defining the composition, function, and evolution of life in the universe.

4. Depending on the circumstances, the occurrence of *extinct life only* on some planet or satellite could be of considerable interest, though as compared to (1), (2), and (3) this category could provide no great biological insight because of the lack of functional material for study. Discussions of some possible cases of this sort are presented by Gilvarry (Chapter V) and Staplin (Chapter II).

If life were passing toward complete extinction on a planet, the excel-lence of preservation should increase as the number of major taxa declined. Everything now known about community metabolism on an ecological scale would demand such a result because of the partition of metabolic functions among members of diverse taxa in ecological communities. Preservation would also be enhanced if the factor initially responsible for extinction also favored preservation (for example, increasing desiccation or decreasing temperature). Carnivores and herbivores of appreciable size would likely succumb early in the extinction process, leaving their own remains in a successively better state of preservation. If any analogy can be made to the Earth, then protistans or protistan-like forms would be expected to be the last survivors. Even the ability of the total protistan community to carry out complete decomposition processes would become more and more limited with time as successive taxa declined toward extinction. The over-all state of preservation would be at least equivalent to that found in anaerobic, desert, and ice-bound regions of the Earth. Whether autotrophs or heterotrophs would be the last survivors is a moot question.

With the development of improved methods and knowledge in the field of paleobiochemistry[5] and an environment of good preservation, considerable reconstruction of original structure and function could be made from extraterrestrial fossil materials. Discrimination between materials belonging to categories (1), (2), and (3) might well be possible on the basis of paleobiochemical analyses and reconstruction.

5. The main difficulty inherent in the hypothesis that *no life ever existed* would be in proving the point; but if accepted, it could be of considerable historical and biogeochemical interest. Such a planet, if it resembled the Earth in other respects, would provide an instructive control to which the Earth could be compared. Evidence of some early stages in biopoesis might be found that could never be expected to survive had life evolved later. Of course, nothing could arise from such studies that would materially affect the course of the biological sciences *per se*.

STABILITY FIELD OF LIVING MATTER

At one time or another, various authors have attempted to describe the physico-chemical limits of life, occasionally on a physiological basis but more often in an ecological sense. These limits pertain to organisms evolved on Earth. We have no conception of where they may lie for life on a cosmic scale. Also, the subject has traditionally been approached haphazardly by isolated and unconnected investigations made with some other purpose in mind, often little more than the study of a biological novelty. It is to be hoped that comprehensive attempts to describe the physiological and environmental stability fields of living matter may be among the fundamental contributions of exobiology. Attention here is devoted primarily to a consideration of the environmental field. A description of the physiological field would, however, be of considerably greater biological interest. The data listed in Table 1 are taken from one of the more recent summaries available on the environmental stability field of living matter on Earth.[6]

TABLE 1. Environmental limits of temperature, Eh (at the prevailing pH), pH, hydrostatic pressure, salinity, and activity of water for growth and reproduction of microorganisms[6]

Factor	Lower limit	Upper limit
Temperature	−18°C (fungi, bacteria)	104°C (sulfate-reducing bacteria under 1000-atm hydrostatic pressure)
Eh	−450 mv at pH 9.5 (sulfate-reducing bacteria)	+850 mv at pH 3 (iron bacteria)
pH	0 (*Acontium velatum*, fungus D, *Thiobacillus thiooxidans*)	13? (*Plectonema nostocorum*)
Hydrostatic pressure	Essentially 0	1400 atm (deep-sea bacteria)
Salinity	Double-distilled water (heterotrophic bacteria)	Saturated brines (*Dunaliella*, halophilic bacteria, etc.)
$a_w{}^a$	0.65–0.70 (*Aspergillus glaucus*)	Essentially 1.0

$^a a_w$ (activity of water) $= p/p_0$, where p is the vapor pressure of water in the material under study and p_0 is the vapor pressure of pure water at the same temperature.

One of the unfortunate limitations of present data in regard to the environmental stability field is that few serious attempts have ever been made to study two or more environmental factors acting simultaneously in extremes. The need for such an approach was probably first demonstrated in connection with temperature–salinity relationships, where it has been common knowledge that many bacteria and fungi can grow and reproduce in saline environments at temperatures well below 0°C.[7,8] Zernow[9] also stressed the ecological significance of saline environments in relation to the occurrence of life at low temperatures. Quite recently, an Antarctic body of water (Don Juan Pond) has been discovered that harbors an apparently distinctive microflora existing at temperatures down to −23°C and perhaps even lower.[10]

In connection with pressure–temperature relationships, ZoBell and Morita[11] and others have noted the basic antagonism between pressure and temperature, in that forms grown under high hydrostatic pressure possess higher temperature optima than pertain at lower pressures. The highest temperature ever reported for the growth and reproduction of any organism is for a sulfate-reducing bacterium isolated from several thousand meters depth in the lithosphere and cultured under 1000-atm hydrostatic pressure at 104°C.[12]

Another interesting case that has not been examined in detail is that of *Cyanidium caldarium*, an alga known to occur in acid hot springs. It has been cultured in 1 N H_2SO_4,[13] but apparently, no study of the upper lethal temperature in acid solution has ever been made to determine the combined effects of high temperature and acidity on the hydrolysis of polymers, etc.

Two special points are worth stressing in relation to the action of thermal energy on organisms. The first of these concerns the thermo-lability of proteins. It is often suggested that the upper lethal temperature limits for living matter are determined by the properties of enzymes. This seems to imply that the effective control is imposed by something inherent in the chemical structure of enzymes themselves. But those who base their thinking on such a logic forget that proteins and enzymes are products of evolution and that they have been formed by organisms living on an Earth that has an average surface temperature close to 13°C. What the thermal denaturation properties of proteins might be in organisms living on planets with considerably higher or lower average temperatures is quite a different question.

The second point concerns statements made to the effect that the limits of water-based life in the universe will probably nowhere exceed the temperature limits of 0 and 100°C. What the authors of such statements actually mean, of course, is that living organisms as we know them are quite unlikely to grow and reproduce at temperatures precluding the existence of water in the liquid state. But these are two quite different statements, the former referring to pure water under 1 atm of pressure and the latter to a much more general set of circumstances. For example, in the presence of dissolved substances of high solubility and low particle weight, water will not freeze until quite low temperatures are reached. In the case of Don Juan Pond, Antarctica, an extreme example, the water contains 474,000 ppm of dissolved substances, mostly $CaCl_2$, and does not freeze until a temperature of −45°C is reached.[10] On other planetary systems, it is conceivable that mixtures of ammonia and water, glycerol and water, etc., could occur as natural antifreezes, permitting life at temperatures well below 0°C. In relation to the upper temperature limit for living matter, it should also be noted that if the atmospheric pressure of the Earth at sea level were one-tenth or ten times its actual value, water would not boil at 100°C but rather at 46°C in the former case and 180°C in the latter. Thus, the conception that life is inherently limited to temperatures in the range of 0 to 100°C is just one more in a long list of geocentric fictions created by the human mind.

BIOPOESIS

Ever since Oparin and Haldane provided the insight on which modern views of biopoesis are based, much attention has been given to the appealing question of how life originated on Earth. Several workers (e.g. Baly[14]) initiated studies on the production of organic compounds under conditions probably similar to those of the primitive Earth. But it was really only ten years ago, with the work of Miller (Ref. 1280), that biopoesis came to be recognized as a discipline amenable to experimental study; and even then, only in its chemical aspects. Oró (Chapter I) and others have since expanded this approach using a variety of cosmochemically reasonable reactants as starting materials. As a result, there is now a legitimate discipline of experimental organic cosmochemistry, a name that would have caused consternation only a few decades ago. Although much remains to be done in the chemical aspects of biopoesis, it is clear that what is really needed now is an *experimental organic cosmobiology* with some reasonable degree of geological plausibility.[15] It is quite unclear at the present time exactly where the insight for this new approach is going to come from.

To date, the subject of biopoesis has really been more attractive philosophically than experimentally. This is exemplified by the fact that many still find it more convenient to treat the subject as a hobby than as a profession. The mechanism of transformation of nonliving into living matter is, however, a fundamental problem that demands scientific explanation. Its solution will be no less epoch-making in the twentieth century than was the nineteenth-century solution to the question of how species originated. One would hope, however, that the discussion may be a little less heated.

It is widely assumed that some sort of selection process was operative in the early stages of biopoesis, and several models of early eobionts have been proposed ranging from organic-clay complexes (Ref. 1030) and self-reproducing nucleic acid–protein preparations or their primitive counterparts (several proponents) to coacervates (Ref. 1149) and proteinoid microspheres (Fox and Yuyama[16] and elsewhere). None of the models produced so far is very attractive, but until something better is proposed, their study must be pushed to logical conclusions, whatever they may be. Some kind of model with an inefficient but readily discernible mechanism of reproduction built into it from the start will probably have to be accepted in the long run. The reason for this is that the eobiontic "fight" for survival against other eobionts and against chemical thermodynamics would be facilitated in all respects if there were some mechanism perpetuating accumulated information (genetic and/or learned) by reproduction. Reproduction is a *sine qua non* for the origin and persistence of the delicate architectural design of living matter. To some, this may seem equivalent to starting the process of biopoesis with life itself; but surely, once the notion of biopoesis is accepted, one is also obliged to admit the former existence of systems which, though best described in over-all terms as nonliving, nevertheless would possess many if not all of the characteristics of living matter though only on very primitive levels. The sterile female is not dead simply because she cannot reproduce herself; nor is the crystal of the tobacco mosaic virus a living organism merely because it can reproduce itself in a suitable environment. Definitions and terminologies in this interregion must be flexible in the years ahead if they are to serve rather than direct thought.

Improved sophistications in experimental design must also be anticipated in future experiments on all aspects of biopoesis, if for no other reason than that they have been lacking in the past. When Miller (Ref. 1280) first reported the production of amino acids on sparking mixtures of primitive Earth gases, many observers seemed to believe that most if not all biologically important monomers, and some polymers as well, could be formed within the confines of a single vessel. But nothing could be further from expectation. At any given time on the primitive Earth, there must surely have been a series of environments E_1, E_2, E_3, ..., each critical for some stage in the perpetuation of the system, whether it be for populations of molecules, eobionts, or organisms. Different birth and death rates (production vs. decomposition rates for chemicals) must have characterized each environment. Environments favorable for production could be quite unfavorable for survival, and vice versa. This is even seen in Miller's original experiment: the synthesis of aminonitriles occurs in the spark with subsequent hydrolysis to amino acids and preservation of amino acids in the aqueous phase. In fact, in all experiments utilizing physical energy sources (sparks, ultraviolet light, heat) for the production of amino acids, the region of greatest synthesis is also the region of most rapid destruction. The accumulation of organic compounds thus depends on a rapid transfer of the product to locations more favorable for survival. Fox has recognized this need for heterogeneity in his studies on the formation of proteinoids and microspheres (e.g. Fox and Yuyama[16]).

All model experiments in abiogenesis to date have been naively simple in a geochemical sense in that they have been lacking in the variety of inorganic substances that could be expected in soils and water bodies of the primitive Earth. Apart from C, H, O, N, and P, the elements most likely to have participated in the abiogenesis of organic compounds and in the structure and metabolism of eobionts are Fe and S. Both are quite abundant geochemically; both would have occurred on the primitive Earth in forms (Fe^{++}, $S^=$, S^0) that could act as energy sources for metabolism on oxidation (from traces of oxygen or ozone formed by the absorption of ultraviolet light by water); and both form relatively insoluble compounds (ferric hydroxide, vivianite, magnetite, hydrotroilite, etc.) that are variously colored or black and thus capable of absorbing visible as well as untraviolet light. Likewise, both elements are subject to geochemically reversible changes in solubility and oxidation state, depending on local conditions. Two additional relationships are noteworthy: (1) the ability of ferric hydroxide to act as a collecting agent for organic compounds in solution and (2) the lipoidal and vulcanization properties of elemental sulfur. It is surprising that even though cyanides have been extensively used in model abiogenetic systems, no one has considered the possible geochemical influences of metallic ions either in lowering effective cyanide concentrations or in causing the formation of colored precipitates or complexes. The inclusion of Fe, S, and P in model experiments is a requisite for the reconstruction of the events of biopoesis.

TIME· AND BIOPOESIS

Knowledge accumulated during the present century has tended to decrease the estimates of time available for the origin of life on Earth. Paleontological discoveries (Chapter III by Barghoorn) and isotope fractionation analysis[17, 18] indicate that living matter was almost certainly present when some of the oldest rocks of the Earth were deposited. Sagan (Ref. 1179) has even gone so far as to divine "a more narrowly circumscribed estimate... that life arose on Earth 4.2 ± 0.2 × 10⁹ years ago." Further extrapolation raises an interesting question: Could life have originated within the course of a very short geological period of time, say, 10^6 years? Could even Sagan's provocative, and perhaps intuitive, guess be an underestimate? The question, of course, begs a definition of life. But assuming that some sort of definition based on consensus can ultimately be arrived at, the question still remains as to whether the time required for biopoesis might not be considerably shorter than is currently thought. Are there selective factors that would favor, or even necessitate, a rapid transformation from nonliving to living matter under geologically reasonable conditions?

Three factors might be considered in this regard. There is the general case of some possible set of environmental factors requisite for biopoesis, whose probability of occurrence decreased with increasing time after the origin of the Earth. The over-all concentration of radioactive nuclides or a decreased rate of formation of certain essential components of the primitive soup might be taken as possible examples. Secondly, it is conceivable that too much chemical evolution in the environment (as distinct from that in eobionts) might hinder the origin of life in the same sense in which Haldane[19] suggested that free enzymes could be a danger to the whole process of biopoesis. It seems important that any catalytically active molecules produced in the environment by chemical evolution be incorporated into eobionts, where they could be used to advantage in energy transfer and utilization. If left free in the environment, they might impede biopoesis by preventing the abiogenetic production of highly ordered macromolecules. Finally, one might argue that there are two ways in which populations of eobionts could be adapted for survival: (1) by making their "houses" strong so that they would need repair only occasionally or (2) by repairing the "houses" often so that they would not have to be strong. Over limited times and conditions, good arguments could be presented for both (1) and (2); but as the length of time increased, forms built on plan (2) would undoubtedly win out in the struggle for survival simply because they would be "pre-adapted" to reproduction. Allen[20] has discussed much the same topic in relation to thermophilic adaptations in microorganisms.

FINAL REMARKS

There is a tendency today to assume that the ability to evolve into life may be one of the properties of matter. George Wald put this very nicely in his introduction to Henderson's *The Fitness of the Environment* (Ref. 1106) when he said that "a physicist is the atom's way of knowing about atoms". However, the fact remains that the Earth is still the only place in the Universe where life is known to occur with certainty. Given such a discrepancy between theory and knowledge, the only possible scientific approach is to gather new knowledge by any and all means available. And that is just about what is going on in exobiology today. At present the subject matter is diffuse, tenuous, and highly speculative; but at the same time it is the beginning of a logical approach to what is perhaps the most significant historical question that any civilization could ask – the origin, nature, and history of life in the Universe.

The first of its kind, this volume gives a good cross-section of current approaches to exobiology. Radically new interpretations are given to old data in some of the chapters; in others there is a full exposition of disciplines that have emerged only within the past ten years. The book will be valuable for these reasons. The reader who approaches it without undue bias for its factual content and ideas will have much profit in store for him providing that he realizes, as biophysicists did some years ago, that it is a hindrance to worry about the definitions of young subjects. Given time, exobiology will define itself.

Biopoesis on a cosmic scale may indeed be something like making a cake. If the right ingredients are mixed in the right proportions and baked for the right time at the right temperature, only one thing can result—a nice, edible cake of some sort. The variety produced will depend on the ingredients, their relative amounts, and the sequence in which they are mixed. But if one of the essential ingredients is missing or the proportions are too unusual, if the temperature is too high or the baking too long, then one ends up not with cake, but with dough, coke, or a thin crust of salt.

REFERENCES

1. PHILLIPS, H. B., On the Nature of Progress, *American Scientist*, vol. 33 (1945), pp. 253–9.
2. SIMPSON, G. G., The Nonprevalence of Humanoids, *Science*, vol. 143 (1964), pp. 769–75.
3. THOMPSON, D'ARCY W., *On Growth and Form*, Cambridge: Cambridge University Press (1942).
4. HUTCHINSON, G. E., The Biogeochemistry of Aluminum and of Certain Related Elements, *Quarterly Review of Biology*, vol. 18 (1943), pp. 1–29, 128–53, 242–62, 331–63.
5. *Organic Geochemistry*, ed. by I. A. BREGER, London: Pergamon Press, Ltd. (1963).
6. VALLENTYNE, J. R., Environmental Biophysics and Microbial Ubiquity, *Annals of the New York Academy of Sciences*, vol. 108 (1963), pp. 342–52.
7. BEDFORD, R. H., Marine Bacteria of the Northern Pacific Ocean, *Contributions to Canadian Biology and Fisheries*, vol. 7, No. 34 (1933), pp. 433–8.
8. ZOBELL, C. E., Microbiological Activities at Low Temperatures With Particular Reference to Marine Bacteria, *Quarterly Review of Biology*, vol. 9 (1934), pp. 460–6.
9. ZERNOW, S. A., On Limits of Life at Negative Temperatures, *Comptes Rendus Hebdomadaires des Séances de l'Académie des Sciences*, vol. 44 (1944), pp. 76–77.
10. MEYER, G. H., MORROW, M. B., WYSS, O., and LITTLEPAGE, J. L., Antarctica: The Microbiology of an Unfrozen Saline Pond, *Science*, vol. 138 (1962), pp. 1103–4.
11. ZOBELL, C. E., and MORITA, R. Y., Barophilic Bacteria in Some Deep Sea Sediments, *Journal of Bacteriology*, vol. 73 (1956), pp. 563–8.
12. ZOBELL, C. E., Ecology of Sulfate Reducing Bacteria, *Producer's Monthly*, vol. 22, No. 7 (1958), pp. 12–29.
13. ALLEN, M. B., Studies With *Cyanidium caldarium*, an Anomalously Pigmented Chlorophyte, *Archiv für Mikrobiologie*, vol. 32 (1959), pp. 270–7.
14. BALY, E. C. C., *Photosynthesis*, New York: D. Van Nostrand Co., Inc. (1940).
15. ABELSON, P. H., Trends in Scientific Research, *Science*, vol. 143 (1964), pp. 218–23.
16. FOX, S. W., and YUYAMA, S., Abiotic Production of Primitive Protein and Formed Microparticles, *Annals of the New York Academy of Sciences*, vol. 108 (1963), pp. 487–94.
17. RANKAMA, K., Origin of Carbon in Some Early Precambrian Carbonaceous Slates From Southeastern Manitoba, Canada, *Geologiska Sällskapet i Finland, Suomen Geologinen Seurai*, No. 27 (1954), pp. 5–20.
18. HOERING, T. C., The Stable Isotopes of Carbon in the Carbonate and Reduced Carbon of Precambrian Sediments, *Carnegie Institution of Washington Yearbook No. 61*, Baltimore: Lord Baltimore Press, Inc. (1962), pp. 190–1.
19. HALDANE, J. B. S., Data Needed for a Blueprint of the First Organism, *The Origin of Prebiological Systems*, New York: Academic Press Inc. (In press).
20. ALLEN, M. B., Utilization of Thermal Energy by Living Organisms, *Comparative Biochemistry*, vol. 1, ed. by M. FLORKIN and H. S. MASON, New York: Academic Press Inc. (1960), pp. 487–514.

CHAPTER I

INVESTIGATION OF ORGANO-CHEMICAL EVOLUTION

J. J. ORÓ

Department of Chemistry, University of Houston, Houston, Texas

ORGANO-CHEMICAL EVOLUTION

Introduction

There are at least five main levels of complexity in the organization of matter at which processes of evolution are more or less clearly manifest. These levels include:

1. Elementary particles
2. Elements (e.g. nuclides and atoms)
3. Molecules (e.g. monomers, polymers, and crystals)
4. Aggregate systems (e.g. planets, stars, and galaxies)
5. Superordinated organic systems (e.g. living objects and living organisms)

The occurrence of evolutionary processes in populations of elements[1-5] (Ref. 36), stars,[6] galaxies,[7] and living organisms[8,9] has been fairly well documented. On the other hand, the serious study of evolutionary processes in populations of elementary particles[10] and of molecules is only now beginning to appear possible. This Chapter is concerned with some aspects of the evolution of organic molecules, in particular those molecules which are essential for the existence of living organisms. Since molecular evolution theory is not yet sufficiently advanced to allow the formulation and application of fundamental principles, only an essentially empirical approach can be followed at this time. The scope of this Chapter is limited to a description and interpretation of some astrophysical observations and experimental results of organic synthesis which have a bearing on the abiogenic formation of biochemical compounds. The formation of these compounds from very simple precursors has been observed to occur under conditions presumed to exist, or to have existed, in cosmic or terrestrial environments[11,12] (Refs. 1038, 1069, 1115, 1149, 1198, 1233, 1237, 1280, 1285, 1290, 1295, 1296).

13

Cosmic Abundance of Organogenic Elements

If we exclude helium, and possibly neon, the four most abundant elements in the universe are hydrogen, oxygen, carbon, and nitrogen.[13-16] In fact, hydrogen constitutes the bulk of the universe, and oxygen, carbon, and nitrogen are each several times more abundant than the next most prevalent element, silicon. It is of particular interest to observe that these four elements are precisely the four major constituent elements of proteins and of most of the organic substances present in living organisms.

Two other important elements, sulfur and phosphorus, which enter into the composition of proteins and nucleic acids, are much less ubiquitous in nature. Interestingly enough, however, their relative proportion in the living cell parallels roughly their relative cosmic abundance.[17] Moreover, if a comparison between the relative abundances of the first thirty-one elements in the cosmos and in living organisms is made, a general parallelism can be observed.[17] The occurrence of such a general correlation, even though certain minor discrepancies may exist, cannot be simply a fortuitous coincidence. Regardless of its cause, it is a remarkable fact that "the composition of living matter turns out to be a better sample of the universe than the dead Earth".[5]

Formation of Organogenic Elements

Hydrogen, carbon, nitrogen, and oxygen, together with helium, constitute a group of elements which are closely interrelated from a nucleo-genetic point of view. Hydrogen is supposed to be the most primordial chemical element in the universe, from which all the others are ultimately formed. The nuclear fusion of hydrogen by operation of the proton–proton cycle results in the formation of helium in young stars.[1,13] Helium "burning", the carbon–nitrogen cycle, and an alpha-particle capture process lead to the formation of carbon, nitrogen, and oxygen, respectively, in more evolved stars, particularly in the so-called carbon stars.[1,13]

It appears that carbon is the first of the light elements, after helium, to be stable at the stellar temperatures at which the helium burning process takes place. This stability, which probably reflects the internal symmetry of the carbon-12 nucleus in its ground state,[13] has important consequences which transcend nuclear chemistry. Not only carbon atoms accumulate in carbon stars, but so do (at the expense of carbon) the atoms of the next elements in the periodic system, nitrogen and oxygen, with which carbon so readily interacts. When such interactions occur in star atmospheres, in the inevitable presence of hydrogen, the end result is the formation of water, molecular hydrogen, nitrogen and oxygen, and the following six diatomic species: C_2, CN, CO, CH, NH, and OH.[13] The latter constitute perhaps the six most characteristic diatomic groups of organic compounds. In fact, by placing all the possible single, double, and triple bonds between the atoms of these diatomic combinations, one obtains the prototypes of the majority of functional groups described in organic chemistry. It is, therefore, tempting to speculate that within the symmetrical structure of the ordinary carbon nucleus lies not only the basis for the stability of this nuclide, but also perhaps a hidden explanation for the almost unique ability[18] of the resulting carbon atom to form, under appropriate conditions, a vast number of molecular combinations.

Very little can be said with regard to the formation of the ordinary nuclides of phosphorus and sulfur, except that the first is formed mainly from sodium, by a neutron capture process, and the second from neon, by an alpha-particle capture process.[1,2] Other thermonuclear reactions also lead to the formation of these elements.[3,4] The large abundance of neon and the more extensive occurrence of alpha-particle capture processes may explain the relatively higher abundance of sulfur as compared to phosphorus.

Distribution of Organogenic Elements

Hydrogen, carbon, nitrogen, and oxygen exist mainly as atoms and as homonuclear and heteronuclear diatomic combinations in the atmospheres of relatively cool stars,[13,19,20] including the Sun,[21] and in interstellar or circumstellar space.[19,20,22] The triatomic molecule, H_2O, is found in relatively large amounts in the atmospheres of carbon stars,[13] which have also been suggested as the sources of interstellar carbon grains or graphite particles.[23] Therefore, in line with the above discussion, these stars should be considered as primary sites of synthesis of the fundamental molecules which are the precursors of organic compounds.

More complex combinations of the above four elements have been detected in planets[24] (Refs. 104, 523, 692), comets,[20,25-28] and meteorites[29-33] (Refs. 848, 854, 858, 866, 878, 884, 893, 901, 927, 940, 947). Meteoritic dust appears to contain carbonaceous matter (Ref. 952), and gaseous emanations from geological igneous formations show the presence of C_1 to C_4 hydrocarbons of supposedly nonbiogenic origin.[34] Thus, it is evident that simple and complex compounds of carbon are found widely distributed in the universe. In principle, these compounds will exist wherever the prevailing temperatures are compatible with the stability of the bonds between carbon and the other elements. If the carbon-containing diatomic combinations C_2, CO, CN, and CH are considered, it is observed that their thermal stability ranges from the low temperatures of interstellar space to the relatively high temperatures prevailing above the surface of stars. In fact, equilibrium calculations show that such diatomic combinations can exist in the atmospheres of carbon stars at temperatures (3100 to 6000°K) at which some of the most thermally stable oxides, namely titanium and zirconium oxides, are generally dissociated into their metallic ions.[13]

The triatomic species, C_3,[27] C_2H,[35] and H_2O,[13] are also quite stable at high temperatures. The production of polycarbon molecules, or graphite grains, which has been calculated to amount to 5×10^{25} g per year per star, is presumed to take place readily at 2000°K.[23] Of course, the relative abundance of each di-, tri-, or polyatomic species depends on other factors besides temperature, such as the relative abundance of the constitutive elements, the C/O ratio, and the total hydrogen content of the stellar atmosphere.[13] Similar considerations should also be applicable to other cosmic environments. If the temperatures are low and the hydrogen content high, the hydrides of carbon, oxygen, and nitrogen may be expected to predominate.

Nitrogen is present in substantial amounts in the form of ammonia and other compounds in comets and in the atmospheres of the Jovian planets. Carbonaceous chondrites contain approximately 0.3% nitrogen,[32] probably in the form of ammonium salts and organic compounds. Terrestrial igneous rocks are also supposed to contain about twenty times more nitrogen, in the form of ammonium ions, than is present in the Earth's atmosphere.[36]

With regard to the distribution of phosphorus, it may be pointed out that this element has been detected in abundances 100 times higher than the cosmic average in a B star,[5] but in most other places it is found in small amounts. Iron meteorites contain phosphorus in the form of iron-nickel phosphide, one stony-iron meteorite contains it in the form of anhydrous magnesium sulfate,[37] and most of the other meteorites in the form of calcium and sodium phosphate minerals. The average P_2O_5 content of carbonaceous chondrites and other meteorites is approximately 0.3%.[32] Somewhat higher values, 0.64% P_2O_5, have been found in the Mokoia meteorite (Ref. 858). It would be of interest to ascertain whether any water-soluble phosphorus compounds are present in carbonaceous chondrites. On the Earth, a very large deposit of apatite of presumably igneous origin is known to exist in the Kola peninsula.[38]

The ubiquity of sulfur is well known. Sulfur is present in the form of sulfides, sulfur, or sulfates in most meteorites. The average for chondrites is about 2%, with the higher values found in carbonaceous chondrites.[32] It is of interest that carbonaceous chondrites reveal the coexistence of elemental sulfur with soluble sulfate (Ref. 886). No extraordinary oxidation reactions seem to be required to account for this situation (Ref. 886).

Models for the Synthesis of Organic Compounds

With the correct interpretation of certain meteoritic[39-42] (Ref. 139) and nucleogenetic[43,44] (Ref. 36) singularities, and with further knowledge about the chronology of the solar system,[39–42,45] we may be able to describe, some day, in a fairly accurate manner, the events that led to the formation of the solar system (Refs. 1518, 1524) and the Earth[46,47] (Refs. 103, 1534). However, until such a day arrives, it would be premature to attempt a detailed description of any cosmic or terrestrial model for the abiogenic synthesis of organic compounds. Therefore, any models suggested here should merely be regarded as tentative working hypotheses. The following possibilities are considered as probable sites of organic synthesis within the solar system:

1. Solar nebula
2. Accretion bodies of the solar nebula
3. Comets
4. Jovian planets
5. Primitive terrestrial planets

1. The solar nebula was probably formed by the gravitational collapse of an interstellar cloud (Ref. 1518), and therefore, it can be expected to have contained, among other things, the fundamental carbon-containing molecules which were previously present in the interstellar medium.[19,20] The degree of organic synthetic activity which took place during this period presumably depended on the temperature, radiation intensity, and other conditions prevailing during the transformation of the interstellar cloud into a nebular disk. If temperatures well above 2000°K are considered for the nebular disk (Ref. 1518), the combinations present under these conditions would be essentially the ones found in cool star atmospheres; that is to say, mainly diatomic and triatomic molecules, radicals, and ions.[13,20] Upon cooling of the nebular disk, polyatomic molecules were probably formed by direct interactions and condensation of the reactive species. Additional contributions to synthesis can also be expected to have been made by the action of electrons derived from the radioactive decay of potassium-40 (Ref. 1518). It is difficult to indicate the nature and complexity of the substances formed. One thing that can be said is that the trend would have been toward increasing complexity as the temperature of the nebular disk decreased to the temperatures at which accretion processes took place.

If instead of using the above high-temperature model, one uses a low-temperature model for the formation of the solar system (Ref. 1524), a major synthesis of organic compounds beyond what was already present in the interstellar cloud probably did not take place until the protosun had evolved into an intensely radiating star. Regardless of which of the above models for the formation and evolution of the solar nebula is accepted, the building up of organic molecules did presumably continue, perhaps with increased intensity, after the first solid aggregates were formed by accretion or condensation of nebular material.

2. Different opinions exist on the nature of the first accretion bodies. Whether they were chondritic aggregates,[46,47] metric planetesimals[43,44] (Ref. 36), or protoplanets[48] does not introduce a serious problem from the point of view of organic synthesis. The amount of carbon compounds present, for instance, in carbonaceous chondrites (up to 5% carbon), is more than sufficient to allow significant reaction rates. The same can be said with respect to the concentration of methane, ammonia, and other compounds present in the medium surrounding the planetesimals.[43] Recent studies (Ref. 1284) indicate that methane and other hydrocarbons may have also been present as gas hydrates (clathrate compounds of gases in a distorted ice matrix), making the conditions for the synthesis of organic compounds still more favorable.

3. The author has considered comets as possible cosmic models for the synthesis of biochemical compounds (Ref. 1290), primarily because comets are supposed to contain large amounts of carbon compounds and because their composition presumably reflects the composition of the primordial solar nebula.[49] The cometary nucleus has been postulated as a discrete mass of solids which may have been formed from typical interstellar material at temperatures of the order of $10-100°K$.[50,51]

With regard to the composition of the model, it is known that the spectra of comets show fluorescence emission bands corresponding to the molecules or radicals CN, CH, CH_2, C_2, C_3, NH, NH_2, and OH, to the radical ions CH^+, OH^+, CO^+, N_2^+, and CO_2^+, and to the atoms of Fe, Ni, Cr, and other elements.[20,25-27,52] These emission bands are observed in the heads or in the tails of comets when these bodies are at less than 3 AU from the Sun. The band corresponding to the CN radical is generally the first emission band to appear on the tails of comets during the travel of these bodies toward the Sun.[25] The CN band is also the band with the largest degree of extension into the comets' heads, followed in intensity by the C_2 (Swan) and C_3 bands.[25,28]

It has been suggested that the above compounds exist in the nuclei of comets in one of the three forms: frozen free radicals,[53-55] "ices" of water, ammonia, methane, etc.,[50,51] or clathrate-type hydrates (Ref. 1284). A fourth possibility is that they exist there in the form of more complex molecules. These species are either vaporized or vaporized and dissociated into radicals by the solar radiation. In general, it is considered that the parent molecules of CN, NH_2, and OH are hydrogen cyanide, or cyanogen, ammonia, and water, respectively.[20,25] The parent molecules of the carbon radicals are supposed to be methane, acetylene, and other hydrocarbons.[20,25,55]

If comets are derived from typical interstellar material,[49-51] from which the primordial solar nebula was also formed, then any knowledge obtained on the formation of organic compounds with cometary models may have a bearing on the probable synthesis of these compounds in preplanetary bodies. No implication of an identical place of origin is made here for comets and preplanetary bodies, since this is precluded by the different orbital characteristics of comets and planets.[56,57] Only a similarity in the chemical composition, and perhaps the state of aggregation of matter, of comets and preplanetary bodies is suggested.

On the basis of this chemical similarity, it is reasonable to assume that the chemical processes which occur in comets by the action of solar radiation when these bodies are at distances of less than 3 AU from the Sun may also have occurred, but on a much larger scale, in preplanetary Mars, Earth, and Venus. Such a correlation would be particularly well justified if one accepted low-temperature theories for the formation of the solar system (Refs. 103, 1524, 1534), which appear to be supported by the presence of thermally labile organic compounds in the chondrules as well as in the matrix of chondrites (Ref. 901).

Additional qualitative details of a cometary model, and its implications with regard to the formation of biochemical compounds on the preplanetary and planetary stages of the Earth, have been presented elsewhere (Refs. 1290, 1295, 1296).

4. The occurrence of organic synthetic processes in the atmospheres of the Jovian planets is suggested by experiments carried out with simulated atmospheres (Ref. 85) and by the coloration of Jupiter's cloud layers. The results of current investigations on this planet[58] are also in line with the existence of intense chemical and physicochemical processes involving methane, ammonia, and probably water.

5. The primitive planetary atmosphere model has been discussed in detail elsewhere in a qualitative (Ref. 1149) and quantitative manner[24,62] (Refs. 103, 104, 1198, 1285). The escape of gases from the primordial atmosphere[59] (Ref. 98) and subsequent geological changes[60] (Refs. 994, 1063, 1177, 1202) bearing directly or indirectly on the problem of synthesis of organic compounds on the primitive Earth have also been treated previously. If the emanation of hydrocarbons from igneous geological formations[34] is confirmed, this would be in strong support of a reducing primitive atmosphere containing significant amounts of hydrocarbon gases. The reducing condition of an atmosphere of magmatic origin is also supported by the fact that the terrestrial rate of oxygen production by photolysis of water is lower than the rate of volcanic carbon monoxide production.[61]

The above models represent different stages in the transformation of the solar nebula into the present cosmic bodies of the solar system. An important condition, which is common to all these models, is that they are essentially reducing or at least nonoxidizing in character, of which we have meteoritic (Ref. 68) as well as geochemical evidence[61,62] (Refs. 169, 1177, 1179). Future investigations may elucidate to what extent the formation of organic compounds took place in preterrestrial cosmic environments[43,44] (Refs. 256, 1290) and on the primitive Earth.

Energy Sources

Several sources of energy were available for the synthesis of organic compounds during the transformation of solar nebula into planets. The main source was, of course, the Sun, providing ultraviolet light and ionizing radiation, probably at a higher rate than observed at the present time.[44] A second source was natural radioactivity (Refs. 1115, 1202, 1324, 1518), and perhaps the heat derived from gravitational compression and radioactivity during the formation of the planets.

However, it should be emphasized that if, as indicated above, some of the primordial constituents of the preplanetary Earth were radicals or reactive chemical compounds, then organic synthesis could have occurred spontaneously at relatively low temperatures prior to the formation of the planets. It is surmised that such syntheses were responsible for the formation of significant amounts of organic and biochemical compounds. Similar views have also been advanced by other investigators (Ref. 256). Furthermore, because of the relatively low prevailing temperatures and the reducing conditions of the preplanetary environment, the compounds thus formed could have been preserved for very long times.

During the further stages of planetary development, additional sources of energy were available on the surfaces and in the atmospheres of the terrestrial planets. It is likely that in addition to ultraviolet light and ionizing radiation, electric discharges and the heat from plutonic processes also contributed to the formation of organic compounds.

Synthesis of Amino Acids and Hydroxy Acids

The abiotic synthesis of amino acids and hydroxy acids under the conditions of postulated cosmic models or primitive Earth models has been accomplished by several investigators using electrical discharges, ultraviolet light, and ionizing radiation. Moreover, when some of the reactive carbon compounds presumed to be present in comets were used, the formation of amino acids and hydroxy acids was observed to occur spontaneously at moderate temperatures.

By electric discharges. References to the early literature on the action of electrical discharges on carbon compounds have been given by Miller (Ref. 1281). In particular, Loeb,[63] Miller[64] (Refs. 1280, 1281, 1282), Hough and Rogers,[65] Abelson,[66] Heyns *et al.* (Ref. 1271), Pavlovskaya and Pasynskii (Ref. 1307), Franck,[67] Oró (Ref. 1293), and Hearn and Oró[68] applied silent and spark discharges to aqueous mixtures of totally reduced (CH_4, NH_3) or partially oxidized carbon and nitrogen compounds. The products obtained include the amino acids—glycine, imino-diacetic, sarcosine, alanine, beta-alanine, methylalanine, alpha-amino-n-butyric acid, alpha-amino-isobutyric acid, glutamic acid, aspartic acid, valine, and leucines, and the hydroxy acids—glycolic, lactic, succinic and hydroxy-butyric acid. The amides of glycine and aspartic acid have also been detected recently (Ref. 1293) in short-time sparking experiments.

The yield of total amino acids in these experiments was usually less than 5% of the theoretical, and the relative yield of each individual amino acid was approximately inversely proportional to the number of carbon atoms in the molecule. When methane was used, the amino acids formed contained almost exclusively from two to four carbon atoms. When methane was partially replaced by ethane or higher hydrocarbons, valine and leucines were formed in addition to the other amino acids.[68] Aside from these and other small variations, the over-all qualitative composition of amino acids obtained in different experiments by several investigators is very similar if not identical.

Although the mechanisms of synthesis have not been studied in detail, it appears that the first phase of one of the possible mechanisms involves the formation of radicals which recombine to form many compounds, including hydrogen cyanide, aldehydes, amines, nitriles, and aliphatic hydrocarbons. The primary formation of methyl radicals has been suggested by the experiments of Franck,[67] using either isooctane or methanol in the presence of ammonia and water. When methanol was used, the observed amino acid yield was increased more than 50% as compared to that obtained from methane. This is in line with the fact that less energy is required to form a methyl radical from methanol than from methane.[69] That methyl radicals are formed can also be deduced from a study of the products formed by the action of electrical discharges upon methane,[70] and upon mixtures of methane and ammonia (Ref. 85). Because of the high thermal stability of the triple-bonded radical C_2H derived from acetylene,[35] one would expect that this radical should act as a trap for other radicals giving rise to the formation of methyl, ethyl, vinyl, and ethynyl derivatives of acetylene. In fact, these compounds were precisely the products identified in the aforementioned experiments.[70] In a similar manner, the nitrile analogs of the above compounds, namely, acetonitrile, propionitrile, acrylonitrile, and cyanogen, should also be expected to be formed from the thermally stable triple-bonded CN radical derived from hydrogen cyanide. Some of these compounds were, in fact, detected by Sagan and Miller (Ref. 85) in model experiments with Jovian atmospheres. References to the early literature bearing on this question may be found elsewhere[71] (Ref. 1281).

The second phase of this mechanism of amino acid synthesis does not appear to occur in the gas phase but rather in aqueous solution. It involves a Strecker condensation of aldehydes with hydrogen cyanide in the presence of ammonia (Ref. 1282). The resulting alpha-amino acid nitriles, which can be detected during the first hours of the reaction,[68] are progressively hydrolyzed into the corresponding amides and acids.

In addition to alpha-aminonitriles, beta-aminonitriles have also been detected in the reaction product. In particular, beta-aminopropionitrile, which is a precursor of beta-alanine and of pyrimidines, has been detected by paper chromatography.[68] This nitrile gives a characteristic green derivative when it reacts with ninhydrin.

An alternative mechanism for the formation of amino acids in the experiments with electrical discharges is suggested by the presence in the reaction product of polymers of hydrogen cyanide which are known to be converted into amino acids (see *From reactive precursors*).

By ultraviolet light. The reduction of carbon dioxide to formaldehyde by ultraviolet light[72] and the photochemistry of carbon compounds[73] have been reviewed previously. Studies on the photochemical synthesis of amino acids in aqueous systems were reported some time ago by several investigators. Baudisch[74] claimed the formation of amino acids from potassium nitrite, carbon monoxide, and ferric chloride. Dhar and Mukherjee[75] observed the formation of glycine from ethylene glycol and of arginine from glucose. Nitrates were used as a source of nitrogen and titanium dioxide or ferrous sulfate as catalyst. More recently, Bahadur and associates (Refs. 1214, 1219, 1220), also using nitrates and ferric chloride, have observed the formation of serine, aspartic acid, and asparagine from paraformaldehyde. Other amino acids formed in these experiments as detected by paper chromatography were glycine, alanine, and threonine and, in particular, C_5 and C_6 amino acids, which are formed with difficulty in the experiments with electric discharges. These include valine, ornithine, arginine, proline, glutamic acid, histidine, leucine, isoleucine, and lysine. The latter amino acids were detected by paper chromatographic methods without the previous separation from amines and other ninhydrin-positive compounds which are also formed in these experiments.[76] Before the results can be accepted without reservation, they will have to be confirmed using carbon-14 formaldehyde, or by analyzing the products by amino acid-free ion exchange resins.[77]

It would be difficult to visualize the presence of nitrates in a primitive Earth environment or in a cosmic body. However, the nitrate ion *per se* should not be considered as the immediate precursor of the amino group of amino acids. It is clear that the nitrates must be reduced at the expense of the oxidation of part of the carbon compounds, such as formaldehyde, which are always present in a large excess in these experiments. In fact, it is known that in the presence of metallic ions and partially reduced carbon compounds, nitrates[78] and nitrites[79] are rapidly reduced by the action of light to some nitrogen compound of a lower oxidation level. Hydroxylamine was suggested by Oró et al. (Ref. 1304) as one of the nitrogen compounds which may be involved more directly in the formation of amino acids. In fact, this could also be deduced from the synthesis of amino acids from formhydroxamic acid and formaldehyde by Baly et al. (Ref. 1228). The preferred participation of hydroxylamine in the comparative photochemical synthesis of amino acids from formaldehyde and either nitrates, nitrites, hydroxylamine hydrochloride, or ammonium chloride has been confirmed in our laboratory.[76] The same conclusion has been arrived at by Ferrari[80,81] from similar comparative photochemical experiments but using more complex carbon compounds instead of formaldehyde.

From theoretical considerations (Ref. 1285) and the results of meteoritic[32,33] and igneous rock analyses,[36] ammonia and ammonium chloride would seem to be the most logical precursors of the amino group of amino acids in cosmic and primitive Earth environments. Experiments carried out by Miller,[64] by Groth,[82] and by Groth and von Weyssenhoff (Refs. 1258, 1259) have given evidence that the amino acids glycine and alanine can be synthesized by irradiation with shortwave ultraviolet light (Krypton 1165, 1235 Å; Xenon 1295, 1490 Å; and mercury vapor, 1850 Å) of aqueous mixtures containing ammonia as the nitrogen source and either methane or ethane as the carbon source. A higher amino acid yield was obtained when ethane was used instead of methane. On exposing a mixture of methane, ammonia, carbon monoxide, and water to the radiation of a hydrogen lamp through a thin LiF window, Terenin (Ref. 1325) observed the formation of the alanines and of several other amino acids.

On the basis of the experimental quantum yields obtained by Groth and recent theories of solar evolution, Sagan (Refs. 85, 282, 1179) has calculated that the synthesized organic compounds in the contemporary atmospheres of the Jovian planets and in the primitive reducing atmospheres of the terrestrial planets are of the order of 1000 g/cm^2 of planetary surface.

Experiments carried out by Pavlovskaya and Pasynskii (Ref. 1271) and also in this laboratory[76].have shown that several amino acids can be synthesized by irradiation with ultraviolet light of aqueous mixtures containing formaldehyde and ammonium salts. The synthesized amino acids, which were separated by ion-exchange resins and detected by paper chromatography, include glycine, serine, alanine, and glutamic acid. The Russian investigators also found valine, isoleucine, phenylalanine, and basic amino acids.

With regard to the mechanism of photochemical synthesis of amino acids, it has been pointed out previously that the amino group may be derived from either ammonia or hydroxylamine. However, very little is known about the mechanism of formation of the hydrocarbon chain. Perhaps monosaccharides of two to six carbons are first formed photochemically and then transformed by redox processes into alpha-keto acids which, upon transamination, are converted into amino acids.

That hexoses and hydroxy acids or their lactides are formed by the irradiation of formaldehyde solutions with ultraviolet light was shown by Baly[83] and Irvine and Francis.[84] Moreover, when the syrupy product thus obtained was heated with a trace of acid at 100°C, it was found to resinify into a polymeric material.[76,84] This suggested the additional presence in the reaction product of polyhydroxyphenols.[84] If phenolic compounds were formed from formaldehyde, these compounds may be the precursors of the aromatic amino acids. That hydroxy acids and also keto acids and dicarboxylic acids react photochemically with ammonia, ammonium salts, or other nitrogen compounds to produce amino acids has been shown by Deschreider[85] and by Cultrera and Ferrari.[86,87] Nonphotochemical transamination reactions are also well known.

The synthesis of amino acids containing straight chains with five or six carbon atoms could be explained by the intermediate formation of C_5 or C_6 monosaccharides, respectively. These compounds become stabilized by the formation of furanose and pyranose cyclic structures, stopping the growth of the monosaccharide chain by preventing the condensation of additional formaldehyde molecules. Therefore, essentially no monosaccharides and amino acids with linear chains of more than six carbon atoms are formed. Branched chain amino acids could be derived from branched chain monosaccharides such as dendroketose.

It is of interest that the same maximum amino acid chain length is observed in these photochemical experiments as in the experiments with electric discharges. Whereas in the present case the maximum chain length may be determined by the stability of cyclic structures in the experiments with electric discharges, it may be the result of the decreased probability of formation of long chains by processes of methyl radical recombination.

By ionizing radiations. The synthesis of organic compounds by ionizing radiation is reviewed by Swallow (Ref. 1324). After the stimulating investigations in this area by Garrison *et al.* (Ref. 1233), the formation of amino acids by the action of ionizing radiations has been studied by several investigators. Hasselstrom *et al.* (Ref. 1269) obtained glycine, aspartic, and possibly diaminosuccinic acid by irradiating with beta-rays an aqueous solution of ammonium acetate. Paschke *et al.* (Ref. 1155) irradiated solid ammonium carbonate with the gamma-rays from a cobalt-60 source and obtained glycine, two other ninhydrin-positive compounds, one of which was tentatively identified as alanine, and ammonium formate.

It is known that formic acid and simple aldehydes are formed by the action of ionizing radiation over aqueous solutions of carbonic acid (Ref. 1233). It is also known that glycolic acid is produced by the irradiation of formic acid.[88] Therefore, it is conceivable that glycine and other amino acids could also be obtained by the irradiation of aqueous solutions of ammonium carbonate, but the yields would, of course, be extremely small.

Even though the above experiments indicate that it is possible to synthesize amino acids from partially oxidized compounds such as ammonium carbonate, it would appear more logical, on the basis of theoretical considerations about the primitive Earth's atmosphere (Refs. 1198, 1285), to study the irradiation of aqueous mixtures of reduced carbon and nitrogen compounds, such as methane and ammonia. This has been done by Dose and coworkers[89] (Ref. 1235), and a large number of amino acids and bases have thus been obtained. Urea and other organic compounds are also formed by proton irradiation of these mixtures (Ref. 1230). More recently, Calvin[11] and Palm and Calvin (Ref. 1305) have irradiated mixtures containing carbon-14-methane, ammonia, and water, among other compounds, with 5-Mev electrons and have obtained a number of amino acids, including glycine, alanine and aspartic acid. This has been confirmed by Oró (Ref. 947), who, in addition, has found glycinamide and other products, which were also found in experiments with electric discharges (Ref. 1293). Radiochemical and nonradiochemical mechanisms of synthesis may be involved in this case, since hydrogen cyanide, which is known to condense into products that yield amino acids, was also formed in substantial amounts in these experiments.

From reactive precursors. As pointed out earlier, it is known from astronomical observations that in the atmospheres of carbon stars, very reactive diatomic combinations of carbon, nitrogen, oxygen, and hydrogen are formed. These combinations diffuse out or are ejected at high speeds[23] and eventually become part of interstellar matter and cosmic bodies, being presumably converted into simple but reactive compounds. These may include hydrogen cyanide, acetylene, carbon monoxide, formaldehyde, acetaldehyde, ammonia, hydrazine, and hydroxylamine, among others. Most of the compounds have also been produced in the laboratory from aqueous ammonia–methane mixtures in experiments with electric discharges or ionizing radiation.

Thus, it was considered of interest to find out whether some of these compounds are sufficiently reactive to yield amino acids and other biochemical compounds in the absence of electric discharges, ultraviolet light, or ionizing radiation.

It was first shown in our laboratory (Ref. 1304) that aqueous mixtures of formaldehyde and hydroxylamine hydrochloride at moderate temperatures and under slightly acidic conditions yield large amounts of glycine and smaller amounts of alanine, beta-alanine, serine, threonine, and aspartic acid, the last three having been identified only by ion-exchange and paper chromatography. Amino acid amides, in particular glycinamide, were found as intermediates, and formic, lactic, and glycolic acids as side products.

It was found (Ref. 1304) that the mechanism of synthesis involves the initial formation of formaldoxime and its dehydration into hydrogen cyanide. Strecker and cyanohydrin condensations yield nitriles which are hydrolyzed first into amides and then into acids. Condensation of formaldehyde with glycinamide is presumed to yield serinamide, which can be converted into serine and alanine.[90] A similar formation of serine and threonine involving aldol-type condensations of formaldehyde and acetaldehyde with methylene-activated glycine derivatives, such as glycine chelates or polyglycine, was also shown by Akabori and coworkers[91,92] (Ref. 1213). It may be added here that when the formaldehyde–hydroxylamine hydrochloride mixtures were made slightly basic, pyridines were also formed in addition to amino acids.

A subsequent study made in our laboratory of the products formed by refluxing aqueous mixtures of formaldehyde and hydrazine revealed the formation of glycine, valine, and lysine as detected by paper chromatography.[93] The mechanism of lysine formation is thought to involve the intermediate formation of hexoses and their reduction–oxidation by hydrazine. It is well known that hexoses are formed from formaldehyde by base catalysis, that hydrazine is formed by the action of electric discharges on ammonia,[94] and that hydrazines can be both reducing[95] and oxidizing reactants.

As mentioned earlier, three of the major compounds which are assumed to exist in comets in addition to methane and carbon dioxide are hydrogen cyanide (or cyanogen), ammonia, and water.[20,25] For this reason, a study of the products formed with mixtures of the latter three compounds was subsequently undertaken in our laboratory. It was observed that the amino acids glycine, alanine, and aspartic acid, and other biochemical compounds were formed spontaneously in these mixtures at moderate temperatures (Ref. 1300). Oligomers of hydrogen cyanide are presumed to be the intermediates of the amino acids. In fact, tetrameric hydrogen cyanide was observed to be one of the first products formed in the above mixtures,[96] and it is known that tetrameric hydrogen cyanide can be degraded hydrolytically into glycine.[97,98] Two possible degradation mechanisms of tetrameric hydrogen cyanide into glycine have been suggested by Loquin[99] and Ruske.[100] Other mechanisms involving processes of reductive deamination can be postulated for the formation of alanine and aspartic acid.

The formation of amino acids in the hydrogen cyanide–ammonia–water mixtures has been confirmed and extended by Lowe et al.[101] In addition to the above three amino acids, Lowe and coworkers[101] have also detected the presence of beta-alanine, alpha, beta-diamino-propionic, alpha-aminobutyric, threonine, glutamic acid, arginine, leucine, and isoleucine in the reaction product. The formation of hydroxy amino acids could conceivably take place in these mixtures if aldehydes were present, since it is known that formaldehyde and acetaldehyde condense with methyleneamino-acetonitrile to form serine and threonine, respectively.[102]

It can thus be seen that, with the exception of the aromatic and sulfur-containing amino acids, most of the building blocks of proteins can be synthesized nonenzymatically in aqueous systems from very simple precursors in the absence of highly activating forms of energy.

With regard to the formation of sulfur-containing amino acids, simple nonenzymatic pathways can also be visualized. Cysteine could be formed in a manner similar to serine by condensation of thioformaldehyde[103] with a methylene-activated glycine derivative, such as glycine nitrile, glycinamide, polyglycine or a metal chelate of glycine. Methionine could be formed by the addition of methylmercaptan to acrolein, followed by the condensation of the resulting methional[104] with hydrogen cyanide and subsequent hydrolysis of the nitrile. One of the possible pathways for the synthesis of aromatic amino acids could be through monosaccharides or similar compounds obtained from formaldehyde.[84]

Synthesis of Monosaccharides

Since the early studies of Butlerow[105] and Loew,[106] it is known that formaldehyde in aqueous solutions condenses into sugars by the action of basic catalysts. As a result of the work of Fischer and other investigators,[107,108,109] fructose, sorbose, and xylulose were identified among other compounds in the formaldehyde reaction product.

Relatively recently, Mariani and Torraca[110] analyzed by two-dimensional paper chromatography the product of the base catalyzed condensation of formaldehyde and confirmed and extended the previous results. They detected the presence of the hexoses galactose, glucose, mannose, fructose, and sorbose, and the pentoses arabinose, ribose, ribulose, xylose, xylulose, and lyxose, in addition to ten more unidentified monosaccharides. More recent studies by Mayer and Jäschke[111] and by Pfeil and Ruckert (Ref. 1308) have shown the formation of glycolaldehyde, glyceraldehyde, dihydroxyacetone, and tetroses in addition to pentoses and hexoses. Dendroketose was also obtained as the product of the condensation of two moles of dihydroxyacetone (Ref. 1308).

The reaction is assumed to be initiated by the condensation of two moles of formaldehyde into glycolaldehyde, which occurs at a very slow rate (induction phase).[112] This is followed by aldol condensations which lead to the formation of trioses, tetroses, pentoses, and hexoses and use up all the formaldehyde in a very short time (autocatalytic phase) (Ref. 1308). The over-all reaction is catalyzed by calcium carbonate, calcium oxide, and other bases.

Since no attempts had been reported on the synthesis of 2-deoxy-pentoses, in particular 2-deoxyribose, we undertook the synthesis of this compound (Ref. 1297), which is the monosaccharide present in deoxy-ribonucleic acid. This deoxypentose and its isomer, 2-deoxyxylose, were obtained in yields of about 5% of the theoretical by the condensation of acetaldehyde with glyceraldehyde in aqueous systems. The reaction takes place very rapidly at room temperature when catalyzed by calcium, magnesium, and other divalent metallic oxides. The lifetime of 2-deoxy-ribose under these conditions is relatively short, the compound probably being transformed into other products. Results from our laboratory have shown that the reaction is also catalyzed by ammonia and other simple nit-rogen bases. In contrast to the fast reaction which divalent metallic oxides catalyze, the reaction occurs in a very controllable manner when am-monium hydroxide is used as catalyst. Furthermore, under these con-ditions 2-deoxyribose appears to be quite stable. In fact, the continuous synthesis of this compound was observed for an uninterrupted period of over two months. It would be of interest to determine whether the catalysis by calcium or magnesium carbonates occurs in such a controll-able manner, since these salts have been detected in carbonaceous chondrites. 2-deoxyribose was also obtained in smaller yields from aqueous solutions of formaldehyde and acetaldehyde in the presence of calcium oxide (Ref. 1297).

Synthesis of Purines and Purine Intermediates

The formation of purines on the primitive Earth or in cosmic bodies poses *a priori* a difficult problem because it requires the formation of two fused heterocyclic structures; an imidazole and a pyrimidine.

In principle, there are, however, two relatively simple mechanisms or pathways which can be visualized for the formation of the purine ring. One involves condensation of a three-carbon compound with a one-carbon reactant to form a 4, 5-disubstituted imidazole, and the other involves condensation of a C_3 compound with a C_1 reactant to form a 4, 5-disubstituted pyrimidine. The reaction terminates by cyclization of either the disubstituted imidazole or the disubstituted pyrimidine with another mole of the C_1 reactant.

It is known that the formation of purines in living organisms occurs by a pathway involving 4, 5-disubstituted imidazole derivatives,[113] and it has also been observed that the acid degradation of adenine yields 4-aminoimidazole-5-carboxamidine as an intermediate.[114] On the one hand, we have the very mild conditions of enzymatic synthesis and on the other hand, the very drastic conditions of acid hydrolysis; yet, in both cases, a 4, 5-disubstituted imidazole shows as an intermediate. On the basis of these observations, it is conceivable that an abiotic synthesis of the purine ring may have proceeded through a pathway involving imidazole derivatives.

The first demonstration of the synthesis of adenine from simple precursors and under the conditions of a postulated model was made not too long ago in our laboratory (Ref. 1288). It is of interest that in line with the foregoing reasoning, 4, 5-disubstituted imidazoles were found in the reaction product along with adenine (Ref. 1288).

Adenine was obtained from the reaction product of a mixture of hydrogen cyanide, ammonia, and water. This purine was synthesized in substantial amounts by heating a solution of hydrogen cyanide (1 to 15 M) in aqueous ammonia for one or several days at moderate temperatures (27 to 100°). The insoluble black polymer of hydrogen cyanide was removed by centrifugation, and adenine was isolated from the red-brown supernatant by chromatographic methods. The main ultraviolet-absorbing compound of the reaction product was identified as adenine˙ by a number of different procedures, including ultraviolet spectrophotometry and the melting point of its picrate derivative. The synthesis was found linear with time at room temperature, and, in a typical experiment, more than 100 mg of adenine per liter of reaction mixture were obtained at the end of four days (Ref. 1302).

Since adenine is an essential building block of nucleic acids and of the most important coenzymes, and since hydrogen cyanide, ammonia, and water are presumed to be common natural constituents of the solar system, these findings were considered to be of special significance in relation to the problem of the origin of life.

In addition to adenine, several purine precursors, namely 4-aminoimidazole-5-carboxamide (AICA), 4-aminoimidazole-5-carboxamidine (AICAI), formamide, and formamidine were also found in the reaction product[115] (Ref. 1303). The mechanism of adenine synthesis is supposed to be initiated by the base catalyzed polymerization of hydrogen cyanide into nitriles.[116] The role played by ammonia in this synthesis is two-fold. It acts as a basic catalyst, and it causes the ammonolysis of hydrogen cyanide into formamidine and of nitriles into amidines. One of the resulting nitriles, possibly aminomalonodinitrile, condenses with formamidine either directly or after transformation to its mono- or diamidine to form AICAI. In the last step, AICAI condenses with another mole of formamidine to yield adenine. This last step has been confirmed in a separate experiment in our laboratory (Ref. 1291).

The other purines were postulated to be formed from 4-aminoimidazole-5-carboxamide (Ref. 1303). Recent experiments in our laboratory have confirmed this assumption (Ref. 1292). It has been observed that AICA and guanidine condense in aqueous ammonia systems to yield guanine. Moreover, when AICA is allowed to react with urea under similar conditions, guanine and xanthine are formed.[117]

The formation of the one-carbon reactants, guanidine and urea, in the absence of free oxygen, poses no special problem, since compounds of this oxidation level, such as urea, were detected by Miller,[64] Berger (Ref. 1230), and Palm and Calvin (Ref. 1305), in their respective experiments with electric discharges, high-energy protons, and high-energy electrons, which were carried out under reducing conditions. It may also be pointed out here that significant amounts of hydrogen cyanide were formed in these experiments (Ref. 1282) and that both guanidine and urea were obtained from hydrogen cyanide solutions by Lowe et al.[101] Other workers have also observed the formation of urea[118,119] from cyanogen or cyanates.

The above experiments on the synthesis of adenine from mixtures of hydrogen cyanide, ammonia, and water have been confirmed by Lowe et al.[101] using isotopic tracer methods. These investigators have also found an additional purine, hypoxanthine, among the reaction products. A significant extension of these experiments has been carried out recently by Calvin,[11] Palm and Calvin,[120] and Ponnamperuma and Lemmon,[121] who have observed the formation of adenine and AICA by irradiating with 5-Mev electrons a mixture containing methane, ammonia, and water among other reduced compounds. AICA is apparently also formed in the ultraviolet irradiation of hydrogen cyanide solutions.[122] In summary, it appears to be well established that the four major biological purines can be synthesized, from very simple precursors, in aqueous systems under possible primitive Earth conditions.

From an historical point of view, it should be said that, at the turn of the last century, cyanogen[123] and hydrocyanic acid[124,125] were thought to be involved in the synthesis of proteins and purines in living organisms. These have since been found to be erroneous concepts. Nevertheless, it is of interest that such early ideas may apply to the abiogenic formation of these compounds. Studies on the polymerization of hydrocyanic acid were initially carried out more than 150 years ago,[116] and therefore it is highly probable that purines, purine intermediates, and other compounds of biological significance have been synthesized in the laboratory many times since then, yet have remained unidentified until the present time. Interesting observations bearing on the synthesis of purines from hydrogen cyanide were made by Gautier,[124] Fischer,[126] Salomone,[127] and Johnson and Nicolet;[128] they are discussed in some detail in a recent paper from our laboratory (Ref. 1303). Aside from these early unsuccessful attempts to synthesize purines from hydrogen cyanide, it should be noted that uric acid was synthesized from glycine and urea by Horbaczewski[129] and purine from formamide and other simple compounds by Bredereck and coworkers.[130,131] However, none of the biochemical purines found in nucleic acids were isolated or identified in these experiments.

Synthesis of Pyrimidines

With regard to the formation of pyrimidines, it was proposed not too long ago (Ref. 1290) that derivatives from the C_3 molecular species found in comets could be the source of these heterocyclic compounds. One of these C_3 derivatives is malonamide semialdimine or its isomer, beta-aminoacrylamide, which could be expected to yield uracil by condensation with urea.

Since beta-aminoacrylamide was not available to us, we tested some of the C_3 compounds which are formed in the experiments with electric discharges and are considered to be intermediates in the formation of beta-alanine. These intermediates are acrylonitrile, beta-aminopropionitrile, and beta-aminopropionamide. When these compounds were allowed to react with urea in aqueous ammonia systems at 130°C, the formation of small amounts of uracil was observed in each case (Ref. 1291). Uracil was characterized by paper and ion-exchange column chromatography and by ultraviolet spectrophotometry. The yields obtained from beta-aminopropionamide were approximately two and five times higher than those obtained from beta-aminopropionitrile and acrylonitrile, respectively. This is what would be expected if acrylonitrile first has to undergo amination into beta-aminopropionitrile, which, in turn, must undergo hydrolysis into beta-aminopropionamide. Since this amide is, in fact, the dihydroderivative of beta-aminoacrylamide, it is obvious that the mechanism of the reaction must involve a dehydrogenation step either before or after the cyclization.

The mechanism of uracil formation involving beta-aminoacrylamide or its isomer, malonamide semialdimine, is in line with the well-known chemical synthesis of uracil from malic acid and urea in the presence of a strong mineral acid[132] (Ref. 1244). A strong mineral acid transforms malic acid into malonic semialdehyde, which then condenses with urea to form uracil.[132] Also in line with the above mechanism, it is known from the work of Bredereck et al.[133] that the pyrimidine ring can be formed in good yield from either aminoacrolein or malonodialdehyde. In theory, the three pyrimidines found in nucleic acids could conceivably be formed in aqueous systems under possibly primitive Earth conditions by the mechanism described above. In addition to beta-aminoacrylamide yielding uracil, beta-aminoacrylamidine and alpha-methyl-beta-aminoacrylamide could be expected to condense with urea into cytosine and into thymine, respectively.

A possible pathway for the conversion of the symmetrical C_3 species of comets into beta-aminoacrylamide or malonamide semialdimine is through the formation of carbon suboxide (C_3O_2), which has been presumed to exist in several cosmic bodies (Ref. 648). By the addition of hydrogen and ammonia to carbon suboxide, malonamide semialdehyde or malonamide semialdimine might be obtained. In fact, malonic acid derivatives are known to be formed from carbon suboxide.[134] Another possibility of pyrimidine synthesis is suggested by the presence of alpha, beta-diaminopropionic acid among the products from the hydrogen cyanide reaction mixture. Reductive deimination of the alpha imino group of the postulated intermediate, alpha, beta-diiminopropionitrile,[135] would give beta-aminoacrylonitrile. Condensation of the amidine and the amide derived from this nitrile with urea would be expected to form cytosine and uracil, respectively.

In addition to purines and pyrimidines, preliminary data have also been obtained on the synthesis of pyridines,[96] pteridines,[96,136] and of other fluorescent and photosensitive pigments[96] (Ref. 1303).

Synthesis of Polypeptides

The early literature on the direct polymerization of unsubstituted amino acids has been reviewed previously in some detail.[137-139] Current studies on the synthesis of peptides and of polymers containing amino acids, under conditions presumed to have existed on the primitive Earth, were initiated by Fox and Middlebrook (Ref. 1247), and by Akabori (Ref. 1212). This work has been reviewed recently (Refs. 1069, 1076, 1077, 1212, 1299) and has been extended by other workers. As a result of these investigations, a number of different pathways for the abiotic formation of polypeptides appear possible.

Polymers containing essentially all the amino acids found in proteins can be prepared by heating a mixture of these amino acids in the presence of an excess of dicarboxylic (Refs. 1102, 1075) or diamino amino acids (Ref. 1099). This synthesis requires anhydrous conditions and heating at high temperatures for relatively short periods of time. Several lines of evidence show that the products formed are heteropolypeptides. Most of these products have the ability to form stable microspheres in appropriate ionic solutions (Ref. 1332). Other thermal polymers, containing certain amounts of histidine, have been found to act as hydrolytic catalysts (Ref. 1076).

The formation of homo- and heteropolypeptides can occur also under aqueous conditions and at moderate temperatures, as shown by other workers. Thus, unsubstituted amino acids[140] (Ref. 1299) and their corresponding amides[140] (Ref. 1277) and nitriles[140-142] have been observed to polymerize directly or by the action of basic (ammonia) or surface (silicates) catalysts. The amides glycinamide and asparagine seem to condense most readily into polypeptides[140] (Ref. 1277). These two amides have been detected as intermediates in some amino acid syntheses (Refs. 947, 1293, 1304).

A pathway which appears to be particularly good for the formation of polypeptides containing serine, threonine, and other amino acids is that of Akabori *et al.* (Ref. 1212), which is based on the condensation of aldehydes and olefins with polyglycine. The natural occurrence of this process would be quite probable, since, as has been shown in our laboratory, polyglycines are readily formed from glycine (Ref. 1299) and glycinamide[140] in aqueous ammonia systems. Furthermore, in practically all the abiogenic syntheses of amino acids studied, glycine has been found to be the predominant amino acid formed.

Another possible pathway has been described recently by Schramm *et al.* (Ref. 1316). Polyarginine (molecular weight 4000 to 5000) was prepared from arginine with the help of polyphosphate esters. Using the same method, polyleucine, polyvaline, and a polymer of serine were prepared in our laboratory.[143] This method, however, requires essentially anhydrous conditions. Furthermore, it would be difficult to visualize the formation of large amounts of ethyl polyphosphate in a cosmic or terrestrial environment. Other problems posed by the chemistry of phosphorus have been discussed by Gulick (Ref. 1092).

In addition to the above pathways of polypeptide formation, other observations have been made which indicate that peptides or polymers containing amino acids can also be obtained by the action of ultraviolet light[144] and electric discharges.[145]

A significant recent development is the isolation of polymers containing several amino acids from the reaction product of mixtures of hydrogen cyanide, ammonia, and water.[101] This is the same reaction mixture that has been shown to give rise to the formation of amino acids, purines, purine intermediates, and pteridines, among other compounds. Since nitriles are formed in this system, it is likely that the above polymers result from nitrile condensation reactions, although other condensation reactions involving amino amides or amino acids are also possible. Hydrogen cyanide has been suggested as an amino acid condensing agent by Calvin (Ref. 1041), and it is known that unsubstituted cyanamide can be used for the synthesis of peptides.[146] Hydrogen cyanide and also cyanamide (formed by combination of CN and NH_2 radicals) were probably abundant in the primordial cosmic bodies of the solar system. It is possible that these reactants may have been responsible for the formation of a number of polymeric compounds, including polypeptides and perhaps also polynucleotides.

Synthesis of High-Energy Phosphate Compounds and Polynucleotides

A possible abiotic mechanism for the formation of a high-energy phosphate compound, carbamyl phosphate, was proposed some time ago.[147] Formiminyl phosphate, obtained by condensation of hydrogen cyanide with an inorganic phosphate, such as monohydrogen, disodium orthophosphate, is suggested here as another possibility of a high-energy phosphate compound. Compounds such as these, and possibly also pyrophosphates, could conceivably be the source of the high-energy phosphate bonds of nucleoside triphosphates such as adenosine-5'-triphosphate (ATP). The formation of ATP by ultraviolet irradiation of an aqueous mixture of adenine, ribose, and a polyphosphate ester has been observed recently by Ponnamperuma and Sagan.[148]

Schramm and coworkers (Ref. 1316) have also shown recently that mononucleosides, mononucleotides and polynucleotides can be synthesized from their constituents at moderate temperatures, with the help of a polyphosphate ester. The preparation of this ester was first described by Langheld,[149] who used it for the synthesis of a phosphorylated leucine. According to the results from this[143] and other laboratories,[150] Langheld's phosphate ester appears to be a mixture of variable amounts of at least two tetrametaphosphate tetraethyl esters. Some of the polynucleotides obtained by Schramm *et al.* show enzymatically the 3', 5'-phosphodiester linkages which are common to RNA and DNA. Strand complementarity, which is involved in molecular self-duplication, and autocatalytic activity have also been observed in the above polynucleotides (Ref. 1316). Further investigations will be needed, however, to assess how realistic it is to consider the polyphosphate ester method as a cosmic or terrestrial model of abiogenesis.

Another recent development in this area is the formation of ribonucleotide polymers by the action of gamma-radiation on aqueous solutions of ribomononucleotides. Again, the presence of 3', 5'-phosphodiester bonds in these polymers is suggested by the fact that enzymatic hydrolysis with RNAase or phosphodiesterase of the irradiated samples produces a hyperchromic effect.[151]

Even though the above results are certainly encouraging, it is obvious that a large amount of work remains to be done in the area of nonenzymatic polypeptide and polynucleotide synthesis. Therefore, a discussion of concepts of evolution of these macromolecules would be a little premature at present. At any rate, interesting ideas have been presented recently on the role that nucleic acids and other macromolecules may have played in directing prebiochemical evolution[152-154] (Refs. 1038, 1041, 1115). More general principles of chemical evolution have been discussed mainly by Pattee[152] and Pullman and Pullman.[155] Also, of general importance in this respect, in addition to the investigations quoted earlier, are some of the ideas expressed by other authors[156,157] (Refs. 1008, 1013, 1021, 1085, 1096, 1167, 1205, 1206, 1361).

Conclusion

There is no doubt that carbon compounds exist widely distributed in the universe. Whether the more complex biochemical compounds described in this paper are present in cosmic bodies other than the Earth will only be answered with certainty by space probes. Probes to the Moon, Mars, and Venus are feasible and should provide valuable information about the organic and inorganic chemistry in these bodies. However, more information about the chemistry prevailing during the beginning of the solar system would be obtained by sending probes to Jupiter and to comets passing sufficiently close to the Earth's orbit.

From the experimental studies presented here, it appears reasonable to say that if the Earth in its preplanetary stage had some of the simple organic constituents of comets, a large number of biochemical compounds, including carbohydrates, amino acids, purines, pyrimidines, pteridines, and polymers containing amino acids would have been synthesized during the development of this cosmic body.

The formation of complex biochemical compounds from simple organic molecules is not in disagreement with thermodynamic principles. In fact, these syntheses can occur because the initial precursors (hydrogen cyanide, nitriles, aldehydes, olefins, etc.) are compounds of high-energy content which, in their tendency to acquire lower energy states and to become stabilized, react and are *ipso facto* transformed into biochemical compounds.

THE FORMATION OF BIOCHEMICAL COMPOUNDS

Introduction

If we exclude the noble gases from consideration because of their inertness, the four most abundant elements of the universe are hydrogen, oxygen, carbon, and nitrogen. In fact, hydrogen is the major constituent of the universe; oxygen, carbon, and nitrogen are each about ten times more plentiful than the next most abundant element, silicon. It is of particular interest that these elements are precisely the four major constituents of organic compounds and living matter. Therefore, as a first approximation, one may state that "The composition of living matter turns out to be a better sample of the universe than the dead Earth."[5]

These four elements exist mainly as atoms and diatomic combinations such as CN, CH, C_2, CO, NH, and OH, in the atmospheres of relatively cool stars, including the Sun, and in interstellar or circumstellar space. They also exist as di- and polyatomic combinations in planets, comets, and meteorites. Thus, simple and complex compounds of carbon are found to be widely distributed in the universe. In principle, these compounds will exist wherever the prevailing temperatures and other physical conditions are compatible with the stability of the bonds between carbon atoms and between carbon and other elements. It follows that wherever such required conditions prevail in the cosmos, the natural synthesis of more or less complex organic compounds will be possible.

The theoretical treatments [mainly by Oparin (Ref. 1149) and Urey (Ref. 1198)], the experimental approach with ionizing radiations by Calvin and his associates (Ref. 1233), and Miller's experiments with electric discharges (Ref. 1280) have given a strong impetus to the study in the laboratory of the abiogenic synthesis of biochemical compounds.

From the results of these experiments, it may be concluded that processes of organic synthesis, which may have occurred in the primitive Earth's atmosphere, or may be occurring in certain cosmic bodies (such as comets and the atmospheres of the Jovian planets), can be partially reproduced in the laboratory. These experiments have opened a new field of investigation, for which the names "experimental organic cosmochemistry" and "primordial organic chemistry" have been suggested.

Possible Models for Organic Synthesis

Because of limited astrochemical and geochemical knowledge, it is premature to make a detailed drawing of any cosmic or terrestrial model for the abiogenic synthesis of organic compounds. Only working hypotheses that are admittedly tentative can be advanced.

As a working hypothesis, we have given some consideration to a comet-like model for the Earth protoplanet, primarily because comets (Fig. 1) appear to contain large amounts of reactive carbon compounds, HCN, ammonia, and water (Fig. 2 and Table 1). Furthermore, it is presumed that their composition approximates the composition of the primordial solar nebula and the protoplanets. Indeed, a recent model for the Earth protoplanet, as suggested by Fowler[44] (Ref. 1518), is quite similar to a cometary model proposed some time ago by Whipple.[50,51]

We do not wish to imply that the Earth protoplanet should be imagined as a gigantic comet; the different orbital characteristics of planets and comets suggest a different origin. We want only to point out the probable existence of a certain similarity in their composition, particularly the presence of simple compounds which are considered to be the precursors of molecules of biological significance. Thus, we assume that the Earth protoplanet also contained carbon compounds, ammonia, and water as they are now observed in comets.

FIG. 1 Whipple–Fedtke comet (1942 g).[26]

The presence of methane and ammonia in the atmospheres of the Jovian planets suggests their presence in the Earth protoplanet. Moreover, according to Oparin and Urey, if the primitive Earth atmosphere was essentially reducing and predominantly composed of methane, ammonia, and water, these same compounds should have been present in the Earth protoplanet.

Assuming this limited similarity between comets and protoplanets, it is conceivable that the chemical processes occurring in comets as a result of solar radiation, when these bodies are at distances of less than 3 AU from the Sun, may also have occurred in the Earth protoplanet on a much larger scale.

Some of the main features of this model are summarized as follows:

1. Relatively high concentrations of reactive carbon compounds, together with ammonia and water, would have been present in the Earth protoplanet at the beginning. Their formation may have been

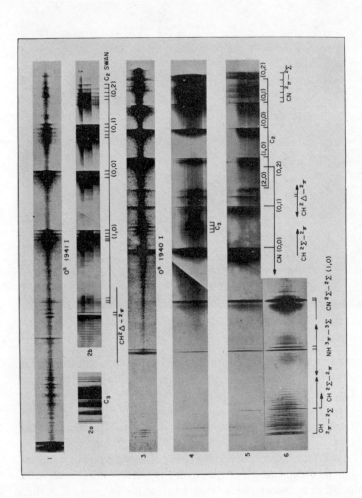

FIG. 2. Comparison of cometary and flame spectra.[25] Spectrogram 1: Comet 1941, I,r (distance from comet to Sun in AU) = 0.73, slit, glass, f/1, McDonald. Spectrogram 2A: λ4050 group of C_3 obtained by L. Herman. Spectrogram 2B: Three spectrographic exposures on a flame of acetylene, stoichiometric mixture and inner cone; main bands: C_2 and CH. Spectrogram 3: Comet 1941, I,r = 0.87, slit, quartz, f/1, McDonald. Spectrogram 4: Spectrum of rich acetylene flame with some addition of ammonia. Main features: bands of OH, NH (Q-branch), CN (violet system), C_3 (and associated continuum extending from λ3200 to λ4600), C_2 and CH; also red continuum of incandescent particles of graphite. Spectrogram 5: Spectrum of acetylene flame in stoichiometric ratio, with traces of ammonia; inner cone and part of outer cone. Present in inner cone: CH ($^2\Sigma - ^2\Pi$), NH, CN (blue, $\Delta\nu = +1.0, -1, -2$), CH ($^2\Sigma - ^2\Pi$), CH ($^2\Delta - ^2\Pi$), C_2 (Swan, $\Delta\nu = +2, +1.0, -1, -2$), CN (red, $^2\Pi - ^2\Sigma$). Present in outer cone: OH, NH, CN (blue and red), extremely weak CH, weak C_2. Spectrogram 6: Spectrum of acetylene flame in

TABLE 1. Chemical species detected in comets and other cometary data

Composition[a]	$CN, CH, CH_2, C_2, C_3, NH, NH_2, OH, CH^+,$ $CO^+, CO_2^+, N_2^+, OH^+,$ and Na
Parent compounds[b]	$HCN, NH_3, H_2O, CO, C_2N_2, CH_4, C_2H_2$ and other hydrocarbons
Average mass[c]	$10^{18\pm3}$ g (10^{18} g minimum mass for Halley's comet)
Probability of collision by the Earth[b]	100 collisions in 5×10^9 yr
Cometary matter trapped by the Earth[b]	$10^{20\pm3}$ g in 5×10^9 yr

[a]From spectrochemical evidence.
[b]Calculated or estimated.
[c]See Chapter-end Ref. 25.

primary (nucleogenetic and related processes) or secondary (action of solar radiation on methane and other compounds).

2. The synthesis of more or less complex organic compounds would have started very early in the history of the protoplanet—as early as the formation of inorganic compounds. Otherwise, a very unreasonable mechanism would have to be postulated preventing the reaction of C, H, O, and N, when all the other elements were able to react.

3. A significant amount of the nonvolatile and polymeric organic compounds would have survived the transformation of the protoplanet into a planet and accumulated on its surface. This should be expected, if we assume a cold origin for the Earth and a reasonably low surface temperature for the primitive planet, as proposed by Urey[158] (Ref. 1534) and others.

EXPERIMENTAL RESULTS

As indicated in Table 1, some of the compounds presumed to exist in comets are hydrogen cyanide, ammonia, water, and C_1 to C_3 hydrocarbons. In addition to these, the random recombination of some of the observed radicals such as $CH, C_2, NH_2, OH,$ and CN should be expected to lead to the formation of a variety of reactive compounds, including formaldehyde, acetaldehyde, hydroxylamine, hydrazine, and nitriles.*

Since 1955, we have been investigating the products obtained when some of these reactive compounds are allowed to react together. Figure 3 shows the simple apparatus used for these experiments in our laboratory. The reaction mixtures studied include formaldehyde–hydroxylamine, formaldehyde–hydrazine, hydrogen cyanide–ammonia, and aldehyde–bases (organic and inorganic). All the experiments of synthesis

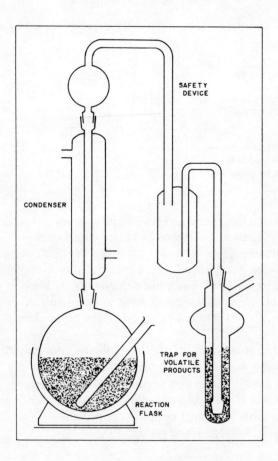

FIG. 3. Apparatus for the formaldehyde–hydroxylamine, formaldehyde–hydrazine, and hydrogen cyanide–ammonia reactions.

---

*It may be pointed out that some of these compounds are also formed by the action of electrical discharges or ionizing radiation on methane–ammonia–water mixtures.

were performed in aqueous systems at temperatures below 150°C (mostly between room temperature and 100°C).

Formation of Amino Amides, Amino Acids, and Hydroxy Acids

Figure 4 and Table 2 show the formation of glycinamide and amino acids in the formaldehyde–hydroxylamine reaction. The product of the reaction was concentrated and treated successively with Dowex 50 and Dowex 2 columns in the usual way. The resulting ampholytic and basic fractions were analyzed by column and paper chromatography. The detailed separation scheme is presented in Fig. 5.

Figure 6 shows the separation of amino acids by ion-exchange column chromatography, and Fig. 7 shows the separation of hydroxy acids and other simple aliphatic acids by adsorption column chromatography. These acids, which include glycine, alanine, beta-alanine, serine, threonine, and aspartic, lactic, glycolic, acetic, and formic, were formed in the reaction between formaldehyde and hydroxylamine. A simple kinetic

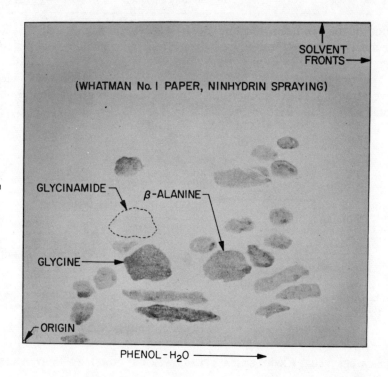

FIG. 4. Paper chromatogram of amino acids from the formaldehyde–hydroxylamine reaction (Whatman No. 1 paper, ninhydrin spraying).

TABLE 2. Amino acids obtained from the formaldehyde – hydroxylamine reaction[a]

Solvent mixtures	R_f values[b] $\times 10^2$		
	Glycine	Glycinamide	β-alanine
ButOH : HAc : H_2O (4 : 1 : 1)	16 (17)	20 (21)	38 (38)
EtOH : HAc : H_2O (8 : 0.5 : 1.5)	64 (64)	81 (82)	63 (65)
n-PrOH : formic acid : H_2O (7.5 : 1.5 : 1)	51 (52)	30 (31)	62 (63)
Pyridine : H_2O (6.5 : 3.5)	62 (62)	78 (80)	45 (45)
Lutidine : H_2O (6.3 : 3.7)	28 (30)	39 (40)	32 (28)
Phenol : H_2O (7.5 : 2.5)	40 (40)	34 (33)	61 (61)
ButOH : EtOH : $(Et)_3N$: H_2O (2 : 1 : 1 : 1)	27 (26)	32 (32)	23 (26)

[a] Ascending chromatography in Whatman No. 1 paper.
[b] R_f values in parentheses correspond to standards, where

$$R_f = \frac{\text{Solute migration}}{\text{Solvent-front migration}}.$$

study of the synthesis of amino acids is shown in Fig. 8, and the likely mechanism for the formation of glycine (and glycinamide) is depicted in Fig. 9.

The reaction of formaldehyde with hydrazine at 100°C also yields several amino acids, among other products. Some of the amino acids obtained in this reaction are listed in Table 3. In addition to glycine,

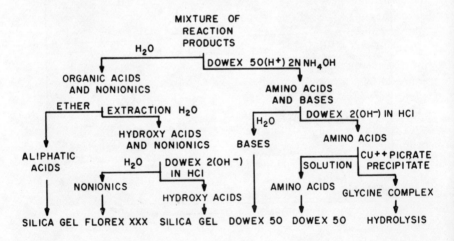

FIG. 5. Separation scheme of the products formed in the formaldehyde–hydroxyl-amine reaction (Ref. 1304).

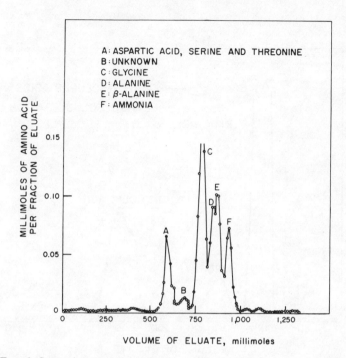

FIG. 6. Separation of amino acids by a Dowex 50 column (Ref. 1304) (A = aspartic acid, serine and threonine; B = unknown; C = glycine; D = alanine; E = beta-alanine; and F = ammonia).

the two amino acids, lysine and valine (formed with difficulty in other experiments), were observed to be formed in formaldehyde–hydrazine aqueous mixtures.

The amino acids, glycine, alanine, and aspartic acid, have also been formed in our laboratory from aqueous mixtures of hydrogen cyanide and ammonia. A number of additional ninhydrin-positive compounds, some of which were presumed to correspond to peptides, were also observed. These particular results have been confirmed and extended by Lowe,[101] who has found in the mixtures essentially all the amino acids present in proteins, with the exception of the sulfur and aromatic amino acids. In addition, a number of polymers containing several amino acids were isolated by Lowe from the reaction product of aqueous mixtures of hydrogen cyanide and ammonia.

The formation of amino acids by electric discharges and ultraviolet light has also been studied in·our laboratory. In addition to the amino acids identified by Miller, valine and leucine(s) were observed to be formed when a mixture of methane, ethane, ammonia, and water was submitted to the action of electric discharges.

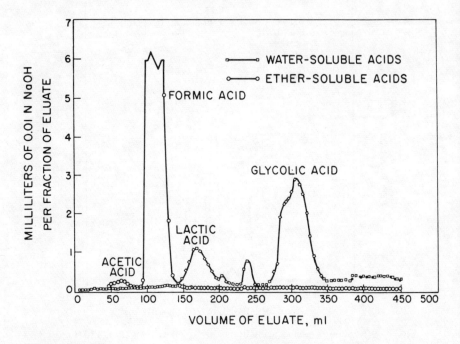

FIG. 7. Separation of hydroxy acids and other aliphatic acids by a silica gel column (Ref. 1304)

TABLE 3. Amino acids obtained from the paraformaldehyde–hydrazine reaction[a]

Solvent mixtures	R_f values[b] $\times 10^2$		
	Glycine	Lysine	Valine
(Et)$_3$N : H$_2$O : EtOH : ButOH (2 : 2 : 2 : 4)	33 (32)	21 (22)	52 (50)
Pyridine : H$_2$O (6.5 : 3.5)	89 (88)	–	88 (88)
Dimethylaniline : EtOH : H$_2$O : ButOH (1 : 3 : 3.5 : 2.5)	73 (73)	52 (45)	54 (52)
ButOH : EtOH : H$_2$O (8 : 2 : 2)	–	23 (23)	42 (42)
n-PrOH : formic acid : H$_2$O (7.5 : 1.5 : 1)	88 (82)	39 (39)	–
EtOH : ammonia (9.5 : 0.5)	84 (85)	36 (36)	–
IsoPrOH : HAc : H$_2$O (7 : 2 : 1)	86 (86)	53 (58)	–
EtOH : HAc : H$_2$O (8 : 0.5 : 1.5)	84 (84)	88 (85)	–
Pyridine : benzene : H$_2$O (6.5 : 1.5 : 2)	49 (49)	–	–

[a] Ascending chromatography in Whatman No. 1 paper.
[b] R_f values in parentheses correspond to standards.

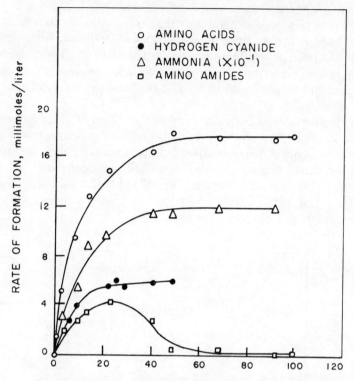

FIG. 8. Rate of formation of amino acids and other products from formaldehyde–hydroxylamine mixtures (Ref. 1304).

$$H_2C = O + H_2NOH \longrightarrow H_2C = NOH + H_2O$$

$$H_2C = NOH \longrightarrow HCN + H_2O$$

$$H_2C = O + NH_3 \longrightarrow H_2C = NH + H_2O$$

$$H_2C = NH + HCN \longrightarrow CH_2(NH_2)CN$$

$$CH_2(NH_2)CN + H_2O \longrightarrow CH_2(NH_2)CONH_2$$

$$CH_2(NH_2)CONH_2 + H_2O \longrightarrow CH_2(NH_2)COOH + NH_3$$

COMPLEMENTARY REACTION:
$$2H_2C = NOH + 2H_2O \longrightarrow H_2C = O + NH_2OH + HCOOH + NH_3$$

FIG. 9. Mechanism of glycine formation.

Formation of Monosaccharides

The formation of monosaccharides by the base-catalyzed condensation of formaldehyde is known since the early work of Butlerow, Lowe, and Fischer. It has been shown more recently by Mariani and Torraca, and others, that essentially all the biological trioses (including glyceraldehyde), tetroses, pentoses (including ribose), and hexoses can be synthesized from formaldehyde.

As no experiments had been done on the formation of 2-deoxyribose in aqueous solutions, the synthesis of this compound was undertaken in our laboratory. This 2-deoxypentose and its anomer, 2-deoxyxylose, have been synthesized from glyceraldehyde and acetaldehyde (Fig. 10) and from formaldehyde and acetaldehyde (Fig. 11). In the latter case, formaldehyde first yields glyceraldehyde, which then condenses with acetaldehyde to form the 2-deoxypentoses.

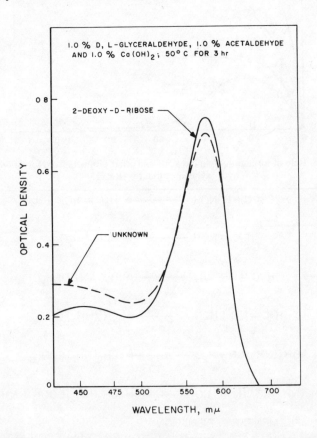

Fig. 10. Spectrum of Dische's derivative obtained from the glyceraldehyde reaction.

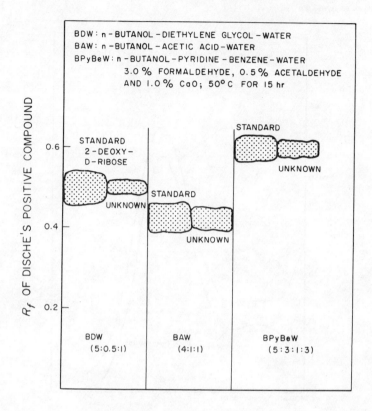

FIG. 11. Paper chromatogram of the product obtained from the formaldehyde–acetaldehyde reaction.

In addition to the ordinary oxides, hydroxides, and carbonates of alkaline-earth metals, ammonia and other nitrogen bases also catalyze the formation of 2-deoxypentoses (Table 4 and Fig. 12).

With the use of calcium oxide, the reaction is fast at room temperature, and even at 0°C has a measurable rate (Fig. 13). Using weak bases such as ammonia, and low temperatures, the deoxypentoses are synthesized slowly and appear to be stable under these conditions for long periods of time.

Formation of Purines

It is well known that in addition to phosphate, ribose and 2-deoxyribose, purines and pyrimidines are required for the formation of nucleic acids. During a study of the polymerization of hydrogen cyanide in aqueous ammonia, the formation of adenine was observed. Figure 14 is a photograph of a chromatogram made with ultraviolet light which shows the

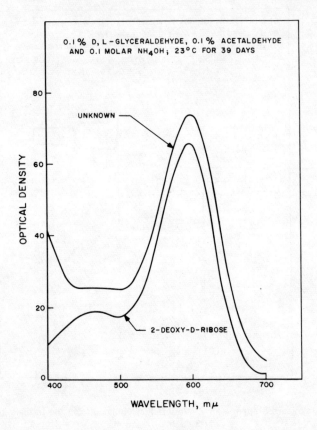

FIG. 12. Spectrum of Dische's derivative obtained using ammonium hydroxide as a catalyst.

TABLE 4. Bases which catalyze the synthesis of 2-deoxyribose and other 2-deoxypentoses

High activity	Moderate activity	
MgO	NH_4OH	LiOH
$Ca(OH)_2$	$(Me)_4NOH$	NaOH
$BA(OH)_2$	$(Et)_4NOH$	KOH

Reaction conditions: 0.1% glyceraldehyde and 0.1% acetaldehyde, 0.1 molar base, 50°C temperature for 1 hr.

presence of adenine in the reaction product (X). A stands for adenine standard and G for guanine standard. The nature of the other ultraviolet-absorbing compounds seen on the chromatogram will be discussed later. Figure 15 is a photograph of the same paper chromatogram with ordinary light after treatment with the specific adenine reagent of Gerlach and Döring.[159] Figure 16 shows the ultraviolet spectra in acid and in base of the compound with the R_f of adenine, compared with that of standard adenine. Figure 17 shows the ultraviolet and visible spectra of the picrate of the compound with the R_f of adenine, compared with the spectra of authentic adenine picrate.

It is clear from this and other data that adenine can be obtained from hydrogen cyanide in aqueous ammonia systems. Perhaps this synthesis becomes less surprising when one considers that adenine is, in fact, pentameric hydrogen cyanide.

The formation of this compound takes place at temperatures below 100°C. As shown in Fig. 18, at 70°C the synthesis was linear for at least five days, and an appreciable amount of adenine was formed. Although no treatment of the samples is necessary for the formation of adenine, the yield of this compound can be increased several-fold by evaporating on the steam bath the crude reaction product in the presence of hydrochloric acid. (See treated and untreated samples in Fig. 18.) At 90°C,

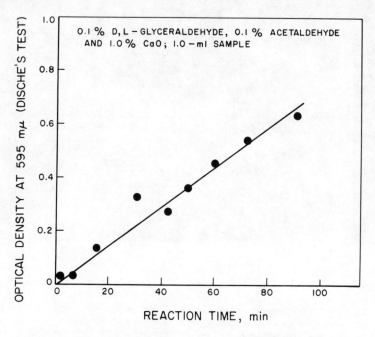

FIG. 13. Rate of 2-deoxypentose formation at 0°C.

the spontaneous formation of adenine reaches its maximum yield in about one day, at which time most of the hydrogen cyanide has been used up (Fig. 19).

In addition to adenine, the reaction product contains several other ultraviolet-absorbing compounds. Some have been found to be 4-amino-5-substituted imidazoles, which are known purine intermediates.

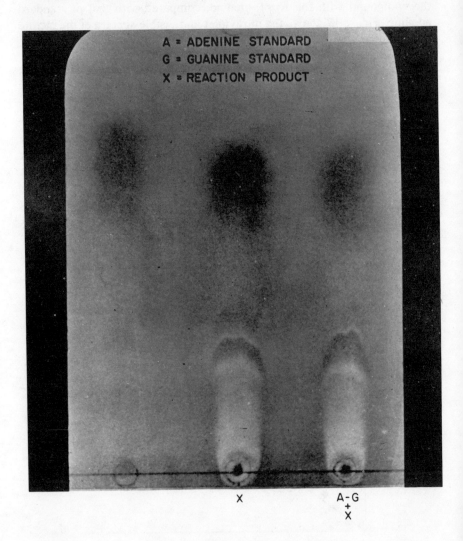

FIG. 14. Chromatographic identification of adenine in the hydrogen cyanide–ammonia reaction product. (Photograph obtained with ultraviolet light—not a contact print. Photographic method distinguishes clearly between ultraviolet-absorbing and fluorescing compounds.)

Figures 20 and 21 show photographs of paper chromatograms which were treated with a reagent* for diazotizable amines. The presence of 4-aminoimidazole-5-carboxamide (AICA) and 4-aminoimidazole-5-carboxamidine (AICAI) can be observed among other compounds. A detailed schematic representation of another chromatogram is shown in Fig. 22. Compound E corresponds to AICA and compound H to AICAI.

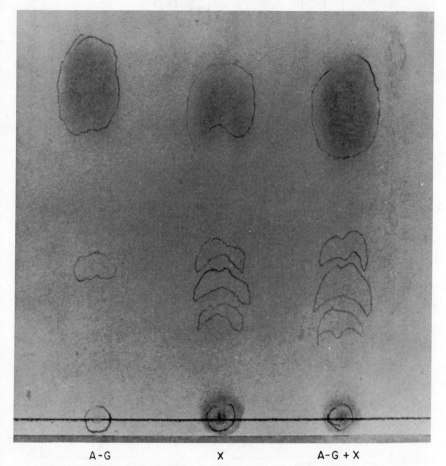

A = ADENINE STANDARD
B = GUANINE STANDARD
X = REACTION PRODUCT

A-G   X   A-G + X

FIG. 15. Identification of adenine by the specific method of Gerlach and Döring.

*The chromatograms were first sprayed with a mixture of equal volumes of 0.5% sodium nitrite and 0.5 N sulfuric acid. After drying, the sheets were sprayed with a 0.5% solution of N-1-naphthylethylenediamine hydrochloride.

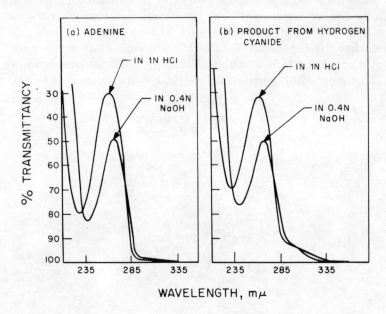

FIG. 16. Spectrophotometric identification of adenine in the hydrogen cyanide-ammonia reaction product.

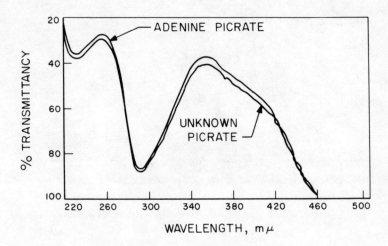

FIG. 17. Ultraviolet and visible spectra of the picrate derivative of the adenine obtained from hydrogen cyanide (Ref. 1302).

The diazotizable compound A shows the infrared spectra of diamino-maleodinitrile; compound B, which shows a strong CN band, may be 4-aminoimidazole-5-carbonitrile. The nature of the other diazotizable amines has not yet been identified. Figure 23 shows the progress of the formation of acidic and basic diazotizable amines. In this experiment, AICA was found to be the predominant component of the acidic fraction and AICAI that of the basic fraction. The graph also shows the rate of amino acid synthesis.

Because of the important part that AICA and AICAI may play in the mechanism of purine synthesis from hydrogen cyanide, these two compounds were isolated from the reaction mixture and characterized more fully. Figures 24, 25, and 26 show the isolation and characterization data on AICA; Figs. 27, 28, and 29 show similar data for AICAI.

Since monocarbon reactants at the oxidation level of formic acid are known to be chemical as well as biochemical precursors in the synthesis of purines, the product of the reaction was also analyzed for the presence of these compounds. Figure 30 is the reproduction of two chromatograms, where the presence of compounds with the R_f of formamide (FA) and formamidine (FAI) can be observed.

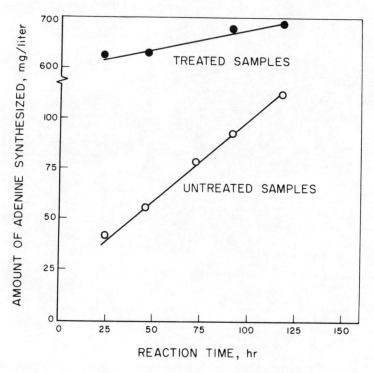

FIG. 18. Rate of adenine synthesis at 70°C (Ref. 1302).

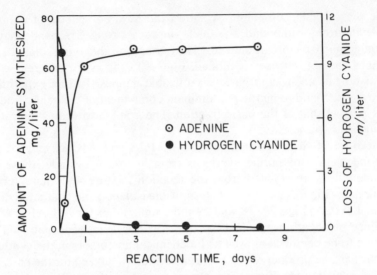

FIG. 19. Rate of adenine synthesis at 90°C compared with the disappearance of hydrogen cyanide (Ref. 1302).

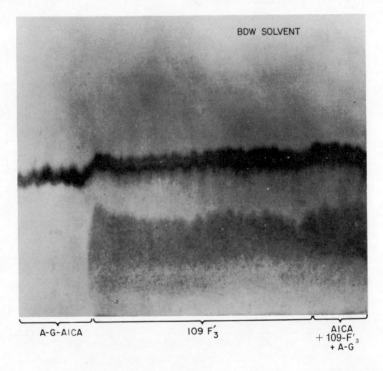

FIG. 20. Paper chromatographic detection by AICA (by diazotization) in the hydrogen cyanide–ammonia reaction product.

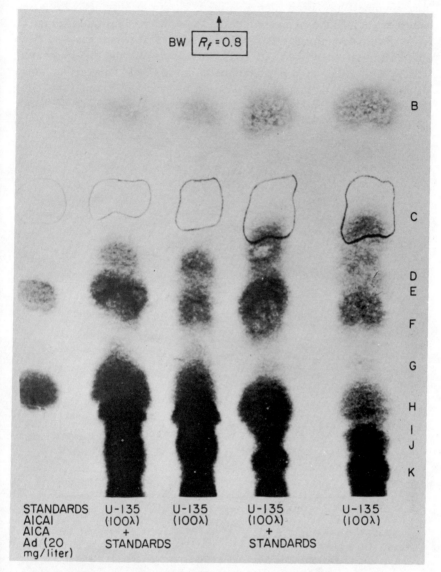

FIG. 21. Detection of adenine (by ultraviolet absorption), AICA, AICAI, and other diazotizable amines in the product from hydrogen cyanide.

An incomplete list of the organic and biochemical compounds formed from hydrogen cyanide in aqueous ammonia is presented in Table 5. On the basis of the data obtained, a mechanism for the synthesis of adenine has been proposed (as shown in Fig. 31). The required last step, which involves the condensation of 4-aminoimidazole-5-carboxamidine with formamidine, has been demonstrated in our laboratory. Proposed syntheses of guanine, hypoxanthine, and xanthine are illustrated in Fig. 32.

As postulated, the synthesis of guanine and xanthine has also been demonstrated recently in our laboratory (Figs. 33 and 34) by heating AICA with either urea or guanidine in aqueous and aqueous ammonia systems. The formation of guanidine from hydrogen cyanide has been shown by Lowe, and the formation of urea by irradiation of methane–ammonia–water mixtures has been shown by Berger, Palm, and Calvin.

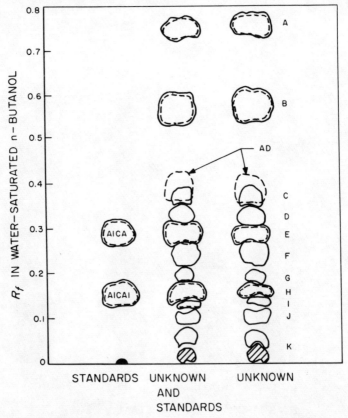

FIG. 22. Diazotizable amines formed from hydrogen cyanide (Ref. 1303).

The synthesis of adenine from hydrogen cyanide has been confirmed by Lowe, who has also detected the presence of hypoxanthine in the reaction product.

Formation of Pyrimidines

As pointed out earlier, the emission spectra of comets show the presence in these bodies of the C_2 and C_3 species. It is conceivable that the interaction of these active species with other molecules or radicals will lead to the formation of a number of molecules such as propiolonitrile, beta-amino acrylonitrile, and their respective amides. Under appropriate conditions, these compounds would be expected to condense with urea to yield pyrimidines such as uracil and cytosine.

Since the above pyrimidine precursors were not available to us, we have studied the condensation of their hydrogenated analogs, i.e. acrylonitrile (AN), beta-aminopropionitrile (APN), and beta-aminopropionamide (APA).

The reaction was carried out at 135°C in aqueous or aqueous ammonia systems. The formation of uracil was observed in each case. Figure 35 shows the ultraviolet spectra in acid and in base of one of the compounds obtained, compared with the spectra of standard uracil. As can be seen, the spectra are essentially identical. Yields of less than 1% were obtained, which are reasonable assuming that a dehydrogenation of the alpha- and beta-carbons of the C_3-compound must take place at some stage before a pyrimidine can be formed. The relative yields from APA, APN, and AN were 5, 2.5, and 1, respectively, which are in agreement with a mechanism involving the direct condensation of the beta-amino-substituted amide with urea. Studies on the formation of the other pyrimidines are in progress.

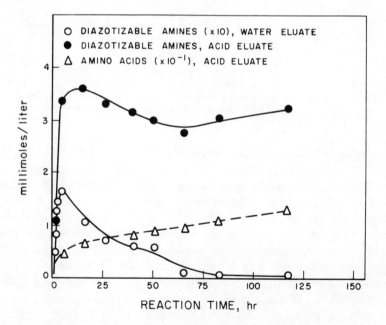

FIG. 23. Rate of synthesis of diazotizable amines from hydrogen cyanide (Ref. 1303).

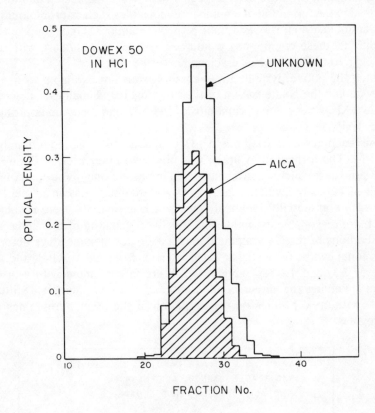

FIG. 24. Isolation by ion exchange column chromatography of the AICA formed
from hydrogen cyanide (Ref. 1303).

Formation of Polypeptides and Polymers Containing Amino Acids

In the majority of the amino acid syntheses from C_1 and N_1 precursors
which have been carried out so far, amino nitriles are formed first. These
are then hydrolyzed into amino amides and finally into amino acids. It
would therefore appear reasonable that one should first study the possibility of peptide formation from amino acids, amino amides, and amino
nitriles under the same aqueous conditions in which they were synthesized. This has been done in our own and other laboratories, and the
formation of homo- and hetero-polypeptides in aqueous systems at temperatures below 150°C has been observed.

Figure 36 shows the infrared spectrum of a polyglycine obtained by
heating glycine at 140°C in aqueous ammonia ($2N$). Degree of polymerization of up to 18 were obtained. From infrared and X-ray diffrac-

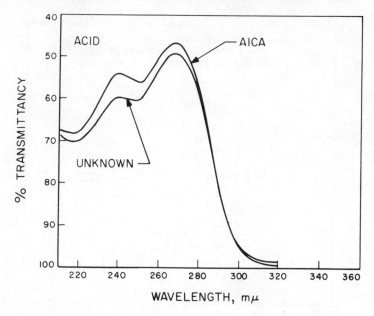

FIG. 25. Ultraviolet spectrum of the isolated AICA (Ref. 1303).

tion data, it has been concluded that the structure of this homo-poly-peptide corresponds exactly to that of polyglycine II. Above 140°C, the yield of polyglycine decreases with the temperature. At 140°C and lower temperatures, the formation of polyglycine increases with time, the yield being of the order of 40% in about four days.

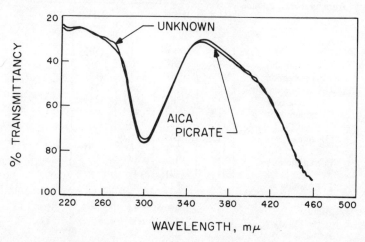

FIG. 26. Ultraviolet and visible spectra of the picrate derivative of the AICA obtained from hydrogen cyanide (Ref. 1303).

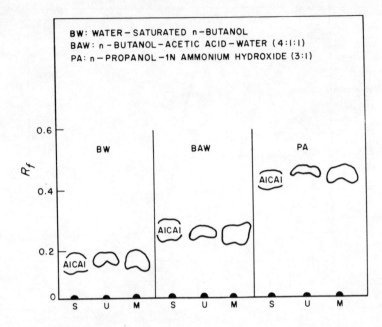

Fig. 27. Paper chromatographic identification of AICAI (Ref. 1303).

TABLE 5. Compounds formed from hydrogen cyanide

Compounds formed from hydrogen cyanide	R_f value$^a \times 10^2$ in different solvents				
	BW	BAW	PA	BDW	PHW
Adenine	42	57	56	50	
	(42)	(58)	(54)	(50)	
4-Aminoimidazole-5 carboxamide	17	26	46	18	
	(15)	(28)	(44)	(17)	
4-Aminoimidazole-5 carboxamide	28	50	56	21	
	(27)	(50)	(56)	(21)	
Glycinamide	18	18	44	38	
	(20)	(19)	(44)	(40)	
Glycine	12	24	26	23	
	(10)	(23)	(28)	(23)	
Formamidine	11	44	48		
	(11)	(43)	(46)		
Formamide	44	61	67		
	(44)	(61)	(67)		
Alanine		35	34		57
		(37)	(35)		(58)
Aspartic acid		24	16		8
		(23)	(17)		(9)

$^a R_f$ values in parentheses correspond to standards.

As shown in Table 6, a number of individual amino acids were observed to condense with glycine, forming copolymers which gave a positive biuret response* and yielded the respective amino acids upon acid hydrolysis. Copolymers containing at least eight different amino acids were also obtained when a mixture of amino acids was copolymerized with glycine under the same aqueous ammonia conditions (Fig. 37).

The polymerization of amino amides in aqueous ammonia systems was also studied. Figure 38 gives the rate of polyglycine synthesis from glycinamide at 100°C. It was observed that the rate of polypeptide formation is faster from glycinamide than from glycine, and that the synthesis of polymers from the amide occurs even at room temperature. X-ray diffraction data showed that the polymers obtained were mixtures of polyglycines I and II (Fig. 39a). Pure polyglycine II was obtained from the mixture by reprecipitation from a solution in 60% aqueous lithium bromide (Fig. 39b). Studies on the polymerization of other amino amides,

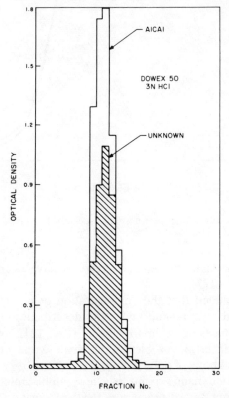

FIG. 28. Isolation by ion exchange column chromatography of the AICAI formed from hydrogen cyanide (Ref. 1303).

*Typical blue–violet color produced by peptides with a dilute cupric ion solution in a strong alkali.

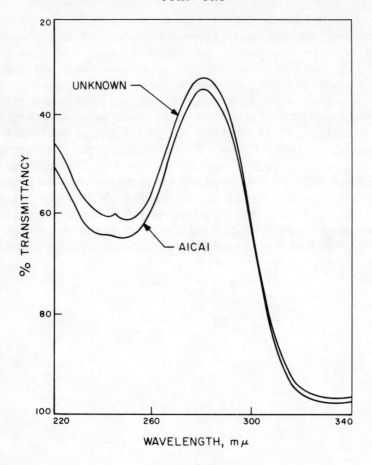

FIG. 29. Ultraviolet spectrum of the isolated AICAI (Ref. 1303).

in particular asparagine, in aqueous systems have been carried out by the Kovacs (Ref. 1277).

It should be added that the demonstration of polyglycine formation from glycine and glycinamide under the described conditions provides an experimental basis for Akabori's theory (Ref. 1212) of heteropolypeptide formation (insertion of olefins, aldehydes, and other groups into a polypeptide backbone of polyglycine).

From a thermodynamic point of view, alpha-amino nitriles would appear to be the preferred precursors for the formation of polypeptides. Yet, because of their reactivity and their partial decomposition into HCN, a variety of secondary products can be expected to be formed, which will make the isolation of polymers difficult. It is possible, however, that in

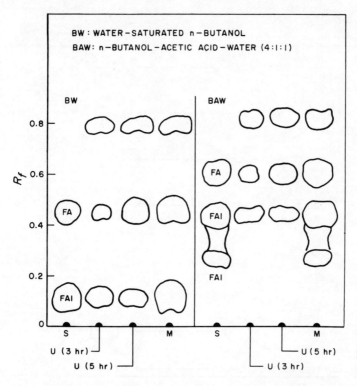

FIG. 30. Paper chromatographic identification of formamide and formamidine (Ref. 1303).

TABLE 6. Biuret response of amino acids copolymerized with glycine[a]

Group A (form insoluble product; biuret test positive)		Group B (do not form insoluble product; biuret test negative)
Glutamic acid	+ 4	Aspartic acid
Glutamine	+ 2	Asparagine
Cystine	+ 3	Methionine
Valine	+ 1	Alanine
Norvaline	+ 1	α-Amino butyric acid
Leucine	+ 1	Threonine
Histidine	+ 1	Serine
Arginine	±	Lysine

[a]A mixture of amino acid (1 g), glycine (2.5 g) and $2N$ NH_4OH (0.7 ml) was maintained at 140°C for 20 hr, then dialyzed for 4 days. The liquid remaining in the dialysis bag was made up to 100 ml and tested by the biuret reaction. No diketopiperazines were present in the final dialyzed product.

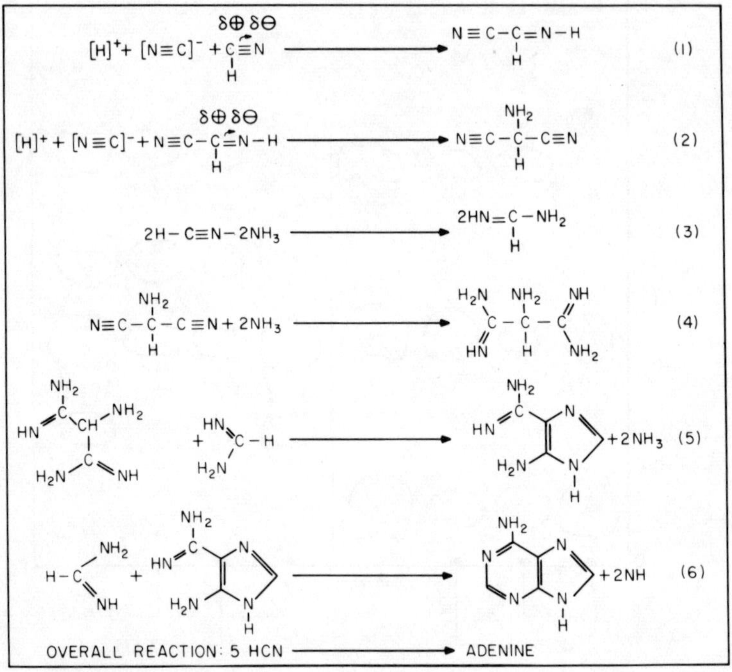

FIG. 31. Mechanism of formation of adenine from hydrogen cyanide (Ref. 1291).

the presence of an adsorbing surface, or in the presence of certain reactants, the nitriles may be stabilized sufficiently to undergo significant polycondensation. In line with this reasoning, small peptides of glycine were obtained by Akabori and his associates from aminoacetonitrile in the presence of clays. Also, polyalanines of relatively large molecular weight were obtained by Losse and Anders[142] from alpha-aminopropionitrile under similar conditions.

Polymers which can be precipitated with trichloroacetic acid and which give, upon hydrolysis, glycine and an unidentified ninhydrin-positive compound (with a similar chromatographic behavior to cysteine) have also been obtained in our laboratory by heating aqueous mixtures of methyleneacetonitrile and ammonium sulfide to 100°C.

Perhaps the most significant results in the context of these studies are those in which the formation of peptides or polymers containing amino acids has been observed in the same experiments which were designed essentially for the synthesis of amino acids. Thus, in his experiments with electric discharges, Miller observed the formation of a compound(s) which was (were) rapidly eluted with acid from a Dowex 50 column. This (these) compound(s) was (were) ninhydrin-positive under the reducing conditions of the Moore and Stein procedure but ninhydrin-negative on paper. The compound was thought to be a polymer. Similar observations have been made in our laboratory in experiments with electric discharges. Ion exchange and paper chromatographic data indicate the formation of peptides in these experiments.

Preliminary studies on the ninhydrin-positive compounds formed from hydrogen cyanide in aqueous ammonia have also revealed the presence of compounds which are thought to be peptides. Interestingly enough, the paper chromatographic behavior of these compounds is similar, if not identical, to those obtained from electric discharges. Some of this work on the products from hydrogen cyanide has been pursued in more detail by Lowe and Rees.[101,160] The formation of polymers containing glycine, alanine, aspartic acid, threonine, and other unidentified amino acids has been established by these investigators by ion exchange column chromatography, electrophoresis, and paper chromatography.

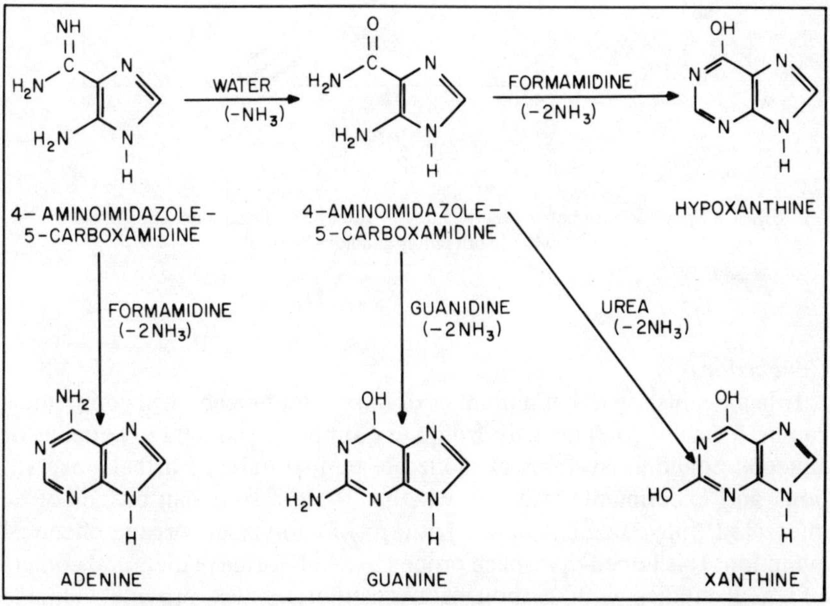

FIG. 32. Proposed mechanism for the synthesis of purines on the primitive Earth.

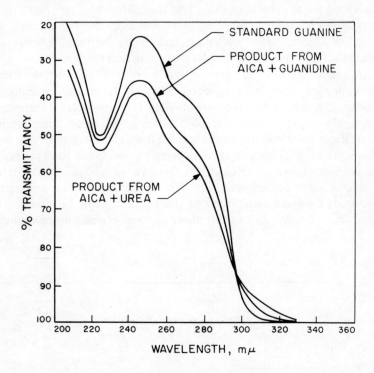

FIG. 33. Spectrophotometric identification of guanine in the condensation product of AICA with either guanidine or urea.

Conclusions

It has been shown that a number of important biochemical compounds can be formed spontaneously from very simple precursors in aqueous or aqueous ammonia systems at moderate temperatures. Further observations and experiments may tell whether these results can or cannot be integrated into a meaningful pattern of universal organo-chemical evolution. It is hoped that space probes to neighboring planets and comets and new studies with carbonaceous meteorites will provide valuable confirmatory evidence of the occurrence in the cosmos of processes of organic chemistry similar to those described here.

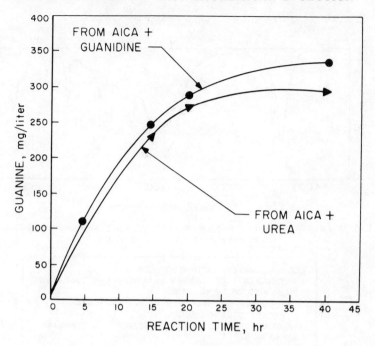

FIG. 34. Rate of guanine synthesis from AICA and guanidine and from AICA and urea.

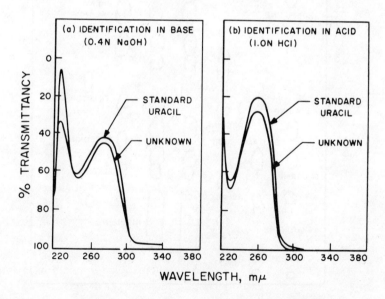

FIG. 35. Spectrophotometric identification of uracil formed by heating an aqueous solution of acrylonitrile, urea, and ammonium chloride.

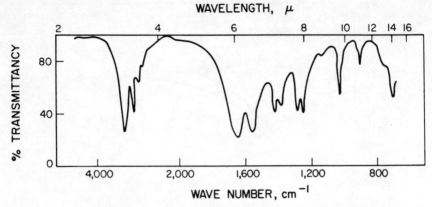

FIG. 36. Infrared spectrum of polyglycine synthesized from an aqueous ammonia
solution of glycine at 140°C (Ref. 1299).

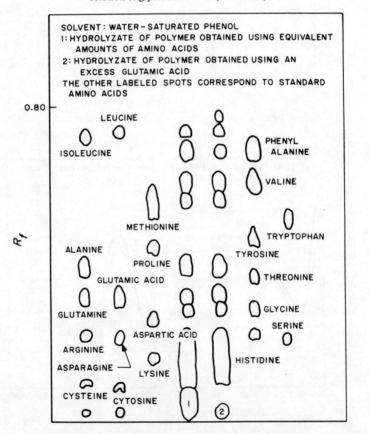

FIG. 37. Reproduction of a chromatogram of the hydrolysates of two polymers
obtained in aqueous ammonia systems from amino acid mixtures.

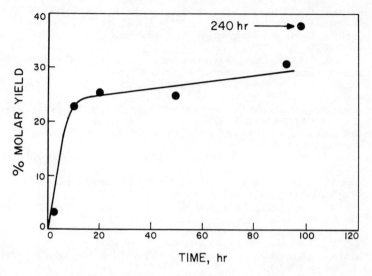

Fig. 38. Rate of polyglycine formation from glycinamide in aqueous ammonia systems (Ref. 1298).

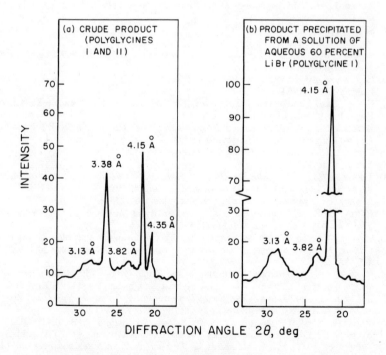

Fig. 39. X-ray diffraction diagrams of polyglycine obtained from glycinamide.

REFERENCES

1. BURBIDGE, E. M., BURBIDGE, G. R., FOWLER, W. A., and HOYLE, F., Synthesis of Elements in Stars, *Reviews of Modern Physics*, vol. 29 (1957), pp. 547–650.
2. BURBIDGE, E. M., and BURBIDGE, G. R., Formation of Elements in Stars, *Science*, vol. 128 (1958), pp. 387–9.
3. CAMERON, A. G. W., Carbon Thermonuclear Reactions and the Formation of Heavy Elements, *The Astrophysical Journal*, vol. 130 (1959), pp. 429–51.
4. CAMERON, A. G. W., Neon and Oxygen Thermonuclear Reactions, *The Astrophysical Journal*, vol. 130 (1959), pp. 895–915.
5. GREENSTEIN, J. L., Stellar Evolution and the Origin of Chemical Elements, *American Scientist*, vol. 49 (1961), pp. 449–73.
6. SCHWARZSCHILD, M., *Structure and Evolution of the Stars*, Princeton: Princeton University Press (1958).
7. ARP, H. C., The Evolution of Galaxies, *Scientific American*, vol. 208, No. 1 (1962), pp. 70–84.
8. DARWIN, C., *The Origin of Species by Means of Natural Selection*, New York: D. Appleton and Co. (1899).
9. *Evolution After Darwin; The University of Chicago Centennial*, vol. I, II, and III, ed. by S. TAX, Chicago: University of Chicago Press (1960).
10. HEISENBERG, W., Die Entwicklung der einheitlichen Feldtheorie der Elementarteilchen, *Die Naturwissenschaften*, vol. 50 (January 3, 1963), pp. 3–7.
11. CALVIN, M., Chemical Evolution and the Origin of Life, *American Scientist*, vol. 44 (1956), pp. 248–63.
12. *Proceedings of the First International Symposium on the Origin of Life on the Earth*, ed. by A. I. OPARIN, A. E. BRAUNSHTEIN, A. G. PASYNSKII, and T. E. PAVLOVSKAYA, New York: Pergamon Press, Inc. (1959).
13. ALLER, L. H., *The Abundance of the Elements*, New York: Interscience Publishers, Inc. (1961).
14. SUESS, H. E., and UREY, H. C., Abundances of the Elements, *Reviews of Modern Physics*, vol. 28 (1956), pp. 53–74.
15. VON KLÜBER, H., *Das Vorkommen der chemischen Elemente im Kosmos*, Leipzig: J. A. Barth (1931).
16. CHERDYNTSEV, V. V., *Abundance of Chemical Elements*, Chicago: University of Chicago Press (1961).
17. EDSALL, J. T., and WYMAN, J., *Biophysical Chemistry*, vol. I, New York: Academic Press, Inc. (1958), Chapter 1, pp. 1–26.
18. SIDGWICK, N. V., *The Chemical Elements and Their Compounds*, vol. I, New York: Oxford University Press, Inc. (1950), p. 490.
19. DUFAY, J., *Galactic Nebulae and Interstellar Matter*, New York: Philosophical Library, Inc. (1957).
20. HERZBERG, G., *Molecular Spectra and Molecular Structure: I. Spectra of Diatomic Molecules*, New York: D. Van Nostrand Co., Inc. (1959).
21. ABETTI, G., *The Sun*, New York: The Macmillan Co. (1957).
22. BATES, D. R., and SPITZER, L., JR., The Density of Molecules in Interstellar Space, *The Astrophysical Journal*, vol. 113 (1951), pp. 441–63.
23. HOYLE, F., and WICKRAMASINGHE, N. C., On Graphite Particles as Interstellar Grains, *Monthly Notices of the Royal Astronomical Society*, vol. 124 (1962), pp. 417–33.
24. KUIPER, G. P., Planetary Atmospheres and Their Origin, *The Atmospheres of the Earth and Planets*, 2nd ed., Chicago: University of Chicago Press (1952), pp. 306–405.
25. SWINGS, P., and HASER, L., *Atlas of Representative Cometary Spectra*, University of Liège Astrophysical Institute, Louvain: Impr. Ceuterick (1956).
26. RICHTER, N. B., *Statistik und Physik der Kometen*, Leipzig: J. A. Barth (1954).
27. SWINGS, P. *et al.*, La Physique des Comètes, Colloque International d'Astrophysique, September 1952, Liège, *Mémoires de la Société Royale des Sciences de Liège*, 4e ser., vol. 13 (1953), pp. 43–429.

28. BREWER, L., and ENGELKE, J. L., Spectrum of C_3, *The Journal of Chemical Physics*, vol. 36 (1962), pp. 992–8.

29. HAIDINGER, W., Die organische Substanz im Meteorsteine von Kaba, *Sitzungsberichte der Akademie der Wissenschaften in Wien*, vol. 34 (1859), pp. 7–8.

30. SMITH, J. L., Solid Carbon Compounds in Meteorites, *Original Researches in Mineralogy and Chemistry*, ed. by J. B. MARVIN, Louisville: J. P. Morton and Co. (1884), pp. 496–514.

31. VDOVIKIN, G. P., Preliminary Results of the Luminescent Bituminous Investigation of Four Carbonaceous Chondrites, *Meteoritika*, vol. 18 (1960), pp. 78–82.

32. MASON, B., *Meteorites*, New York: John Wiley and Sons, Inc. (1962).

33. ANDERS, E., On the Origin of Carbonaceous Chondrites, *Annals of the New York Academy of Sciences*, vol. 108 (1963), pp. 514–33.

34. PETERSILIE, I. A., Is There a Stream of Flammable Gases From the Depths of the Khibini? *Izvestiya Akademii Nauk SSSR, Seriya Geologicheskaya*, No. 12 (1961), pp. 24–9.

35. PLOOSTER, M. N., and REED, T. B., Carbon–Hydrogen–Acetylene Equilibrium at High Temperatures, *The Journal of Chemical Physics*, vol. 31 (1959), pp. 66–72.

36. STEVENSON, F. J., On the Presence of Fixed Ammonium in Rocks, *Science*, vol. 130 (1959), pp. 221–2.

37. DuFRESNE, E. R., and ROY, S. K., A New Phosphate Mineral From the Springwater Pallasite, *Geochimica et Cosmochimica Acta*, vol. 24 (1961), pp. 198–205.

38. PALACHE, C., BERMAN, H., and FRONDEL, C., *The System of Mineralogy*, 7th ed., vol. II, Collophane, New York: John Wiley and Sons, Inc. (1951), p. 885.

39. REYNOLDS, J. H., Determination of the Age of the Elements, *Physical Review Letters*, vol. 4 (January 1, 1960), pp. 8–10.

40. KURODA, P. K., and CROUCH, W. H., JR., On the Chronology of the Formation of the Solar System. 2. Iodine in Terrestrial Rocks and the Xenon 129/136 Formation Interval of the Earth, *Journal of Geophysical Research*, vol. 67 (1962), pp. 4863–6.

41. FISH, R. A., and GOLES, G. G., Ambient Xenon: A Key to the History of Meteorites, *Nature*, vol. 196 (1962), pp. 27–31.

42. MERRIHUE, C. M., Excess Xenon 129 in Chondrules From the Bruderheim Meteorite, *Journal of Geophysical Research*, vol. 68 (1963), pp. 325–30.

43. FOWLER, W. A., GREENSTEIN, J. L., and HOYLE, F., Deuteronomy. Synthesis of Deuterons and the Light Nuclei During the Early History of the Solar System, *American Journal of Physics*, vol. 29 (1961), pp. 393–403.

44. FOWLER, W. A., Nuclear Clues to the Early History of the Solar System, *Science*, vol. 135 (1962), pp. 1037–45.

45. MURTHY, V. R., and UREY, H. C., The Time of Formation of the Solar System Relative to Nucleosynthesis, *The Astrophysical Journal*, vol. 135 (1962), pp. 626–31.

46. RINGWOOD, A. E., Present Status of the Chondritic Earth Model, *Researches on Meteorites*, ed. by C. MOORE, New York: John Wiley and Sons, Inc. (1962), pp. 198–216.

47. WOOD, J. A., Chondrules and the Origin of the Terrestrial Planets, *Nature*, vol. 194 (1962), pp. 127–30.

48. KUIPER, G. P., The Formation of the Planets, Part I, pp. 57–68 (March–April); Part II, pp. 105–21 (May–June); Part III, pp. 158–76 (July–August); *The Journal of the Royal Astronomical Society of Canada*, vol. 50 (1956).

49. KUIPER, G. P., Comets and the Dissipation of the Solar Nebula, *Mémoires de la Société Royale des Sciences de Liège*, 4e ser., vol. 13 (1953), pp. 401–25.

50. WHIPPLE, F. L., A Comet Model. I. The Acceleration of Comet Encke, *The Astrophysical Journal*, vol. 111 (1950), pp. 375–94.

51. WHIPPLE, F. L., On the Structure of the Cometary Nucleus, *The Solar System: vol. IV, The Moon, Meteorites, and Comets*, ed. by B. M. MIDDLEHURST and G. P. KUIPER, Chicago: University of Chicago Press (1963), pp. 639–62.

52. LILLER, W., The Nature of the Grains in the Tails of Comets 1956h and 1957d, *The Astrophysical Journal*, vol. 132 (1960), pp. 867–82.

53. HASER, L., La conservation des radicaux libres à basse température et la structure des

noyaux de comètes, *Comptes Rendus Hebdomadaires des Séances de l'Académie des Sciences*, vol. 241 (1955), pp. 742–3.

54. DONN, B., and UREY, H. C., On the Mechanism of Comet Outbursts and the Chemical Composition of Comets, *The Astrophysical Journal*, vol. 123 (1956), pp. 339–42.

55. GLASEL, J. A., Stabilization of NH in Hydrocarbon Matrices and Its Relation to Cometary Phenomena, *Proceedings of the National Academy of Sciences of the United States of America*, vol. 47 (1961), pp. 174–80.

56. OORT, J. H., Inferences on the Origin of Comets Derivable From the Distribution of the Reciprocal Major Axes, *Mémoires de la Société Royale des Sciences de Liège*, 4e ser., vol. 13 (1953), pp. 364–71.

57. PAGE, T., Recent Statistical Studies in Astronomy, *Science*, vol. 132 (1960), pp. 1870–5.

58. JASTROW, R., and PANAGAKOS, N., The Planet Jupiter, *Science*, vol. 139 (1963), pp. 351–4.

59. SUESS, H. E., Die Häufigkeit der Edelgase auf der Erde und im Kosmos, *The Journal of Geology*, vol. 57 (1949), pp. 600–7.

60. TUREKIAN, K. K., Probable Aquatic Environments of the Pre-Cambrian, *Preprints of the International Oceanographic Congress*, Washington, D.C.: American Association for the Advancement of Science (1959), pp. 81–3.

61. KUIPER, G. P., Origin, Age, and Possible Ultimate Fate of the Earth, *The Earth and Its Atmosphere*, ed. by D. R. BATES, New York: Basic Books, Inc. (1957), pp. 12–30.

62. HOLLAND, H. D., Model for the Evolution of the Earth's Atmosphere, *Petrologic Studies: A Volume to Honor A. F. Buddington*, ed. by A. E. J. ENGEL, H. L. JAMES, and B. F. LEONARD, New York: The Geological Society of America (1962), pp. 447–77.

63. LOEB, W., Über das Verhalten des Formamids unter der Wirkung der stillen Entladung. Ein Beitrag zur Frage der Stickstoff-Assimilation, *Berichte der deutschen chemischen Gesellschaft*, vol. 46 (1913), pp. 684–97.

64. MILLER, S. L., The Formation of Organic Compounds on the Primitive Earth, *Annals of the New York Academy of Sciences*, vol. 69 (1957), pp. 260–75.

65. HOUGH, L., and ROGERS, A. F., Synthesis of Amino Acids From Water, Hydrogen, Methane and Ammonia. *The Journal of Physiology* (London), vol. 132 (March 23–24, 1956), pp. 28–30.

66. ABELSON, P. H., Paleobiochemistry: Inorganic Synthesis of Amino Acids, *Carnegie Institution of Washington Yearbook No. 55*, Washington, D.C.: Carnegie Institution of Washington (1956), pp. 171–4.

67. FRANCK, B., Synthese von Aminosäuregemischen aus Methanol und aliphatischen Kohlenwasserstoffen, *Berichte der deutschen chemischen Gesellschaft*, vol. 93 (1960), pp. 446–54.

68. HEARN, L. E., and ORÓ, J., Unpublished experiments.

69. PITZER, K. S., Repulsive Forces in Relation to Bond Energies, Distances and Other Properties, *The Journal of the American Chemical Society*, vol. 70 (1948), 2140–5.

70. GUNESCH, H., and STADMÜLLER, R., Separarea și Dozarea Acetilenelor Superioare, Rezultate Prin-Cracarea Gazului Metan in Arc Electric, Prin Metoda di Chromatografie de Repartitie Gaz-lichid. *Revista de Chimie (Bucharest)*, vol 9 (1958), pp. 35–8.

71. GLOCKER, G., and LIND, S. C., *Electrochemistry of Gases and Other Dielectrics*, New York: John Wiley and Sons, Inc. (1939).

72. RABINOWITCH, E. I., *Photosynthesis and Related Processes*, vol. I, New York: Interscience Publishers, Inc. (1945), p. 81.

73. NOYES, W. A., JR., and LEIGHTON, P. A., *The Photochemistry of Gases*, New York: Reinhold Publishing Corp. (1941).

74. BAUDISCH, O., Über Nitrat- und Nitritassimilation, *Zeitschrift für angewandte Chemie*, vol. 26 (1913), pp. 612–13.

75. DHAR, N. R., and MUKHERJEE, S. K., Photosynthesis of Amino Acids *in vitro, Nature*, vol. 134 (1934), p. 499; Photosynthesis of Amino Acids, *Journal of the Indian Chemical Society*, vol. 11 (1934), pp. 727–35.

76. FRITZ, R., *Photochemical Synthesis of Amino Acids*, Master's Thesis, University

of Houston, Houston, Texas, 1960.

77. STEVEN, F. S., and TRISTRAM, G. R., The Presence in Commercial Sulphonated-Polystyrene Resins of Some Amino Acids, *The Biochemical Journal*, vol. 83, No. 2 (1962), p. 245.

78. ANDERSON, W. T., JR., The Photolysis of Potassium Nitrate Solutions, *The Journal of the American Chemical Society*, vol. 46 (1924), pp. 797–802.

79. KRISHNAN, K. S., and GUHA, A. C., The Absorption Spectra of Nitrates and Nitrites in Relation to Their Photodissociation, *Proceedings of the Indian Academy of Sciences, Section A*, vol. 1 (1934), pp. 242–9.

80. FERRARI, G., Sintesi fotochimica di amminoacidi da composti azotati inorganici e sostanze organiche ternarie. Nota II., *Annali di Chimica (Rome)*, vol. 49 (1959), pp. 2017–22.

81. FERRARI, G., Sul meccanismo della sintesi fotochimica di amminoacidi. Nota I., *Gazzetta Chimica Italiana*, vol. 90 (1960), pp. 1522–9.

82. GROTH, W., Photochemische Bildung von Aminosäuren und anderen organischen Verbindungen aus Mischungen von H_2O, NH_3 und den einfachsten Kohlenwasserstoffen, *Angewandte Chemie*, vol. 69, No. 21 (1957), p. 681.

83. BALY, E. C. C., Photosynthesis, *Industrial and Engineering Chemistry*, vol. 16 (1924), pp. 1019–21.

84. IRVINE, J. C., and FRANCIS, G. V., Examination of Photosynthetic Sugars by the Methylation Method, *Industrial and Engineering Chemistry*, vol. 16 (1924), pp. 1022–3.

85. DESCHREIDER, A. R., Photosynthesis of Amino Acids, *Nature*, vol. 182 (1958), p. 528.

86. CULTRERA, R., and FERRARI, G., Sintesi fotochimica di amminoacidi da composti azotati inorganici e sostanze organiche ternarie, *Annali di Chimica (Rome)*, vol. 49 (1959), pp. 1629–48.

87. FERRARI, G., and CULTRERA, R., Sul meccanismo della sintesi fotochimica di amminoacidi. Nota II., *Gazzetta Chimica Italiana*, vol. 90 (1960), pp. 1637–44.

88. GARRISON, W. M., BENNETT, W., and COLE, S., Synthesis of Products of Higher Molecular Weight in the Radiolysis of Aqueous Solutions of Formic Acid, *Radiation Research*, vol. 9 (1958), pp. 647–59.

89. DOSE, K., and ETTRE, K., Die radiationschemische Synthese von Aminosäuren und verwandten Verbindungen, *Zeitschrift für Naturforschung*, Pt. b, vol. 13 (1958), pp. 784–8.

90. CHAMBERS, R. W., and CARPENTER, F. H., Ammonolysis of Peptides: A Method of Determining C-Terminal Amino Acids, *The Journal of the American Chemical Society*, vol. 77 (1955), pp. 1527–31.

91. SATO, M., OKAWA, K., and AKABORI, S., A New Synthesis of Threonine, *Bulletin of the Chemical Society of Japan*, vol. 30 (1957), pp. 937–8.

92. AKABORI, S., OTANI, T. T., MARSHALL, R., WINITZ, M., and GREENSTEIN, J. P., A Synthesis and Resolution of DL-Serine, *Archives of Biochemistry and Biophysics*, vol. 83 (1959), pp. 1–9.

93. MASTER, F., *Natural Synthesis of Amino Acids*, Master's Thesis, University of Houston, Houston, Texas, 1957.

94. HICKLING, A., and NEWNS, G. R., The Synthesis of Hydrazine by Glow-Discharge Electrolysis of Liquid Ammonia, *Proceedings of the Chemical Society* (London), (November 1959), pp. 368–9.

95. AYLWARD, F., and SAWISTOWSKA, M., Reduction of Organic Compounds by Hydrazine, *Chemistry and Industry* (April 1, 1961), p. 404.

96. ORÓ, J., Unpublished experiments.

97. LANGE, O., Über eine neue Verbindung von der Zusammensetzung der Cyanwasserstoffsäure, *Berichte der deutschen chemischen Gesellschaft*, vol. 6 (1872), pp. 99–101.

98. WIPPERMAN, R., Über Tricyanwasserstoff, eine der Blausäure polymere Verbindung, *Berichte der deutschen chemischen Gesellschaft*, vol. 7 (1874), pp. 767–72.

99. LOQUIN, R., Sur les éthers et les acides alpha-cétoniques ou composés homo-pyruviques, VI, *Bulletin de la Société Chimique de France*, vol. 31 (1904), pp. 1147–53.

100. RUSKE, W., Über Tri- und Tetramere Blausäure, *Die chemische Technik (Berlin)*,

vol. 6 (1954), pp. 489–94.

101. LOWE, C. V., REES, M. W., and MARKHAM, R., Synthesis of Complex Organic Compounds from Simple Precursors: Formation of Amino Acids, Amino Acid Polymers and Purines from NH₄CN, *Nature*, vol. 199 (1962), p. 222.

102. MAHAJANI, P. B., and RAY, J. N., Synthesis of Some Amino Acids and Related Products, Part I, *Journal of the Indian Chemical Society*, vol. 33 (1956), pp. 455–8.

103. SCHMIDT, M. and BLAETTNER, K., Tetramere Thioformaldehyde, *Angewandte Chemie*, vol. 71 (1959), pp. 407–8.

104. ORÓ, J., GUIDRY, C. L., ZLATKIS, A., The Odor of Methional Purified by Gas Chromatography, *Food Research*, vol. 24 (March–April 1959), pp. 240–1.

105. BUTLEROW, A., Formation synthétique d'une substance sucrée, *Comptes Rendus Hebdomadaires des Séances de l'Académie des Sciences*, vol. 53 (1861), pp. 145–7.

106. LOEW, O., Über Formaldehyd und dessen Kondensation, *Journal für praktische Chemie*, vol. 33 (1885), pp. 321–51.

107. FISCHER, E., and PASSMORE, F., Bildung von Acrose aus Formaldehyd, *Berichte der deutschen chemischen Gesellschaft*, vol. 22 (1889), pp. 359–61.

108. EULER, H., and EULER, A., Über die Bildung von *i*-Arabinoketose aus Formaldehyd, *Berichte der deutschen chemischen Gesellschaft*, vol. 39 (1906), pp. 45–51.

109. SCHMITZ, E., Über den Mechanismus der Acrose-Bildung, *Berichte der deutschen chemischen Gesellschaft*, vol. 46 (1913), pp. 2327–35.

110. MARIANI, E., and TORRACA, G., The Composition of Formose. A Chromatographic Study, *The International Sugar Journal*, vol. 55 (1953), pp. 309–11.

111. MAYER, R., and JÄSCHKE, L., Zur Umwandlung von Formaldehyd in Kohlenhydraten, *Annalen der Chemie*, vol. 635 (1960), pp. 145–53.

112. BRESLOW, R., On the Mechanism of the Formose Reaction, *Tetrahedron Letters*, No. 21 (December 1959), pp. 22–6.

113. BUCHANAN, J. M., and HARTMAN, S. C., Enzymic Reactions in the Synthesis of the Purines, *Advances in Enzymology*, vol. 21, ed. by F. F. NORD, New York: Interscience Publishers, Inc. (1959), pp. 199–294.

114. CAVALIERI, L. F., TINKER, J. F., and BENDICH, A., A Synthesis of Adenine. The Incorporation of Isotopes of Nitrogen and Carbon, *The Journal of the American Chemical Society*, vol. 71 (1949), pp. 533–6.

115. ORÓ, J., Formation of Purines Under Possible Primitive Earth Conditions, *Federation Proceedings of the Federation of American Societies for Experimental Biology*, vol. 20 (Pt. 1), (1961), p. 352.

116. VÖLKER, T., Konstitution und Bildung der polymeren Blausäuren, *Angewandte Chemie*, vol. 69, No. 22 (1957), pp. 728–9.

117. ORÓ, J., and KAMAT, S. S., Unpublished experiments.

118. WÖHLER, F., Sur la formation artificielle de l'urée, *Annales de Chimie (Paris)*, 2ᵉ ser., vol. 37 (1828), pp. 330–4.

119. VARNER, J. E., and BURRELL, R. C., Prebiological Chemistry of Nitrogen Compounds of Metabolic Importance, *Euclides (Madrid)*, vol. 15 (1955), pp. 1–8.

120. PALM, C., and CALVIN, M., *Primordial Organic Chemistry: Evidence for Production of Purines and Pyrimidines From Simple Gases by Electron Irradiation*, Bio-organic Chemistry Quarterly Report 9900, E. O. Lawrence Radiation Laboratory, University of California, Berkeley, 1961, pp. 51–64.

121. PONNAMPERUMA, C., and LEMMON, R., Unpublished results.

122. LEMMON, R., Private communication.

123. PFLÜGER, E., Beiträge zur Lehre von der Respiration. I. Über die physiologische Verbrennung in den lebendigen Organismen, *Pflügers Archiv für die gesamte Physiologie*, vol. 10 (1875), pp. 251–367.

124. GAUTIER, A., Nouvelle méthode de synthèse de composés organiques azotés; synthèse de la xanthine et de la méthylxanthine, *Bulletin de la Société Chimique de France*, 2ᵉ ser., vol. 42 (1884), pp. 141–6.

125. JOHNSON, T. B., The Origin of Purines in Plants, *The Journal of the American Chemical Society*, vol. 36 (1914), pp. 337–45.

126. FISCHER, E., Über die angebliche Synthese des Xanthins aus Cyanwasserstoff,

Berichte der deutschen chemischen Gesellschaft, vol. 30 (1897), pp. 3131–3.

127. SALOMONE, G., Sui prodotti di esplosione dell' acido cianidrico, *Gazzetta Chimica Italiana*, vol. 42 (1912), pp. 617–22.

128. JOHNSON, T. B., and NICOLET, B. H., Researches on Pyrimidines. LXVI. The Formation of Pyrimidines from Diethyl Aminomalonate and Aminomalonic Nitrile, *The Journal of the American Chemical Society*, vol. 36 (1914), pp. 345–55.

129. HORBACZEWSKI, J., Synthese der Harnsäure, *Monatshefte für Chemie und verwandte Teile anderer Wissenschaften*, vol. 3 (1882), pp. 796–7.

130. BREDERECK, H., ULMER, H., and WALDMANN, H., Purin aus Formamid. Methylierung und Bromierung des Purins (Synthesen in der Purinreihe, VII. Mitteilung), *Berichte der deutschen chemischen Gesellschaft*, vol. 89 (1956), pp. 12–18.

131. BREDERECK, H., EFFENBERGER, F., and RAINER, G., Eine neue einfache Purin-Synthese, *Angewandte Chemie*, vol. 73 (1961), p. 63.

132. DAVIDSON, D., and BAUDISCH, O., The Preparation of Uracil From Urea, *The Journal of the American Chemical Society*, vol. 48 (1956), pp. 2379–83.

133. BREDERECK, H., GOMPPER, R., and HERLINGER, H., Darstellung, Eigenschaften und Umsetzungen des Pyrimidins, *Berichte der deutschen chemischen Gesellschaft*, vol. 91 (1958), pp. 2832–49.

134. DASHKEVICH, L. B., Preparation of Malonic Acid and its Ethers From Carbon Suboxide, *Doklady Akademii Nauk SSSR.*, vol. 132 (1960), pp. 1319–21.

135. BREDERECK, H., SCHMÖTZER, G., and BECKER, H. J., Zur Konstitution der tetrameren Blausäure und ihrer Acyl-Derivative, *Annalen der Chemie*, vol. 600 (1956), pp. 87–95.

136. RUSKE, W., Polymere Blausäure, *Wissenschaftliche Zeitschrift der Humboldt-Universität zu Berlin*, vol. 8 (1958), pp. 557–72.

137. KATCHALSKI, E., Poly-Alpha-Amino-Acids, *Advances in Protein Chemistry*, vol. 6, New York: Academic Press, Inc. (1951), pp. 123–85.

138. BAMFORD, C. H., ELLIOTT, A., and HAMBY, W. E., *Synthetic Polypeptides*, New York: Academic Press, Inc. (1956).

139. KATCHALSKI, E., and SELA, M., Synthesis and Chemical Properties of Poly-Alpha-Amino-Acids, *Advances in Protein Chemistry*, vol. 13, New York: Academic Press, Inc. (1958), pp. 243–492.

140. GUIDRY, C. L., *Thermal Synthesis of Polypeptides in Aqueous Systems*, Doctoral Thesis, University of Houston, Houston, Texas, 1962.

141. HANAFUSA, H., and AKABORI, S., Polymerization of Aminoacetonitrile, *Bulletin of the Chemical Society of Japan*, vol. 32 (1959), pp. 626–30.

142. LOSSE, G., and ANDERS, K., Die Polymerisation von Alpha-Amino-Propionitril an mineralischen Trägern als Modell für die primäre Bildung von Eiweissstoffen auf der Erde. *Zeitschrift für physiologische Chemie*, vol. 323 (1961). pp. 111–5.

143. NOONER, D. W., and ORÓ, J., Unpublished experiments.

144. PERTI, O. N., BAHADUR, K., and PATHAK, H. D., Photosynthesis of Peptides in Aqueous Solutions of Glycine, Glutamic Acid and Tyrosine, *Proceedings of the National Academy of Sciences, India*, Section A, vol. 30 (1961), pp. 206–20.

145. OTOZAI, K., KUME, S., NAGAI, S., YAMAMOTO, T., and FUKUSHIMA, S., Polymerization by Electric Discharge, *Bulletin of the Chemical Society of Japan*, vol. 27 (1954), pp. 476–7.

146. LOSSE, G., and WEDDIGE, H., Neue Möglichkeiten zur Knüpfung der Peptidbindung, *Annalen der Chemie*, vol. 636 (1960), pp. 144–9.

147. JONES, M. E., and LIPMANN, F., Chemical and Enzymatic Synthesis of Carbamyl Phosphate, *Proceedings of the National Academy of Sciences of the United States of America*, vol. 46 (1960), pp. 1194–1205.

148. SAGAN, C., Private communication.

149. LANGHELD, K., Über Metaphosphorsäure-Äthylester und dessen Anwendung in der organischen Chemie, *Berichte der deutschen chemischen Gesellschaft*, vol. 43 (1910), pp. 1857–60.

150. VAN WAZER, J. R., Phosphorus and Its Compounds, *Chemistry*, vol. I, New York: Interscience Publishers, Inc. (1958), p. 278.

151. CONTRERAS, G., ESPEJO, R., MERY, E., OHLBAUM, A., and TOHÁ, J., Polymerization

of Ribomononucleotides by γ-Radiation, *Biochimica et Biophysica Acta,* vol. 61 (1962), pp. 718–27.
152. PATTEE, H. H., On the Origin of Macromolecular Sequences, *Biophysical Journal,* vol. 1 (1961), pp. 683–709.
153. RICH, A., On the Problems of Evolution and Biochemical Information Transfer, *Horizons in Biochemistry,* New York: Academic Press, Inc. (1962), pp. 103– 26.
154. MULLER, H. J., Genetic Nucleic Acid, *The Graduate Journal,* vol. 5 (1962), pp. 133–59.
155. PULLMAN, B., and PULLMAN, A., Electronic Delocalization and Biochemical Evolution, *Nature,* vol. 196 (1962), pp. 1137–42.
156. ULBRICHT, T. L. V., The Origin of Optical Activity and the Origin of Life, *Comparative Biochemistry,* vol. IV, ed. by M. FLORKIN and H. S. MASON, New York: Academic Press, Inc. (1962), pp. 16–25.
157. KLISS, R. M., and MATTHEWS, C. N., Hydrogen Cyanide Dimer and Chemical Evolution, *Proceedings of the National Academy of Sciences of the United States of America,* vol. 48 (1962), pp. 1300–6.
158. UREY, H. C., Boundary Conditions for Theories of the Origin of the Solar System, *Physics and Chemistry of the Earth,* ed. by L. H. AHRENS *et al.,* London: Pergamon Press, Inc. (1957), pp. 46–76.
159. GERLACH, E., and DÖRING, H. J., Schnell-Identifizierung von Adenin, Adenosin, Adenosin-Phosphorsäuren und Pyridinnukleotiden in Papierchromatogrammen, *Die Naturwissenschaften,* vol. 42 (1955), p. 344.
160. LOWE, C. V., and REES, M. W., *Synthesis of Amino Acids and Polypeptides Under Possible Primitive Earth Conditions,* Society for Pediatric Research, 32nd Meeting, Atlantic City, N. J., 1962.

ACKNOWLEDGEMENTS

The author is indebted to Professor M. Calvin and to Doctor S. L. Miller for discussions of some of the ideas contained in this Chapter, and to the National Science Foundation (research grant G-13, 117) and the National Aeronautics and Space Administration (research grant NsG-257-62) for supporting the experimental work carried out in this laboratory. Permission from the New York Academy of Sciences to reproduce part of the text of Ref. 1295 is gratefully acknowledged.

CHAPTER II

ORGANIC REMAINS IN METEORITES

F. L. STAPLIN

Imperial Oil Limited, Calgary, Canada

THE material in the Chapter is divided into three sections: (1) Chemical analyses of carbonaceous chondrites, (2) organized elements and possible microfossils, and (3) origin and significance of carbonaceous chondrites.

Definite conclusions as to the meaning of the organic substances and possible fossils in the carbonaceous chondrites must be left to the future. Much of the work is still incomplete, and experimental evidence must be found to prove or disprove a number of the assumptions.

The organic matter may or may not be interpreted as biogenic in origin. Either way, it does have profound implications with regard to life. If it is not direct evidence of life from outside of our planet, then perhaps it holds the key to the origin of life. The indigenous occurrence of the complex hydrocarbons and other organic molecules in the carbonaceous chondrites is no longer disputed.

Experimentation is proceeding in a number of laboratories. Bernal (Refs. 842, 843, 844) has pointed out that perhaps only 50 kg of carbonaceous meteorite have been collected. Unless the research work is carefully coordinated and the various groups from diverse disciplines cooperate, irreplaceable evidence may be lost. The chondrites are not homogeneous in substance, adding a further difficulty, especially with regard to the possible microfossils that offer the only direct evidence for the existence of life on the meteorite parent body.

CHEMICAL ANALYSES OF CARBONACEOUS CHONDRITES

Older Work

Carbonaceous substances in a stony meteorite (Alais) were first noted by Berzelius (Ref. 854), but he decided that these substances were not developed through biogenic agencies. It was believed that organic constituents in Kaba had a biological origin. In the early work, simple solvents were used to extract the organic matter. Tentative attempts

77

at identification were made by means of the gross physical properties of the extracts. Only in the last ten years have modern spectrometric, chromatographic, infrared, and microscopic techniques been applied. The early work is summarized by Cohen (Ref. 879).

Hahn (Ref. 898) reported fossils, but a large number of these objects were demonstrated to be mineral substances. Not until 1961 (Ref. 871) was the question of fossils or "organized elements" again put forth.

Inorganic Constituents

Rose[1] proposed the two-fold classification of stony meteorites into chondrites and achondrites. Chondrites have growths, aggregates or spherules of olivine or pyroxene. Tschermak[2] and Brezina[3] modified the classification by subdivision into groups according to structure and color. This classification was unsatisfactory because it was based largely on superficial or secondary characteristics.

The Prior–Mason classification,[4,5] based on chemical composition, recognizes five groups of chondrites (Table 1).

TABLE 1. Prior–Mason classification of chondrites[a]

Group	Number known[b]	FeO/FeO + MgO mol %	Total Fe %	Wiik type[c]
1. Enstatite	9	0	28.5	
2. Olivine–bronzite ⎫	±800	15-22	26.0	
3. Olivine–hypersthene ⎭		22-32	22.0	
4. Olivine–pigeonite	11	32-40	26.0	III
5. Carbonaceous	14	40-50	26.0	I + II

[a]From Mason.[5]
[b]Numbers differ in various papers.
[c]Ref. 989.

The mineralogical composition is related to chemical composition, and, according to Mason, the classification of an individual chondrite can be determined rapidly by the presence or absence of olivine and the composition of the olivine.

Urey and Craig (Ref. 987) and Wiik (Ref. 989) suggested that two main groups existed among the chondrites, high iron with about 26% total Fe and low iron with about 22% Fe. Only the olivine–hypersthene group of Mason falls into the low iron group.

Wiik recognized three types of carbonaceous chondrites on the basis of mean values of certain constituents:

	SiO$_2$	MgO	C	H$_2$O	S
Type I	22.56	15.21	3.54	20.08	10.32
Type II	27.57	19.18	2.46	13.35	5.41
Type III	33.58	23.74	0.46	0.99	3.78

Type III or olivine–pigeonite chondrites are characterized by the predominance of olivine, some pigeonite, oligoclase and troilite, and accessory taenitic nickel–iron.[5] Some have sufficient carbonaceous material to produce a black color.

Carbonaceous chondrites are defined by Mason as containing little or no iron as metal or sulfide, containing carbon and carbonaceous compounds in excess of 0.5%, and considerable amounts of combined water. Sulfur is present as free sulfur, sulfur in organic compounds, or oxidized sulfur compounds. Total iron (water-free basis) amounts to 23–26%. Types I and II of Wiik are differentiated as follows:

Type I – Low density ($\sim$ 2.2), high amorphous hydrated silicate content, much of sulfur as water-soluble sulfate, no chondrules, magnetic (mostly as spinel).

Type II – Density 2.5–2.9, high serpentine content, weakly or non-magnetic, much of sulfur in free state, chondrules of olivine and enstatite. Traces of nickel – iron may be present.

Some basic analyses of carbonaceous chondrites, after Wiik (Ref. 989), DuFresne and Anders (Ref. 886), and Briggs (Ref. 866) are condensed in Table 2. The figures represent atoms per 100 atoms of silicon unless otherwise noted.

Among minerals present in the carbonaceous chondrites, dolomite has been found in Orgueil and Ivuna (Ref. 866). Serpentine is reported for all type II chondrites by Mason, but its exact nature is uncertain. Comparative X-ray diffraction patterns presented by DuFresne and Anders show that minerals are present in Murray, Mighei, and Cold Bokkeveld that can be compared with serpentines and chlorite but do not have identical diffraction patterns. These minerals are considered by DuFresne and Anders to be alteration products of olivine. The same authors found monoclinic pyroxenes in Murray (10–15%) but not in eight others examined. Only Ornans of the group tested lacked elemental sulfur in coexistence with soluble sulfate (largely epsomite). Minerals similar to chrysotile or chlorite were found in Murray, Orgueil, Mighei, Mokoia, Haripura, and others. Breunnerite occurs in Orgueil.

The water-soluble salts often occur in distinct veins or cracks in the rock. Any hydration of the sulfate is almost certainly terrestrial. Isotopically, the low-temperature water fraction is close to terrestrial water

(Ref. 855). Boato also found abundant deuterium in the higher-temperature water fractions (over 180°C) of Ivuna and Orgueil that probably is extraterrestrial and possibly bound to silicates.

TABLE 2. Basic analyses of some carbonaceous chondrites[a]

Name	Type	Fe	Mg	Si	Al	Na	Ca	Ni	S	C[b]
Alais	I									
Ivuna	I	90.0	105.2	–	8.4	6.4	8.9	4.73	55.3	4.83
		(27.41)	(32.14)	(30.43)	(2.56)	(1.95)	(2.71)	(1.44)	b	
Orgueil	I	87.8	104.5	–	8.6	6.3	5.8	4.4	45.6	3.10
		(27.34)	(32.48)	(31.12)	(2.68)	(1.97)	(1.81)	(1.37)	b	
Tonk	I	85.7	90.9	–	10.1	27.9	6.4	3.43	49.1	2.70
Al Rais	II									2.49
Bells	II									
Boriskino	II	83.9	107.8	–	13.7	7.8	8.9	4.41	7.1	2.06
Cold Bokkeveld	II	82.1	102.1	–	9.9	4.3	6.1	4.38	20.4	1.52
Crescent	II									
Erakot	II									2.14
Haripura	II	86.6	101.8	–	10.0	5.1	8.2	5.2	38.7	4.0
Mighei	II	82.1	104.2	–	9.1	4.4	6.4	4.42	24.7	2.48
Murray	II	79.7	102.6	–	6.9	1.5	7.2	4.21	18.3	2.78
Nawapali	II	83.4	98.4	–	9.1	3.9	8.7	4.58	19.4	2.5
Nogoya	II	84.9	104.3	–	10.2	1.3	9.9	4.52	22.5	1.62
Renazzo	II									
Santa Cruz	II	84.6	107.3	–	6.8	3.3	8.4	4.50	21.0	2.54
Felix	III	82.2	104.2	–	10.1	3.4	7.0	4.10	11.0	
Grosnaja	III									0.56
Indarch	III									
Kaba	III									1.99
Lance	III	82.7	105.4	–	10.4	3.4	8.5	4.62	13.3	0.46
Mokoia	III	77.5	106.9	–	8.9	3.0	8.2	3.95	13.8	1.36
Ornans	III	–	106.1	–	–	3.2	6.4	–	13.1	
Vigarano	III									1.12
Warrenton	III	80.8	100.8	–	7.4	3.8	6.7	4.21	10.0	
Bali	?									
Simonod	?									
St. Caprais	?									

[a] Atoms per 100 atoms of silicon (Ref. 139).
[b] Per cent (Refs. 866, 917).

"Thermometer" minerals have been investigated by Mueller (Ref. 927) and DuFresne and Anders (Refs. 139, 886). A strained glass in Mighei becomes annealed at 180°C within a few weeks. The combination of unpyrolized organic material with elemental sulfur and the lack of sulfides or sulfites resulting from the reduction of SO_4 in the presence of carbon and organic material also indicate a rather low-temperature history subsequent to the aggregation of the chondrites of types I and II. Thin fusion crusts offer the only evidence of contact with the Earth's atmosphere, but much of the meteorite has been lost by ablation.

In an earlier summary (Ref. 973), it was suggested that fragments of the Orgueil meteorite superficially resemble carbonaceous siltstone with fine veins of magnesium sulfate. Type I chondrites are especially friable. Other stony meteorites show brecciation, veining, and primary and secondary mineral formation. The veins and brecciation may be shock-induced.[6,7] Detailed petrographic and petrofabric comparisons of the stony meteorites are needed, and evidence of sorting, grading of size fractions, and of the movement of solutions should be sought.

Excellent summaries of the physics, chemistry, and origin of meteorites are presented by Wood[8] and Anders.[7]

Organic Analyses

Mueller (Ref. 927) reported 2.2% carbon, after decomposition of carbonates with dilute acid, for the Cold Bokkeveld chondrite, or an approximate content of 22 mg of carbon per gram of chondrite. Briggs (Ref. 866) determined that the major fraction of the organic matter removed from chondrites has a carbon content of about 47%. On the assumption that carbonates and inorganic compounds are present only as traces, or at most as small percentages, roughly 44 mg of organic matter per gram of meteorite is estimated for Cold Bokkeveld. The roughness of estimates prepared in this manner is evident when it is pointed out that one extract made by Mueller contained only 24% carbon, and Briggs obtained carbon analyses of Mokoia samples that varied from 0.5 to 2.1%. The carbon distribution is heterogeneous. Estimates of per cent carbon are given in Table 2.

Estimates of organic material based on loss of weight on ignition (Ref. 989) are inaccurate because of weight changes due to oxidation, loss of water, sulfur, and other constituents, and the high temperatures required for the complete conversion of carbon to carbon dioxide.

Ultraviolet absorption spectra of water extracts of the Murray and Orgueil chondrites in acidic and basic solutions were obtained by Calvin (Ref. 1039). The absorption wavelengths and variations in these lengths induced by the addition of acids were suggestive of cytosine, a basic component of nucleic acids which are components of living cells. Evidence of purines and imidazoles has been reported for Orgueil, Murray, and Mokoia meteorites by Briggs (Ref. 858). Twenty amino acids, three sugars, and two amino sugars, cytosine, uracil and/or hypoxanthine were found in the Bruderheim chondrite and the Murray type II chondrite (Ref. 884), but on the basis of experimental evidence, it was concluded that the organic constituents "are with great probability terrestrial in origin".

The fraction of the organic matter extractable with various common organic solvents and water from Cold Bokkeveld (Ref. 927) and Haripura and Mokoia (Ref. 866) is optically inert and contains, on an ash-free and elemental sulfur-free basis, the following elements:

	Cold Bokkeveld	Mokoia	Haripura
C	24.26	46.43	48.05
H	8.12	5.03	5.27
N	4.00	2.13	4.87
S	8.78	3.99	2.75
Cl	5.89	1.06	1.74
O	48.95	39.36	37.32

With the exception of sulfur and chlorine, the elemental composition is similar to that of humic acids from terrestrial soils (Kononova, 1961, as reported in Ref. 866). The organic chlorine may result from the use of $CHCl_3$ and CCl_4 in extraction procedures. The infrared absorption spectra of the soluble fraction from Murray (Ref. 868) and from Mokoia and Haripura (Ref. 866) suggest a mixture of compounds with aromatic, carboxylic acid, aliphatic, phenolic, and possibly chlorine-substituted groupings. In the ultraviolet, a pH-sensitive absorption around 260 m suggests a compound such as cytosine. Various aromatic acids are probably present (Ref. 858).

An important fact is that the identified substances discussed later constitute a small percentage of the total organic material of the meteorites. This is also true of extracts of terrestrial sediments. Briggs (Ref. 866) suggests that these compounds may include polymeric aromatic acids and hydrocarbon polymers of high molecular weight. Much of the remaining material is probably asphalt and insoluble organic matter, which also constitute the major part of terrestrial sediment extracts. Pyrobitumens may be present.

Nagy et al. (Ref. 940) determined quantitatively a number of saturated hydrocarbons belonging to n-paraffins, monocycloalkanes, bicycloalkanes, and tetracycloalkanes. Meinschein et al. (Ref. 921) determined the hydrocarbons on 9:1 benzene–methanol extracts of Orgueil and Murray. Humble paraffin–naphthene type analyses were prepared from mass spectra of the n-heptane, CCl_4, and benzene eluates. Paraffins, noncondensed naphthenes, 2- to 6-ring naphthenes, alkyl benzenes, naphthalenes, acenaphthenes, pyrenes, chrysenes, and other organic compounds were identified. The elemental sulfur-free residues represent, according to Briggs, 3 to 8% of the total meteorite organic matter.

Interpretation of the Results of Organic Analyses

Agreement is now general that the organic constituents are indigenous to the chondrites. There is no agreement, however, as to how these materials were formed. Meinschein *et al.* firmly support a biogenic origin for the organic materials. In this, they are supported by geochemists who have performed analyses on ancient and recent terrestrial sediments. The number of sediments analyzed by both academic institutions and petroleum corporations amounts to several thousand. Saturated hydrocarbons from sediments, plants, and animals have been analyzed.

Hydrocarbons extracted from relatively recent sediments have compositions and properties equivalent to hydrocarbons in ancient crude oils.[9] The great interest in source rocks of petroleum must be thanked for the large amount of data that has been accumulated on hydrocarbons, asphalts, and pyrobitumins in terrestrial sediments. Hydrocarbon oils extracted from nonreservoir rocks are similar in physical and chemical properties to natural crude oils,[10] with the same paraffins, naphthenes, aromatics, and other compounds. Work at Esso and Magnolia laboratories showed that the average sediment contains 20 to 80 ppm of C_{14} and larger hydrocarbons[10,11] and constitutes 10 to 30% of most extracts. Organic oxygen, sulfur, and nitrogen compounds make up most of the remaining 70 to 90% (Ref. 921).

Comparison of chromatographic data shows clearly that extracts of the Orgueil chondrite fall within the terrestrial sediment range. Infrared spectra of the chondrite extracts have absorption bands similar to those of sedimental extracts, particularly marine sediments (Ref. 162). Like most marine sediments, Orgueil and Murray extracts suggest a complex mixture of carbonyl compounds, significant quantities of aromatic hydrocarbons, and free sulfur. The aromatic fractions of the chondrites are relatively simple, approaching those of recent terrestrial samples but unlike those of crude oils and ancient sediments (Ref. 922). Phenanthrenes, pyrenes, and chrysenes are suggested by ultraviolet and mass data. It is suggested that more restricted varieties of organisms existed in the meteorite parent material, and that this may account for the differences in aromatic fractions. Meinschein *et al.* conclude that the saturated hydrocarbons isolated from Orgueil and Murray have infrared spectra, molecular weights, and cracking patterns that resemble those of sedimental saturated hydrocarbons. In a later paper, Meinschein (Ref. 921) further emphasized the similarities between the benzene-extractable fractions of the Orgueil meteorite and recent marine sediments: "Chromatographic analyses of benzene extracts of the Orgueil meteorite and recent marine sediments agree within one standard deviation of the sedimental extracts." Mass spectrometric, saturated hydrocarbon-type analyses of the n-C_7 eluates of meteoritic, terrestrial sedimental and biological saturated hydrocarbons are similar. Evidence is quoted from several authors that some of the saturated hydrocarbons in terrestrial sediments are unaltered remnants of former life.[9, 12-16]

Briggs and Mamikunian (Ref. 866) champion an abiogenic origin for the organic constituents of the chondrites. The compounds, in common with paraffins of most terrestrial organisms and sediments, largely lack branched carbon chains. Abiogenic syntheses for paraffins generally yield a mixture of unbranched and branched compounds, the latter predominating. Recent work by Wilson[17] has increased the chain length of palmitic acid up to C-19 without any side chain formation by a discharge system in methane over a palmitic acid monolayer. Oró (Ref. 1290) is also doing important work on nonbiological syntheses under conditions assumed to approach primitive Earth environments.

Wilson (Ref. 1327) showed that electron discharges acting on a mixture of methane, ammonia, and hydrogen above a conducting salt solution, such that the discharge continually strikes the liquid–gas interface, will produce high-molecular-weight compounds largely composed of carbon and hydrogen. The waxy material that accumulates on surfaces in the electron-beam pathway in electron microscopes is discussed in textbooks. Waxy coatings have been identified on cosmic nickel fragments (Ref. 952). High-molecular-weight organic material, "probably similar to the discharge polymers and to the organic coatings on cosmic nickel fragments", may be present in the carbonaceous chondrites on the basis of the presence of carbon amorphous to X-rays, and flat translucent fragments that char on heating (Ref. 866). It should be pointed out, however, that similar substances are present in terrestrial sediments, particularly ancient ones.

Briggs and Mamikunian (Ref. 866) suggest that thermal cracking of high-molecular-weight hydrocarbons would yield a mixture of volatile paraffin hydrocarbons similar to that obtained by Meinschein et al. (Ref. 921). Briggs and Mamikunian further state that "The lack of branching in the paraffin molecules could be due to a synthesis via a reaction mechanism involving attack by methyl free radicals onto an adsorbed surface layer of organic compounds. In this manner little side chain formation could occur as a result of steric blocking" (Ref. 187). Complex mixtures of organic compounds have been produced from simple inorganic materials by radiation, electrical discharge, and proton bombardment (Ref. 1230).

The experience of organic chemistry shows that it is unlikely that these substances could have been formed by nonbiological chemical processes. Many coincidences would have to occur in order for natural abiogenic methods to produce a mixture of organic constituents so similar in type and relative amounts to that of terrestrial sediments and recent organisms. At the present time, a belief that nature may have produced an array of carbonaceous compounds that are indistinguishable, by the best available analytical methods, from the organic compounds in certain former biospheres on Earth is only speculation.[18] Briggs and Mamikunian, on the other hand, would seem to be saying that theories, no matter how sound when examined in the light of present-day knowledge, may be overturned when new additions are made to the known facts.

ORGANIZED ELEMENTS AND POSSIBLE MICROFOSSILS

Considerable controversy arose when Claus and Nagy (Ref. 871) reported organized elements similar to the pellicles of single-celled algae and the incertae sedis fossil group of hystrichospheres from the Orgueil, Ivuna, and Murray carbonaceous chondrites. Crushed fragments, thin sections, and acid-resistant extracts were examined. During 1962, additional finds were made by Engel, Palik (Ref. 949), Ross, Skuja (reported in Ref. 985), Staplin (Ref. 973), Timofeev (Ref. 981), and van Landingham.[19] Other "microstructures" were illustrated by Briggs and Kitto (Ref. 865) and Mamikunian and Briggs (Ref. 913).

Claus and Nagy described elements from Orgueil and Ivuna but also reported poorly defined particles from Murray and Mighei. The ordinary stony meteorites, Bruderheim and Holbrook, lacked these elements. Five types of "organized elements" were described—small circular forms $(4-10 \mu)$, spinose or furrowed forms $(8-30 \mu)$, shield-shaped bodies $(circa\ 15\ \mu)$ cylindrical forms $(circa\ 10 \times 20\ \mu)$, and a hexagonal body with three tubular protrusions with striate excrescences. Approximately 1700 particles per milligram of sample were reported. The "high concentrations ... could have developed only in an environment where moisture was continuously present for a prolonged period of time." Later (in 1962), Claus and Nagy proposed formal names for a number of the elements. With Hennessy (Refs. 936, 937), they also found organized elements in Alais and Tonk.

From the Orgueil meteorite, Staplin (Ref. 973) described a number of acid-resistant bodies in the $10-100\ \mu$ range. One type is hexagonal, lenticular, and yellow in color, often with a partial black sheathing and an internal particle of black pyrito-organic (doubtful) material. Mueller (Ref. 929) considers these bodies to be limonite pseudomorphs after troilite, but this does not seem to be supported by the apparent wall structure, shape, and optical appearance. There are a number of black hexagonal bodies in the sample that are interpreted as mineral by Staplin. Recent heat probe tests failed to volatilize or change the shape of the bodies described by Staplin, so they are certainly mineral in composition; however, their origin remains in doubt. Another is a thick-walled granulose sphere, dark amber red in color, sometime united in twos or threes. Small, spherical, featureless bodies and several types of tissue were noted. One tissue (Ref. 974) must be regarded with skepticism, as it may have been introduced from the Canada balsam used to seal the residue to the slide.

Ross found a smaller number of elements than that reported by Claus and Nagy (Ref. 985), but discovered objects like "collapsed spore membranes, small circular forms (type I of Claus and Nagy), and two bodies with a general umbrella or mushroom shape." He stated that the majority of the objects looked like fossil hystrichospheres. Skuja (cited in Ref. 985) also reported organized elements, and Engel obtained numerous bodies that "looked like small pellicles with the interiors destroyed". Timofeev (Ref. 981) found a number of collapsed spherical vesicles in Mighei, yellow in color, $10–12\mu$ in diameter, and with ornamentation and sculpture "characteristic of spores of water plants of the Late Cambrian mire". Palik (Refs. 948, 949) describes various organized elements. His preliminary report discusses filamentous structures suggestive of algae. Others who have identified structures that they consider to be indigenous fossil remains are Cholnoky (Ref. 869) and Reimer (cited in Ref. 876).

Mamikunian and Briggs (Ref. 913) illustrated circular vesicle-like bodies from Haripura that resemble those shown by Timofeev and a hexagonal body from Cold Bokkeveld that resembles those described by Staplin. They conclude, however, that the "variety of rare microstructures in the $20-\mu$ size range ... are unusual mineral grains or terrestrial materials that have contaminated the meteorite during museum storage. However, conclusive identifications are not possible."

Fitch and Anders (Ref. 891), also with Schwarcz (Ref. 892), claim that the organized elements described by Claus and Nagy are mineral grains, hydrocarbon droplets, and contaminants, They divide the organized elements into "two classes—particles of simple and of highly-structured morphology, respectively. Particles of the first class are definitely indigenous, although their numbers seem to have been overestimated. The particles of the first class are in morphological no-man's-land, and to establish their possible biological origin, new techniques and new criteria will have to be developed. As for particles of the second class, proof must be given that they are not terrestrial contaminants."

Fox (Ref. 1070) has suggested that the objects are nonbiological organic matter, droplets of sulfur, and contaminating organisms. Deflandre (Ref. 883) dismisses the organized elements of Claus and Nagy as contaminants or artifacts.

Interpretation of the organized elements continues to be a perplexing problem. Some of the presumed fossils are mineral in composition, like diatoms, radiolarians, and other groups. The simplest acid-resistant spherical bodies are comparable to the vesicles of some algae and ancient incertae sedis such as *Protoleiosphaeridium*. The presence of a definite cell wall or pellicle, demonstrated in section, may be the best evidence that this type of element is fossil. Other minute bodies, without definite structure, could well be organic and mineral–organic complexes.

One major difficulty is that no single expert is able to identify with certainty all of the objects that belong in his own field of study, let alone objects from other fields. A vast majority of the fossil fungi have not been studied. Many algal groups remain poorly known. Mamikunian and Briggs suggest that the complex objects should be studied first. If the objects are terrestrial contaminants, some degree of identification should manifest itself. A number of qualified people have examined the elements, but their identifications have been singularly divergent. Some of the comments and suggestions are useful and deserve exploration. For example, Horst[20] suggests that comparisons should be made with the resinous bodies, artifacts, and partly converted organic matter, both organized and unorganized, in coal ash. J. M. Schopf,[21] with regard to the filamentous and fibrous objects illustrated by Mamikunian and Briggs, points to the abundance of such material in the atmosphere, both as a result of combustion and from plant and animal fibers. The abundance of such objects may be demonstrated by placing a sticky microslide on a window sill for a day.

Care must be exercised not to generalize observations that are valid for one element to others. Claus, Nagy, and Europa (Ref. 876) point this out but then proceed to fall into the pit themselves with regard to a comparison of hystrichospherids and *Ambrosia* pollen. It is pointed out that the spines of *Ambrosia* pollen are solid, while those of the genus *Hystrichosphaeridium* are hollow. They then generalize what is true for *Hystrichosphaeridium* (a dinoflagellate group that probably is still extant, although very poorly known) to various Cambrian hystrichospheres that are unrelated to the dinophytes and which have spines whose nature is in dispute (not yet definitely demonstrated by microtome sections).

Biological staining, fluorescence tests, acid treatments, density separations, and magnetic determinations have been used by various people to demonstrate the nature of the organized elements. Most of these tests are dubious in significance. During diagenesis, the chemical and physical properties of fossil material undergo profound changes, including simplification of organic composition, loss of structural detail, replacement by mineral matter, and infilling or coating with carbonaceous and/or pyrito-organic matter as a result of local increased reduction caused by the interaction of the elements' own organic matter with the enclosing mineral matter and fluids. What is often preserved in fossils is the "skeletal" wall structure and sculpture. Remains of structures not composed of mineral matter, pseudochitinous or cellulosic material or altered derivatives of these, are preserved only in exceptional cases in terrestrial sediments and are no more likely to be preserved in meteoritic materials.

The electron probe X-ray microanalysis of organized elements (Ref. 938) has considerable significance as opposed to the tests mentioned above. For Orgueil, it was shown that several of the organized elements contain major amounts of Fe, some Cl, and/or Ni. Morphologically less well developed microstructures are composed of hydrous Fe–Mg silicates. Acid-resistant pellicles that were obtained when powdered preparations of Orgueil were boiled in 6N HCl are composed of carbonaceous matter. "The finding of Fe, Cl, and Ni in organized elements . . . shows that these particles are very probably not terrestrial contaminations. Electron microscopy of the HCl treated particles revealed organized structures, which suggests, but does not prove, biological origin."

Materials stained or treated in various ways may appear very different, and interpretations are hampered. The type V element of Claus and Nagy, with Gridley staining, does not look like any known pollen to palynologists experienced with unstained material or material stained with dyes such as safranin. Fitch and Anders[22] stained *Ambrosia elatior* and *A. trifida* pollen by the Gridley method, emphasizing internal features and reducing the outer exinal layer to semi-obscurity, thereby duplicating the type V element.

The meteorites have been stored under museum or cabinet conditions, exposed to air and airborne contamination, in contact with organic labeling and packing materials, and have been handled and sampled at various times. The relatively dry conditions of museum storage have not provided a fertile environment for the growth of fungal or bacterial contaminants. Sources of contamination fall into three categories: (1) materials incorporated during transit through the atmosphere and upon impact with the Earth, (2) materials which coated or penetrated the fragments during storage and display, and (3) materials introduced during the processing that yielded the organized elements. Contaminants have been recognized, in spite of special precautions on the part of most investigators. They include cellulosic, mostly gymnospermous tissues, bacteria, a few spores of fungi, some algae, fly ash, and rare pollen and spores. Even in the carefully controlled sterile environments, it is difficult to eliminate all contamination from the air, containers, chemicals, and apparatus. Sisler (Ref. 966) detected, while working at the germ-free laboratory of the United States Institute of Health, a viable unidentified aerobic species of bacteria in the interior of the Murray chondrite that is probably a contaminant. The motile bacteria cultured by Bairyev and Mamedov[23] from a "powdery mass of meteorite" heated to 150° and placed in a nourishing medium must also be considered suspect. A few specimens of Cretaceous or Tertiary pollen and one fern spore were reported among contaminants by Staplin (Ref. 974). Since the pollens were rare in laboratory preparations, especially in relation to other species, it was suggested that they could have been incorporated at impact. Claus and Nagy reported sponge spicules (perhaps from cleaning compounds) in one Orgueil specimen. Mamikunian and Briggs illustrate what appears to be a diatom frustrule from Mokoia. Anders *et al.*[24] report contaminants from a hitherto untested specimen of Orgueil.

In spite of the presence of modern contaminants, much of the unknown material is altered and poorly preserved, suggesting an ancient source. It is difficult to explain as contaminants those elements that have been observed in thin sections to be locked in the rock itself.

ORIGIN AND SIGNIFICANCE OF CARBONACEOUS CHONDRITES

Theories on the origin of carbonaceous chondrites have been summarized by Anders[25] as follows:

1. High-iron group chondrites altered by infiltration of water, carbonaceous matter, and hydrogen sulfide from some other source (Ref. 987).
2. Primitive material accreted at low temperatures from solar nebula[26,27] (Ref. 914). Other chondrites were derived from this material by heating and reduction.
3. Primitive material expelled from the Sun at high temperatures,[28] accreted at low temperatures into asteroidal sized bodies[28,29] (Ref. 890), altered by liquid water and sulfur compounds (Ref. 886).

Mason (Ref. 917) calls the chondrites "representative samples of the dust that made up much of the primitive solar nebula." Ideas of what primordial material is like are based on spectra of comets and thermodynamic calculations of stellar abundances. These suggest richness in H_2O, CH_4, H_2S, NH_3, and other condensed volatiles.

DuFresne and Anders (Ref. 886) assume that the primordial material that accumulated to form the parent bodies of meteorites would, essentially, produce iron-rich olivine. As a result of internal heating, condensed volatiles would be driven toward the surface, altering the original composition. The olivine and metal would be destroyed and redistributed in the form of salts, some water-soluble. Excess volatiles would eventually be lost. Orgueil and Ivuna, having no olivine or free metals, would be considered the end product of the alteration of an iron-rich olivine.

Mason[5] (Ref. 914), on the other hand, suggests that the parent material of all meteorites was highly oxidized, its original state similar to carbonaceous chondrites such as Orgueil and Ivuna. Other groups of meteorites were produced by dehydration and progressive reduction, including heating and recrystallization that would drive off volatiles and their less stable compounds.

Urey (Refs. 1535, 987) also considers chondritic material, with the exception of the volatiles, to be near to the fundamental composition of cosmic matter. The presence of organized elements and complex organic substances, however, led him to the view that the water, carbonaceous matter, and hydrogen sulfide may come from another source. He suggests that these bodies could have formed through the tremendous forces set up when the Earth captured the Moon. The anomalous material was splashed up from the Earth, and the meteorites contain a combination of material from both the Earth and the Moon (Ref. 987).

A number of theories on the origin of chondrites fail to take into account the possibility that all meteorites may have a common origin. If the metallic and stony meteorites in all of their diversity are considered from the viewpoint of a common origin, it is difficult to escape an assumption that the parent body was large. Within a large body, the energy necessary for segregation and alteration of the magnitude involved would be available. Current theories favor small parent bodies.

If it is assumed that the meteorite parent body (or bodies) resulted from the aggregation of primordial particles of the dust cloud of the solar nebula, the original composition should be rather homogeneous. If the parent bodies were small, segregation is improbable. The dust cloud may have been zoned in composition, and the accreting bodies may have been formed in the different zones, but this seems improbable when the range from metallic to carbonaceous meteorites is considered.

No concrete evidence of sorting of materials has been adduced from the meteorites themselves. This may be due either to the possibility that the evidence has not been sought for sufficiently or that the meteorites themselves do not constitute a sufficiently representative sample. Carbonaceous chondrites and certain other types of stony meteorites are impossible to recognize in the field once the fusion crust and other obvious characteristics are lost. Meteorites that show brecciation, veining, and similar features suggestive of either physical or chemical mixing may point toward segregation and sorting processes on a large body and not entirely to shock phenomena.

If the organized elements and complex organic substances are biogenic in origin, either a suitable environment, including water, must have existed on the parent body, or the dual origin of the chondrites as proposed by Urey, are possible explanations. The parent body must have been at least of lunar size for water to have been retained for any time. It has been suggested that life could have evolved in small subterranean pools in asteroid-sized bodies, but as Urey (Ref. 984) suggests, this seems improbable. Our present knowledge of the closer planets of our own system suggests that conditions are too rigorous for life to exist or, at best, are marginal. The same is true for the asteroidal belt. Solar radiation, internal heat of the planetary bodies, and spatial relationships of the solar system could have been somewhat different in times preceding the origin of the meteorites. Other possibilities are that the parent body is a piece of the primitive Earth or that the chondrites come from another solar system.

If the organic materials are not biogenic, Mason (Refs. 914, 917) and Bernal (Ref. 1015) have an equally interesting hypothesis. Mason suggested that the nuclei for condensation would be minute particles of hydrous iron magnesium silicate formed directly from solar gases. These particles would accumulate ice, methane, ammonia, and H_2S from the volatiles in the dust cloud surrounding the Sun. As the cloud dissipated through particle aggregation, these substances would evaporate, leaving a thin skin of polymerized carbonaceous material produced by the action of cosmic ray and solar particles. Bernal cites the observation of Mueller (Ref. 927) that Cold Bokkeveld resisted boiling HF for 140 hr because each silicate particle was coated with carbonaceous matter (this is also true of certain organic-rich terrestrial shales in which the organic material is biogenic in origin). The carbonaceous meteorites may represent "the primary accumulation of elements and free energy for the first synthesis of life on this Earth rather than the end products of chemical evolution on some other celestial body" (Ref. 842). Mason (Ref. 917) states that if the Earth was formed by accretion of material of meteoritic composition and this material brought with it complex organic substances, the development on Earth of self-replicating compounds of nucleic acid and protein molecules (i.e. primitive organisms) would be easier to understand. In other words, Mason and Bernal suggest that the carbonaceous chondrites may hold the key to the origin of life on our planet.

REFERENCES

1. ROSE, G., Systematisches Verzeichniss der Meteoriten in dem mineralogischen Museum der Universität zu Berlin, *Monatsberichte der deutschen Akademie der Wissenschaften zu Berlin* (1862), pp. 551–8.
2. TSCHERMAK, G., Die Meteoriten des k. k. mineralogischen Museums am 1. Oktober 1872, *Mineralogische und petrographische Mitteilungen* (Vienna) (1872), pp. 165–72.
3. BREZINA, A., The Arrangement of Collections of Meteorites, *Proceedings of the American Philosophical Society*, vol. 43, No. 176 (1904), pp. 211–47.
4. PRIOR, G. T., The Classification of Meteorites, *The Mineralogical Magazine and Journal of the Mineralogical Society*, vol. 19, No. 90 (1920), pp. 51–63.
5. MASON, B., *The Classification of Chondritic Meteorites*, American Museum Novitates, No. 2085, American Museum of Natural History, New York, May 24, 1962.
6. FREDRIKSSON, K., DE CARLI, P. S., and AARAMÄE, A., Shock-Induced Veins in Chondrites, *Space Research III, Proceedings of the 3rd International Space Sciences Symposium*, ed. by W. PRIESTER, Amsterdam: North–Holland Publishing Co. (1963).
7. ANDERS, E., *Origin, Age, and Composition of Meteorites*, C00-382-47, EFINS

64–27, Enrico Fermi Institute of Nuclear Studies, University of Chicago, Chicago, Illinois, 1964.

8. WOOD, J. A., Physics and Chemistry of Meteorites, *The Solar System, vol. IV: The Moon, Meteorites, and Comets,* ed. by G. P. KUIPER and B. M. MIDDLEHURST, Chicago: University of Chicago Press (1963).

9. SMITH, P. V., JR., The Origin of Petroleum: Occurrence of Hydrocarbons in Recent Sediments, *Bulletin of the American Association of Petroleum Geologists,* vol. 38 (1954), pp. 377–404.

10. HUNT, J. M., and JAMIESON, G. W., Oil and Organic Matter in Source Rocks of Petroleum. *Bulletin of the American Association of Petroleum Geologists,* vol. 40 (1956), pp. 477–88.

11. STEVENS, N. P., BRAY, E. E., and EVANS, E. D., Hydrocarbons in Sediments of Gulf of Mexico, *Bulletin of the American Association of Petroleum Geologists,* vol. 40 (1956), pp. 975–83.

12. MEINSCHEIN, W. G., Origin of Petroleum, *Enciclopedia del Petrolio e del Gas natural,* Rome: Carlo Colombo Publishing Co. (In press).

13. WHITMORE, F. C., Review of API Research Project 43B, *Fundamental Research on Occurrence and Recovery of Petroleum, 1944–45,* American Petroleum Institute, Baltimore, Maryland: Lord Baltimore Press (1949), p. 99.

14. OAKWOOD, T. S.,   Notes on the Accomplishments of Project 43B, *Fundamental Research on Occurrence and Recovery of Petroleum, 1952–3,* American Petroleum Institute, Baltimore, Maryland: Lord Baltimore Press (1954), pp. 167–8.

15. BENDORAITIS, J. G., BROWN, B. L., and HEPNER, L. S., Isoprenoid Hydrocarbons in Petroleum, Isolation of 2, 6, 10, 14–Tetramethylpentadecane by High Temperature Gas-Liquid Chromatography, *Analytical Chemistry,* vol. 34 (1962), pp. 49–53.

16. DEAN, R. A., and WHITEHEAD, E. V., The Occurrence of Phytane in Petroleum. *Tetrahedron Letters,* No. 21 (1961), p. 768.

17. BRIGGS, M. H., Personal communication.

18. MEINSCHEIN, W. G., Personal communication.

19. VAN LANDINGHAM, S. L., *Acid Resistant Microfossils from the Alais and Orgueil Meteorites,* Manuscript (1962).

20. HORST, V., Personal communication.

21. SCHOPF, J. M., Personal communication.

22. FITCH, F. W., and ANDERS, E., Organized Element: Possible Identification in Orgueil Meteorite, *Science,* vol. 140 (1963), pp. 1097–1100.

23. BAIRYEV, C., and MAMEDOV, S., Traces of Life in Rocks from Outer Space, *Pravda* (June 25, 1962), p. 6.

24. ANDERS, E. *et al., Contaminated Meteorite,* EFINS 64–46, Enrico Fermi Institute of Nuclear Studies, University of Chicago, Chicago, Illinois, 1964.

25. ANDERS, E., *On the Origin of Carbonaceous Chondrites,* EFINS 62–67, Enrico Fermi Institute of Nuclear Studies, University of Chicago, Illinois, 1962.

26. MASON, B., Reply to DR. HAROLD C. UREY's Criticism of the Paper by BRIAN MASON 'The Origin of Meteorites', *Journal of Geophysical Research,* vol. 66 (1961), pp. 3979–80.

27. RINGWOOD, A. E., Chemical and Genetic Relationships Among Meteorites, *Geochimica et Cosmochimica Acta,* vol. 24 (1961), pp. 159–97.

28. WOOD, J. A., *Silicate Meteorite Structures and the Origin of Meteorites,* Technical Report No. 10, Smithsonian Astrophysical Observatory, Cambridge, Massachusetts, 1958.

29. WOOD, J. A., Chondrules and the Origin of the Terrestrial Planets, *Nature,* vol. 194 (1962), pp. 127–30.

CHAPTER III

MICROORGANISMS OF MIDDLE PRECAMBRIAN AGE FROM THE ANIMIKIE SERIES, ONTARIO, CANADA

E. S. BARGHOORN* and S. A. TYLER†

ALTHOUGH an element of scepticism has traditionally prevailed both on the part of geologists and biologists with regard to the existence and nature of Precambrian life, evidence is now rapidly accumulating to demonstrate the occurrence of widespread and abundant biological activity as far back in the geologic record as one-half the presently accepted age of the Earth. Geochemical evidence and evidence from the mineralogical and petrographic characteristics of Precambrian rocks are equivocal regarding the time of origin of life and the physical setting of biogenesis. However, fossils showing three-dimensionally preserved morphology are now known from sediments of an age approaching 2000 million years (Ref. 1008).[1] It is the purpose of this Chapter to extend discussion of these currently oldest known Precambrian fossils with respect to their geologic occurrence, morphology and certain corollary chemical studies of their retained organic matter. No attempt will be made to review the voluminous literature on Precambrian fossils. This has recently and excellently been done by Glaessner[2] and Rutten (Ref. 1177).

GENERAL GEOLOGY

The term "algal cherts" has long been applied to certain facies of the Gunflint iron formation of the northern Lake Superior region of Canada and adjacent Minnesota. The Gunflint iron formation is one of two

*Harvard University, Cambridge Massachusetts.

†The investigations reported here are the result of joint studies with the late Stanley A. Tyler, Department of Geology, University of Wisconsin. For a period of years since 1953, the author was fortunate to have this association with Professor Tyler, whose knowledge of the Precambrian shield rocks of North America was profound and ever stimulating both in the field and in the laboratory. The discussion of the geology and petrology of the Gunflint formation in this Chapter is taken almost entirely from his work as are also aspects of the Section on paleoenvironments.

93

structurally conformable units, of which the Rove shale is the overlying member. Together, the Gunflint and the Rove comprise the recognizable Animikie series in the Thunder Bay district of Ontario. The term Animikie rather than Huronian is used here because of the impossibility of direct stratigraphic correlation with the classical tripartite Huronian sequence in the Lake Huron–Georgian Bay area to the east. As will be discussed later, the absolute age of the Gunflint formation is approximately 2000 million (2.0 × 10⁹) years,[3] hence placing the formation in the lower third of the Middle Precambrian.

The Gunflint sediments extend eastward some 110 mi from the vicinity of Gunflint Lake on the U.S.–Canada international boundary to Loon Lake, Ontario (Fig. 1). Isolated remnants of the formation occur on the mainland and upon islands in Lake Superior in the Rossport–Schreiber area some 67 mi east of Loon Lake. In the Gunflint sequence of Minnesota, four major members may be distinguished: Lower Cherty, Lower Slaty, Upper Cherty, and Upper Slaty.[4] In many exposures of the formation, however, one or more of the upper members has been removed by erosion. However, Gill[5] extended Broderick's work on the subdivisions of the Gunflint formation by recognizing and tracing the four members from Gunflint Lake to Mink Mountain, a distance of about 50 mi. Goodwin[6] presented additional information regarding lithofacies of the Gunflint and emphasized the cyclical nature of sedimentation during Gunflint time. Moorhouse[7] and Goodwin[8] present an excellent summary of the Gunflint and related general geology of the Animikie series in the Port Arthur and Whitefish Lake regions.

The structurally preserved organisms originally described by Tyler and Barghoorn[1] were discovered in dense black cherts collected from the Lower Algal member of the Gunflint formation near Schreiber, Ontario. Structurally preserved organisms have also been observed in the Lower Algal chert member at several other localities in exposures of the formation in the Thunder Bay area and west to Nolalu, Ontario. The organisms preserved in the black cherts are known to occur at the same stratigraphic horizon over a distance of approximately 120 mi along the strike of the formation. Preservation is best in the Schreiber locality, and discussion of the detailed geologic occurrence of the chert will be limited here to this area, although the organisms have been secured from several other localities as well.

Small erosion remnants of Animikie sediments occur on the shore of the mainland between Schreiber Beach and Winston Point; also on a small island south of Horn, locally known as Flint Island, on Powder Island in Pays Plat Bay; and on small islands near Rossport. These occurrences have been described by Tanton,[9] Hopkins,[10] and Harcourt.[11] The Animikie sequence in this area consists of a basal clastic member

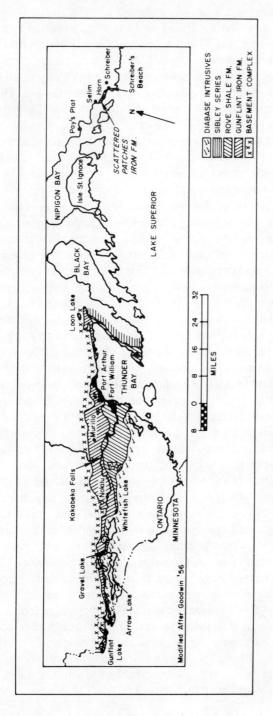

FIG. 1. General areal geology of Gunflint range north of Lake Superior (Note isolated eastern outlier of Gunflint formation above N on directional arrow. Most structurally preserved organisms are from this easternmost outcrop.)

ranging in thickness from 1 to 6 ft, followed by 4 to 10 ft of iron formation, which in turn is overlain by 15 to 35 ft of thin-bedded fissile black
shale. In places where the Gunflint rests upon red porphyritic granite,
the basal member is a dark colored, poorly sorted clastic consisting of
rounded to angular quartz grains set in a dark gray, shaly matrix. South
of Horn, Ontario, where the Animikie sediments rest upon ellipsoidal
greenstones, the basal clastics consist of a foot or two of poorly sorted
and poorly lithified massive shaly material composed of angular to sub-
angular greenstone fragments which are partially altered to IM muscovite
associated with well rounded to angular grains of quartz, jasper, chert,
and greenstone, with occasional grains of fresh pink feldspar. The clastics
are cemented by a minor amount of carbonate and chert.

The basal 6 to 18 in. of the iron formation contain an abundance of
structurally preserved organisms. Numerous algal domes ranging in size
from a few inches up to 5 ft in diameter and 6 to 18 in. in height are present.
The domes are often developed preferentially upon greenstone boulders
of the underlying basal conglomerate. The gross internal structure of the
domes consists of somewhat irregular layers of white, coarsely crystalline,
structureless quartz alternating with layers of fine-grained black chert or
flint. The individual layers are usually several inches in thickness. The
black chert is characterized by discontinuous anastomosing pillars
oriented roughly perpendicular to the gross algal dome. The dimensions
of individual pillars show considerable variation in width, ranging from
a fraction of a millimeter up to a centimeter, the length up to 4 cm or more,
and the height up to 10 cm or more. The pillars often tend to bifurcate
upward. The internal structure of the pillars consists of a series of laminae
produced by variations in grain size of the chert or by concentrations of
pyrite and organic matter. The laminae are oriented convex upward, with
the individual layers steepening and tending to become tangent to the
borders of the pillars. The general appearance is that of a nest of thimbles.
The interpillar zone ranges in width from 1 to 10 mm and is usually filled
with white, light gray, greenish, or black granular and oolitic chert embedded in a fine-grained cherty matrix. The granules and oolites appear
to be clastic particles which became entrapped between the pillars during
the growth of the algal colonies. Occasionally, the area between the pillars
is occupied by an iron-bearing carbonate or by white, coarsely crystalline
quartz with drusy cavities or, more rarely, by anthraxolite.

The upper 3 to 4 ft of the iron formation is composed of lenses of white
to gray chert a fraction of an inch to several inches in thickness, alternating
with iron-bearing carbonate layers. Structurally preserved organisms are
rare in these lenses, although the algal pillar structure is often conspicuous.

The algal cherts are overlain conformably by a fissile, black, pyritic
shale interbedded with limey argillites. The total thickness of the black

shale unit and the character of the overlying rocks are unknown, since the shales dip southeastward and disappear beneath the waters of Lake Superior. The general stratigraphic position of the black shale unit of the Gunflint is uncertain; it may represent the equivalent of what is known in the western portion of the Gunflint iron range as the Rove shale, which is usually recognized as a separate formation overlying the Gunflint formation.

PETROGRAPHY OF THE CHERT

The rocks of the Lower Algal horizon of the Gunflint formation are composed predominantly of dense black chert, associated with subordinate amounts of gray, green, red, and white cherts. The red and green colors are due to the presence of fine-grained hematite and siderite, respectively. The black cherts owe their color to an abundance of fine-grained pyrite and, more particularly, to the presence of yellow, brown, and black organic matter. These constituents, especially the organic matter, have exerted a strong influence upon the texture of the rock, for there is a close correlation between the grain size of the chalcedony and quartz and the abundance of finely disseminated organic matter. The organic matter has had a pronounced effect in inhibiting grain growth.

The chert consists of chalcedony grains which average 100 to 400 μ in diameter but attain a maximum size of 500 μ (some even larger) in local areas. The chalcedony grains form a mosaic pattern, with the grain boundaries ranging from roughly linear to highly sutured. When observed with polarized light, a dark, rather narrowly defined line marking the extinction position sweeps across the grains, indicating a sheaf-like structure. Chalcedony grains 200 μ and larger exhibit a pronounced radial structure. Quartz with undulating extinction occurs in subordinate amounts in localized areas. The quartz grains range in size from 200 to 400 μ or even larger. The chalcedony and quartz which occur as a matrix to chert granules and oolites in the areas between the algal pillars are often coarse-grained. The abundance of chalcedony and the pronounced local variation in grain size of both chalcedony and quartz indicate that the Gunflint cherts of the Lower Algal horizon have suffered little if any thermal or regional metamorphism. This conclusion is substantiated by the abundance of IM muscovite at several horizons in the Gunflint formation.

Carbonate is usually present in the black cherts of the Lower Algal horizon as a minor constituent occurring as scattered rhombs in the chert matrix, as fracture fillings or as irregular borders along narrow fractures. The rhombs range in size up to 300 μ and generally have well developed outlines. The carbonate is younger than the chert, for the borders of chert granules and the successive zones of chert oolites are often partially enclosed within carbonate rhombs.

Apatite occurs in the Lower Algal cherts as doubly terminated crystals which range from less than a micron up to about 15 μ in size. The apatite is present in the chert groundmass as isolated crystals, irregular clusters of crystals, partial borders to chert granules, and as ovoid bodies or granules with a subordinate chert matrix.

The interface between the red algal jasper and black chert reveals an interesting transition zone. Bedding in the algal pillars is marked by discontinuous wispy lenses 100 to 1000 μ in thickness of black chert containing pyrite and organic matter alternating with gray chert. As the jasper interface is approached, the gray chert becomes light red and alternates with lenses of black chert. The black chert lenses gradually give way to red jasper. Bedding in the red jasper is made evident by slight differences in the hematite content of adjacent laminae. The grain size of the hematite shows a marked increase from the light red transition zone, where the individual hematite particles are a micron or less in diameter, into the red jasper, where aggregates of hematite range in size up to about 50 μ.

The transition from the black to red algal cherts probably reflects a change from reducing to oxidizing conditions at the time of deposition. This change appears to have been gradual, as indicated by the alternating light red and black laminae in the pillars. The occurrence of oolites in the interpillar zones with jasper centers and black outer zones indicates (1) that the hematite is primary in origin and (2) that reducing conditions persisted in the interpillar depressions at a time when the upper portion of the individual algal pillars extended into a more strongly oxidizing environment. Jasper oolites that were formed in the oxidizing environment occasionally were trapped in the narrow depressions between the algal pillars and continued to grow in a reducing environment.

AGE OF THE GUNFLINT FORMATION

The Gunflint iron formation has been correlated by Leith, Lund, and Leith[12] and others with the Biwabik iron formation of Minnesota and the Ironwood, Negaunee, and Vulcan iron formations of Michigan. This correlation is based upon similarity in lithology and general position in the Precambrian stratigraphic sequence. Whether or not these formations are time equivalents remains to be determined.

Recent studies by Hurley and coworkers[3] on the $K^{40}-Ar^{40}$ ratios and the $Rb^{87}-Sr^{87}$ ratios in several suites of unmetamorphosed minerals from diverse localities in the Gunflint sequence have yielded remarkably consistent absolute ages. Granules of a K-rich mica extracted from a tuff-argillite band in the Lower Gunflint exposed in the Port Arthur district showed a potassium content of 4.69% with Ar^{40}/K^{40} of 0.146, indicating an age of 1600 ± M.Y. Argillaceous material from the basal cherty unit of the Lower Gunflint at the Schreiber Beach locality showed a potassium content of 4.45%, with an Ar^{40}/K^{40} ratio of 0.145, indicating an age of 1580 ± 50 M.Y. A replicate but less pure sample from the Schreiber Beach locality containing 2.01% potassium showed an Ar^{40}/K^{40} ratio of 0.146, indicating an age of 1600 ± 70 M.

Regarding the true age of the Gunflint, the authors[3] state: "It is therefore expected that, owing to the ideal conditions for preservation of the clay minerals in this area the measured age values should represent at least 80% of the true age of the Gunflint sedimentation." If this correction were applied, the true age of the Gunflint sediments, based on the authigenic minerals, would be 1900 ± 200 M.Y.

It is of interest to note in connection with the age of the Gunflint sediments that the unconformably underlying granite in the Kakabeka Falls locality yields an Ar^{40}/K^{40} ratio of 0.332 (biotite concentrate), with age 2570 ± 75 M.Y. $Rb^{87}-Sr^{87}$ ratios of this same granite yield ratios indicating 2365 ± 70 M.Y.[3]

TYPES OF PRESERVATION OF ORGANISMS

The organic remains present in the Gunflint cherts are preserved in several different ways. These are: (1) organic residues and films, (2) fine-grained pyrite, (3) solid pyrite, (4) carbonate, and (5) hematite.

Organic Residues and Films

This type of preservation consists of tenuous films, varying in thickness, of a light to dark brownish material, which outline the organic structures. When the chert is dissolved in hydrofluoric acid, the brown material floats on the surface of the liquid and aggregates into black opaque masses. This material is readily volatilized upon ignition. Local recrystallization of the chert to a coarser grain size leads to the elimination of the brownish material and the accumulation of a black, opaque substance along the grain boundaries of the quartz. This opaque material resembles anthraxolite. The organic forms are also preserved in the chert by a diffuse, light yellow substance. This type of preservation resembles a stain. The yellow substance is clearly an organic compound or group of compounds, since it grades into the brownish films and accumulates as anthraxolite on grain boundaries in areas in which chalcedony has recrystallized to quartz. The yellow material is also observed to preserve or represent morphologically the substance of organic remains such as filaments and spore-like bodies within disseminated carbonate rhombs in the chert.

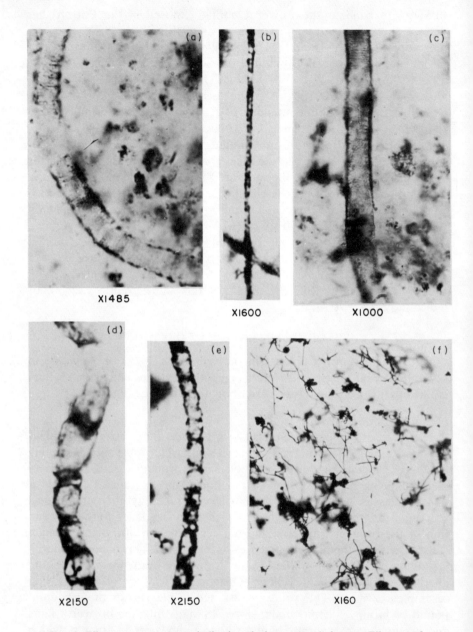

Fig. 2. Filamentous structures indicating algal-type morphology. a, Filament of blue-green algal type. (Note remnants of transverse septae.) b, c, Filaments of blue-green algal type. d, Algal filament showing transverse septae. (Note variation in cell size.) e, Algal filament showing transverse septae. f, Group of filaments and occasional spore-like bodies in random assortment. (Organic remains are partially carbonized and nearly opaque to transmitted light.)

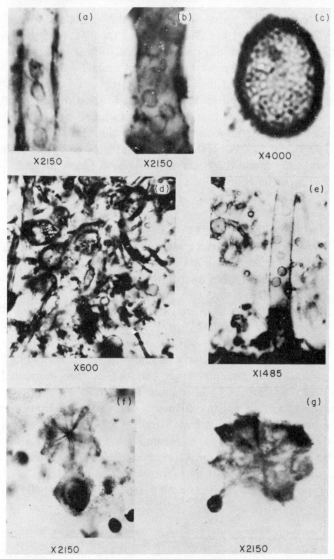

FIG. 3. Filamentous structures containing spore-like bodies. a, Portion of non-septate filament containing ovoid spore-like bodies. b, Nonseptate filament with numerous internal spore-like bodies. c, Thick-walled, spheroidal spore-like body showing surface reticulum. d, Aggregation of filaments enmeshed with spore-like bodies of varying size. e, Nonseptate filament with internally contained spores. (Organization of filaments and spores of this general type occurs in both extant iron bacteria and blue-green algae.) f, g, Structures occurring in great profusion in Gunflint chert from Kakabeka Falls locality. (Basic organization consists of basal bulbous swelling, slender stipe connecting with parasol- or umbrella-shaped, radially organized upper structure. Structures occur in chert at different angles of orientation, three-dimensionally preserved, thus presenting wide range of morphological diversity.)

Where preservation of morphology of the contained organisms is best (Fig. 2a, c, d, and e; Fig. 3c, d, and e; Fig. 4a, c, d, e), thin sections of the chert, when viewed in transmitted light, appear light amber to dark brown in color when 50 μ or less in thickness (Fig. 5). It is evident that the remains of the organisms in which structure is best retained are represented by the altered remnants of the original organic matter and that the structures are not pseudomorphs produced by condensation or polymerization of material which entered the chert prior to crystallization of the chalcedonic matrix. This is further attested to by the remarkable three-dimensional mode of preservation of both filaments and spherical structures (Fig. 2a and c; Fig. 4a, c, d, and e; Fig. 5a–f).

Pyrite

The color of the black cherts of the Gunflint results from the presence both of pyrite and of organic matter. The pyrite occurs as individual crystals and aggregates. It ranges in size from a maximum of 3 to 4 mm down to particles less than a micron in diameter. The grains are usually closely associated spatially with organic matter. Crystals which fall in the size range of 5 to 10 μ are observed in some instances to occur closely spaced along organic filaments, producing an effect resembling a string of beads. The pyrite grains less than a micron in diameter tend to outline the organic structures in a manner similar to stippling (Fig. 4g). As the pyrite grains become larger — about 1 μ — the individual grains become more distinct and the organic forms take on a grainy aspect. In a few instances, the organic filaments and spore-like bodies are composed of solid pyrite. Individual filaments of solid pyrite have been observed to pass laterally and continuously into carbonaceous films containing scattered pyrite grains less than a micron in diameter (Fig. 2f). The association of fine-grained pyrite with organic matter is the most common type of preservation of organic structures in the algal cherts.

FIG. 4 (*opposite*) Microstructures in thin sections in the Schreiber Beach area. a, b, c, Three of a total of 150 specimens found in cherts from Schreiber Beach locality. (Organization consists of inner sphere on whose surface small spheroidal bodies are attached in random distribution; entire structure is surrounded by a thin outer sphere, represented by outer circumferential membrane. Objects are nearly spherical in external form and appear to have been free-floating. No internal contents have been observed within inner sphere.) d, Multibranched radially organized structure showing complex organization. (Organic residue is translucent brown in transmitted light. Basic organization is reminiscent of that in certain hydrozoan coelenterates.) e, Two thick-walled spheroidal bodies in approxima-tion. (Whether attenuation of right-hand sphere is post-depositional or original cannot be determined.) f, Filaments of blue-green algal type in random orienta-tions in chert. g, Contorted filament showing ghost-like outlines of original walls. (Shape of outline of filament is more that of certain coenocytic green algae than of blue-green algae.)

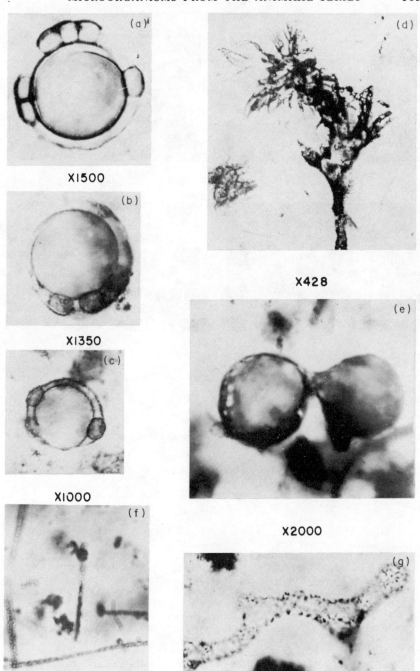

X1500

X1350

X1000

X1300

X428

X2000

X1000

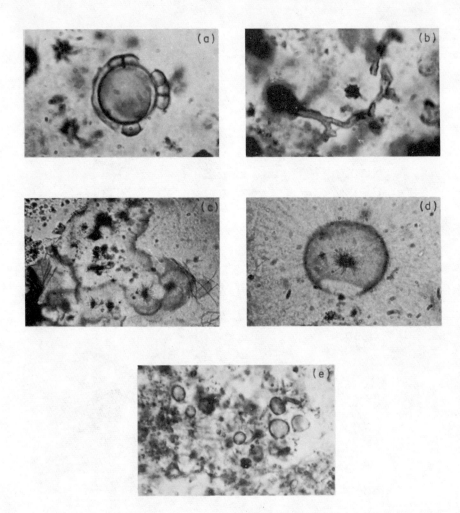

FIG. 5. Photomicrographs of thin sections of Gunflint chert showing optical properties of organic structures in transmitted white light of 3200 K intensity. a, Same organism shown in Fig. 4a. (Note remnants of outer sphere membrane at left side of object.) b, Branched filament devoid of septae. (Seeming attachment to opaque spore-like object at left is probably fortuitous and due to superposition of opaque mass in thin section.) c, Actinomorphic clusters of filaments surrounded by drusy chalcedony crystal aggregates forming mammillary masses. (Outlines of drusy aggregates are probably formed by extrusion of organic matter during crystallization. Clear areas surrounding drusy aggregates are composed of micro-crystalline randomly oriented chalcedony.) d, Single isolated aggregate comparable to those shown in c. (Actinomorphic filamentous center is clearly organic, but outline of globular structure is composed of extruded organic matter associated with hematite forming a sharp boundary with surrounding chalcedony.) e, Typical appearance of more organic phase of Gunflint chert showing variety and form of spheroidal spore-like bodies and filaments.

Carbonate

Filaments, spore-like bodies, and other organic structures are preserved in some instances by carbonate imbedded in a chert matrix The carbonate may form a continuous body which outlines the filament, or it may occur as a series of lenses along the axis of the filament. The small size of the carbonate filaments — 1 μ or less in diameter — and the fact that they are enclosed in chert prevents determination of the type of carbonate present. The carbonate preservation of organic entities in the Gunflint chert is not to be confused with the phenomena described elsewhere,[13] in which carbonate trails are appendaged to ambient pyrite crystals that have moved through the solid chert matrix forming tubular pseudo-fossils.

Hematite

The black algal cherts pass locally into red algal jaspers. Thin sections of black chert — jasper interfaces show filaments outlined by carbonaceous films and pyrite grains passing as continuous bodies into the jasper, where hematite outlines the filament. Spore-like bodies and other organic structures are also preserved by hematite. The hematite often occurs as disseminated particles less than a micron in diameter set in a red-stained chert groundmass. The occurrence is similar to that of pyrite, suggesting that the hematite may represent oxidation of pyrite. However, the common occurrence of filaments and spore-like bodies composed of solid hematite as compared to the rareness of solid pyrite filaments in the black cherts suggests that the hematite may be replacing original organic matter in many cases. One aspect of the structural preservation of the organisms in the Gunflint chert which should be emphasized is the fact that their gross physical alteration has been extraordinarily minimal considering their antiquity and geologic history. As will be discussed later, it is most probable that the microorganisms were entrapped in amorphous silica (gel?), which, upon dehydrating to solid opal, provided an incompressible matrix with minimal deformation. The resistance of opal and the subsequently crystallized chalcedony (chert) to pressure and crushing provided the physical environment permitting their three-dimensional preservation as well as a minimum of the pressure–time effects by which organic matter is degassed and "coalified". Moreover, the crystallization of the chert to the chalcedonic structure commonly had little effect on the morphology of the organisms. The vast majority of the countless organic structures (filaments, spore-like bodies, etc.) show no primary deformation in relation to the chalcedony grains. This may be readily seen by comparing the organic structure in normal transmitted light with the same in polarized transmitted light. In the latter case, it can be observed that the organic structures pass without alteration across the crystal boundaries of the chert grains.

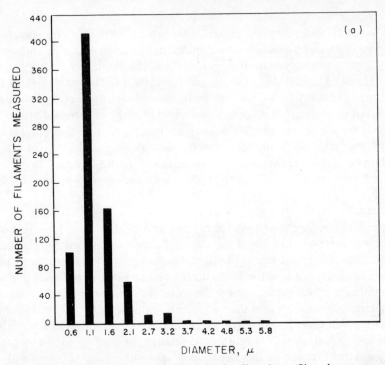

FIG. 6. Size distributions of organisms in Gunflint chert. (Size classes were selected on the basis of discrimination by ocular micrometer units; it is evident that a continuous range in size exists between smallest and largest. Distribution of this type indicates a diversity of organisms or entities rather than normal distribution of a single "species" or entity.) a, Algal filaments.

STRUCTURALLY PRESERVED ORGANISMS

Paleontologic study of the Gunflint chert has been carried out by use of thin sections, acid maceration, and other chemical techniques. The tenuous and friable nature of the organic residues of the organisms, even when best preserved, necessitates the use of thin sections for optimum results with white-light microscopy. Macerations, even when carried out very slowly using dilute hydrofluoric acid, result in nearly complete fragmentation of the more delicate structures and partial fragmentation of the more thick-walled organic remains. Thick-walled filaments, initially several hundred microns in length, tend to break up into small segments when freed in maceration. Of the spore-like bodies, only the more massive-walled forms can be freed intact by maceration. All photomicrographs in this Chapter, Figs. 2–5 inclusive, are from thin ground sections of the chert, averaging 30 to 60 μ in thickness.

It is not intended in the following discussion to present detailed descriptions of the whole range of microstructures thus far observed in the

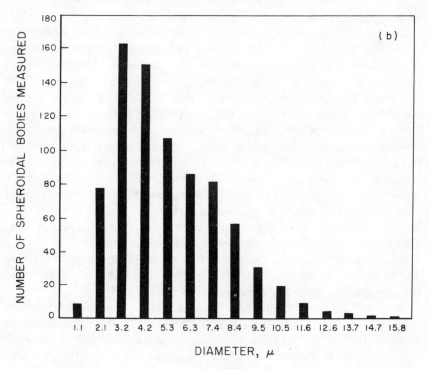

FIG. 6. b, Spheroidal bodies.

Gunflint chert, nor to present formal taxonomic treatment and nomen-clatural designations of the forms figured. It is intended rather to por-tray the major categories and representative microorganisms with which the chert abounds. Of the more abundant structures such as filaments and spore-like bodies, several square centimeters of thin sections of the chert may show the presence of thousands of discrete entities. The more complex forms such as those shown in Fig. 3f and g and those shown in Fig. 4a, c, and d, are far less abundant. The absolute frequency of the morphologically better preserved entities is a rather meaningless value owing to extremely wide variation within relatively short distances in the rock matrix.

The most abundant organisms in the Gunflint assemblage are filaments of diameter ranging from 0.5 to 6.0 μ or occasionally larger. The length of the filaments is exceedingly variable, ranging from fragments which have resulted from the segmentation of the larger filaments, apparently before death and mineralization, to filaments several hundred microns in length. The maximum length of the filaments is difficult or impossible to ascertain inasmuch as they are distributed in an undulating fashion in the chert matrix and pass in and out of the section interface, where parts of the filaments have been ground away in preparation of the thin section. In the most favorably preserved state, the filaments are found to be both septate and nonseptate (compare Fig. 2a, c, d, and e with Fig. 3a, b, and e and Fig. 5b). In most cases, as may be noted in Fig. 2b, it is not possible to determine with certainty whether the filament was septate or devoid of cross walls because of postdepositional changes in the organic residue or deposition of pyrite granules. The septate types exhibit a basic morphology very comparable to that found in certain extant filamentous blue-green algae such as *Oscillatoria* and *Lyngbya*. Among the nonseptate filaments forms occur, although very rarely, showing internally contained spores or endogonidia (Fig. 3a, b, and e). Structures morphologically comparable to these occur in a few extant genera of the blue-green algae and also in the iron bacteria (*Crenothrix*).

Filaments which show evidence of branching are exceedingly rare, and in the few cases in which any vestige of branching has been found, the filaments are devoid of cross walls or septae (Fig. 5b).

As noted previously, the size of the filaments with respect to cross-sectional diameter ranges from approximately 0.5 to over 6.0 μ. Measurement of 1000 filaments (Fig. 6a) reveals the fact, however, that nearly 50% of the 1000 filaments are in one size class, viz. 1.1 μ. It is probable, although certainly not definitely demonstrable, that this preponderance of one size class represents the near dominance of one "species" of blue-green alga. By analogy with mixed populations of modern blue-green algae from a variety of environments, it seems reasonable to infer that the size range exhibited by the Gunflint algal assemblage represents a mixed population of blue-green algal species and not the size range to be expected in a random sampling of a single species (Fig. 6a).

The spheroidal spore-like bodies which are ubiquitously but irregularly distributed through the chert matrix exhibit a wide range in size, thickness of wall, external wall structure and, to a certain extent, shape. The range in size of the spore-like bodies is from approximately 1 to over 16 μ (Fig. 6b). Their shape varies from spherical (Fig. 3d and e) to ellipsoidal (Fig. 3a and c). Thickness of the wall is highly variable, ranging from an almost diaphanous membrane to relatively thick or coarsely reticulate (Fig. 3a–e; Fig. 4e). The differences in the original structure of the wall and those induced by mode of preservation or precipitation of pyrite adjacent to the wall are difficult to distinguish from differences which existed in original biological structure. However, it is apparent that the spore-like bodies are of diverse and heterogeneous origin. Several of the more reasonable possibilities are: (1) unicellular blue-green algae of the *Chroococcus* type among living forms, (2) endogenously produced endospores of filamentous blue-green algae or iron bacteria, (3) free-swimming dinoflagellates, or (4) fungus spores. The latter possibility seems quite remote in view of the absence or extreme scarcity of filamentous structures resembling those of fungi, i.e. freely branching hyphae.

Among the more distinctive looking organisms which are of quite uncertain biological affinity with respect to living forms or groups are those shown in Fig. 3f and g, and those in Fig. 4a, c, and d. The organisms shown in Fig. 3 are largely restricted to the known Gunflint chert outcrops in the locality near Kakabeka Falls. In the dense black chert from this locality, the structures may be observed in thin sections by the thousands. The morphology is distinct in showing a tripartite organization of basal bulb, slender stipe, and a crown of umbrella-like shape. The realtive size of these three units of the organism differs widely, although in general, the size of the basal bulb varies inversely with the size of the umbrella-like crown or mantle. The crown or mantle possesses from six to eight distinct vein-like thickenings, the most common number being eight. The "veins" sometimes dichotomize and terminate in the points of the mantle. The size of the organisms ranges from $12.0\,\mu$ to slightly over $30.0\,\mu$. They occur within the same thin section in all directions of orientation, and when viewed from directly above the mantle appear somewhat similar in form to discoasters, an analogy which was erroneously drawn by the author in a previous paper.[1] The affinity of this organism, provided any living counterpart exists, is difficult to assign. In shape and basic organization, the structural features are reminiscent of certain coelenterates, particularly the hydrozoans. The size of the organism is extraordinarily small, however, and if size is a criterion of prime importance, the structure must be excluded from consideration as a coelenterate. In this connection, it should be pointed out that in life, this organism may have been three to four times its present size, considering shrinkage in the transition from the hydrated silica gel to the chalcedonic phase of the silica matrix. Efforts to find analogies to this structure among the dinoflagellates living and fossil, the chitinozoans, protozoa, and the myxobacteria have been unsuccessful.

The organism shown on Fig. 4a, c, and d and Fig. 5a presents similar problems in seeking an existing biological counterpart. The organism is limited in occurrence among the Gunflint chert outcrops to that at the Schreiber Beach locality, where it occurs in very sparse numbers in the dense black cherts. Detailed observation of several hundred thin sections has revealed only 155 organisms which show this general organization. Of these, a number are fragmental, although over 100 fairly intact specimens have been examined in detail. The basic organization consists of a central, relatively thick-walled sphere on which are distributed a variable number of spheroidal tubercle-like bodies, and the entire structure is surrounded by a tenuous outer layer, which is almost invariably ruptured in one hemisphere or parts of both. The structure is essentially a sphere within a sphere, the two spheres being separated by the tubercle-like spheroids. The number of the latter varies from none to as many as fifteen. The tubercles are distributed over the surface of the inner sphere without any discernible geometric pattern as may be ascertained by optically sectioning the object. When the number of the tubercles is small, or if they are absent, the outer sphere is fragmented and often undetectable. The structures, if intact, range from approximately 28.0 to 32.0 μ, and many of them show a tendency toward flattening to a rounded lenticular shape, although they are never highly compressed.

Objects similar to this structure among living organisms are unknown to the authors. Analogies have been drawn by other observers to öogonia of aquatic fungi and to certain colonial algae. However, none of these comparisons bears close scrutiny. It is most probable that the structure was a free-floating colonial photosynthetic organism, and it is possible that the small tubercles were involved in vegetative reproduction. Despite careful search in many thin sections of the chert from the Schreiber locality, no intermediate, or what might be called ontogenetic, stages have been found.

In concluding this discussion of the structurally preserved organisms, it should be noted that the organisms described do not represent the total range of structures which have thus far been found in the Gunflint chert. They do, however, represent some of the most common and most distinctive forms observed to date. None of the organisms are contaminants to the chert in preparation, since they have all been observed and photographed in their solid transparent silica matrix of chalcedonic chert.

CHEMICAL STUDIES OF THE ORGANIC MATTER

The antiquity of the organic matter in the Gunflint chert and its definite biogenic origin evoke much interest in various chemical aspects of the Gunflint formation, particularly with reference to problems of the ultimate antiquity of life and the nature of very ancient organic matter. Inasmuch as the Gunflint formation is probably the least metamorphosed Middle Precambrian formation now known in the geologic record, the possibilities of securing meaningful bio-geochemical data are attractive. With this in view, a number of studies have been made, some of which will be summarized here. Further studies are in progress, and it is hoped that additional information may become available in this difficult field of investigation.

The organic fraction of the darker and more highly carbonaceous samples of the chert ranges from 0.2 to 0.6% by dry weight, the average of the darker samples being 0.37 or 3700 ppm. Although there is some presumptive evidence of the presence of amino acids, careful reruns have yielded such low values that the data are inconclusive. No porphyrins can be detected.

Destructive distillation of the chert at 400°C yielded the following hydrocarbons and their relative proportions:

Hydrocarbon	ppm*
Methane	87.0
Ethane	4.0
Propane	0.8
Normal pentane	0.2
Cyclopentane	0.1
2-methyl pentane	0.1
Normal hexane	0.5
Cyclohexane	0.1
Normal heptane	0.07
Normal octane	0.01
Benzene	0.34
Toluene	0.15
Xylenes	0.45
Isopropyl benzene	0.13

* Data secured from Dr. John Hunt, Jersey Production Research, Tulsa, Oklahoma.

The organic residue of the Gunflint chert after demineralization in HF yields small amounts of extractable compounds when eluted with benzol and methanol. These extractives fluoresce strongly in ultraviolet light. Data recently obtained by W. G. Meinschein show the following extracts by weight secured by eluting the organic residue from 1824 g of chert after dissolution of the silica:

N-heptane eluate	2.1 mg
Carbon tetrachloride eluate	1.3 mg
Benzene eluate	0.3 mg
Methanol eluate	10.9 mg

Of these extractables, the heptane and carbon tetrachloride fractions are presumably all alkane hydrocarbons and the benzene eluate aromatic hydrocarbons, probably consisting primarily of phenanthrenes as shown by ultraviolet absorbtion. The methanol nonhydrocarbon eluate was subjected to infrared absorbtion, with the result shown in the spectrum in Fig. 7. It will be noted that the infrared absorbtion indicates the presence of carbonyl bonding and alcohol and ester linkages.

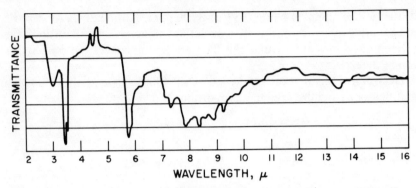

FIG. 7. Infrared absorption spectrum of methanol eluate secured from HF freed organic fraction of Gunflint chert. (Peaks above 10 μ indicate highly condensed ring structures.)

One aspect of the carbon chemistry of the Gunflint organic matter of much interest is the nature of its stable carbon isotopic composition. Several determinations have been made of the C^{13}/C^{12} ratio of the organic fraction. By use of the Peedee belemnite standard and correction for O^{17}, S. R. Silverman secured a C^{13}/C^{12} ratio of $-33.1\% 0\delta$. This value falls close to the low end of the range for solid and liquid contemporary biogenic carbon (i.e. organic matter photosynthetically depleted in C^{13}). Such C^{13} depletion is putative evidence that the Gunflint organic matter was produced by photosynthesis if analogy is made with contemporary photosynthetic products such as wood or with known fossil products of photosynthesis such as peat lignite and coal.[14] Further evidence in this direction has been secured by T. Hoering in the analysis of the C^{13}/C^{12} ratio in the organic carbon of the Gunflint and its comparison with the C^{13}/C^{12} ratio of the carbonate fraction in the *same rock sample*. The value for the organic carbon C^{13}/C^{12} ratio was $-29.2\% 0\delta$ and that for the inorganic $CaCO_3$ fraction $-11.63\% 0\delta$ (values with reference to the Solenhofen Limestone N.B.S. Reference Sample # 20). The differences here between the reduced (organic) carbon and the $CaCO_3$ carbon attest further to the photosynthetic origin of the Gunflint chert organic matter and are of interest in speculations on the oxidizing vs. reducing paleoenvironment of Gunflint time.

PALEOENVIRONMENT OF DEPOSITION

It is generally recognized that the Precambrian banded siliceous iron-bearing formations such as the Gunflint are sedimentary deposits, but there is no general agreement as to the source, method of transportation, and manner of deposition of the iron and silica. Interpretation of paleoenvironment is based to a large extent upon knowledge gained from the study of the physical and chemical processes operating in similar environments today. In the case of the siliceous iron formations of the Precambrian type there does not exist a modern example; nor is there known a single place where sediments of this type are being deposited today. Furthermore, similar sediments are either very rare or are absent in Paleozoic, Mesozoic, and Cenozoic stratigraphic sections. Thus, reconstruction of the paleoenvironment of the siliceous iron-bearing sediments depends upon circumstantial evidence restrained only by the laws of physics and chemistry. This situation has led to a wide variety of interpretations and controversial points of view.

Van Hise and Leith[15] concluded that in the Lake Superior region, the iron and silica were derived partly by weathering of pre-existing basic igneous rocks and partly by direct magmatic contribution or reaction of sea water with hot lavas. The weathering hypothesis has since been strongly supported by Gruner,[16] Woolnough,[17] Sakamoto,[18] James,[19] Alexandrov,[20] and Hough.[21] The direct magmatic or hot-spring origin has received support from Collins, Quirke, and Thompson,[22] Moore and Maynard,[23] Magnüsson,[24] Dunn,[25] Goodwin,[6] and Oftedahl.[26]

There seems to be general agreement that the Precambrian iron formation accumulated in a subaqueous environment. The specific nature of this environment is open to question. The site of deposition of the iron formation is specified by Van Hise and Leith[15] and Oftedahl[26] as the sea; Gruner[16] and Moore and Maynard[23] as lakes or the sea; Tyler and Twenhofel,[27] James,[19] and Goodwin[6] as marginal basins with restricted connections with the sea; Woolnough,[17] Sakamoto,[18] Alexandrov,[20] and Hough[21] as lakes; and Collins, Quirke, and Thompson[22] as pools, ponds, and irregular flow of water over a surface intermittently exposed to the air.

An intensive study of the physical and chemical attributes such as chemical composition, mineralogy, grain morphology, textures, structures, and relationships to other sediments should provide the necessary clues to define the environment of deposition of the iron formation. The chemical composition of these rocks is rather well known (this applies only to the major constituents) in areas which have stimulated economic interest, but there are extensive areas in which we have little or no information. Thus, a statistical approach to the composition of the siliceous iron formations is heavily weighted by economic concepts and does not provide the basic information necessary for paleoenvironment interpretation.

Minerals are rather sensitive indicators of environment; thus, the occurrence of specific minerals or mineral associations might be expected to have important environmental significance. This type of approach holds great promise from a theoretical point of view, but there are formidable practical difficulties. The Precambrian iron formations are very old rocks. In most areas, these rocks have suffered metamorphism of some type during their history; hence, the present mineralogy may date largely from this period rather than from the time of deposition of the sediment. Iron-bearing sediments are particularly sensitive to oxidizing and reducing environments that may have existed at any time throughout their history, and thus, the present oxidation state of the iron may not reflect conditions at the time of deposition. These factors are inherent in the problem and must be taken into consideration in any study dealing with paleoenvironmental interpretation. Van Hise and Leith[15] concluded from their extensive studies of iron formations in the Lake Superior region that the original minerals were, "... greenalite, siderite, chert, and perhaps some hematite, magnetite and limonite...".

As the result of studies in the Iron River district of Michigan, James[19] extended the sedimentary facies concept originally proposed by Van Hise and Leith[15] to include the oxide and sulphide facies. James considers magnetite, which is a major component of his oxide facies, as a primary mineral. He also redefines iron formation so as to include graphitic, pyritic slates as the dominant component of the sulphide facies. James[19] assumes that the minerals which occur in the areas of lowest metamorphic grade (in Michigan and Minnesota) are primary minerals. This assumption is not necessarily valid, for there is no compelling reason that unmetamorphosed iron formation should occur in these areas. The eastern portion of the Gunflint range contains probably the least metamorphosed iron formation known. This area is truly a window through the Precambrian metamorphic veil. The minerals present in the Gunflint formation have suffered a minimum amount of change and, thus, more nearly reflect the original environment of deposition.

It seems certain that the Gunflint waters were silica rich. However, the source of this silica, the manner of transportation, and the mechanism of deposition are unknown. Krauskopf's[28] studies indicate that silica is soluble to the extent of about 120 ppm at 25°C in both fresh and sea waters in the pH range from 0 to 9. Any silica that occurs in excess of this amount will be present in the colloidal state. Most silica-bearing solutions in nature are very dilute (5 to 30 ppm), except for certain connate waters (20 to 60 ppm) and hot spring waters such as those in Yellowstone Park, where the silica content may reach 700 ppm. Colloidal silica may be deposited by evaporation, freezing, coprecipitation with other colloids, and by electrolytes. Organisms such as diatoms, radiolaria, and some varieties of sponges have the ability to precipitate silica from very dilute solutions. The silica which now occurs in the form of chalcedony and quartz in the Gunflint formation may have been deposited by organisms in the form of silica gel. Such a hydrous gel would slowly lose water through syneresis, passing into opal, and finally crystallizing as chalcedony and quartz.

Interpretation of primary textures and structures of the Precambrian iron formations in terms of environment has received inadequate attention. The Gunflint iron formation contains granular, oolitic, and dense nongranular cherts. The granules range in size from 0.1 to 1.0 mm (or even larger) and show no regular internal structure. Van Hise and Leith,[15] Gruner,[16] and Gill[29] concluded that the granules represent colloidal globules or aggregates that were deposited in the gelatinous state. Hotchkiss[30] and Huber[31] suggest than the wavy-bedded granular cherts on the Gogebic range were formed in shallow waters under conditions of strong wave activity.

The granular cherts in the Lower Algal zone of the Gunflint contain chert oolites and granules, IM muscovite granules, pyroclastic granules, and occasional clastic quartz grains. The morphology of the granules and the intimate association with clastic grains suggest that they were not deposited as colloidal globules or aggregates but are clasts that were deposited in an environment of strong wave or current activity. Goodwin[6] has noted well developed cross-laminated units in the Lower East Taconite facies of the Gunflint. Similar structures may be observed in the Lower Cherty horizon on the Mesabi range. The occurrence of cross-laminated units in the granular cherts indicates that the granules behaved as clasts and that currents were responsible for their transportation and deposition.

The occurrence of large numbers of algal domes in the Lower Algal zone of the Gunflint formation indicates that the waters were sufficiently shallow, probably less than 60 ft, to allow light to penetrate to the water–sediment interface. The presence of granular chert associated with oolites and quartz clasts in this zone suggests current activity. The cherts of the Lower Algal zone are predominantly black, gray, or green, with red and white cherts occurring in subordinate amounts. The black, gray, and green colors are due to the presence of pyrite, organic matter, and iron-bearing carbonates. The algal domes and the granular cherts suggest shallow, agitated waters. The pyrite, organic matter and the iron-bearing carbonates indicate reducing conditions.

The local conditions of the environment as they affected the organisms preserved in the Gunflint chert are amenable only to inferential generalizations. The assumption that the filamentous structures constituting much of the organic fraction in the chert were truly algal and hence photosynthetic is based on the following deductions: (1) their morphology conforms to that of existing primitive filamentous blue-green algae; (2) the gross structure of the domes containing the organisms conforms to similar algal domes or biostromes of blue-green algae extant today in shallow waters; and (3) the fractionation of the stable carbon isotopes as determined in the organic carbon of the chert would most reasonably be explained on the basis of photosynthetic fractionation. The oxygenous environment produced by photosynthesis in the Gunflint sedimentary basin might have been very localized and adjacent to the algal colonies only. If heterotrophic oxygen-consuming organisms were among the mixed population of the organisms observed, it might well account for the evidence (based on mineralogy) of oxidizing and reducing conditions closely adjacent to each other. Such contrasts in conditions of eH can be found in many biologically highly active sedimentary environments today.

Extrapolation on the nature of the gaseous composition of the Earth's atmosphere during Gunflint time on the basis of the paleontologic evidence provided by the Gunflint fossils is scarcely justified. However, it is tempting to consider that if the Gunflint assemblage was largely a photosynthetic biosystem, and if it is representative of a geographically more widespread or a world-wide biosystem of photosynthetic organisms, the period of Gunflint time may represent an intermediate stage in the evolution of the highly oxygenic atmosphere which must have prevailed at the beginning of Cambrian time.

ACKNOWLEDGMENTS

The following acknowledgments are made on behalf of the late Professor Stanley Tyler by the present author. For their able assistance in photographing the organisms of the chert, thanks are due to G. W. Andrews, K. E. Siefert, J. T. Mengel, and T. E. Hendrix. The assistance in the field of R. W. Marsden, G. H. Spencer, Jr., D. Ferreira and A. M. Goodwin is gratefully acknowledged.

The author wishes to express appreciation to J. M. Hunt, T. Hoering, S. R. Silverman and W. G. Meinschein for their invaluable contributions in chemical and isotopic studies.

Financial support for this research was provided by the Wisconsin Alumni Research Foundation and by the National Science Foundation –Grant NSF–G 18858.

REFERENCES

1. TYLER, S. A., and BARGHOORN, E. S., Occurrence of Structurally Preserved Plants in the Precambrian Rocks of the Canadian Shield, *Science,* vol. 119 (1954), pp. 606–8.
2. GLAESSNER, M. F., Pre-Cambrian Fossils, *Biological Reviews of the Cambridge Philosophical Society,* vol. 37 (1962), pp. 467–94.
3. HURLEY, P. M., *et al.,* Unmetamorphosed Minerals in the Gunflint Formation Used to Test the Age of the Animikie, *The Journal of Geology,* vol. 70 (1962), pp. 489–92.
4. BRODERICK, T. M., Economic Geology and Stratigraphy of the Gunflint Iron District,

Minnesota, *Economic Geology and the Bulletin of the Society of Economic Geologists*, vol. 15 (1920), pp. 422–5.

5. GILL, J. E., Gunflint Iron-Bearing Formation, *Memoir of the Department of Mines and Technical Surveys, Geological Survey of Canada*, Summary Report, Part c (1924), pp. 28–88.

6. GOODWIN, A. M., Facies Relations in the Gunflint Iron Formation, *Economic Geology and the Bulletin of the Society of Economic Geologists*, vol. 51 (1956), pp. 565–95.

7. MOORHOUSE, W. W., Gunflint Iron Range in the Vicinity of Port Arthur, *Reports of the Ontario Department of Mines*, vol. 69 (1960), pp. 1–40.

8. GOODWIN, A. M., Gunflint Iron Formation of the Whitefish Lake Area, *Reports of the Ontario Department of Mines*, vol. 69 (1960), pp. 41–63.

9. TANTON, T. L., Fort William and Port Arthur and Thunder Cape Map Areas, Thunder Bay District, Ontario, *Memoir of the Department of Mines and Technical Surveys, Geological Survey of Canada*, vol. 167 (1931).

10. HOPKINS, P. E., Schreiber–Duck Lake Area, *Reports of the Ontario Department of Mines*, vol. 30 (1921), pp. 1–26.

11. HARCOURT, G. A., The Southwestern Part of the Schreiber Area, *Reports of the Ontario Department of Mines*, vol. 47 (1938), pp. 1–22.

12. LEITH, C. K., LUND, R. J., and LEITH, A., Pre-Cambrian Rocks of the Lake Superior Region, *United States Department of the Interior, Geological Survey, Professional Papers*, Paper No. 184 (1935).

13. TYLER, S. A., and BARGHOORN, E. S., Ambient Pyrite Grains in Precambrian Cherts, *American Journal of Science*, vol. 261 (1963), pp. 424–32.

14. CRAIG, H., The Geochemistry of the Stable Carbon Isotopes, *Geochimica et Cosmochimica Acta*, vol. 3 (1953), pp. 53–92.

15. VAN HISE, C. R., and LEITH, C. K., The Geology of the Lake Superior Region, *United States Department of the Interior, Geological Survey*, Monograph 52 (1911).

16. GRUNER, J. W., Hydrothermal Oxidation and Leaching Experiments; Their Bearing on the Origin of the Lake Superior Hematite–Limonite Ores, *Economic Geology and the Bulletin of the Society of Economic Geologists*, vol. 25 (1930), pp. 697–719.

17. WOOLNOUGH, W. G., Origin of Banded Iron Deposits; A Suggestion, *Economic Geology and the Bulletin of the Society of Economic Geologists*, vol. 36 (1941), pp. 465–89.

18. SAKAMOTO, T., The Origin of the Precambrian Banded Iron Ores, *American Journal of Science*, vol. 248 (1950), pp. 449–74.

19. JAMES, H. L., Sedimentary Facies of Iron Formation, *Economic Geology and the Bulletin of the Society of Economic Geologists*, vol. 49 (1954), pp. 235–93.

20. ALEXANDROV, E. A., Contribution Studies of Origin of Precambrian Banded Iron Ores, *Economic Geology and the Bulletin of the Society of Economic Geologists*, vol. 50, No. 5 (1955).

21. HOUGH, J. L., Fresh Water Environment of Deposition of Precambrian Banded Iron Formation (Lake Superior District), *Journal of Sedimentary Petrology*, vol. 28, No. 4 (1958), pp. 414–30.

22. COLLINS, W. H., QUIRKE, T. T., and THOMPSON, E., Michipicoten Iron Ranges, *Memoir of the Department of Mines and Technical Surveys, Geological Survey of Canada*, vol. 147 (1926), pp. 1–141.

23. MOORE, E. S., and MAYNARD, J. E., Solution, Transportation and Precipitation of Iron and Silica, *Economic Geology and the Bulletin of the Society of Economic Geologists*, vol. 24 (1929), pp. 272–303.

24. MAGNÜSSON, N. H., The Evolution of the Lower Archaen Rocks in Central Sweden and Their Iron, Manganese, and Sulphide Ores, *Geological Society of London Quarterly Journal*, vol. 367 (1936), pp. 332–59.

25. DUNN, J. A., Banded Hematite Ores, *Economic Geology and the Bulletin of the Society of Economic Geologists*, vol. 37 (1941), pp. 426–30.

26. OFTEDAHL, C., A Theory of Exhalative-Sedimentary Ores, *Geologiska Foreningens i Stockholm Forhandlingar*, vol. 80, No. 492 (1958).

27. TYLER, S. A., and TWENHOFEL, W. H., Sedimentation and Stratigraphy of the Huronian of Upper Michigan, *American Journal of Science*, vol. 250 (1952), Part I, pp. 1–27; Part II, pp. 118–51.
28. KRAUSKOPF, K. B., Dissolution and Precipitation of Silica at Low Temperatures, *Geochimica et Cosmochimica Acta*, vol. 10 (1956), pp. 1–26.
29. GILL, J. E., Origin of the Gunflint Iron-Bearing Formation, *Economic Geology and the Bulletin of the Society of Economic Geologists*, vol. 27 (1927), pp. 687–728.
30. HOTCHKISS, W. O., Geology of the Gogebic Range and Its Relation to Recent Mining Developments, *Engineering and Mining Journal*, Reprint 1–30 (September 13, 20, 27, and October 4, 1919).
31. HUBER, N. K., Some Aspects of the Origin of Ironwood-Iron Formation of Michigan and Wisconsin, *Economic Geology and the Bulletin of the Society of Economic Geologists*, vol. 54 (1959), pp. 82–118.

CHAPTER IV

THE SURVIVAL CAPABILITIES AND THE PERFORMANCE OF EARTH ORGANISMS IN SIMULATED EXTRATERRESTRIAL ENVIRONMENTS

S. M. SIEGEL, G. RENWICK, O. DALY, C. GIUMARRO,
G. DAVIS, and L. HALPERN

Union Carbide Research Institute, Tarrytown, New York

BIOLOGICAL APPROACH TO ENVIRONMENTAL SIMULATION

FROM the engineering viewpoint, the evaluation of performance under stress of materials, components, and systems is a highly exacting endeavor. This is particularly the case when performance of systems designed for space missions is considered.

Biologists have worked according to engineering specifications and standards in the study of simulated extraterrestrial environments, yet the biological information generated has not constituted a fair return on the investment of time, labor, and materials in the electronics and "hardware" required.

We cannot hope to duplicate the "environment" of Mars in the laboratory, because any planet possesses a virtual infinity of environments consisting of many elements in a state of continuous change. Furthermore, the limitations inherent in methods of remote measurement (spectroscopy, radiometry, etc.) make it impossible to determine with certainty even an average set of extraterrestrial conditions.

We can, however, approximate some extraterrestrial conditions remarkably well, others only passingly well, and some poorly or not at all. The individual factors, properly evaluated, can be combined into a near-simulation of a specific environment. But only by the study of various factors individually can the nature of their interplay be understood.

Our approach rests heavily upon the concept that the total of earthly environments is part of a greater bioecological continuum within the cosmos, and that virtually any rational and systematic alteration in the factors which comprise a terrestrial condition must approximate a part of some other planetary ecosystem, known or unknown. In other words, the *raison d'être* for environmental simulation as an experimental tool is the evaluation of the capabilities of familiar life forms in order that we may better assess the directions in which they might depart if the environment and selection pressures changed in a particular manner.

Specifically, we may select factorial combinations which can be designated as "simulated high altitude", "simulated Martian equatorial summer", etc. Then, having the factors in mind singly and in lower orders of combination, we can move in simile from Earth to 60,000 ft, toward Mars, or in any other reasonable direction with some confidence that the biological performance—survival, acclimatization, adaptation—will give us meaningful information toward a picture of organic evolution on a cosmic scale.

If this philosophy and methodology are adhered to, we believe that a host of new morphological and biochemical phenomena, as well as practical techniques such as extraterrestrial farming, will surely make their appearance as a matter of course.

EXPERIMENTAL PROCEDURES

Selection of Reference Systems

Emphasis was placed upon variations in partial and total oxygen pressures because it is reasonable to suppose that the universe offers many anaerobic conditions as well as aerobic environments covering a range of partial and total pressures. Indeed, the microenvironments on this planet cover an appreciable range of oxygen pressures. Convenient reference points include the biotic zone of the Himalayas (elevation: 20,000 ft, $P_{total} \sim 380$ mm Hg, $P_{O_2} = 76$ mm Hg); air pressures equivalent to 50,000–60,000 ft; and completely anaerobic conditions.

Pure oxygen at 1 atm is assumed to be rare in nature but is useful for studying the phenomenon of oxygen poisoning, a possible hazard in artificial environments. Furthermore, oxygen in the normal atmosphere will rapidly kill plants grown in a low-oxygen or oxygen-free atmosphere.

Temperature cycles of several kinds constitute additional factors, including the summer equatorial temperature cycle adopted for Mars (8 hr of 20 to 25°C day temperature and 16 hr of −20 to −30°C night temperature). Cycles involving other times and temperatures are included as well as single high- and low-temperature shock treatments.

Water supply is one of the most controversial factors in a simulated Martian environment, and a variety of experimental variations have been devised. Values for condensable atmospheric water in the range of 0.01–0.05 g/cm² have been adopted. An alternative procedure is the application of 1 cm of water ice to the substratum at 2- to 4-week intervals.

Factors such as centrifugal simulation of gravity, radiation, and substratum have so far received only preliminary study.

Other factorial combinations include the anaerobic desert (produced in a chamber operating at $P = 1$ atm, 100% N_2 or 98% $N_2 + 2\%$ CO_2, dew point $-60°C$, temperature $\sim 25°C$) and the diurnal freezing cycle under aerobic conditions.

The most important reference system to be considered here is the "nearly simulated Martian equatorial summer". This environment is approached factorially as a tripartite biological screen for evaluating competence of seed germination at suitable temperature, atmospheric, and water conditions, followed by the combination of factors. This approach will be considered in a later Section.

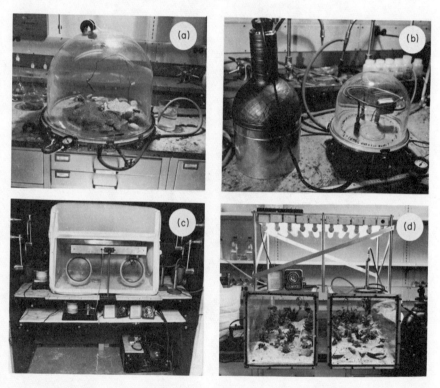

Fig. 1. Environment-simulating equipment. a, Large Plexiglas chamber used for turtle colony. b, "Snow dome" used for controlled water supply to seeds. c, Nearly simulated Martian equatorial summer. d, Anaerobic desert chamber.

A number of facilities have been used for establishing single and multifactorial simulated conditions (Fig. 1). The large Plexiglas dome used for turtles and lower plants is equipped for gassing, watering, draining, and feeding. The small Plexiglas dome for seed and insect work has a refrigerator coil for liquid nitrogen and an electric vibrator for dislodging frost from the coil to simulate snow (frost) fall. Both domes can be operated at reduced pressures. The large foam-insulated box may be operated anaerobically and programmed for specific warm–light and cold–dark cycles. The anaerobic desert chamber, which passes 3–4/min of N_2 or $N_2 + CO_2$ at dew point $-60°C$, has been used to select species resistance to desiccation and to study the course of water deficiency injury in organisms.

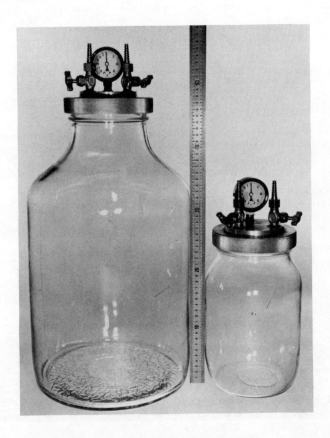

FIG. 2. Anaerobic jars used in screening atmosphere effects.

Routine screening of atmospheric effects on seed germination, insect behavior, and other processes has been studied in 4- or 16-liter anaerobic jars (Fig. 2), which can be placed in controlled temperature and light conditions.

TABLE 1. Organism studied

Group	Examples	Extent of testing	Environments used	Basis for selection
Seed plants	Legumes Cereals Composites Mustards	Nearly 300 species and cultivated varieties	General, low oxygen $P_{O_2} = 760$ mm Hg	Most random, some ecological
Cryptogamic plants Autotrophic	Ferns Mosses Hornworts and liverworts	6 species	Low pressure, low oxygen, $P_{O_2} = 760$ mm Hg, low water	Paleobotanical
Heterotrophic	Fungi	About 12 species, not all identified	Contaminants in anaerobic desert and Mars factorial	By their presence in simulators
Protista	Mastigophora Ciliata	6 species	Low pressure	Paleontological
Metazoa Invertebrate	Coelenterata Platyhelminthes Nemathelminthes Mollusca Insecta Crustaces	20 species	Low pressure, low oxygen, $P_{O_2} = 760$ mm Hg, low temperature, salinity, and desiccation	Part random, part ecological
Vertebrate	HeLa cells Amphibia (tadpoles) Reptilia (turtles)	One species of each	Low oxygen, $P_{O_2} = 760$ mm Hg, freezing, simulated high altitude	Principally biological

Organisms

Nearly 300 species and varieties of seed plants, 24 species of lower plants and protista, and over 20 species of animals have been studied in various ways in this laboratory (Table 1). In a few instances, selections have been made on a specific ecological basis. For example:

1. The peanut was expected to germinate with little or no oxygen, in recognition of the subterranean development of the peanut seed.
2. Some of the grasses and cereals are native to cold semiarid regions of relatively high altitude, hence were expected to withstand appreciable cold at reduced oxygen levels.

The protista and lower plants, on the other hand, were viewed as more or less direct descendants of forms which may have lived when the atmosphere had far less oxygen than at present. Seed selection was made principally on a random basis, whereas the turtle was chosen purely by intuition.

The most striking biological performance in many respects was shown by organisms which had not been introduced intentionally into the Mars equatorial summer and anaerobic desert conditions. Fungi, presumably introduced as spores, grew well during simulator operation. The species isolated in pure culture and identified will be discussed in a later Section.

Standards of Response and Performance

The simplest order of response under environmental stress is death. Of course, up to a point, test organisms in the process of failing may be rescued from some situations. The standards of response and performance are summarized in Table 2.

TABLE 2. Standards of response and performance

Stage	Designation	Condition	
		Plant	Animal
1	Suitable environment – no challenge or stress	Growth and reproduction	Growth, reproduction, locomotion (if normal)
2	Retardation, suboptimal conditions, moderate stress	Growth; little or no reproduction	As with plants; locomotion impeded
3	Survival (maintenance)	No growth; inactivity or dormancy	
4	Failure	Progressive decline in function and structure	
5	Death	Irreversible loss of function	

Two mechanisms for circumventing failure—acclimatization and dormancy—would be expected to occur between Stages 3 and 4; that is, before the process of decline. The failing organism may recover by direct resuscitation or wholesale restoration, or regeneration of severely damaged structures may be required. The ways in which organisms exhibit failure or other responses will be described in detail later.

Genetic heterogeneity within a population will have a bearing on stress response, and it appears that new areas of phenotypic expression result from experimental environments which create hitherto nonexistent (or rare) types of selection pressure.

GENERAL STUDIES: VARIATIONS IN AIR AND OXYGEN PRESSURE

Plant and Animal Performance at the High Mountain Level

The flora and fauna of the upper biotic zone in the Himalayan range (18,000–20,000 ft, $P_{atm} = 0.5$ mm Hg) are not abundant forms but include flowering plants–grasses, sedges, composites; higher invertebrates–reptiles, bees, flies, spiders; and transient vertebrates–birds, rodents, carnivores.

In examining the factors of the upper Himalayan environment, total pressure and oxygen pressure have been studied independently. Experiments were performed at $P_{total} = 760$ mm Hg, $P_{O_2} = 76$ mm Hg (remainder N_2 or Ar), and at $P_{air} = 380$ mm Hg.

It has long been known that 380 mm Hg air pressure is far from the incipient anoxic level, even for many mammals. Symptoms of oxygen deficiency are not displayed by cats and dogs until $P_{air} = 250–270$ mm Hg or by rabbits until $P_{air}^{-} = 200$ mm Hg. The frog is not disturbed until $P_{air} \cong 100$ mm Hg.

In our experience, wasps (*Vespa*), bees (*Bombus*), ants (*Monomorium*), beetles (*Adalia, Passalus*), other insects, and the common turtle (*Pseudemys*) can live actively, at least for weeks, in 10% oxygen at sea-level pressure or in air at a simulated 20,000 ft. Neither ground locomotion nor flight is impaired, although the air density at 20,000 ft is near the lower limit for sustained wasp or bee flight.

Nematodes and protozoa in water appear unaffected by reductions in pressure to 380 mm Hg, and the hatching rate of the brine shrimp *Artemia* is higher at 380 than at 760 mm Hg.

The fungus *Alternaria* grows at twice the sea-level rate in a simulated 20,000 ft atmosphere. The germination of beet, marigold, rice, and turnip is optimal in 10% oxygen rather than in air; the germination of tomato, tobacco, and cockscomb (*Celosia*) seed is the same in air and 10% oxygen.

Cockscomb, cucumber, and barley seedling growth rates are about 30–40% higher in 10% oxygen than in air; the shoot of peppermint elongates 42% faster in 10% oxygen. Optima for some species may lie at even lower partial pressures of oxygen. Thus, if barometric pressure or P_{O_2} were determining factors in mountain ecology, the high altitudes should be teeming with plant and animal life. In the Himalayas, the desiccating gale-force winds, low mean year-around temperatures, and comparatively warm seasons may determine the relative scarcity of organisms. Indeed, the beneficial effects of 10% oxygen at $P_{total} =$ 760 mm Hg or $P_{air} = 380$ mm Hg (which seem to be biologically equivalent) may aid organisms to withstand the rigors of other stress factors at 20,000 ft.

Plant and Animal Performance at $P_{0_2} = 1$ atm (760 mm)

In contrast to the beneficial effects of a moderately subatmospheric oxygen level on plants and its ready acceptance by animals, pure oxygen at 1 atm comes close to being a "universal poison" (Table 3). It is known that man cannot function for more than brief periods in 1 atm of pure oxygen, and the "Prolonged exposure... eventually produces inflammation of the lungs, respiratory disturbances, various heart symptoms, numbness of fingers and toes, and nausea." (Ref. 299.)

The Responses of Invertebrates to Air Pressures < 0.2 atm (< 150 mm Hg)

There is a wide difference in atmospheric pressures and partial pressures of oxygen between the biotic zone of the high mountains and the surface of Mars. This gap of about one order of magnitude in total pressure and two orders in oxygen pressure presumably has been filled in many other planetary systems. In this solar system, it may be filled in the future either in orbital stations or at ground-based lunar or Martian stations, and it is important that its biological effects be known.

Atmosphere tests were carried out in 4- or 16-liter glass jars closed with gasketed and threaded aluminum caps equipped with gassing valves and vacuum gages. Some tests were carried out under Plexiglas hemispheres (radius *circa* 10 cm) which could be sealed onto O-ring-gasketed bases at 1 atm and then evacuated or gassed. No specialized equipment was required for the study of smaller invertebrates. The Leighton tissue culture tube fitted with a rubber stopper containing gassing or evacuating tubes was useful for microscopic observation of protozoa and nematodes because it possesses flat polished surfaces.

In one series of experiments, the ambient air pressure was lowered at a rate of about 0.002 atm/sec until a behavioral change in the insects was noticed (Table 4). The first change was shown by the wasps and bees, which ceased normal flight at about 0.4 atm but remained highly active otherwise. All the forms studied tolerated quite low air pressures (0.1–0.17 atm) for at least ·3 days. Ten wasps maintained for 5 days at 0.16 atm readily flew again when restored to 1 atm. Stag beetles and harlequin bugs were kept at their respective tolerable pressures for 8 days and termites for 10 days.

TABLE 3. Biological responses to 100% oxygen at 1.0 atm[a]

Organism	Process	Response
Bean	Seed germination	Suppressed 90% (4 days)
Pea		Suppressed 100% (4 days)
Portulaca		Suppressed 71% (3 days)
Pea	Shoot growth	Length suppressed 55% (14 days)
		Weight suppressed 62% (14 days)
Corn		Weight suppressed 51% (9 days)
Euphorbia	Leaf abscission	All leaves fallen (4 days)
Mimosa		All leaves fallen (7 days)
Mimosa	Touch sensitivity	Desensitized (15 hr)
Funaria (moss)	Spore germination	Germination tube inhibited 75% (3–4 weeks)
Pteris (fern)		Germination tube inhibited 55% (4 weeks)
Colpidium (ciliate)	Survival time	Dead (18 hr)
Paramecium (ciliate)		Dead (18 hr)
Planaria (flatworm)		Dead (14 days)
Gryllus (insecta)		Dead (24 hr)
Monomorium (insecta)		Dead (48 hr)
Adalia (insecta)		Dead (48 hr)
Bombus (insecta)		Flight impaired (4 hr); dead (20 hr)
HeLa cells (man)		Cells rounded; dying (48 hr)

[a]Control: 93 days.

TABLE 4. General responses of insects to reduced air pressure

Insect	Behavior at pressure indicated, atm			
	Apparently normal, at least 3 days	Loss of equilibrium	Complete immobilization	Activity restored after 1–15 min
Wasp (Vespa)	0.16[a]	<0.16	0.02	0.03
Bumble bee (Bombus)	0.16[a]	<0.16	0.07	0.10
Grasshopper (Melanoplus)	0.10[b]	0.07	0.03	0.07
Stag beetle (Passalus)	0.10	0.03	0.02	0.03
Ladybird beetle (Adalia)	0.17	0.03	<0.03	0.07
Harlequin bug (Murgantia)	0.10	0.07	0.01	0.07
Termite (Reticulotermes)	0.10	0.05	0.03	0.05
Ant (Monomorium)	0.10	0.05[c]	0.03	0.07

[a]But no flight below 0.4 atm.
[b]Unimpaired jumping; no flight.
[c]Only about 50% were impaired; the others moved normally.

The wasp and the bumble bee can fly in 1 atm at $P_{O_2} = 0.05$ atm, but the former does much better at $P_{O_2} = 0.1$ atm.

Flying ability of these insects was studied in a series of atmospheres of varying density but constant (10%) oxygen content. As the atmospheric density was lowered from that of 90% Ar + 10% O_2, through less dense mixtures, down to air at 0.5 atm, a nearly three-fold reduction, flight was unimpaired. A modest additional reduction resulted in markedly restricted flight, and at one-fifth of normal air density flight ceased completely. Further lowering of pressure caused the wasps and bees to lose coordination among walking appendages, resulting in pronounced "listing" of the body, toppling, and difficulty in righting the body once toppled. This phase was also reversible, at least within 1–2 days, when sea-level pressures were restored. Other insects were even more tolerant of low pressure. Complete immobilization generally required pressures well under 0.1 atm. In the final stages of immobilization, wasps, grasshoppers, and stag and ladybird beetles survived for 24 hr and recovered when a higher pressure was restored. Other insects, if kept immobilized more than 2 hr, displayed severe impairment of the appendages or died soon after activity was restored.

Half of a colony of 300 *Monomorium* ants maintained at 0.05 atm had impaired locomotion; however, the remainder gave a prompt, positive phototaxic response to unilateral illumination. Several trials showed the normal aerobic response time of about 5 sec (for half of the mobile population to move to the illuminated side of the vessel) to be essentially unchanged by the twentyfold reduction in pressure.

Wasps fly normally at a total pressure of 0.5–1.0 atm, $P_{O_2} = 0.1$ atm, and the bumble bee was observed in flight at $P_{O_2} = 0.05$ atm. Loss of flying ability in air at $P = 0.4$ atm does not arise primarily from an oxygen deficiency but from lowered atmospheric density (Table 5).

TABLE 5. Atmospheric density–flight relations of *Vespa communis*

P_{total} atm	P_{O_2} atm	Diluent gas for oxygen	Density at 25°C, g/liter	Flying ability
1.0	0.1	Ar	1.588	Unrestricted
1.0	0.1	N_2	1.155	Unrestricted
1.0	0.1	$N_2 + H_2$ (1:1)	0.691	Unrestricted
1.0	0.1	$N_2 + H_2$ (1:2)	0.496	1–2 cm elevation in 1-sec bursts
1.0	0.1	H_2	0.203	None
0.5	0.1	Air	0.588	Unrestricted
0.2	0.1	Ar	0.235	None
1.0	0.2	Air	1.177	Unrestricted

Locomotion and behavior of the contractile vacuole in ciliate proto-
zoans have been examined at low oxygen pressures. *Vorticella, Stentor,
Paramecium,* and *Colpidium* species were maintained in pond water
at 0.013-atm headspace pressure for 3 days without visible harm. The
only behavioral change was the retention by *Vorticella* and *Stentor* of
their contracted swimming forms rather than their obviously stalked
forms.

The flatworm *Planaria* is rather tolerant of high oxygen concentration;
nevertheless, it can live over 3 weeks in 5% oxygen and more than a day
in 0.1% oxygen (Table 6).

TABLE 6. Lifespan of unfed *Planaria* in
various atmospheres

% oxygen at 1 atm	Days to extinction[a]
0.0	0.5
0.1	1.2
1.0	1.5
2.0	11.0
5.0	21.0
10.0	25.0
21.0	93.0
100.0	13.0

[a]Based on 50–175 animals.

The "eggs" of the brine shrimp *Artemia salina* are notable for their
shelf life of some years and ease of hatching in fresh water, sea water,
or concentrated brine. The hatching rate in 1% sodium chloride was
observed to be higher when the headspace pressure was reduced from
$P_{air} = 1$ atm to $P_{air} = 0.5$ atm. Further reductions in pressure delayed
hatching; however, about 60 out of 300 eggs still produced viable larvae
under $P_{air} = 0.25$ atm and *circa* 20 out of 300 eggs hatched under a
synthetic Martian atmosphere (0.1% O_2, 2.3% CO_2, 1.5% Ar, remainder
N_2) at $P_{air} = 0.1$ atm (Fig. 3). Larvae hatched at normal pressure were
readily disintegrated by decompression, but those hatched at reduced
pressures remained active for periods of 4–6 days. It was of interest to
note that, although a few eggs hatched in 1% NaCl under the rarefied
Martian atmosphere, none hatched when the salt level was increased
to 3% or more.

Thus, even without the benefit of adaptation, selection, or acclimatization, a variety of invertebrates (14 out of 15 tested) show marked capabilities under unusual atmospheric conditions. The notable exceptions
were flight of insects, apparently restricted for aerodynamic rather than
metabolic reasons, and survival of the planarians. In addition, mollusks
have been reported by others to tolerate anaerobiosis indefinitely.

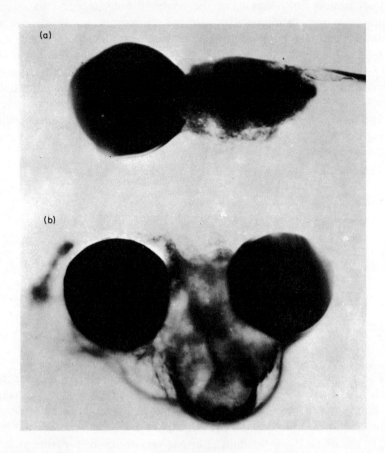

FIG. 3. Hatching of brine shrimp at reduced pressure and oxygen levels (mean
egg diameter = 0.16 mm). a, Larva emerging in synthetic Martian atmosphere
(0.1% O_2) at $P = 0.1$ atm. b, Larva emerged in $P_{air} = 0.25$ atm.

The Effects of Subatmospheric Oxygen Levels on Plants

Spores of mosses (e.g. *Funaria*) and ferns (e.g. *Pteridium*) can germinate
in 5% $O_2 + 95\%$ Ar or N_2, but at one-third the rate in 10% oxygen;
however, subsequent growth is slow.

The thallus stages of the liverwort *Marchantia* and the hornwort
Anthoceros become discolored and shrivelled within 2 weeks at air
pressures of 75–80 mm Hg. In contrast, *Marchantia* has been kept in a
green, unshrivelled condition for 6 weeks in 0–2% oxygen at 760 mm Hg
total pressure, but no growth was observed.

Survival tests under 0.5% oxygen (argon added to 760 mm Hg) were
run on 3–5-week-old, air-grown seedlings or cuttings. These plants were

maintained in potting soil. Survival times were based upon the irreversible wilting which occurred when the plants were returned to air. Only minimum values were obtained in some instances, and for many species only a few plants were used. Hence, the results are approximate. *Alyssum,* *Salvia,* and *Chrysanthemum* survived for more than 24 hr; *Digitaria,* *Oxalis,* and *Plantago* survived more than 40 hr. The maximum survival time for *Coleus* was between 150 and 175 hr and for 10-day-old *Acer,* between 250 and 275 hr. Tomato could not tolerate as much as 25 hr. If watered with 0.005 M KNO_3, *Coleus* tolerated an additional 100 hr and *Acer* an additional 25 to 40 hr.

In general, air-grown plants can survive for a limited time only in extremely low levels of oxygen, even though the same species can be germinated and grown with little or no oxygen. Winter rye and cucumber are examples, and will be discussed separately.

Seed germination in anaerobic and microaerobic conditions will be considered later, but germination capabilities of twenty species are given in Table 7. The Table shows remarkably high germination of virtually all species in 5% oxygen, of most in 2% oxygen, and of 6 in the complete absence of oxygen.

TABLE 7. Seed germination percentage in low-oxygen atmospheres after 3–6 days

Seed	Atmosphere			
	Ar (or N_2)	2% O_2 + 98% Ar	5% O_2 + 95% Ar	Air
Lettuce	0	78	78	98
Marigold	0	33	60	57
Zinnia	0	22	60	57
Celosia	22	81	90	89
Alyssum	0	21	80	80
Portulaca	0	50	50	55
Carrot	0	50	65	32
Onion	0	65	70	69
Cucumber	17	88	96	100
Bean	0	0	60	53
Coleus	0	0	54	91
Tomato	0	2	33	91
Dianthus	7	50	50	82
Ageratum	0	30	33	84
Cabbage	0	9	71	95
Turnip	0	16	21	90
Beet	0	34	40	50
Rye	40	50	95	95
Barley	0	10	28	80
Corn	29	42	80	80
Rice	17	24	24	23

Growth of *Celosia* is substantial in 5% oxygen and 2% oxygen:

	Air	5%O$_2$	2%O$_2$
Relative whole seedling weight	100	111	29
Relative root length	100	115	42

Turnip shoot growth also shows striking capabilities:

	Air	5%O$_2$	2%O$_2$
Relative shoot height	100	170	43

Other species showing good growth in low oxygen include peppermint, tomato, and cucumber (Figs. 4 and 5).

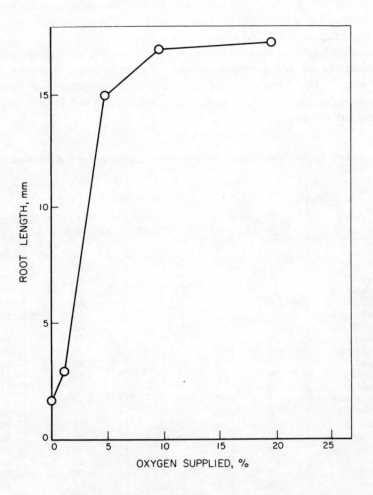

FIG. 4. Oxygen dependency in cucumber root growth.

FIG. 5. Sturdy appearance of 8-day-old cucumber seedlings grown in 2% O_2.

When the garden bean (*Phaseolus vulgaris*) is grown from seed in 5% O_2 + 95% Ar at 100% relative humidity, its appearance at 2 weeks does not differ greatly from that of air-grown plants (Fig. 6a). If, however, the same plants are permitted to remain in an atmosphere of *circa* 50% relative humidity for 1–2 hr, in well-watered soil, the appearance of air-grown plants is unchanged, whereas low-oxygen-grown plants collapse (Fig. 6b).

Speculations as to the chemical differences which could account for such novel behavior led to the discovery of constitutional and metabolic changes which are no less striking. Comparisons of these plants are summarized in Tables 8 and 9. Appreciable growth takes place in 5% oxygen, primarily of those structures already present in the embryo.

FIG. 6. Effect of atmosphere on 2-week-old bean plants. a, Immediately after removal from growth vessels. b, After 1–2 hr in 50% air.

The foregoing studies and many others have assured us that higher plants can be grown in low-oxygen atmospheres.

Reproduction in higher plants has not yet been achieved at extremely low pressures or oxygen partial pressures, although the opening of the flower bud of the desert succulent *Faucheria* and apparent beginnings of fruit growth have been observed in atmospheres containing 0.5% oxygen.

Efforts to study flowering and other plant developmental processes in experimental atmospheres continue, although there are theoretical arguments that would preclude flowering at extremely low oxygen levels. Such levels must be well under 10%, because that concentration is found at the biotic limits (*circa* 20,000 ft) in the Himalayas, where several families of flowering plants are represented.

TABLE 8. Comparison of linear growth of bean plants grown in air and in 5% oxygen

Organ	Linear growth, cm		Growth ratio $\left(\dfrac{5\% \, O_2}{air}\right)$
	Plants grown in air	Plants grown in 5% O_2	
Hypocotyl length	13.0	9.0	0.69
Epicotyl length			
Internode I	9.2	5.6	0.61
Additional internodes	9.3	1.6	0.17
Total stem length	31.5	16.2	0.52
Hypocotyl diameter	0.36	0.49	1.36
Cotyledon			
Length	2.0	2.6	1.30
Width	0.46	0.85	1.85
Thickness	0.25	0.38	1.52
Primary leaf			
Petiole length	3.4	1.5	0.44
Lamina length	3.9	2.1	0.54
Lamina width	3.5	2.3	0.66

TABLE 9. Comparison of weight of bean plants grown in air and in 5% oxygen

Organ	Plants grown in air		Plants grown in 5% O_2		Weight ratio $\left(\dfrac{5\% \, O_2}{air}\right)$
	Weight, g	$\dfrac{Fresh}{Dry} \times 100\%$	Weight, g	$\dfrac{Fresh}{Dry} \times 100\%$	
Root					
Fresh	0.91	5.6	0.82	5.0	0.90
Dry	0.05		0.04		0.80
Hypocotyl					
Fresh	1.50	5.4	1.58	5.1	1.05
Dry	0.08		0.08		1.00
Epicotyl internode					
Fresh	0.51	6.0	0.42	4.8	0.82
Dry	0.03		0.02		0.67
Additional internode					
Fresh	0.31	9.9	0.02	5.0	0.07
Dry	0.03		0.001		0.03
Primary leaves					
Fresh	0.40	7.5	0.10	10.0	0.25
Dry	0.03		0.01		0.33
Cotyledons					
Fresh	0.12	25.0	0.40	12.5	3.33
Dry	0.03		0.05		

The Turtle in Experimental Atmospheres

Several preliminary studies involving oxygen pressure and other variables have been undertaken with the common red-eared turtle *Pseudemys scripta-elegans*.

1. Two turtles were still active after exposure to 0.5 atm for 31 hr.
2. Ten animals were placed in a chamber containing argon at 1 atm to determine anaerobic tolerance. All animals were sluggish after 12 hr, and by the 24th hr all were comatose. On being returned to air, all recovered within 12–20 hr. Several weeks after this treatment, all animals appeared to be healthy and active.
3. Ten animals were placed in 100% oxygen at 1 atm. No effects of this treatment were seen after 24 hr nor in many subsequent weeks.
4. Three turtles were placed in a large anaerobic jar lying on its side and containing an island of mounded sand, several small rocks, and water to a depth of 5 cm. Under constant evacuation and bleed-in of air, the pressure was maintained at 0.5 atm for 3 days, then reduced to 0.2 atm and held for an additional 3 days. All three turtles appeared normal. The pressure was then reduced to 0.1 atm, representing the P_{total} (but not P_{O_2}) of Mars. All three turtles remained active for an additional 4 days, but on the 5th morning, with the pressure at 0.075 atm, one turtle was dead. The pressure was brought up 1 atm with argon, and under a constant argon flush, the dead turtle was removed. The two remaining turtles were fed for the first time in 11 days. At reduced oxygen pressure, the turtles apparently need less food. Evacuation to 0.1 atm was resumed, and the two turtles were still alive after 54 days total elapsed time.
5. Twelve animals were placed in a sand–rock–water environment in a large Plexiglas dome (Fig. 1). Several thimbles containing food were suspended by magnets from the top of the dome. When the pressure had fallen to 0.33 atm, one animal showed distress symptoms—possibly internal hemorrhage—and a second was inactive. Both were removed, and the decompression was resumed and held at 0.1–0.12 atm.

On the 8th day, all animals were active and healthy. On both the 9th and 12th days, an additional death occurred. On the 12th day, 500,000 units each of penicillin and mycostatin and 1 g of streptomycin were introduced into the water, and the animals were fed for the first time. An additional death occurred on the 15th day, but the remaining animals continued to be active through the 34th day. At this time, the experiment was terminated, some animals were set aside in air for observation and others were bled for hematological study.

These preliminary observations indicate clearly that the turtle is in the first rank as a candidate animal for stress and space research.

GENERAL STUDIES: TEMPERATURE, WATER, AND OTHER FACTORS

The Centrifuge

Although simulated high g values have pronounced effects on mammals, the results with simple organisms suggest that few highly novel or especially interesting responses will be generated. Bacterial cells, other cells, viruses, and subcellular particles are prepared routinely in functional states by centrifugation at more than 10,000 g.

Dry or partially imbibed rye seeds were exposed to 100,000 g for periods of as long as 5 hr (at 0°C, *in vacuo*). Subsequently, germination and growth were delayed transitorily, but the seedlings soon became indistinguishable from those grown from control seed. Although subcellular organization may well be disturbed by such forces, the magnitude required is clearly a matter of laboratory rather than planetary interest.

Dense cultures of *Paramecium* exposed to a single "pulse" of 100,000 g (5 min to maximum rpm from rest and 5 min for return to rest) were totally disintegrated. Three consecutive 50,000-g pulses had no perceptible effect upon structure or behavior. A 62,500-g pulse produced no apparent structural change, but locomotion in many individuals was impaired and erratic. In contrast, the *HeLa* cell, which lacks the tough wall or pellicle of *Paramecium,* survived 30 min at 100,000 g; and the nematode *Cephalobus,* a metazoan which has about ten times more bulk than *Paramecium,* withstood centrifugation at 100,000 g for hours with no evident impairment of locomotion or activity.

The effect of more modest centrifugal acceleration on seed germination was also studied (Table 10). Seeds were centrifuged for 3 days in stoppered test tubes at about 30°C (heating effect in centrifuge). Control groups were kept for the same length of time in stoppered tubes in darkness at 30°C and also under conventional conditions in unstoppered vessels at 25°C. Centrifugation caused greater inhibition of germination than either control condition.

TABLE 10. Effects of centrifugation at a constant 100 g during germination (3 days)

Species	Germination, %		
	Control group A, 25°C, open tubes	Control group B, 30°C, stoppered tubes	Centrifuged group, 30°C, stoppered tubes
Celosia	74	82	16
Turnip	100	38	0
Coleus	87	23	0
Amaranthus	85	72	13
Carnation	95	22	9
Spinach	90	20	20
Radish	90	24	7

Plants (and Some Animals) at Low Temperatures

Representatives of Gramineae (grasses), Cactaceae (cacti), and Crassulacae (succulents) were subjected to low-temperature shock treatments ranging from exposure to $-36°C$ to immersion in liquid nitrogen ($-180°C$). Exposure ranged from a few seconds to 5–10 min. Some results with the jade plant (*Crassula* sp.) are summarized below:

Plant No.	Temperature, °C	Rate of cooling, °C/sec	Atmosphere during thaw	New leaves after 33 days
8	−37	0.63	Air	10
9	−37	0.63	Argon	17
10	−55	0.77	Air	4
11	−55	0.77	Argon	12

The regeneration of leaves was thus demonstrated, and it appears that thawing in the absence of oxygen increases regenerative ability. The leaves stripped from these plants after cold treatment all rooted when planted with the cut surface in sand.

Grass clumps wholly immersed in liquid nitrogen for 5 min retained their viability when thawed at 22°C but not when subjected to accelerated warming at 40–50°C.

Another succulent, *Sempervivum tectorum*, exposed for 1 min to various low temperatures, showed root initiation in 1 month, as follows:

Temperature, °C	Roots on 5 plants in 30 days
22–25 (control)	28
−23	12
−52	9
−80	13

Plants were hard-frozen at $-10°C$, and it appears that their ability to initiate roots was not further reduced by exposure to temperatures below that point.

A cactus (*Mammilaria*) exposed to $-83°C$ for 1 min promptly showed damage (shrinkage and discoloration of the tip) but had produced two new branches 1 month after freezing.

Thus, two desert types—the dry, siliceous grass and the hydrophilic colloid-rich, thick-skinned succulent—exhibit regenerative abilities after brief exposure to extremely low temperature. In contrast, *Coleus, Ageratum,* and *Plantago* were readily killed by all temperatures below $-20°C$.

Some seeds show an increased rate of germination following immersion in liquid nitrogen:

Species	Time of germination count, hr	Per cent of germination after immersion in liquid N_2 for				
		0 hr	1/12 hr	1 hr	3–4 hr	16–19 hr
Lima bean	64	13	13	33	27	47
Winter rye	18	0	24	36	20	80
Peanut	144	5	25	10	15	35
Piñon pine	312	4	–	28	20	28
Flax	312	8	–	20	36	52

Germination of cucumber, red kidney bean, and radish was unaffected by exposures to liquid nitrogen up to 16 hr. However, the radish seedlings grown from such seeds were 50% heavier than the controls.

Germination of seeds following 24-hr low-temperature cycling for 1 week was as follows:

Seed	Per cent of germination after 1 week at			
	22°C, 16 hr 4°C, 8 hr	22°C, 8 hr 4°C, 16 hr	22°C, 16 hr −30°C, 8 hr	22°C, 8 hr −30°C, 16 hr
Mustard	+	+	+	−
Bachelor's button	+	−	−	−
Radish	+	+	+	−
Beets	+	−	−	−
Carrot	+	+	−	−
Cabbage	+	+	+	−
Brussels sprout	+	+	−	−
Cucumber	+	+	−	−
Chard	+	−	−	−
Turnip	+	+	−	−
Xeranthemum	+	+	+	+
Rutabaga	+	+	−	−
Bean	+	−	−	−
Rye	+	+	+	+

+ denotes ≥ 10% germination.

All the forms above show at least 80% germination under normal laboratory conditions. Most species cannot withstand 8 hr of severe freezing per day, yet a few are hardy enough to continue the germination process.

Low-temperature work with animals has consisted of only a few exploratory experiments:

1. The nematode *Cephalobus* can be lowered to − 30°C and stored for

at least several days without impairment in activity when returned
to ordinary temperatures.

2. Some individuals of the beetle *Passalus* remain active while the
   ambient temperature is reduced from $+5°C$ to $-20°C$ during 45 min.
   After 12 hr at $-20°C$, all resume activity at $+20°C$.

3. Specimens of the turtle *Pseudemys* have survived temperatures of
   $-5°C$ for 30 min; of $-2°C$ for 18 hr; and in one case, continued to be
   active for 30 min at $-13°C$.

4. The feeding medium was drained from a 5-day-old culture of *HeLa*
   cells and the culture flask immersed in liquid nitrogen for 18 hr. The
   flask was then thawed at $25°C$ and 500,000 cells inoculated into a
   fresh culture medium. After 24-hr incubation, the viable cell count
   was 64,000. Thus, some 13% of the cells survived prolonged liquid
   nitrogen temperatures. However, when cells were allowed to
   contact liquid nitrogen directly, they all died.

The Anaerobic Desert, High-Altitude Salt Marsh, and Snow Dome Environments

Xerophytes such as *Faucheria, Haworthia, Sedum, Mammilaria,
Sempervivum,* and *Pachyphytum* have been maintained in anaerobic
conditions (e.g. 100% N_2 or CO_2, or 70% $N_2 + 30\%$ CO_2), with the
atmospheric dew point *circa* $-60°C$ and no water save that brought
in with tissues. The atmosphere was changed continuously at 7 ft³/hr
in chambers of about 3 ft³. Plants preconditioned in the $N_2 + CO_2$ mixture
for 4 days prior to being placed in 100% carbon dioxide were healthy
and undesiccated after 3 weeks. Those in either nitrogen or carbon
dioxide were generally shrivelled; and in carbon dioxide, the normal
green color of the plants gave way to a pale, watery straw coloration.
Plants in nitrogen were more normal in appearance, but their weight loss
($> 50\%$) was higher than that of plants in carbon dioxide.

In general, irrespective of appearance, plants anaerobically conditioned
for 3–4 weeks could not survive a return to air. Within 24 hr, the greenish
plant body became grayish with streaks or spots of pink, red, brown, and
black pigmentation and became desiccated in spite of unlimited water.
The "Tiger Jaw" *Faucheria* opened a flower bud in one instance, and the
beginnings of fruit development were observed.

Rutabaga and turnip roots will grow shoots readily if left in the laboratory atmosphere without supplementary water. In the chamber conditions
described above, these roots failed to support existing shoots or to grow
new ones, and the rate of shrinkage of the roots was higher than for other
plants tested.

Coleus, which is easily wilted in air if not watered, was severely
desiccated when in the chamber for a few hours. If, however, one intact

branch is enclosed in a polyethylene bag containing water, the remaining exposed portion of the plant can survive 1–2 weeks of desert chamber. A defoliated stem cannot carry out the required absorptive functions (Fig. 7).

FIG. 7. Effect of feeding water to *Coleus* through a leafy branch on resistance to desiccation.

Many seeds are coated with extremely hydrophilic polysaccharide mucilages, which begin to hydrate and swell rapidly when the seed encounters water. Range and semidesert grasses such as "alkali sacaton" (*Sporobolus* sp.) and open dryland forms such as flax, wild mustard, plantain, etc., are common examples of seeds with water-holding coats. Conceivably, this is the sort of adaptation one would expect in any area which had moved slowly from a well watered to a desert condition—a possible situation on Mars.

Many common seeds native to the moister regions lack such an adaptive device, but it can be conveyed upon them in an approximate way by embedding them in 2% agar del. Disks of the seed-containing agar were placed on dry perlite in the "desert" chamber under nitrogen.

Thirteen species were tested in 5-day trials. Sunflower, onion, and nasturtium failed to germinate. Chinese cabbage, carnation, cockscomb, and okra yielded up to 10% germination; morning glory, spinach and cucumber up to 30%; and hibiscus and winter rye over 50%.

Other observations made in the desert chamber indicate that:

1. After 6 weeks in nitrogen, the common xerophytes were dead and so desiccated that they crumbled when touched; however, they exhibited superficial patches of a filamentous material. Several of these patches were identified as the phycomycete *Mucor mucedo*, complete with sporangiophores and sporangia (Fig. 8). Other fungi included a dense, white, imperfect form as yet unidentified and another form which might be *Botrytis*.

2. *Passalus,* the Texas Stag Beetle, and *Pseudemys,* the turtle, can withstand the nitrogen desert for 24 hr without mortality. They are active for about half of this period, then rapidly become sluggish and comatose, but can be revived in air.

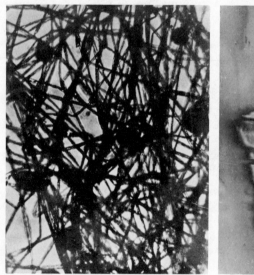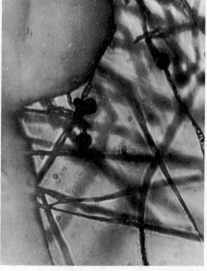

Fɪɢ. 8. Mold *Mucor* growing and sporulating on dead surface of a xerophyte in desert chamber.

Another means for examining a dual stress condition involving water and atmosphere is the "high-altitude salt marsh", which appears to offer as much promise as the alternative anaerobic desert. The salt marsh consists of a perlite substratum covered to a depth of 1–2 cm by a moderately concentrated solution of sodium chloride or $NaCl + Ca(NO_3)_2$ in a vessel evacuated to $P = 0.1$ atm. Fluorescent tubes of about 400 ft-cd supply illumination.

In a mixed salt solution totaling 5500 ppm, rye began to germinate after 18 hr, carnation and lima beans after 48 hr, and cockscomb *(Celosia)* after 4 days. Borage did not germinate until the 8th day, okra after 2 weeks, and *Ageratum* failed completely. At the end of 2 weeks, four species out of seven had passed the emergence phase, and the growth of the plants was as follows:

Species	Height, cm	Leaves/plant
Rye	25	2
Carnation	Roots only	–
Lima bean	15	4
Celosia	3	2
Borage	4	2
Okra	Roots only	–
Ageratum	Failed	–

In sodium chloride alone at 12,000 ppm, rye germination began in 2 days and reached 20% in 8 days. At this time, shoots were 0.1 cm high. In $NaCl + Ca(NO_3)_2$ at 24,000 ppm, 100% germination occurred in 8 days, the seedlings being 0.2 cm tall. In $NaCl + Ca(NO_3)_2$ at 24,000 ppm in air, germination at normal pressure was also 100%, but 5-cm-high seedlings had grown. Lima beans could not germinate at all in these higher salt levels.

The "snow dome" (Fig. 1) has been used to study seed germination at $P_{air} = 0.1$ atm and with low water supply. A shallow dish containing 5 ml of water is placed in the dome. In one type of experiment, water simply evaporates into the atmosphere — about 3 ml being transported in 5–6 days. Alternatively, water vapor in the atmosphere is condensed on liquid nitrogen cooling coils, and the resulting "snow" is dislodged by a vibrator onto seeds planted below. By condensing snow for 1 hr in each 24, all the water is deposited as a layer of 0.033 g/cm² during the 5-day period.

Germination percentages with and without freezing are:

Species	Water as Vapor	"Snow"
Cucumber	0.0	0
Carnation	0.4	10
Cockscomb	10.0	16
Rye	27.0	56

Atmosphere-Conditioned Cold Resistance in Cucumbers and Beetles

The interaction of low temperature and low oxygen pressure as environmental factors is illustrated by the difference in cold resistance of cucumber seedlings grown in air as compared to those grown in 2% O_2 + 98% Ar (Figs. 9a and b).

FIG. 9. Difference in cold resistance of 3-week-old cucumber seedlings. (Both groups were kept at −10°C for 1 hr and allowed to thaw for 1 hr before being photographed.) a, Air-grown seedlings damaged by freezing. b, Freezing-resistant seedlings grown in 2% O_2 + 98% Ar.

Seedlings were lowered to − 10°C, held there for 1 hr, and then allowed to thaw at room temperature. Every air-grown seedling suffered mechanical damage and was collapsing, yet not one of the low-oxygen plants displayed any sign of injury either at the time of thawing or several weeks later.

Species	Germination, % 98% Ar 2% O_2	Air
Turnip	33	0
Kale	48	7
Cabbage	31	0

The temperature–atmosphere interaction can also occur during germination, as shown by Japanese turnip, cabbage, and kale at 6°C. In contrast, anaerobic conditions do not increase the relative germination of rye, onion, or barley at low temperature.

Air pressure has a profound influence upon the effects of cooling the beetle *Passalus* from +25 to −7°C. Behavior during cooling, persistence of activity at −7°C, and recovery were all markedly different at reduced air pressures as compared to air at normal pressure.

Air pressure, atm	Responses during cooling period	Activity at −7°C	Recovery — at 72 hr
1.0	Convulsions	None	2 out of 3 dead, 1 normal
0.5	Locomotion slowed gradually	None	3 out of 3 normal
0.1	Locomotion slowed gradually	1 out of 4 still moving	4 out of 4 normal

Effect of Substratum on Growth

A comparison between perlite and hematite (each supplied with inorganic nutrients) as growth media at air pressures of 1 and 0.1 atm has been carried out with rye and cucumber. The experiments were short-term (8 days), but significant differences were noted.

Winter Rye

$$P_{air} = 760\ mm\ Hg$$

Measurement	Perlite	Hematite	H/P
Shoot length, cm	8.2	12.5	1.53
Root length, cm	9.0	6.0	0.67
Fresh weight, g	0.13	0.33	2.54

$$P_{air} = 76\ mm\ Hg$$

Shoot length, cm	0.7	12.3	17.6
Root length, cm	0.9	9.7	10.8
Fresh weight, g	0.06	0.40	6.7

Cucumber

$$P_{air} = 760 \, mm \, Hg$$

Measurement	Perlite	Hematite	H/P
Shoot length, cm	1.2	1.6	1.33
Root length, cm	4.6	4.0	0.87
Fresh weight, g	0.09	0.19	2.11

$$P_{air} = 76 \, mm \, Hg$$

Shoot length, cm	0.7	1.1	1.56
Root length, cm	1.1	5.3	4.82
Fresh weight, g	0.19	0.40	2.11

In both species, it is evident that hematite has a similar pattern of effects upon ordinary aerobic growth, but its stimulatory effect upon the rye seedling and upon cucumber roots at low pressure is truly striking. Plants were well supplied with nutrients, both exogenous and endogenous, including soluble iron. Many experiments have shown that iron salts do not stimulate growth at reduced oxygen levels. Thus, the cause of stimulation resides in other properties of the growth medium.

The stimulatory effect of elemental sulfur upon germination was even more surprising than the effects of hematite. Sulfur was combined with about one-tenth its volume of silica gel and "whipped" with slow addition of water until it had the consistency of a stiff paste. Seeds were placed upon the sulfur surface just as they are routinely placed on moist filter paper. Under 2% O_2 + 98% Ar, the effect of sulfur after 5 days was as follows:

	Germination, %	
Species	On filter paper	On sulfur
Lettuce	8	24
Turnip	16	24
Cucumber	50	81

Under 5% O_2 + 95% Ar, its effect after 2 days was

Lettuce	61	83
Turnip	21	43
Cucumber	16	64

Anaerobes germinated in argon were affected by sulfur, but seeds germinated in 100% oxygen were not. When sulfur is melted and cast in dishes, whether melting took place under air or argon, the stimulatory effect of the powdered sulfur disappears.

	Root length of cucumber, mm	
	On filter paper	*On sulfur*
In Ar, 5 days	2.0	6.1
In air, 1 day	12.3	14.2

In an unsuccessful attempt to explain these wholly mystifying effects with sulfur, a number of compounds from periodic group VI were tested with cucumber and rye under 5% oxygen and air. These include $S^=$, $SO_3^=$, $SO_4^=$, $Se^=$, $Se_2^=$, $SeO_3^=$, $SeO_4^=$, and $TeO_3^=$. Only tellurite at $0.01-0.02$ M concentrations increased germination in cucumber and rye but inhibited root and shoot growth moderately; surprisingly, none inhibited seedling growth markedly. To illustrate:

1. Cucumber in water in 5% oxygen yielded 15-mm-long roots in 3 days; in 0.01 M K_2TeO_3, 12-mm-long roots had grown, and in 0.02 M, roots grew to 9 mm. Germination rates were somewhat elevated with tellurite.
2. Rye in water in 5% oxygen yielded 46-mg seedlings at 3 days; in 0.02 M K_2SeO_3, 33-mg seedlings were produced, and in 0.01 M selenite, seedlings were 42 mg in fresh weight.

Similar results were obtained with selenate, selenide, and diselenide.

High Temperature and Radiation—Some Preliminary Notes

Seeds are noted for longevity and heat resistance. They can be exposed to temperatures of 75–100°C—and sometimes higher—for minutes to hours without losing viability. The more resistant types include some of the grasses and especially oil-rich seeds such as the mustards and flax. Heat damage increases with increasing oxygen pressure and water content of the seed.

Bean

Oxygen during heating, %	*Growth after exposure to 105°C for 60 min, % unheated control*
21.0	10
10.0	10
0.005	42

Crabgrass

Water content of seed, %	Germination after exposure to 75°C for 30 min, % unheated control
9	50
27	29
34	27
40	1

Preheating of seed can also condition subsequent responses to light:

Seed	Normal effect of light	Treatment changing light effect
Crabgrass	Nil	75°C, 60 min → absolute light requirement
Radish	Nil	100°C, 60 min → severe photo inhibition
Dandelion	Slight stimulation	100°C, 60 min → photo inhibition

Brief exposures to heat—for example, 50–60°C for periods of 15–30 min—can actually stimulate seed germination, an effect which has been seen in corn, rice, and cucumber.

Some seeds can also tolerate combined low- and high-temperature shock, such as treatment with liquid nitrogen to 100°C, with good viability and vigor.

These are only token observations to indicate that high temperature as a shock or conditioning factor merits study. What is true for the seed is also commonly true for spores of other organisms. In any broad environmental picture, it is necessary to take into account the ability of life to withstand extremes of environmental variation when in a state of dormancy.

The aerial organs of the begonia plant were discolored and dying after a dose of *circa* 5×10^8 ergs/cm² of 2537-Å radiation, commonly recognized as mutagenic and sterilizing. This dosage of ultraviolet had no immediate effect on sansevaria, but after nearly 2 weeks some delayed injury was evident. Ivy was not extensively affected by a somewhat higher ultraviolet dosage. The annual ultraviolet radiation above 3000 Å on Earth and Mars is about 10^{10}–10^{11} ergs/cm².

Turtles exposed to *circa* 3×10^8 ergs/cm² of 2537-Å radiation were unharmed even in 100% oxygen ($P_{O_2} = 1$ atm). The animals did not try to avoid the radiation but rested with their necks fully stretched and eyes directed toward the source.

With respect to ionizing radiation, relatively large dosages are required to prevent germination and seedling growth, as the following examples show:

Dose, Kr (250 KVP)	Relative growth of flax 1 month after seed irradiation (control = 100)		
	Root	Hypocotyl	Epicotyl
0.0	100	100	100
2.3	106	85	98
10.7	115	84	98
19.1	113	85	113
44.3	85	49	55
76.4	76	39	13

Dose, Kr (250 KVP)	Relative growth of bean embryos 3 days after irradiation (control = 100)		
	Main axis	Root hairs	Branch roots
0	100	100	100
20	92	80	40
40	92	85	0
60	91	75	0
75	91	55	0
150	91	0	0

BIOCHEMICAL AND PHYSIOLOGICAL OBSERVATIONS ON ORGANISMS IN SIMULATED ENVIRONMENTS

It is impossible at present to attempt an analysis of the biochemistry of nonterrestrially conditioned Earth organisms. The biosphere as it is now constituted contains organisms equipped to cope with stress factors such as anaerobiosis and desiccation. The anaerobic bacteria and other microorganisms can carry out all of the essential processes involved in the synthesis of nucleotides, nucleic acids, and proteins.

It is somewhat surprising, therefore, that biochemists still emphasize mechanisms of aerobic metabolism and energetics as if they were the essential mode of existence, when this is clearly untrue. The highest orders of animal life on this planet require oxygen, but this should not mislead us into projecting too literally the need for highly specific earthly elements of life support onto other planetary systems. This becomes especially evident in view of what has been demonstrated, namely, that environmental factors and systems quite different from present terrestrial conditions are suitable for some terrestrial forms, even without the benefit of genetic selection.

Chemical Support for Anaerobic Germination of Rye and Other Seeds

The response of seed germination to variations in oxygen pressure is highly variable according to species (Fig. 10a). Lettuce shows an almost all-or-none response, being incapable of germinating in 1% oxygen but almost fully capable in 2% oxygen. Cucumber also shows a steep response curve, beginning with a clearly anaerobic component to which the introduction of oxygen adds the activation of members which are obligate aerobes. The requirements of a tomato seed population are spread over a considerable range of oxygen concentrations, whereas rice is essentially "indifferent".

The major product that distinguishes aerobic metabolism from fermentation is ATP, erroneously designated "high-energy phosphate", which provides, in the free energy of the pyrophosphate bond, the driving force for many biosynthetic reactions and biochemical work. Can ATP replace oxygen in anaerobic conditions? The answer is equivocal in most situations because ATP supplied externally may be hydrolyzed *en route* to its target. Nevertheless, a clear affirmative answer has been obtained in a few instances, most strikingly in the case of the germination of cockscomb (Fig. 10b). This species is a capable facultative anaerobe but responds quantitatively to oxygen. In the presence of ATP, the gradual anaerobic curve approaches the steep aerobic curve for germination vs. time.

In addition to the elimination of the need for oxygen by supply of its metabolically produced equivalent, the use of alternate electron acceptors has been considered. These include Fe (111), Ce (IV), Fe $(CH)_6^-$ and NO_3^-. Only the last of these has given definitive results, as shown in this example with winter rye:

KNO_3, mol/liter	Germination, %
0.0	60
0.001	78
0.005	99
0.01	89
0.05	88

On the other hand, rye gives evidence of possessing a completely different metabolic system, known as the Stickland reaction and found in the obligate anaerobic genus *Clostridium*:

$$H_2NCH_2COOH + ADP + H_2PO_4^- + R(SH)_2 \rightarrow$$
$$CH_3COOH + ATP + NH_3 + RS_2$$

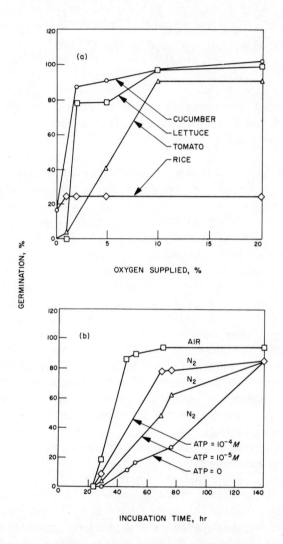

FIG. 10. Response of seed germination to type of atmosphere. a, Dependency of germaination rate upon P_{02}. b. Effect of ATP upon germination of *Celosia* under anaerobic conditions.

When rye was supplied the components of this system singly and in combination under anaerobic conditions, the results at 7 days were:

Substance	Germination, %	Shoot length, mm
K_2HPO_4, 0.01 M	35	1.0
K_2HPO_4, 0.01 M + glycine, 0.01 M	45	2.9
K_2HPO_4, 0.01 M + ADP, 0.01 M	60	2.1
K_2HPO_4, 0.01 M + ADP, glycine, 0.01 M	80	3.1
ADP, 0.01 M + glycine, 0.01 M (without phosphate)	40	2.5

It was assumed that under anaerobic conditions, thiols need not be added. Under low-oxygen conditions, the reducing power of seedlings builds up appreciably, and therefore, the $R(SH)_2$ should be continuously regenerated.

Carbon monoxide is among the unusual metabolic products of seeds germinating in low-oxygen or anaerobic conditions. Approximately 50 cm^3 of loosely packed seeds and an equal volume of oxygen-free water were introduced into 500-cm^3 polyethylene vessels which were evacuated, filled with 5% O_2 + 95% Ar, and held at 25°C. After 2 days, winter rye, Alaska peas, Marketer cucumber, purple-top white globe turnip, and black-seeded Simpson lettuce had formed traces of carbon monoxide, whereas golden bantam corn, red kidney bean, and Marglobe tomato had not. The same results were obtained whether or not the seeds were sterilized in 0.5% sodium hypochlorite. After 5 days, appreciable quantities of carbon monoxide were present in the atmospheres of several species (Table 11). Schiff tests showed that volatile aldehydes are generated by some species and not by others, but the results were too variable to suggest a relationship between aldehydes and carbon monoxide.

Infrared spectroscopy and gas chromatography indicate that rye germinated in 5% oxygen or less generates small quantities of butyric acid and C_4 or C_5 alcohol.

Rye, cucumber, soy-bean, and other seeds also produce hydrogen during germination at subatmospheric oxygen levels. It has not been proven that the highly sterilization-resistant bacteria within the integuments of the seed are not responsible for this phenomenon. In any case, there is reason to suspect the existence of a mutualistic feature to hydrogen production in seeds involving the dependence of the bacteria upon seed metabolites, the relation between growth and hydrogen formation, the beneficial effects upon germination of lowered oxygen pressure, and the direct stimulation of seed germination by hydrogen. Thus, a low-oxygen environment may bring forth new symbiotic relationships in recognizable form.

TABLE 11. Carbon monoxide production by seeds after 5 days at reduced oxygen levels; Schiff test for aldehydes

Seed	Weight, g	CO level		Schiff test[a]
		ppm	μg/g seed	
Rye	39	25	1.95	N
Maize	44	0	0.0	W
Pea	44	10	0.36	P
Bean	42	0	0.0	W
Tomato	14	0	0.0	N
Cucumber	34	15	1.04	P
Turnip	35	10	0.69	N
Lettuce	24	10	0.48	PP

[a]N = negative, P = positive, PP = intense positive, W = weak.

Bean Plants Grown in 5% O_2 + 95% Ar

Some growth and morphological characteristics of beans grown in 5% oxygen were given earlier in this Chapter. Tables 12–15 show the essentials of elementary analyses, constitutional changes during seedling growth, amounts of selected enzymes and other constituents, and the differential carbon disposition on an atom-of-carbon basis.

TABLE 12. Elementary composition and weight data for red kidney bean seedlings grown in air or subatmospheric oxygen levels

Stage	Constituent dry matter, wt %						Total dry matter, mg	Water, mg	Total plant weight, mg
	C	H	O	N	S	Ash			
Seed	42.3	6.3	38.9	4.5	0.4	6.1	530	24	554
Seedling (grown 2 weeks in air)									
Root	41.5	6.2	34.4	6.6	0.8	8.5	50	860	910
Shoot	42.2	6.6	37.8	6.6	0.6	6.0	200	2920	3120
Cotyledon	41.4	6.3	37.0	4.2	0.8	9.2	60	180	240
Seedling (grown 2 weeks in 5% O_2 + 95% Ar)									
Root	43.1	6.2	35.1	6.6	0.6	7.7	40	780	820
Shoot	42.6	6.5	36.3	6.4	0.8	5.2	120	2100	2220
Cotyledon	41.9	6.6	37.4	5.4	0.5	7.8	100	700	800

TABLE 13. Changes in elementary constituents of bean seedlings cultivated in air and in 5% O_2 +95% Ar

Stage	Constituent, mg/plant or plant part					
	C	H	O	N	S	Ash
Seed	224.2	33.4	206.2	23.9	2.1	32.3
Seedling (grown 2 weeks in air)						
Root	20.8	3.1	17.2	3.3	0.4	4.3
Shoot	84.4	13.2	75.6	13.2	1.2	12.0
Cotyledon	24.8	3.8	22.2	2.5	0.5	5.6
Total seedling	130.0	20.1	115.0	19.0	2.1	21.9
Δ Seedling − seed	− 94.2	− 13.3	− 91.2	− 4.9	0.0	− 10.4
Seedling (grown 2 weeks in low oxygen)						
Root	17.2	2.5	14.0	2.6	0.3	3.1
Shoot	51.1	7.8	43.6	7.7	1.1	6.2
Cotyledon	41.9	6.6	37.4	5.4	0.5	7.8
Total seedling	110.2	16.9	95.0	15.7	1.9	17.1
Δ Seedling − seed	− 114.0	− 16.5	− 111.2	− 8.2	− 0.2	− 15.2
$\dfrac{\Delta\ 5\%\ O_2}{\Delta\ \text{Air-grown}}$	1.19	1.24	1.22	1.67	−	1.46

TABLE 14. Comparison of bean plants grown in air and in 5% O_2: chemical composition, selected enzyme activities, and spectrophotometric data

a. Chemical constituents

Constituent and organ	Dry matter, %		Ratio $\left(\dfrac{5\%\ O_2}{\text{air}}\right)$
	Plants grown in air	Plants grown in 5% O_2	
Chloroform extractables			
Root	8.7	9.1	1.04
Stem	15.8	7.3	0.46
Cotyledon	5.7	0.0	0.0
Glucose			
Root	0.44	1.06	2.41
Stem	0.34	0.63	1.85
Cotyledon	0.0	0.41	−
Sucrose			
Root	1.86	6.61	3.56
Stem	1.08	2.95	2.74
Cotyledon	3.95	5.47	1.39
Lignin			
Stem	5.8	2.4	0.41

TABLE 14. Comparison of bean plants grown in air and in 5% O_2: chemical composition, selected enzyme activities, and spectrophotometric data (Cont'd)

b. Enzymes

Enzyme and organ	Plants grown in		Ratio $\left(\dfrac{5\% \, O_2}{\text{air}}\right)$
	Air	5% O_2	
Peroxidase (μmol pyrogallol oxidized/min)			
Root			
per gram dry weight	172.0	203.0	1.18
per plant	8.6	8.2	0.95
Epicotyl			
per gram dry weight	375.0	2183.0	5.82
per plant	23.5	43.7	1.86
Catalase (μmol H_2O_2 decomposed/min)			
Root			
per gram dry weight	300.0	742.0	2.47
per plant	15.0	29.7	1.98
Epicotyl			
per gram dry weight	3450.0	3000.0	0.87
per plant	208.0	60.0	0.29
Lipoxidase (Δ absorbency 232.5 mμ/min)			
Root			
per gram dry weight	28.5	20.0	0.70
per plant	1.5	0.8	0.53
Epicotyl			
per gram dry weight	19.2	40.0	2.08
per plant	1.2	0.9	0.75

c. Spectrophotometry of extracts

Object of measurement	Plants grown in	
	Air	5% O_2
Acetone leaf extract (30 ml/g fresh leaf)		
λ_{max}	430, 662	430, 662
Abs. at λ_{max}	0.847, 0.420	0.692, 0.393
Chloroform stem extract (5 ml/g fresh stem)		
λ_{max}	238[sh], 278, 320[sh]	238, 272, 320[sh]
Abs. at λ_{max}	0.527, 0.351, 0.110	0.855, 0.493, 0.152
Ethanol–HCl stem extract (150 ml/g fresh stem)		
λ_{max}	272, 315	278
Abs. at λ_{max}	0.277, 0.129	0.655

Beans grown in low oxygen and in air contain similar percentages of carbon, hydrogen, and oxygen, but low-oxygen seedlings contain a higher

TABLE 15. Representative carbon distribution in representative compounds in bean
plants grown in air and in 5% O_2 + Ar

Compound	Carbon in specified compound, atoms/1000 atm total C	
	Plants grown in air	Plants grown in 5% O_2 + Ar
Glucose (total)[a]	8.4	20.1
Fructose	5.2	14.1
Lignin	90.5	37.5
Methoxyl	14.0	11.5

[a]Free reducing sugar plus that combined in sucrose.

percentage of protein nitrogen. On an absolute weight basis, beans grown
in low oxygen lose more carbon, hydrogen, oxygen, nitrogen, and ash
than those grown in air. Loss of nitrogen as ammonia was detected,
suggesting a lowered metabolic efficiency.

Data on glucose, fructose, lignin, and methoxyl carbon contents
recalculated on a total carbon basis show that beans grown in low
oxygen contain more carbon as sugars than as lignin and methoxyl. An
altered cell-wall chemistry is suggested.

The low-oxygen plant is higher in general reducing power, higher in
sucrose and glucose content, and lower in chloroform solubles and lignin.
The low-oxygen epicotyl contains far more peroxidase, slightly less
catalase, and about twice the lipoxidase found in air-grown epicotyls.
The low-oxygen root differs little in peroxidase content but contains
appreciably more catalase and somewhat less lipoxidase than air-grown
roots. Various tissue extracts from plants grown in air or 5% oxygen were
compared with respect to absorption spectra. The measurements taken
suggest that the leaf pigments are not greatly different, whereas the low-
oxygen stems appear richer in the ultraviolet regions, suggesting olefins,
phenols, and phenols with side-chain conjugation.

Cucumber Seedlings in Various Atmospheres

Cucumber germination and growth have been discussed earlier in
this Chapter. Unlike the bean, which is strictly aerobic, cucumber seed
populations contain both aerobes and anaerobes. Cucumber anaerobes
are relatively sluggish, but seedlings grow exceedingly well in 1–5%
oxygen. Elementary changes in the cucumber are shown in Table 16
and Fig. 11.

On a percentage basis, cucumbers grown in air and in low oxygen show
marked differences after only 4 days. Tissue oxygen varies directly with
atmospheric oxygen. Two-week-old seedlings grown in 5% O_2 + 95% Ar
are more juvenile with respect to chemical composition than their air-
grown counterparts.

Losses in carbon, hydrogen, oxygen, and nitrogen content were
greater for plants grown in air rather than in low-oxygen atmospheres.

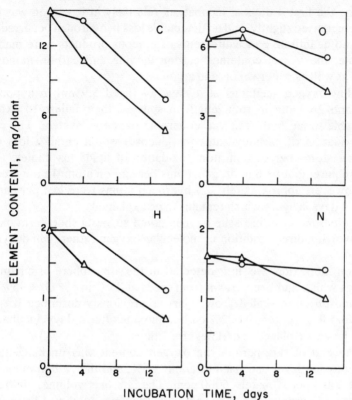

FIG. 11. Changes in C, H, O, and N content of dark-grown cucumber seedlings
in air (o – o) or 5% O_2+95% Ar ($\triangle$ – $\triangle$).

Loss of nitrogen as ammonia was detected in the air-grown group. An
exceptionally small loss in hydrogen was noted in the low-oxygen group,
whereas a gain in oxygen relative to the seed occurred.

TABLE 16. Elementary composition of cucumber seeds and seedlings
grown in various atmospheres

Stage	Constituent dry matter, wt %						Total dry matter, mg	Water, mg	Total plant weight, mg
	C	H	O	N	S	Ash			
Seed	57.1	7.7	23.9	6.0	0.5	4.9	26	1	27
Seedling grown 4 days in									
Air	50.6	7.0	28.6	7.2	0.5	6.1	22	142	164
5%O_2 + 95% Ar	55.2	7.6	26.9	5.9	0.4	3.8	26	55	81
Seedling grown 2 weeks in									
Air	40.5	6.0	34.5	8.6	0.7	9.2	12	203	215
5%O_2+95% Ar	44.0	6.7	32.7	8.3	0.7	7.7	17	303	320
1%O_2+99% Ar	46.5	7.1	28.3	7.5	0.7	8.0	21	209	230

During the first 4 days of incubation, relatively little carbon was lost, oxygen increased slightly, and no detectable loss in hydrogen occurred. Although no quantitative measurements of gaseous products were made at that time, the vessel contained carbon dioxide and carbon monoxide oxygen as well as water vapor, and argon.

The low-oxygen seedlings at 4 days averaged 5.9 mm in hypocotyl length and 26.9 mm in root length in spite of their failure to expend appreciable tissue hydrogen via an aerobic oxidative system. The complete oxidation of carbohydrates (as glucose) would entail a loss of 2 hydrogen atoms per carbon atom, oxidation of lipids (as linoleic acid) would require about 1.6 hydrogen atoms per carbon atom. In the present case, however, approximately 0.4 hydrogen atoms were lost per carbon atom at 4 days, a figure which remains to be explained.

The initial increase in tissue oxygen noted suggests short-term oxidations involving direct addition of molecular oxygen rather than dehydrogenation.

Carbon monoxide was first detected in the atmosphere of cucumber seedlings which had been grown from seeds at 25°C in 5% O_2 + 95% Ar. The atmosphere in sealed growth jars as previously described was adjusted to 5.0% oxygen, 0.002% carbon dioxide after 4 days' incubation, and the jars were placed in darkness for 7 days.

At the end of this period, the oxygen content was unchanged, the carbon dioxide level had risen to about 3.5%, and the carbon monoxide content was approximately 6000 ppm. The jars (gas volume, 7000 cm³) contained 38 completely achlorophyllous seedlings totaling 12 g in fresh weight. Accordingly, some 4.2 mg of carbon monoxide per gram of fresh weight had been generated. It should also be noted that the 38 seedlings doubled in height during this period, elongating some 30 mm on the average.

In a subsequent experiment, cucumber seeds were germinated in an atmosphere containing < 0.5% oxygen and about 0.24% carbon dioxide in argon. After 10 days in darkness, when the seedlings had grown to 15 mm in height, their atmosphere showed no change in oxygen, increased carbon dioxide (1.5%), and 0.04% (400 ppm) carbon monoxide. During an additional 8 days in darkness, the seedlings increased approximately 20 mm more in height. At that time, oxygen in the atmosphere continued unchanged, but carbon dioxide had increased to more than 5%, and carbon monoxide had fallen to 10 ppm.

Cucumber seedlings grown in air produce no detectable carbon monoxide, whether maintained in air or placed for as long as 7 days in low oxygen.

Preliminary analyses for DNA, RNA, and protein have been run on cucumber seedlings grown for 2 weeks in 10% O_2 + 90% N_2. Ribonucleic acid was determined by the orcinol + $FeCl_3$ method; DNA with diphenyl-amine; and protein with $CuSO_4$ + phenol reagent. Expressed as ratios, the analyses yielded:

	$\dfrac{RNA}{DNA}$	$\dfrac{Protein}{RNA}$	$\dfrac{Protein}{DNA}$
Air	2.02	0.56	1.13
10% O_2 + 90% N_2	0.86	2.47	2.13

Without additional data, it can only be said that the changes in these ratios imply that significant alterations in the transfer of information in protein biosynthesis must have taken place, and perhaps in the replication process as well. The present state of genetic knowledge leads to the expectation that a change in DNA–RNA–protein relations should involve (1) changes in the levels of different specific enzymes, and (2) variations in the protein moieties of specific enzymes. Expectation (1) has been verified by the change in amounts of two oxidizing enzymes, ascorbic acid oxidase and peroxidase (Table 17). The ascorbic acid oxidase content rises slightly, whereas peroxidase falls markedly, suggesting that enzyme changes do not reflect a change in total but, rather, in specific proteins.

TABLE 17. Effect of oxygen level on the activity of two oxidases in cucumber seedlings

Enzyme and organ	Seedlings grown in		Ratio $\left(\dfrac{5\% \, O_2}{air}\right)$
	Air	5% O_2 + 95% Ar	
Ascorbic acid oxidase (units/unit fresh weight)			
Leaf	8.86	9.12	1.03
Stem	1.42	1.65	1.16
Peroxidase (units/unit fresh weight)			
Leaf	6.76	3.17	0.47
Stem	1.32	0.83	0.63

Expectation (2) has been verified by demonstrating, via starch-gel electrophoresis, that cucumber peroxidase is heterogeneous both in electrophoretic mobility and substrate range (Fig. 12). Changes with oxygen level therefore do indeed affect specific protein synthesis.

From the preceding information, it is reasonable to propose the sequence

Altered oxygen level → DNA–RNA–protein relationship → Changes in protein of specific enzymes → Altered metabolism and biosynthesis → Altered growth and form

But only the future will reveal its generality.

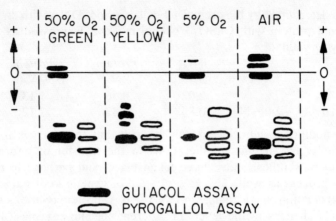

FIG. 12. Iso-peroxidases in cucumber seedlings grown in various O_2 atmospheres. ("Green" designates seedlings of normal healthy appearance in 50% O_2; "yellow" designates seedlings exhibiting advanced senescence [20% of population] in 50% O_2.)

Pigments in Rye Seedlings

Rye seedlings can make chlorophyll when seeds are germinated in argon, hydrogen, nitrogen, carbon monoxide, and nitrous oxide, as well as low partial pressures of oxygen. It is obvious that there are many questions to be answered about biosynthetic processes in these unusual atmospheres.

Quantitatively, the appearance of chlorophylls a and b, and red anthocyanin pigment have been compared in rye grown in air and in 1% O_2 + 99% Ar. The emerging coleoptiles were harvested over several days. Growth, coloration, and chlorophyll from acetone extracts are recorded in Table 18. With respect to growth and chlorophyll a, day 7

TABLE 18. Comparison of rye coleoptile pigments in seedlings grown in air and in 1% O_2 + 99% Ar

Object of measurement	Seedlings grown in				
	Air			1% O_2 + 99% Ar	
Incubation time, days	2	3	6	3	7
Coleoptile length, mm	13	34	160	15	35
Pigment					
Anthocyanin[a]	+	++	−	−	−
Chlorophylls					
(μg/g fresh tissue)					
a	42	81	441	9	98
b	20	19	119	2	52
a+b	62	100	560	11	150
a/b	2.1	4.3	3.7	−[b]	1.9

[a]Extracted from acidified ethanol with n-amyl alcohol. Typical anthocyanin λ_{max} at 540 mμ.
[b]Uncertainty in these low figures makes ratio meaningless.

at 1% O_2 is similar to day 3 in air. This relationship does not apply to chlorophyll b, however, as it rose on day 7 to nearly threefold the amount in 3-day air-grown plants. Thus, the ratio a/b, which is in the ordinary range in air, is changed markedly in low oxygen. Furthermore, no red pigment whatsoever appeared up to day 7 in low-oxygen plants.

Effects of Subfreezing Temperatures on Plant Tissue Chemistry

Only the atmospheric factor has been examined to any degree with respect to biochemical changes. A few observations have been made, however, with xerophyte (succulent) leaves exposed to liquid nitrogen for 10 sec, and with xerophytes kept under winter conditions in various atmospheres for 3 months.

Succulent leaves exposed to acute freezing in liquid nitrogen show the following changes during several subsequent days at 25°C:

1. A slight decrease in Millon reagent-positive protein.
2. A more marked decrease in Benedict-positive reducing sugar.
3. An increase in Schiff-positive aldehyde.
4. An enormous increase in KI_3-positive starch.
5. Sizable increases in the enzymes peroxidase and phosphorylase.
6. An enormous increase in molybdate-positive orthodiphenols.

Leaf pigmentation is grossly unchanged. These leaves are still viable; in soil, they can produce plantlets from the leaf base.

Chronic exposure (i.e. prolonged, but moderate stress) of succulent tissues to cold also brings about changes, but they are strongly dependent upon oxygen level during the freezing period. In the presence of air, chlorophyll was rapidly lost and the leaf color became a bleached yellow. When only traces of oxygen were present, chlorophyll was normal in spectrum. Peroxidase, phosphorylase, aldehydes, reducing sugars, and starch were lacking in air-grown plants. Air-grown plants were dead, whereas those under nitrogen were still viable, if not vigorous.

Changes in the Turtle at Reduced Pressure: Preliminary Notes

Turtles returned to $P_{air} = 760$ mm Hg after 54 days at 70–80 mm appeared entirely normal in head and eye movements and limb coordination; swimming and walking were normal. The one external distinction noted was the formation observable over a period of hours of heavy, black circumorbital rings which appeared to be regular zones of melanization rather than typically irregular hematomas. After several weeks in air, these rings slowly faded and vanished.

Control and experimental animals were given preliminary hematological analyses (Table 19). Very little can be said concerning them at this time, except to note the following phenomena occurring with increasing time at low pressure:

1. Red count is irregular but may exhibit a falling trend.

2. White count fluctuates irregularly.

3. Hemoglobin content falls markedly.

4. Specific white cell types become less diversified.

Exploratory starch-gel electrophoresis of control and 34-day sera showed no γ-globulin in either sample; a strong control α_3-globulin had no counterpart in the low-pressure serum. In all, 12 bands were resolved in control turtle serum, although most are still not identified. In the low-pressure group, only five of these "normal" bands were still present, but one new band has actually appeared.

TABLE 19. Hematological changes in the blood of *Pseudemys* maintained at $P_{air} = 0.1$ atm

a. General analysis

Days at reduced pressure	Erythrocyte count (per mm³)	Leucocyte count (per mm³)	Hemo-globin (g/100 cc)	Hematocrit (vol. % formed elements)
None (controls)	347,250 ± 70,000	155,600 ± 60,000	4.88 ± 1.1	19.9 ± 0.8
19	462,000	160,700	2.25	17
34	90,000	129,000	2.60	16
54	220,000	185,000	1.25	–

b. Differential white cell analysis

Days at reduced pressure	Percentage of				
	Monocytes	Juvenile metamyelocytes	Lymphocytes	Neutrophiles	Eosinophiles
None	92	2	3	1	2
34	76	1	15	5	3
54	99	0	0	0	1

FACTORIAL APPROACH TO SPECIFIC SIMULATION

In the preceding Sections, a variety of conditions and responses have been described and discussed in more or less detail, and random references have been made to Martian conditions. In order to evaluate the potentialities of biological systems under simulated or nearly simulated Martian equatorial summer conditions, a factorial screen was set up for three major determinants of the Martian environment complex. Seed germination was selected as a means for bio-evaluation of atmosphere, temperature, and water availability.

Screening Seed Populations for Primary Capabilities

Screen 1 (Table 20) was set up to select anaerobic species, varieties, or individuals in seed populations. The atmosphere was argon with possible traces of oxygen. No carbon dioxide was introduced but was generated by the seeds themselves, raising the chamber level to about 2–3% by the end of the test period.

Screen 2 (Table 21) was devised to test for cryobic forms by incubation of seeds on the diurnal patterns: 4°C, 16 hr/22°C, 8 hr; − 30°C, 8 hr/22°C, 8 hr; and −30°C, 16 hr/22°C, 8 hr.

Screen 3 (Table 22) was devised to select xerobic forms; that is, seeds capable of germinating against a water deficit. Two media were used for incubation, namely 10% agar and 1 M mannitol. Osmotic methods for creating a water deficit may or may not be physiologically distinguishable from literal xeric conditions. Additional techniques must certainly be used as well. We believe that work against a concentration gradient and extraction of water from a hydrophilic colloid are means for studying the water-accumulating efficiencies of various species.

TABLE 20. Screen 1; familial listing of genera, species, and varieties of seed screened for anaerobic capabilities

Family	Genus, species, variety	Germination percentage[a] (after 5 days at 25°C)
Acanthaceae	1. *Thunbergia alata*	0
Aceraceae	2. *Acer platanoides*	0
	3. *Acer saccharinum*	0
Aizoaceae	4. *Cryophytum crystallinum*	0
Amaranthaceae	5. *Amaranthus caudatus*	
	a. Globe buddy	0
	b. Molten fire	5
	6. *Amaranthus tricolor*	5
	7. *Celosia argenta*	
	a. Empress	92
	b. Fire feather	48
	c. Forest fire	50
	d. Giant plume golden feather	9
	e. Golden feather	36
	f. Toreador	33
Amaryllidaceae	8. *Allium Cepa*	
	a. Southport yellow globe	2
	b. Evergreen bunching	3
	c. White Portugal	3
	9. *Allium Porrum*	
	a. American flag	2
Apocynaceae	10. *Vinca minor*	0
Balsaminaceae	11. *Impatiens Balsamina*	0

TABLE 20. Screen 1; familial listing of genera, species, and varieties of seed screened for anaerobic capabilities (Cont'd)

Family	Genus, species, variety	Germination percentage[a] (after 5 days at 25°C)
Begoniaceae	12. *Begonia Pieta*	0
	13. *Begonia semperfloreus*	0
Boraginaceae	14. *Anchusa azurea*	0
	15. *Borago officinalis*	0
	16. *Cynoglossum amabile*	0
	17. *Heliotropium arborescens*	1
	18. *Myosotis scorpioides*	0
Cactaceae	19. *Cephalocereus sinilis*	0
	20. *Mammileria* sp.	0
	21. *Opuntia* sp.	0
Campanulacae	22. *Campanula medium*	0
	23. *Campanula rotundifolia*	0
Capparidaceae	24. *Cleome spinosa*	0
Caryophyllaceae	25. *Cerastium tomentosum*	0
	26. *Dianthus barbatus*	0
	27. *Dianthus Caryophyllus*	
	a. Chabauds giants	15
	b. Sparkly bright scarlet	6
	28. *Gypsophila paniculata*	
	29. *Lychnis chalcedonica*	1
	30. *Lychnis viscaria*	0
Chenopodiaceae	31. *Beta vulgaris*	
	a. Detroit dark red	0
	b. Ruby queen	0
	c. Wonder	0
	d. var. *cicla*	6
	32. *Kochia scoparia*	0
	33. *Spinaca oleracea*	
	a. Bloomsdale savoy	0
Compositae	34. *Achillea Ptarmica*	0
	35. *Artemisia dracunculus*	0
	36. *Aster* sp.	0
	37. *Aster panacetifolium*	0
	38. *Brachyome iberidifolia*	0
	39. *Centaurea cyanus*	
	a. Bachelor's button	0
	b. Dusty miller	0.7
	c. Snowman	0
	40. *Chrysanthemum* sp.	0
	41. *Chrysanthemum morifolium*	0
	42. *Chrysanthemum parthenium*	0
	43. *Cichorium Endivica*	0
	44. *Cichorium Intybus*	0
	45. *Coreopsis* sp.	0
	46. *Cosmos bipinnatus*	0
	47. *Cremanthodium reniforme*	10
	48. *Dahlia pinnata*	0
	49. *Dimorphothaecae sinuata*	0
	50. *Felicia Bergeriana*	0
	51. *Gaillardia* sp.	0
	52. *Helianthus annuus*	3

TABLE 20. Screen 1; familial listing of genera, species, and varieties of seed screened for anaerobic capabilities (Cont'd)

Family	Genus, species, variety	Germination percentage[a] (after 5 days at 25°C)
	53. *Helichrysum bracteatum*	0.4
	54. *Helipterum roseum*	0
	55. *Lactuca sativa*	
	a. Black-seeded Simpson	0
	b. Grand Rapids	0
	c. Early curled Simpson	0
	d. New York No. 12	0
	e. White Boston	0
	f. White curled Simpson	0
	56. *Scorzonera hispanica*	0
	57. *Tagetes tenufolia*	0
	58. *Taraxacum officinale*	0
	59. *Tithonia diversifolia*	0
Convolvulaceae	60. *Quamoclit pennata*	0
	61. *Quamoclip* sp.	0
	62. *Convolvulus japonicus*	40
Crassulaceae	63. *Sedum Himalaium*	0
Cruciferae	64. *Aubrietta deltoidea*	0
	65. *Arabis procurrens*	0
	66. *Brassica caulorapa*	0
	67. *Brassica napobrassica*	0
	68. *Brassica nigra*	
	a. Florida broadleaf	2
	b. Giant curled	
	southern	0
	69. *Brassica Oleraceaea*	
	a. var. *acephala*	4
	b. var. *botrytis*	0
	c. var. *capitata*	
	1. Jersey queen	2
	2. Red acre	4
	d. var. *gemmifera*	
	1. Jade cross	0
	2. Catskill	0
	e. var. *italica*	3
	70. *Brassica pekinensis*	15
	71. *Brassica rapa*	
	a. Purple-top white	
	globe	0
	72. *Cheiranthus cheiri*	0
	73. *Hesperis* sp.	0
	74. *Iberis* sp.	0
	75. *Lunceria annuus*	0
	76. *Matthioloa bicornis*	
	a. Dwarf (10 weeks)	0
	b. Trisomic (7 weeks)	2
	77. *Raphanus sativus*	
	a. Champion	2
	b. Crimson giant	5
	c. Round black Spanish	3

TABLE 20. Screen 1; familial listing of genera, species, and varieties of seed screened for anaerobic capabilities (Cont'd)

Family	Genus, species, variety	Germination percentage[a] (after 5 days at 25°C)
	d. Scarlet turnip white top	1
	e. Sparkler	1
Cucurbitaceae	78. *Citrullus vulgaris*	0
	79. *Cucumis melo*	
	a. Summer crookneck	0
	80. *Cucumis sativus*	
	a. Black diamond	90
	b. Long Green	72
	c. Straight 8	79
	d. West Indian gherkin	62
	e. Wisconsin	29
	81. *Cucurbita Pepo*	0
	82. *Lagenaria siceraria*	
	a. Small orange	0
	b. Ornamental bottle	0
Dipsacaceae	83. *Scabiosa atropurpurea*	0
Ericaceae	84. *Vaccinium retosum*	0
Euphorbiaceae	85. *Euphorbia marginata*	0
	86. *Euphorbia corollata*	0
	87. *Ricinus communis*	0
Geraniaceae	88. *Geranium maculatum*	0
	89. *Geranium sanguineum*	0
Gesneriaceae	90. *Saintpaulia ionantha*	0
	91. *Sinningia speciosa*	0
Gramineae	92. *Agrostis alba*	0
	93. *Avena sativa* var. *Sieghafer*	0
	94. *Briza maxima*	0
	95. *Coix lacryma–Jobii*	0
	96. *Festuca rubra*	3
	97. *Hordeum vulgare*	50
	98. *Oryza sativa*	
	a. var. *Patna*	17
	100. *Phleum pratense*	0
	101. *Secale cereale*	96
	102. *Triticum vulgare*	0
	103. *Zea Mays*	
	a. Midget sweet	75
Hydrophyllaceae	104. *Nemophila menziesii*	0
	105. *Phacelia tanacetifolia*	0
Iridaceae	106. *Iris Clarkii*	0
	107. *Tigridia Pavonia*	0
Labiatae	108. *Coleus Blumei*	0
	109. *Lavandula officinalis*	0
	110. *Marrubium vulgare*	0
	111. *Majorana hortensis*	0
	112. *Mentha piperita*	0
	113. *Mentha spicata*	0.2
	114. *Molucella piperita*	0
	115. *Nepeta cataria*	0

TABLE 20. Screen 1; familial listing of genera, species, and varieties of seed screened for anaerobic capabilities (Cont'd)

Family	Genus, species, variety	Germination percentage[a] (after 5 days at 25°C)
	116. *Nepeta mussinii*	0
	117. *Ocimum Basilicum*	0
	118. *Rosmarinus officinalis*	0
	119. *Salvia splendens*	0
	120. *Satureja hortenses*	2
	121. *Thymus vulgaris*	0
Leguminosae	122. *Arachis hypogaea*	
	a. Virginia giant	50
	123. *Glycine max*	0
	124. *Lathyrus odoratus*	0
	a. Floribunda salmon	7
	b. Shirley Temple	0
	125. *Lathyrus latifolius*	0
	126. *Lupinus pubesceens*	0
	127. *Mimosa pudica*	0
	128. *Phoseolus multiflorus*	0
	129. *Phoseolus vulgaris*	
	a. Black valentine	0
	b. Red kidney	0
	130. *Pisum sativum*	0
	131. *Vicia faba*	50
Liliaceae	132. *Asparagus officinale*	0
	133. *Asparagus plumosa*	0
	134. *Fritillaria imperealis*	0
	135. *Kniphofia uvaria*	0
	136. *Lilium gigantium*	0
	137. *Lilium regale*	0
	138. *Smilax herbacea*	0
Linaccae	139. *Linum usitatissimum*	0
Lobeliaceae	140. *Lobelia erinus*	
	a. var. *compacta*	0
	141. *Lobelia gracilis*	0
Malvaceae	142. *Althaea rosea*	
	a. Double mixed	1
	b. Old fashioned	1
	143. *Hibiscus militaris*	1
	144. *Hibiscus esculentus*	45
Menispermaceae	145. *Menispermum canadense*	0
Nyctaginaceae	146. *Mirabilis jalapa*	1
Onagraceae	147. *Clarkia elegans*	0
	148. *Godetia amoena*	0
	149. *Oenothera biennis*	0
Oxalidaceae	150. *Oxalis*	0
Papaveraceae	151. *Eschscholzia californica*	0
	152. *Papaver nudicaule*	0
	153. *Papaver orientale*	0
Plumbaginaceae	154. *Limonium*	0
	155. *Plumbago*	0
Polemoniaceae	156. *Phlox divaricata*	0
	157. *Phlox Drummondii*	0
Polygonaceae	158. *Rheum mobile*	0

TABLE 20. Screen 1; familial listing of genera, species, and varieties of seed screened for anaerobic capabilities (Cont'd)

Family	Genus, species, variety	Germination percentage[a] (after 5 days at 25°C)
	159. *Rheum palmatum*	0
Portulacaceae	160. *Portulaca grandiflora*	0
Primulaceae	161. *Cyclamen persicum*	0
	162. *Primula sinensis*	0
Ranunculaceae	163. *Aconitum*	14
	164. *Aquilegia canadensis*	0
	165. *Aquilegia*	0
	166. *Arctotis*	0
	167. *Delphinium Ajacis*	0
	168. *Delphinium cardinale*	0
	169. *Ranunculus sceleratus*	0
	170. *Thalictrum chelidonii*	0
Resedaceae	171. *Reseda odorata*	0.7
Rosaceae	172. *Fragaria virginiana*	0
	173. *Geum triflorum*	0
	174. *Rosa bracteata*	0
	175. *Rosa cathayensis*	0
Rubiaceae	176. *Coffea arabica*	4
Rutaceae	177. *Citrus Aurantium*	0
	178. *Citrus grandis*	0
	179. *Citrus Limon*	0
Scrophulariaceae	180. *Antirrhinum majus*	0
	181. *Digitalis purpurea*	0
	182. *Linaria dalmatica*	
	a. var. *grandiflora*	0
	183. *Nemesia* sp.	0
	184. *Veronica longifolia*	0
Solanaceae	185. *Capsicum frutescens*	
	a. var. *longum*	0
	186. *Nicotiana tabacum*	0
	187. *Lycopersicon esculentum*	0
	188. *Petunia hybrida*	0
	189. *Physalis Alkekengi*	0
	190. *Salpiglossis sinuata*	0
	191. *Schizanthus pinnatus*	0
	192. *Solanum Melongena*	
	a. Black beauty	0.7
	b. Florida highbush	0
Tropaeolaceae	193. *Tropaeolum majus*	
	a. dwarf	0
	b. golden gleam	7
	c. mahogany	0
	194. *Tropaeolum peregrinum*	0
Typhaceae	195. *Typha latifolia*	80
Umbelliferae	196. *Anethum graveolens*	0
	197. *Carum carvi*	0
	198. *Coriandrum sativum*	0
	199. *Daucus carota*	0
	200. *Foeniculum vulgare*	2
	201. *Pastinaca sativa*	0
	202. *Trachymene coerula*	0

TABLE 20. Screen 1; familial listing of genera, species, and varieties of seed screened for anaerobic capabilities (Cont'd)

Family	Genus, species, variety	Germination percentage[a] (after 5 days at 25°C)
Verbenaceae	203. *Lantana Camara*	
	a. var. *hybrida*	0
	204. *Verbena*	
Violaceae	205. *Viola tricolor*	
	a. var. *hortensis*	0

[a]Based on triplicates totalling at least 300 seeds.

Screen 1 shows three patterns of response. Some populations consist of obligate aerobes; others contain a minor percentage of facultative anaerobes (5b, 17, 40b, for example) in a major population of strict aerobes; and some populations consist of significant proportions (or almost entirely) of facultative anaerobes (7a, 62, 144, for example). Extreme varietal differences are apparent in some cases—in species 7 (*Celosia argentea*) and species 80 (*Cucumis sativus*), for example. Of 249 species and varieties given, 15% are weakly anaerobic (< 15% germination) and 9% are strongly anaerobic. In all, Screen 1 required the use of a total of about 70,000 seeds.

Screen 2 presents a selection of 41 species from Screen 1, half of which have anaerobes in the population. Approximately 12,000 seeds were employed altogether. Those capable of any germination at all on the 16-hr − 30°C cycle are unquestionably low-temperature competent. There are five such species, all of which are anaerobic to some degree. Eighteen species germinate to some extent on the short subfreezing cycle, and they are equally divided between aerobic and anaerobic classifications. However, to be more selective, only those showing 90% germination or more on the 8-hr at − 30°C cycle were ranked with the five from the 16-hr, − 30°C cycle condition. Of these few, three are anaerobes. Hence, eight out of nine of the forms showing good low-temperature performance represent populations containing anaerobic members.

Screen 3, which involved about 8,000 seeds, shows that only six species can germinate against osmotic stress: the great difference between mannitol and agar suggests that the latter be discarded as a reference standard. Arbitrarily, the two species 68b and 7c, which germinate over 90% on agar, are included with those succeeding in mannitol. Of these eight species, half performed well on Screen 2, half did not; five out of eight were from populations with anaerobic abilities. There apppears to be a positive relationship between anaerobic and cryobic abilities but only a random relation between these factors and osmotic stress.

TABLE 21. Screen 2; selected species from Screen 1 tested for cryobiotic capabilities

Species No. (from Screen 1)	Screen 1 performance[a]	Germination percentage after 5 days at		
		+4°C, 16 hr +22°C, 8 hr	−30°C, 8 hr +22°C, 16 hr	−30°C, 16 hr +22°C, 8 hr
6	+	90	0	0
8a	+	92	100	12
15	−	67	0	0
26	−	90	80	0
27a	+	92	5	5
27b	+	90	20	3
31d	+	0	0	0
33	−	80	10	0
51	+	0	0	0
54a	−	100	0	0
58	−	0	0	0
62	+	40	0	0
67	−	95	0	0
70	+	100	0	0
77b	+	55	33	0
77c	+	40	73	0
77d	+	100	100	10
80a	+	68	84	0
81	−	0	0	0
94	−	38	90	0
95	−	0	0	0
97	+	92	0	0
98	+	90	66	0
101	+	98	90	20
103	+	0	0	0
112	−	25	5	0
117	−	0	0	0
122	+	16	0	0
123	−	90	0	0
129a	−	0	0	0
129b	−	75	0	0
130	−	0	0	0
131	+	0	7	0
139	+	0	0	0
144	+	0	0	0
150	−	80	80	0
172	−	20	5	0
183	−	25	3	0
191	−	0	0	0
193b	−	0	0	0
201	−	5	39	0

[a] + denotes the 20 best anaerobes from Screen 1; − denotes a random selection of aerobes.

If the 28 species receiving triple screening are evaluated for over-all performance by adding their "+" responses (Table 23), three receive "0", that is, show no stress capabilities; 17 have only single-factor competence; four have two-factor capabilities. The final group, representing

TABLE 22. Screen 3; selected species from Screen 1 tested for xerobiotic capabilities

Species No. (from Screen 1)	Screen 1 performance	Screen 2 performance	Germination percentage after 3 days in	
			1 M mannitol	10% agar
6	+	−	0	60
7c	+	+	0	93
8a	+	−	0	33
15	−	+	0	48
27b	+	+	0	45
31a	−	+	0	5
33	−	−	0	63
40a	−	−	0	48
51	+	−	0	36
62	+	−	0	24
67	−	−	12	18
68b	−	−	0	96
69c$_1$	+	−	0	51
69c$_2$	+	−	5	55
69d$_1$	−	−	0	25
70	+	+	18	87
77d	+	+	6	60
80a	+	+	0	21
80e	+	−	0	87
98	+	+	0	0
101	+	+	35	100
103	+	−	0	33
122	+	−	0	0
144	+	−	0	0
176	+	−	0	0
193b	+	−	0	0
196	−	−	6	9
199	−	+	0	15

triple-factor capability, consists of 7c, *Celosia argentea* (forest fire); 70, *Brassica pekinensis;* 77d, *Raphanus sativus* (scarlet turnip white tip); and 101, *Secale cereale* (winter rye). Of these, winter rye is the most outstanding and *Celosia* is second. The other two, both members of the mustard family (Cruciferae), are relatively poor anaerobes.

The (Partially) Simulated Martian Environment

Several experiments using the full complex of environmental factors have shown that our general approach to simulation is feasible and useful, if not yet optimal (Table 24a and b). Consistent with its behavior in other respects, winter rye is the only species which has shown substantial promise in these experiments.

To date, simulation is inaccurate in the following ways:

1. The warm phase is too long.
2. The low temperature may not be low enough.

TABLE 23. Triple screen score: selected species from Screens 1–3

Species No. (from Screen 1)	Screen 1 performance	Screen 2 performance	Screen 3 performance	Over-all score
6	+	−	−	1
7c	+	+	+	3
8a	+	−	−	1
15	−	+	−	1
27b	+	+	−	2
31a	−	+	−	1
33	−	−	−	0
40a	−	−	−	0
51	+	−	−	1
62	+	−	−	1
67	−	−	+	1
68b	−	−	+	1
$69c_1$	+	−	−	1
$69c_2$	+	−	+	2
$69d_1$	−	−	−	0
70	+	+	+	3
77d	+	+	+	3
80a	+	+	−	2
80e	+	−	−	1
98	+	+	−	2
101	+	+	+	3
103	+	−	−	1
122	+	−	−	1
144	+	−	−	1
176	+	−	−	1
193b	+	−	−	1
196	−	−	+	1
199	−	+	−	1

3. The atmospheric pressure is too high (760 mm Hg) and in some cases lacks carbon dioxide.
4. The light regime is not yet realistic in visible-plus-ultraviolet energy distribution.
5. The substratum is too simple.
6. The water problem is not solved.

These factors are under continuous review and are subject to improvement. The method of supplying water suffers from being discontinuous. This will be rectified by distributing the ice continuously over a period of days or weeks. It should be noted, however, that the surface water condition is modified by the continuous flow of dry atmosphere. Psychrometric readings have been attempted only once after addition of ice to the surface and showed that with the existing flow-through of gas at dew point −60°C, the humidity 10 cm above the melting ice was so low that differential wet–dry bulb differences went off the scale on standard tables.

The results show that in addition to its "inherent" capability, winter rye performance can be improved by a number of chemical agents which may substitute for the oxidizing power of oxygen. Quinones and nitrates may serve in this way directly. Adenosine triphosphate, although a product of oxidation, replaces oxygen only to a small extent. Glycine may support the Stickland reaction described in an earlier Section. Combinations of these substances have a remarkably good effect and suggest that there are two or more limiting pathways to be examined. The effect of carbon dioxide supports the concept of intracellular oxygen production; however, it may reflect buildup of metabolites in a high enough state

TABLE 24. Operating conditions and plant performance in exploratory Mars simulator runs

a. Operating conditions

Environmental factors	Simulator run				
	II	III	IV	V	V-A
Thermocycle					
Max/min, °C	+20/−20	+20/−20	+20/−20	+20/−20	+20/−20
Hr ⩾ 0°C	10	10	10	12	12
Hr at min	12	12	12	10	10
Photocycle					
Intensity, ft-cd	250	250	250	250	250
Spectral character	Warm white fluorescent	Warm white fluorescent	Warm white fluorescent	Warm white fluorescent	Warm white fluorescent
Period, hr	12	12	12	16	16
Atmosphere					
N_2, %	> 99.9	> 99.9	> 99.9	97	97
O_2, %	< 0.1	< 0.1	< 0.1	< 0.1	< 0.1
CO_2, %	< 0.1	< 0.1	< 0.1	3	3
Dew point, °C	− 60	− 60	− 60	− 60	− 60
Flow rate, liters/min	4	4	4	4	4
Surface					
Substratum	Perlite	Perlite	Perlite	Perlite	Perlite
Water g/cm²	0.3 (ice)	0.15 (ice)	0.3 (ice)	0.3 (ice)	soaked
Frequency	2 weeks	2 weeks	2 weeks	4 weeks	seed
Species	Winter rye, corn, cucumber, cockscomb, peanut	Winter rye, morning glory, peanut	Winter rye	Winter rye	Winter rye
Special conditions	None	Some of rye soaked in quinones	First ice layer was 0.5 M in KNO_3	Some seeds presoaked anaerobically in 0.01 M KNO_3	Test of glycine ATP, KNO_3 effects

TABLE 24. Operating conditions and plant performance in exploratory Mars simulator runs (Cont'd)

b.   Plant performance

Simu-lator run	Period of run	Species	Responses	Remarks
II	28	Winter rye	Germination 39% Root 13.5 mm Shoot 6.9 mm	Cockscomb should have succeeded, but very small seedlings desiccated. Other species affected mainly by freezing.
		Corn	Germination 65% Root 3.1 mm No shoot	
		All others	Failed	
III	14	Winter rye $+ 10^{-6} Mp$-benzoquinone	Germination 1%	Morning glory root tips dried out.
		2,5-dichloro-	36%	
		2,5-dihydroxy-	21%	
		Morning glory	Germination 62%, then died	
		Peanut	Failed	
IV	7	Winter rye	1st shoots above ground	KNO$_3$ has double rate of Run No. II; seedlings comparable to Run II in size.
	14	Winter rye	Germination 39% with green shoots	
V	14	Winter rye	Emergence comparable with run IV	Without additional water but with CO$_2$ and KNO$_3$, the best performance to date recorded.
	28	Winter rye	Germination 45% Roots 15–20 mm (heavily branched) Shoots 20–25 mm	
V-A	10	Winter rye a. Water b. 0.05 M glycine c. 0.01 M KNO$_3$ d. 0.01 M ATP b + c b + d c + d b + c + d	Germination 0% 10% 10% 5% 15% 35% 10% 45%	

of oxidation to serve as electron acceptors (organic acids, for example).

In addition to the higher forms, we unintentionally screened a variety of fungi in the simulator. These organisms were isolated from macroscopic (up to 1 cm²) growths on or around young seedlings. The seedlings were not necessarily infected; hence, the fungi may have grown on leachates from the seed. Some have been identified as follows:

Environment	Minimum number of forms distinguished	Forms identified
Anaerobic desert	2	*Mucor mucedo*
Mars II[a]	4	*Aspergillus niger*
		Botrytis sp. (tentative)
		Torula sp. (yeast)
Mars III[a]	3	None
Mars IV	5	*Aspergillus* sp.
		Aspergillus niger
		Torula sp.
Mars V[a]	4	*Aspergillus* sp.
		Botrytis sp. (tentative)

[a]The Mars simulator runs are described in Table 24a.

EXPERIMENTAL BIOLOGY OF SIMULATED ENVIRONMENTS: CONCLUSIONS

Although environmental simulation has been practised by many investigators under a variety of general names such as "stress physiology or "physiological ecology", the rise of exobiology and space biology has created intense interest in the concepts of extraterrestrial environments and their simulation. The use of such terms as space biology or exobiology does not alter the status of this area as a legitimate part of general and comparative experimental biology, and the study of exobiology may contribute significantly to many branches of ordinary terrestrial physiology, biochemistry, embryology, microbiology, genetics, and other sciences. Meanwhile, exobiological simulation has become a powerful tool of research, calling upon many physical, chemical, and engineering specialties for support.

Simulation is a means for applying stress to the biochemical system, and has helped in the elucidation of new metabolic processes and products. More important, perhaps, it is a unique tool for creating familiar and unique selection pressures. Indeed, the flowering plant has now been tested under conditions that ceased to exist long before its rise to prominence during the Cretaceous period (or have never existed on this planet). As simulation techniques become more refined and diversified, it may be possible, by combining physiological stress and genetic selection, to produce organisms with novel and "unearthly" properties which permit them to thrive in ecosystems quite different from our own, including those characteristic of Mars.

READING LIST

A few references pertinent to specific topics treated in this Chapter are presented under the corresponding topical headings below. The principal authority and guide in simulation studies is G. de Vaucouleurs, *Physics of the Planet Mars*, London: Faber and Faber, Ltd. (1953). Information pertinent to the physical features of extraterrestrial environments has been included in the Bibliography.

GENERAL STUDIES: VARIATIONS IN AIR AND OXYGEN PRESSURE
Plant and Animal Performance at the High Mountain Level and
The Responses of Invertebrates to Air Pressures $<$ 0.2 atm ($<$ 150 mm)

GLICK, P. A., *The Distribution of Insects, Spiders and Mites in the Air*, Technical Bulletin No. 673, U. S. Dept. of Agriculture, May 1939, pp. 1–150.

GORDON, M. S., Anaerobiosis in Marine Sandy Beaches, *Science*, vol. 132 (1960), p. 616.

HESSE, R., SCHMIDT, K. P., and ALLEE, W. C., *Ecological Animal Geography*, New York: John Wiley and Sons, Inc.(1937).

KENNINGTON, G., The Effects of Reduced Atmospheric Pressure on Populations of *Tribolium castaneum* and *Tribolium confusum*, *Physiological Zoology*, vol. 26 (April 1953), pp. 179–203.

PACKCHANIAN, A., *The Effect of Simulated Altitude on Certain Insects*, Report No. 2, U. S. Air Force School of Aviation Medicine, Randolph Field, San Antonio, Texas, September 1953, pp. 1–17.

PACKCHANIAN, A., Altitude Tolerance of Normal and Infected Insects, *Journal of Economic Entomology*, vol. 47 (1954), pp. 230–8.

PAYNE, N. M., Freezing and Survival of Insects at Low Temperatures, *The Quarterly Review of Biology*, vol. 1 (1926), pp. 270–82.

SIEGEL, S. M., HALPERN, L. A., GIUMARRO, C., RENWICK, G., and DAVIS, G., Martian Biology: The Experimentalist's Approach, *Nature*, vol. 197 (1963), pp. 329–31.

SIEGEL, S. M., DALY, O., HALPERN, L., GIUMARRO, C., and DAVIS, G., The General and Comparative Biology of Experimental Atmospheres and Other Stress Conditions: Some Notes on the Behavior of Insects and Other Invertebrates, *Aerospace Medicine* (In press).

SIEGEL, S. M., ROSEN, L. A., and GIUMARRO, C., Experimentation With Plants at Sub-Atmospheric Oxygen Levels, *Nature* (In press).

SOKOLOFF, A., and SHRODE, R. R., Survival of *Tribolium castaneum* Herbst after Rocket Flight into the Ionosphere, *Aerospace Medicine*, vol. 33 (1962), pp. 1304–17.

TAYLOR, L. R., Mortality and Viability of Insect Migrants High in the Air, *Nature*, vol. 186 (1960), p. 410.

Plant and Animal Performance at $P_{0_2} = 1$ atm (760 mm)

BAKER, W. K., The Oxygen Effect and the Mutation Process in 'Mutation', *Brookhaven Symposium in Biology*, Brookhaven National Laboratory, Upton, New York, vol. 8 (1956), pp. 191–200.

BECKER, N. H., and GALVIN, J. F., Effect of Oxygen-Rich Atmospheres on Cerebral Lipid Peroxides, *Aerospace Medicine*, vol. 33 (1962), pp. 985–7.

DICKENS, F., The Toxic Effects of Oxygen on Brain Metabolism and Tissue Enzymes, *The Biochemical Journal*, vol. 40 (1946), pp. 145–87.

DIXON, K., Deposition of Globular Lipid in Arterial Cells in Relation to Anoxia, *The American Journal of Pathology*, vol. 39 (July 1961), pp. 65–74.

GABLE, W. D., and TOWNSEND, F. M., Lung Morphology of Individuals Exposed to Prolonged Intermittent Supplemental Oxygen, *Aerospace Medicine*, vol. 33 (1962), pp. 1344–8.

GERSCHMAN, R., *Considerations on the Problem of Oxygen Toxicity—Progress Report*, U. S. Air Force School of Aviation Medicine, Randolph Field, San Antonio, Texas, 1955–6.

GERSCHMAN, R., GILBERT, D. L., NYE, S. W., DWYER, P., and FENN, W. O., Oxygen

Poisoning and X-Irradiation: A Mechanism in Common, *Science*, vol. 119 (1954), pp. 623–6.

GILBERT, D. L., GERSCHMAN, R., COHEN, J., and SHERWOOD, W., Influence of High Oxygen Pressures on the Viscosity of Solutions of Sodium Desoxyribonucleic Acid and Sodium Alginate, *The Journal of the American Chemical Society*, vol. 79 (1957), pp. 5677–80.

ROSEN, L. A., and SIEGEL, S. M., The Effect of Oxygen Tension on the Course of Ethylene- and Gibberellin-Induced Foliar Abscission, *Plant Physiology*, vol. 38 (March 1963), pp. 189–91.

SIEGEL, S. M., Effects of Reduced Oxygen Tension on Vascular Plants, *Physiologia Plantarum*, vol. 14, No. 3 (1961), pp. 554–7.

SIEGEL, S. M., Observations on Peroxide Toxicity in Seed Germination, *Physiologia Plantarum*, vol. 15, No. 1 (1961), pp. 21–6.

SIEGEL, S. M., The Protection of Plants Against Airborne Oxidants: Cucumber Seedlings at Extreme Ozone Levels, *Plant Physiology*, vol. 37 (May 1962), pp. 261–6.

SIEGEL, S. M., and GALSTON, A. W., Peroxide Genesis in Plant Tissues and Its Relation to Indoleacetic Acid Destruction, *Archives of Biochemistry and Biophysics*, vol. 54 (January 1955), p. 102.

SIEGEL, S. M., and GERSCHMAN, R., A Study of the Toxic Effects of Elevated Oxygen Tension on Plants, *Physiologia Plantarum*, vol. 12, No. 2 (1959), pp. 314–23.

SLAGER, U. T., *Space Medicine*, Englewood Cliffs, New Jersey: Prentice-Hall, Inc. (1962), p. 284.

Space Handbook: Astronautics and Its Applications, Staff Report, Select Committee on Astronautics and Space Exploration (Committee Print No. 1545, 85th Congress, 2nd Session), Washington, D.C.: United States Government Printing Office (1959), pp. 110–11.

The Effects of Subatmospheric Levels on Plants

BERGMAN, H. F., Oxygen Deficiency as a Cause of Disease in Plants, *The Botanical Review*, vol. 25 (July–September 1959), pp. 417–85.

CLEMENTS, F., *Aeration and Air-Content*, Washington, D. C.: Carnegie Institution of Washington (1921).

SIEGEL, S. M., ROSEN, L. A., and GIUMARRO, C., Effects of Reduced Oxygen Tension on Vascular Plants. IV. Winter Rye Germination Under Near-Martian Conditions and in Other Non-Terrestrial Environments, *Proceedings of the National Academy of Sciences of the United States of America*, vol. 48 (May 15, 1962), pp. 725–8.

GENERAL STUDIES: TEMPERATURE, WATER, AND OTHER FACTORS
High Temperature and Radiation – Some Preliminary Notes

CROCKER, W., *The Growth of Plants; Twenty Years of Research at the Boyce Thompson Institute*, New York: Reinhold Publishing Corp. (1948).

CROCKER, W., and BARTON, L. V., *Physiology of Seeds*, Waltham, Massachusetts: Chronica Botanica (1953).

SIEGEL, S. M., Effects of Exposures of Seeds to Various Physical Agents: I. Effects of Brief Exposures to Heat and Cold on Germination and Light Sensitivity, *The Botanical Gazette*, vol. 113 (1952), pp. 57–70.

SIEGEL, S. M., Effects of Exposures of Seeds to Various Physical Agents: II. Physiological and Chemical Aspects of Heat Injury in Red Kidney Bean Seed Embryo, *The Botanical Gazette*, vol. 114 (1953), pp. 297–312.

BIOCHEMICAL AND PHYSIOLOGICAL OBSERVATIONS ON ORGANISMS IN SIMULATED ENVIRONMENTS
Chemical Support for Anaerobic Germination of Rye and Other Seeds

CROCKER, W., and DAVIS, W. E., Delayed Germination in Seeds of Alisma Platago, *The Botanical Gazette*, vol. 58, No. 4 (1914), pp. 285–321.

EDWARDS, T. I., The Germination and Growth of *Peltandria Virginica* in the Absence of Oxygen, *Bulletin of the Torrey Botanical Club,* vol. 60 (1933), pp. 573–81.

MATHER, K., *Statistical Methods in Biology,* 4th ed., London: Methuen and Co., Ltd. (1960).

MORINAGA, T., The Favorable Effect of Reduced Oxygen Supply Upon the Germination of Certain Seeds, *American Journal of Botany,* vol. 13, No. 2 (1926), pp. 159–66.

SIEGEL, S. M., RENWICK, G., and ROSEN, L. A., Formation of Carbon Monoxide During Seed Germination and Seedling Growth, *Science,* vol. 137 (1962), pp. 683–4.

SIEGEL, S. M., and ROSEN, L. A., Effects of Reduced Oxygen Tension on Germination and Seedling Growth, *Physiologia Plantarum,* vol. 15, No. 3 (1962), pp. 437–44.

STICH, C., Die Atmung der Pflanzen bei verminderter Säuerstoff Spannung und bei Verletzungen, *Flora oder allgemeine botanische Zeitung* (Jena), vol. 74 (1891), pp. 1–57.

WINDISCH, F., HEUMANN, W., and NORDHEIM, W., Anoxygene, mit Gärung und Glykolyse nicht identische Energieversorgung der Zelle, *Enzymologia, Acta Biocatalytica,* vol. 21, No 4 (1960), pp. 261–70.

**Bean Plants Grown in 5% O_2 + 95% Ar and
Cucumber Seedlings in Various Atmospheres**

CHANCE, B., Cellular Oxygen Requirements, *Federation Proceedings,* vol. 16 (September 1957), pp. 671–99.

FALK, J. E., PORRA, R. J., BROWN, A., MOSS, F., and LARMINIE, H. E., Effect of Oxygen Tension on Haem and Porphyrin Biosynthesis, *Nature,* vol. 184 (1959), pp. 1217–19.

FRITZ, G., MILLER, W. G., BURRIS, R. H., and ANDERSON, L., Direct Incorporation of Molecular Oxygen Into Organic Material by Respiring Corn Seedlings, *Plant Physiology,* vol. 33 (May 1958), pp. 159–61.

SIEGEL, S. M., RENWICK, G., and ROSEN, L. A., Formation of Carbon Monoxide During Seed Germination and Seedling Growth, *Science,* vol. 137 (1962), pp. 683–4.

SIEGEL, S. M., *The Plant Cell Wall,* New York: Pergamon Press, Inc. (1962).

CHAPTER V

THE POSSIBILITY OF A PRIMORDIAL LUNAR LIFE

J. J. GILVARRY

Space Science Laboratory, General Dynamics/Astronautics
San Diego, California

INTRODUCTION

OVER the preceding century, the view was prevalent that both the craters and the maria of the Moon were features primarily of volcanic origin. Gilbert[1] cast serious doubt on this idea by recognizing that the relative dimensions (ratio of depth or rim height to diameter) of the craters and maria do not generally conform to those observed for terrestrial volcanoes. He hypothesized an origin for both types of lunar features in the impact of large meteorites. A missing link in the argument was supplied by Gifford,[2,3] who pointed out that such collisions would yield circular craters even for oblique impact, since they would, of necessity, be explosive in nature. Strong evidence for the genesis of the craters in explosions was provided by Baldwin (Ref. 205). He showed that the curve of diameter vs. depth for explosion craters on the Earth exhibits a continuous variation through the analogous curve for terrestrial meteoritic craters into the corresponding curve for those lunar craters which are the least eroded and presumably the youngest. That meteorite impacts at astronomically possible velocities actually generate pressures and temperatures of explosive magnitude was demonstrated by Gilvarry and Hill[4,5] in a calculation from first principles rather than on empirical grounds.

Throughout this development of ideas on the origin of the craters, the dark and smooth appearance of the maria was viewed as sufficient evidence to identify their surfaces as lava flows, in spite of the virtual absence of identifiable volcanic features on the Moon otherwise. The last consideration led Baldwin (Ref. 205) to propose that the lava was released from the Moon's interior through fissures rent by meteorites on impact. Since such a source of the lava was incompatible with his theory of a cold origin of the Earth and Moon, Urey (Ref. 103) postulated a mechanism of mare formation in which the lava is supplied by fusion

179

of large planetesimals impinging with velocities low enough so that
the temperature merely reaches the melting point. The theory of Kuiper[6]
differs in that the lava is formed by radioactive heating of a Moon formed
by accretion.

This view (which will be referred to as the lava hypothesis) of the
nature of the surfaces of the lunar maria has been challenged by Gold
(Ref. 623), who argues strongly against lava as the agent producing the
smooth dark surfaces. The reasoning is based in part on the paucity
of volcanic formations otherwise, but more strongly on the difficulty
in correlating time sequences as inferred from lava intrusion into craters
and maria and as established by less inferential means, such as the degree
of erosion of crater rims. He presumes the maria to arise in the first
instance merely as meteoritic craters considerably larger (in general)
than the average, without any intervention of lava at all. The smooth
surfaces of the maria are explained by an erosive process which creates
dust in the highlands, coupled with a transport mechanism which deposits
it in the lower maria. However, it is not obvious that suggested erosive
and transport processes are adequate explanations.[7] Radiation damage
is suggested as the process creating the dark superficial color of the dust
in the maria. In this connection, Gilvarry[8] showed by a theoretical
analysis that the eclipse observations of Pettit[9] excluded the possibility
of exposed lava specifically on Mare Vaporum, and by implication on
any mare, in accordance with Gold's views. In addition, this work
yielded the first indication from observations that the maria as well as
the highlands were covered with dust; it was pointed out that this result
vitiated in large part the reasoning for the presence of lava, for which
no evidence on the basis of measurements exists.

The arguments for lava presuppose the absence of a lunar atmosphere
or hydrosphere lasting any significant length of time. This presumption
is in accordance with the calculations of Sir James Jeans[10] and of Baldwin
(Ref. 205) on thermal escape of a lunar atmosphere. During the past few
decades, however, it has become increasingly clear that the terrestrial
atmosphere and hydrosphere were formed by exudation from the Earth's
interior. Gilvarry (Ref. 233) has considered the possibility of an analogous process in the case of the Moon. Needless to say, such a possibility changes the entire complexion of the problem of thermal escape
treated by Jeans and Baldwin. On the basis of reasonable physical
assumptions, it is found that a lunar hydrosphere and atmosphere lasting
for periods astronomically significant are indeed possible. In this connection, such time periods are considered to be measured in billions of years,
in view of the Earth's age (about 4.5×10^9 yr).

The maria are much shallower relative to their diameter than extrapolation from the largest crater on Baldwin's curve would imply. As

was noted, this correlation of the dimensions of lunar craters applies only to those which are the least eroded (the youngest). To explain the relative dimensions of the older craters, showing a much shallower relative depth, Baldwin had to invoke an erosive process of unknown origin filling the bottom at the expense of the rim after crater formation. This suppositious mechanism was presumed to operate with relatively high efficiency on an airless and waterless Moon.

Gilvarry (Ref. 233) has shown that the correlation of diameter vs. depth for the older craters can be understood in terms of the former presence of a lunar hydrosphere, which affected the relative depth at the time of crater formation by meteoritic explosions. Furthermore, this correlation of crater dimensions includes the lunar maria and implies that these features are the relics of ancient seas, showing sedimentary floors rather than the lava cover generally assumed. Thus, the presence of a lunar hydrosphere of the age calculated yields a direct explanation of the progression of relative dimensions of the craters of different ages, of the origin of the maria and of the nature of the mare floors. It is ironical that, on these views, the name mare is correct on the basis of provenance.

In a later paper,[11] the correlation of dimensions of the lunar maria was extended to the terrestrial ocean basins, on the hypothesis that these features were formed by explosive impact of large meteorites at a pristine time far back in the Precambrian, when the terrestrial hydrosphere covered the Earth uniformly. A similar hypothesis has been made by Dietz[12] and Harrison,[13] but without quantitative demonstration of the correlation of dimensions. Since this theory raises issues not entirely germane to the present discussion, the detailed argument in this connection will not be reviewed here. However, these considerations suggest strongly that the ancient maria were seas representing the selenological equivalents of the terrestrial oceans.

If the analogs of terrestrial oceans were once present on the Moon, it is reasonable to inquire about the presence of a former lunar life. It is in these bodies of water on the Earth that Oparin (Ref. 1146) postulates the spontaneous generation of the first living organism. In this manner, Oparin cleared the impasse created by Pasteur's demonstration that life does not arise spontaneously at the present time, and the indisputable fact that it does exist. Specifically, he proposes that the primeval atmosphere was reducing in character. This condition would favor synthesis of complex organic compounds, which accordingly would be present in large quantities in the oceans of the primitive Earth. From this viewpoint, the first organisms to appear were necessarily heterotrophic. The possible steps in the evolution of a simple heterotrophic organism into an autotrophic one, by development of the ability to synthesize cell constituents, have been outlined by Horowitz (Ref. 1111).

If the maria are indeed ghosts of former seas, and if Oparin's views are correct, one can argue that the dark color of the sediments now covering the mare floors is derived from a pristine indigenous biota on the Moon, as postulated by Gilvarry (Ref. 233). In this manner, all the conflicts of evidence involved in the lava hypothesis would be avoided. A detailed argument leading to this conclusion will be presented later in this Chapter, as given by Gilvarry.[14] Admittedly, the case made is inferential and therefore speculative. Of necessity, the argument must rely heavily on logical considerations rather than direct evidence, since the present body of information on the Moon's surface obviously admits conflicting interpretations. The availability of photographs at short range or samples of material from the lunar surface would restrict drastically the possible domain of speculation in the following discussion. Unfortunately, efforts over the last few years by both the Americans and the Russians have been singularly unsuccessful in securing these data. The approach followed is taken in default of such evidence.

PRISTINE HYDROSPHERE AND ATMOSPHERE OF THE MOON

By comparing the cosmic and terrestrial abundances of the inert rare gases, Brown[15] and Suess[16] have demonstrated that any element which existed primarily as a gas at the time of the Earth's formation could not have been retained to a significant extent in its atmosphere. It follows that the present atmosphere and hydrosphere of the Earth are not residual from primordial antecedents but are almost entirely of secondary origin, formed by leakage from the underlying Earth through its surface. Rubey[17] has advanced purely geological arguments yielding precisely the same conclusion for the terrestrial hydrosphere.

In view of the Moon's smaller mass, the conclusion follows *a fortiori* that it could have retained no residue of any primordial atmosphere or hydrosphere. However, the Moon necessarily was formed at essentially the same distance from the Sun, at approximately the same time, and under roughly the same conditions as the Earth. Thus, it is reasonable to hypothesize that the Moon once possessed a secondary hydrosphere and atmosphere, formed by a degassing process from the interior exactly analogous to that demanded from the Earth. To determine the corresponding lifetimes, one must know the initial amounts of each constituent, and to answer this question a scaling law must be invoked. It will be postulated that, initially, the total masses of a constituent in the secondary hydrosphere and atmosphere (combined) for the Moon and Earth should be proportional to the corresponding masses of these bodies, from which they exuded. Let Q_i represent the mass of molecules above unit area in the Moon's surface for the ith constituent in its hydrosphere and atmosphere combined, and let Q_i^* be the corresponding quantity for the Earth. This assumption yields

$$\frac{Q_i}{Q_i^*} = \left(\frac{R^*}{R}\right)^2 \frac{M}{M^*}$$ (1)

where R and R^* are the radii and M and M^* the masses of the Moon and Earth, respectively, in each case. If the difference in mean density between the Moon and Earth is ignored, Eq. (1) simplifies to

$$\frac{Q_i}{Q_i^*} = \frac{R}{R^*}$$ (2)

In applying Eq. (2), it clearly is necessary to consider in Q_i^* the total amounts on the Earth of any compound of hydrospheric or atmospheric provenance. In the case of H_2O, for example, one must include the contribution from continental ice, and in the case of CO_2, the fossil quantity locked in sediments (mainly as carbonates). Values of Q_i^* for compounds on the Earth are shown in Table 1 from data of Wildt (Ref. 111); in each case, the present amount in different locations in the hydrosphere, atmosphere, or lithosphere is specified. Note that considerably more CO_2 and O_2 of atmospheric provenance exist in sediments than in the atmosphere. For each fluid, the sum of values of Q_i^* from different locations has been used to compute the total Q_i for the Moon according to Eq. (2), as given in Table 2. As can be noted, the value of Q_i for H_2O exceeds by a large margin those for the other fluids, as a consequence of the large mass of water in the terrestrial oceans. It is clear that the dominant constituent of the lunar atmosphere must have been water vapor, at least in the later stages.

For computational simplicity, it will be assumed that the secondary lunar hydrosphere and atmosphere were formed by exudation in a time short compared to the corresponding lifetime. For the ith constituent, the lifetime L_i is then fixed by

$$L_i = \frac{Q_i}{J_i}$$ (3)

where J_i is the thermal escape rate of Jeans, determined by the gravitational field of the Moon and the temperature of the escape level. Equation (3) presupposes that loss of a constituent (water vapor, for example)

TABLE 1. Columnar densities Q_i^* for compounds of atmospheric provenance on the Earth

Compound	$\dfrac{Q_i^*}{\text{g/cm}^2}$	Location
H_2O	278×10^3	Sea water
	6×10^3	Hydrated and colloidal sediments
	45×10^2	Continental ice
	1×10^2	Fresh water
	30×10^{-1}	Water vapor
CO_2	656×10	Fossil, in sediments
	31×10^2	Coal, bitumen, humus, biosphere
	2×10	Dissolved in sea water
	4×10^{-1}	Atmosphere
O_2	400 ± 144	Fossil, in sediments
	23×10	Atmosphere
	2	Dissolved in sea water
N_2	755	Atmosphere

TABLE 2. Columnar densities Q_i^* and Q_i of fluids on the Earth and Moon, respectively

Fluid	$\dfrac{Q_i^*}{\text{kg/cm}^2}$	$\dfrac{Q_i}{\text{kg/cm}^2}$
H_2O	289	79
CO_2	9.7	2.6
O_2	0.78^a	0.21
N_2	0.76	0.21

[a] Value for O_2 is a maximum.

TABLE 3. Heights ζ^* and ζ of the escape layer for the Earth and Moon, respectively

Time	$\dfrac{\zeta^*}{\text{km}}$	$\dfrac{\zeta}{\text{km}}$
Day	670	3,200
Night	480	2,300

from the atmosphere can be compensated by gain from the hydrosphere, and thus it applies to the hydrosphere and atmosphere combined. Further, Eq. (3) represents an approximation, since it presumes a constant escape flux J_i. Note that the escape of a constituent of an atmosphere is not exponential in the time, in general, for reasons given by Gilvarry.[18,19]

The escape flux J_i is given in terms of the molecular mass m_i and the corresponding number density n_1 and escape velocity v_e at the base of the exosphere by

$$J_i = n_i m_i v_e f_i \qquad (4)$$

where f_i represents the fraction of molecules of the ith constituent with velocity in excess of the escape value, as determined by the Maxwell distribution for the temperature at the critical level for escape. If ζ is the height of this critical level above the Moon's surface, v_e is fixed by

$$v_e = \left(\frac{2\gamma M}{R + \zeta}\right)^{1/2} \qquad (5)$$

in which γ is the gravitational constant. Jeans' expression for f_i has been cast by Gilvarry[19] in the form

$$f_i = \tfrac{1}{2}\pi^{-1/2} x_i^{-1/2}(1 + x_i)\, e^{-x}{}_i \qquad (6)$$

by introducing the dimensionless parameter

$$x_i = \frac{\tfrac{1}{2}m_i v_e^2}{kT} \qquad (7)$$

fixed by the absolute temperature T at the escape layer (k is Boltzmann's constant). In this formulation of the escape problem, it is unnecessary to consider the correction factor A_i of Gilvarry[19] or B of Spitzer,[20] since introduction of these parameters is obviated when a direct estimate of Q_i is available.

The thermal escape rate J_i depends sensitively on the choice of the height ζ of the escape layer above the surface in the case of a relatively small body such as the Moon. For the Earth, the corresponding height ζ^* of this layer has been determined by Gilvarry[21] from data obtained by observation of satellite orbits. The values of ζ^* appearing in Table 3 exhibit a diurnal variation. Theoretically, the height ζ' of the escape layer above the level at which mixing stops is fixed by Gilvarry's[18] relation

$$\zeta^1 = H \ln(\pi\sigma^2 q + 1) \qquad (8)$$

where H is the mean scale height in the region below the escape layer and down to the level (the mictopause) at which diffusion sets in, q is the number of particles in a vertical column of unit cross-section between these two levels, and σ is the mean collision diameter. Equation (8) has been used to scale the values of ζ^* for the Earth to the case of the Moon, by ignoring the presence of convective mixing layers, by taking the ratio of scale heights as the inverse ratio of surface gravities, and by approximating q for the Moon from the total content (3 g/cm^2) of water vapor in the Earth's atmosphere. The resulting values of ζ for day and night conditions appear in Table 3.

In computing lifetimes of gases on the Moon, ζ was chosen as the lower value of Table 3 for night conditions, rather than the average for night and day. The reason for this choice is that ζ' of Eq. (8) is proportional to the mean absolute temperature corresponding to H, which one expects (for the same solar flux) to be lower for an atmosphere of H_2O than for one containing N_2 and O_2 dominantly, since the water molecule can radiate in the infrared. This height ζ was assumed constant in the calculation of lifetimes. The mean temperature of the escape layer for the Earth varies between 1000 and 2000°K diurnally.[21] A possible upper limit of 3000°K was taken for the escape temperature of the Moon, which is about the value apparently required to explain the loss of atmospheric He^4 from the Earth.[19]

The lifetime L_i on the assumptions made is shown in Fig. 1 as a function of assumed temperature of the escape layer, for H_2O, CO_2, O_2, and N_2. One sees that the lifetime of H_2O is the longest by a large margin for any temperature above 1000°K. Moreover, this lifetime is measured in billions of years and thus is comparable with the age (of order 4.5×10^9 yr) of the Moon and Earth. The computations of the lifetime of H_2O on the Moon made previously by Jeans and Baldwin yielded values insignificant on an astronomical scale for two reasons: First, the possible existence of a lunar hydrosphere continuously replenishing the atmosphere was ignored. Secondly, Jeans' expression for the lifetime was used in default of direct estimates of Q_i, which ignores the need for the large correction factor B of Spitzer[20] or A_i of Gilvarry.[19]

The model presumes that the entire hydrosphere of the Moon was gaseous. The fact that it was liquid lengthens the actual lifetime over that computed, since the water must first evaporate. The rate of transit of the vapor to the escape layer is limited by diffusion, as first pointed out

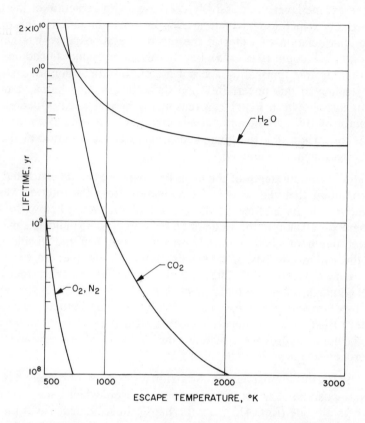

FIG. 1. Lifetime L_i of various constituents of primitive lunar atmosphere and hydrosphere as a function of assumed temperature in escape layer. (Curves for O_2 and N_2 are indistinguishable on scale used.)

by von Harteck and Jensen (Ref. 184) in the case of the Earth. Terrestrially, the existence of a cold trap above the micropause is very significant in the limitation, as is the extreme dryness of the stratosphere.[22] In this connection, note that the rate of evaporation from an open surface of water under an atmosphere is not fixed simply by the equilibrium vapor pressure; it is a complicated function of the wind velocity and other parameters.[23]

The assumption of Eq. (3) with a constant height ζ of the escape layer is strictly applicable only for a minor atmospheric constituent.[19] For the major constituent (H_2O in this case), the fact that the height of the escape layer progressively decreases with depletion of the atmosphere acts to increase the lifetime over the value computed in this manner. Photodissociation of water at the top of the atmosphere has not been taken into account (Ref. 475), but the reaction product O should have a lifetime against thermal escape not greatly less than that for H_2O. Corresponding to this uncertainty and those in assumed initial values, the estimates shown in Fig. 1 can reasonably be increased or decreased by a factor of $10^{1/2}$, giving an over-all spread of a factor of 10 in the results. The conclusion that the lunar hydrosphere lasted a period of the order of 10^9 yr remains unaffected.

The maximum depth of the lunar hydrosphere can be estimated on the assumption that the time of its exudation from the interior was short compared to its lifetime. If the surface of the Moon below the hydrosphere were smooth, the value of Q_i for water would indicate a maximum water depth of about 1 km. However, about half the visible surface of the Moon consists of highlands about 2 km higher on the average than the lowlands (Ref. 205), which, if true for the other face, would yield a mean water depth of roughly 2 km. Height estimates for the averted face are not possible since only a few crude photographs are available.[24] In spite of this uncertainty, it is clear that sufficient water existed in the lunar hydrosphere at one time to drown all the lowlands and to encroach significantly on the highlands.

The Earth's atmosphere is now oxidizing because of the effect of photodecomposition of water in producing hydrogen, which escapes thermally at high altitude (Ref. 475), and (perhaps primarily) because of the photosynthetic activity of plants. Thus, the data of Fig. 1 are not intended to imply a composition of the primitive lunar atmosphere. The essential import lies in the long lifetime implied for water on the lunar surface. Subsequent to Gilvarry's work, Watson, Murray, and Brown[25] pointed out the possibility that ice may be retained on the Moon to the present in areas permanently shaded from the Sun.

PHYSICAL EFFECTS OF THE LUNAR HYDROSPHERE

In this section, the possible physical effects of the former presence of a lunar hydrosphere will be considered. Primarily, the presence of water should have an effect on the dimensions of lunar craters, appearing as a correlation in their mensuration. Certain ancillary evidence should appear also, as will be discussed.

Craters on Land

If it is indeed true that the Moon possessed an appreciable hydrosphere throughout a large fraction of its history, it follows that the level floors of the maria were formed by sediments deposited from the water in the course of its dissipation. Compaction of these sediments should yield a softer rock than that forming the highlands, and this circumstance should, to some degree, be reflected systematically in the mensuration of the corresponding craters. Evidence of a systematic difference between craters formed in the highlands and the maria will be sought in an extension of Baldwin's correlation of diameter and depth to include the effect of crater formation in hard or soft rock. Baldwin's curve of diameter versus depth for the lunar craters of Class I (presumably the youngest) exhibits a continuous variation through the analogous curve for terrestrial meteorite craters into the corresponding curve for explosion craters on the Earth. This correlation is one of the strongest arguments that the lunar craters were formed by explosion of meteorites on impact. It can be shown that such explosions necessarily occur close to the surface.[4,5]

It will be assumed that the relation between the diameter D and depth d of a crater can be written as the quadratic form,

$$D = a_1 d \left(1 + \frac{d}{a_2}\right) \tag{9}$$

with the set of coefficients a_1 and a_2 different in the cases of hard and soft rock. The coefficients a_1 for hard and soft rock were determined from measurements of the dimensions of craters formed by explosion of chemical charges in basalt and sedimentary rock, respectively.[26] These experiments were carried out under closely controlled conditions, with the center of mass of the charge at ground level. The resulting least-squares linear relations $D = a_1 d$ for the two cases are shown (dashed in part) in Fig. 2. As a check, data points for the craters formed by the nuclear explosions Jangle (S) and Jangle (U) in compacted desert alluvium are shown also;[27] the latter was an underground explosion, but the scaled depth of burst was sufficiently small for it to approximate a surface explosion. One sees that agreement of the two points with the line for soft rock is excellent.

Of the craters in Baldwin's Class I, 80 have been classified in Class IH, occurring in the highlands, 84 in Class IS, occurring in the floors of the maria, and 30 as ambiguous on this score. With the values of a_1 fixed as above for hard and soft rock, the corresponding values of a_2 were determined by a least-squares fit to the data of Baldwin for the dimensions of the craters of Class IH and IS, respectively. The resulting curves are shown in Fig. 2. They become nearly identical for large diameter and depth, as is clearly necessary, since the larger craters on the floor of a mare must extend into the harder rock below the sediments. The association of the lunar craters of Classes IH and IS with hard and soft rock, respectively, is inferential; one sees that the difference between the two curves computed on this assumption is too small in the region of large dimensions to be of diagnostic value.

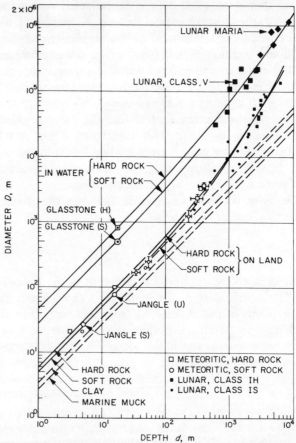

FIG. 2. Correlation of diameter vs. depth for various classes of craters and lunar maria. (Solid curves correspond to fitted functions for craters on land and in water for hard and soft rock. In general, points for only every tenth lunar crater in Classes IH and IS appear.)

However, a significant difference does appear for the two curves in question for the intermediate range of depth and diameter. To show that the difference is real, recourse will be made to the data for terrestrial meteoritic craters. Ten such craters for which dimensions are known with relative accuracy were classified in Class IH, formed in hard rock, and Class IS, formed in soft rock. The basis of distinction between hard and soft rock is the shear strength, primarily; granite and dolomite are regarded as hard, and limestone and sandstone as soft. Schist and gneiss are considered soft, in view of their low shear strength along planes of foliation and banding, respectively. The craters of Class IH are Brent,[28] Chubb,[29] Holleford,[30] Sall,[31] and Dalgaranga;[32] those of Class IS are Barringer (Arizona) (Ref. 205), Le Clot,[33] Merewether,[34] Odessa 1 (Ref. 205), and Odessa 2 (Ref. 205). The dimensions of these craters are plotted in Fig. 2, as differentiated into the two classes.

The close correlation between the data points for terrestrial meteoritic craters of Classes IH and IS and the corresponding curves constructed on the assumption that the lunar craters of Classes IH and IS were formed in hard and soft rock, respectively, is obvious from the Figure. Furthermore, one notes that no data on the dimensions of terrestrial meteoritic craters were used in the construction of the curves in question, as is not the case for Baldwin's curve. In spite of this fact, the curves correctly yield a separation of the terrestrial meteorite craters into two classes, for hard and soft rock. When corresponding coefficients of correlation are obtained for each type of crater, one finds that in all instances the values from this work exceed, or at least are equal to, those obtained using Baldwin's equation.

The considerations of this review suggest strongly (but are insufficient to prove) that the rocks of the mare floors are sedimentary in origin. On this basis, they should be softer than the rocks of the highlands and not basalt from lava flows. This view is diametrically opposed to those generally current. That the maria are vast pits filled with dust, as asserted by Gold, is rendered highly unlikely by observed dimensions of craters formed in clay and marine muck.[26] Least-squares lines for craters in these materials, analogous to those for hard rock and soft rock, appear in Fig. 2; the order of decreasing shear strength corresponding to the curves is to the right. Since dust has negligible shear strength, the points for the lunar craters of Class IS with smallest dimensions should be displaced far to the right in Fig. 2 if Gold's hypothesis (Ref. 623) were correct. Hence, the dust on the Moon, the presence of which is revealed by analysis of eclipse and radio observations,[8] is superficial in distribution.

Craters in Water

Baldwin's correlation curve applies only to lunar craters of Class I, as do the curves discussed in the preceding section. The remaining craters have been classified by Baldwin in Classes II, III, and IV, in order of increasing age on the basis of apparent degree of erosion. When the dimensions of these craters are plotted in a diagram of the type of Fig. 2, the points lie in a broad band above the curves for Class I, at distances correlated roughly with the ordinal numbers of the classes. The nine craters of Class IV for which the representative points are displaced farthest from the curves for Class I have been placed in a separate Class V by Gilvarry (Ref. 233). These craters are Hörbiger, Grimaldi, Schickard, Hipparchus, Ptolemaeus, Neper, Letronne, Hansteen, and Encke. The locus of the corresponding representative points in Fig. 2 represents the upper bound of the band in which all the lunar craters lie.

Baldwin explained the upward progression of the representative points with ordinal class of the craters in a plot similar to Fig. 2 as purely an effect of some unknown erosive process, filling the bottom at the expense of the rim after crater formation (Ref. 205). A similar explanation is inherent in Gold's arguments (Ref. 623), but suggested erosive agents[7] seem insufficient. It will be asserted that the basic cause is a progressive change of the circumstances in which the craters were formed initially, corresponding to the gradual loss of the Moon's hydrosphere. Specifically, the relative dimensions of a crater were fixed by the depth of the water in which the meteorite exploded to produce the crater. The craters of Class V are the oldest and were formed when the hydrosphere was at its maximum depth. It is not denied that erosion is of some consequence in modifying the relative dimensions of lunar craters, but the process is assigned a secondary role in this connection; however, the correlation of age and eroded appearance of a crater is assumed valid.

The mechanism by which the presence of a water layer affects the relative dimensions of craters formed in an underlying rock stratum is easily understood. The physical arguments of Gilvarry and Hill[4,5] can be used to show that the impinging meteorite must explode close to the surface of the water. At the instant of impact, a shock wave starts to run back into the meteorite to arrest its motion, and another races into the water layer below. In traversing the water, the latter shock wave is considerably attenuated from its strength at the surface and reaches the rock stratum below with considerably reduced intensity. The attenuation by the water affects the distribution of peak pressures in the rock below and causes a change in the relative dimensions of the resulting craters from one formed on land. Other effects are produced by the tsunami created in the explosion.

Glasstone[35] gives curves for the dimensions of craters formed by nuclear bombs in strata lying under water, with the seat of the explosion close to the water surface. The curves apply specifically to a water depth of 18 m for a bottom of soft rock, but conversion factors for a bottom of hard rock are given. It has already been established that the maximum depth of the lunar hydrosphere was at least 1 km and possibly 2 km.

Inspection of Fig. 2 reveals that these figures represent the order of the depths for craters of Class V. Accordingly, the dimensionless parameter μ defined by

$$\mu = \frac{\delta}{d} \tag{10}$$

in terms of the water depth δ must have had closely the value unity for these craters, on the assumption that they are among the oldest. Therefore, to relate the lunar craters of Class V with terrestrial explosion craters, it is reasonable to make the correlation with explosion craters for which $\mu = 1$. The dimensions of two craters satisfying this prescription, Glasstone (H) and Glasstone (S) for a bottom of hard and soft rock, respectively, have been obtained from Glasstone's data and plotted in Fig. 2.

Since the points in Fig. 2 for the lunar craters of Class V lie at an extreme displacement from the curves for Class I, it will be assumed that they were formed in hard rock, in agreement with the relative positions of the points for Glasstone (H) and Glasstone (S). Their dimensions were fitted by a relation of the form

$$D = a_1 d \left[1 + \left(\frac{d}{a_2} \right)^n \right] \tag{11}$$

where a_1 was fixed by means of Glasstone (H), and the coefficient a_2 and exponent n were determined by a least-squares fit to the data. The corresponding curve is shown in Fig. 2 (labeled hard rock). One sees that the points for Glasstone (H) and Class V lie on one smooth curve, roughly parallel to those obtained for the craters of Class I. The curve is not changed appreciably by an alternative choice of the dimensions of Glasstone (H) if the parameter μ of Eq. (10) lies in the range $1/2 < \mu < 2$.

The lunar maria can be divided into two broad classes. One class shows irregular borders. The other, of which Mare Imbrium is the archetype, is characterized by a nearly circular outline and the presence of an encircling ring of mountains, with an escarpment on the inner wall and a gradual slope on the outer face. It will be hypothesized that the maria of Imbrian type were formed by explosions of large meteorites, occurring at a time when the lunar hydrosphere exhibited roughly its maximum depth. If such had been the case, the dimensions of these maria should show a correlation with those of the craters of Class V and Glasstone (H).

Values for the diameters of the maria have been given by Baldwin; the diameter was considered to extend fully to the encircling mountains (the Altai in the case of Mare Nectaris). The maximum height of these mountains can be taken as a first approximation to the corresponding crater depth; values were taken from results of Schmidt.[36] Representative points determined in this manner are shown in Fig. 2 for Mare Imbrium, Nectaris, Serenitatis, Crisium, and Humboldtianum. One sees that the points lie closely on the curve already determined from mensuration of Glasstone (H) and the craters of Class V.

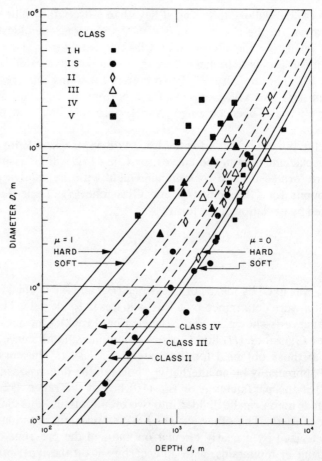

Fig. 3. Correlation curves of diameter vs. depth for lunar craters of Classes II, III, and IV (dashed), for comparison with those for Classes I and V (solid). (In general, points for only every tenth or fifth lunar crater in each class appear, except for Class V.)

If the dimensions of the lunar craters of Classes II, III, and IV (exclusive of V) are fitted separately in each case, the corresponding curves lie between those for Class I and the curve determined by Glasstone (H) and the craters of Class V, in a progression corresponding to the ordinal number of the class, as appears from Fig. 3. On the present thesis, this progression corresponds to formation of craters at temporal stages in the dissipation of the lunar hydrosphere, when the average water level was below the maximum. Terrestrial analogs of these craters of intermediate type probably exist in the Campo del Cielo crater field[37] in Argentina. The meteorite fall occurred in marshland; the dimensions of one of the largest craters are known with reasonable accuracy from excavation, and the corresponding point occupies an intermediate position relative to the curves of Fig. 2. In Fig. 3, the curves for soft rock on land and hard rock in water are not quite identical with those appearing in Fig. 2; they represent curves as modified somewhat in a subsequent publication to conform to a physical principle for consistency.[38]

It is obvious from Fig. 3 that the present theory yields dimensional correlations for all the classes of lunar craters, as well as the maria. On the other hand, Baldwin's correlation applies only to the craters of Class I. In this connection, the statistics on the number of craters in the various classes are of interest. Of the craters in Baldwin's list, 195 are in Class I, 44 in Class II, 26 in Class III, and 55 in Class IV, to yield a total of 320. Thus, of the total number of craters listed, Baldwin's theory yields a correlation of dimensions for only 61%.

Very recently, as the manuscript of this review was in process of completion, a second work by Baldwin appeared.[39] The assignment of craters to various classes (other than Class V) adopted by Gilvarry corresponds to that in Baldwin's first book. There seem to be some differences in assignment in the second work. In particular, note that Class V of Gilvarry is not the same as Class 5 of Baldwin's second book (which did not appear in the first volume).

As noted, Baldwin in his first work ascribed the deviation from his curve of the representative points for craters other than those of Class I to some unknown erosive process, filling the bottom at the expense of the rim after crater formation. In the second volume, he concludes that possible erosive processes are inadequate, as emphasized here and as had previously been stressed by Gilvarry[7] (Ref. 233). He resorts to isostatic readjustment as the mechanism explaining the relative shallowness of craters other than those belonging to Class I. However, invocation of this process for craters on the Moon as small as 20 km in diameter conflicts directly with the fact that the Moon as a whole is not itself in hydrostatic equilibrium, in view of its strongly triaxial shape. The semiaxis of the Moon pointing toward the Earth is about 1 km greater than the mean radius in the plane of the sky,[39] and the weight of this bulge must be supported by a strength of the underlying rock which is incompatible with any significant degree of isostatic compensation of the craters (Ref. 103).

Ancillary Evidence

In the preceding argument, the direct evidence on the association of water with the origin of the maria consists essentially in a correlation of dimensions. Conceivably, the correlation could arise by some mechanism other than the effect of water. For this reason, ancillary evidence on the pristine presence of water on the Moon will be considered in this Section.

If the floors of the maria are sediments formed by drying up of oceans over periods of some billion years, certain features can be predicted. First, for the larger craters formed in the ocean bottom when water existed, relics in the form of "ghost craters" should exist, visible through the slight traces of their rims in the mare surface. Such is indeed the case. Moreover, the process of sediment deposition is a gradual one, and hence the filling of a ghost crater should leave the rim essentially undistorted from a circular form, as is true. On the other hand, the flow over the mare surface of a dense liquid like lava would be expected to push over and level crater walls in the path. Thus, the presence of myriads of ghost craters on the mare floors is difficult to understand if the surface is lava, whether the lava came from the Moon's interior, as suggested by Kuiper and Baldwin, or whether it arose from melting of the impinging planetesimal that created the mare, as urged by Urey.

As a second consequence, the distribution of craters on the mare floors should correspond to a different epoch in the distribution in time of the frequency of meteorite falls, since final dessication of the mare floors required some billions of years from the time of the Moon's formation. Since the planets and the Moon presumably owe their origin to accretion of planetesimals, it follows that the rain of meteorites must have been of much greater intensity on the primordial Moon and Earth than is observed at the present time, which corresponds to a terminal phase of the bombardment. One expects the frequency curve for fall of meteorites to decrease approximately as an exponential in the time. In agreement with this picture, the frequency per unit area of craters with diameter up to a particular value is some 10 to 50 times higher in the highland areas of the Moon than in the floors of the maria.[40,41,42,43] Within each of these major subdivisions (highlands and maria), the crater distribution is essentially random (except for the relatively rare crater chains). Thus, this feature of the distribution of craters on the Moon's surface receives a simple and direct explanation on the present theory. Kreiter[41] has attempted to use the statistics in question to date the formation of Mare Imbrium, but his method is vitiated by the assumption that the rate of meteoritic bombardment has been uniform throughout past time.

The facts of the frequency of craters in the highlands and maria require an artificial and forced element in any theory invoking lava as the material of the mare floors. Since the rate of fall of meteorites at any one epoch must have been essentially uniform over the lunar surface, the lower frequency of craters in the maria can be explained reasonably only by a time delay. Baldwin assumes that the meteoritic impact that created Mare Imbrium triggered the release of lava from the Moon's interior. In his first book, he states that the lava flow in this mare occurred after more than 90% of the craters appeared, corresponding to the required delay in time. Thus, the triggering effect of the initial impact must have been retarded in its action for a very long period of time, as he seems to imply in his first work (Ref. 205) and admits explicitly in the second.[39] Urey assumes that the impinging planetesimal provided the lava that covers Mare Imbrium.[44] Basing his argument on the time required for lava to cool, he asserts that the formation of the maria took place in a very short interval of time (possibly some thousands of years) after the Moon's formation.[45] This time scale for formation of mare floors entails avoidance of the mare surfaces in subsequent meteoritic infall.

As the oceans of the maria dried up, their surfaces should assume the appearance of a dry lake, or playa. Thus, a circular depression covering the major part of the central region should appear, as is characteristic of large playas. This depression arises because the fractional compaction of any vertical column of sediment throughout the playa is essentially constant, but the total compaction is greatest in the central region where the sediment thickness is greatest. Precisely such a central depression concentric with its rim appears in Mare Imbrium and, to a smaller extent, in Mare Crisium and the other maria. Baldwin (Ref. 205) ascribes the existence of the central depression in Mare Imbrium to a large pre-existing crater of which the depression is the "ghost"; this forced explanation presumes that the ghost crater survived the explosion which produced Mare Imbrium proper. The implications of the present theory agree with the conclusions of Alter (Ref. 194), who finds definite observational evidence of subsidence throughout the maria.

If the maria once were lunar seas, one should expect that the regions of maximum erosion on the Moon would be the margins of these areas, because of the high rate of erosion by wave action which one observes on a terrestrial coast line. For the Moon, it obviously is difficult to discriminate between such an agency and effects associated directly with the explosion that produced the mare. However, as a general rule, the erosion observed on the Moon is greatest in the immediate neighborhood of the edges of the maria. Usually, the large craters bordering the rim of a mare show the most ruined appearance. In the majority of cases, these craters (as Sinus Iridum) show no obvious rim on the seaward side. However, this effect may be partially due to breaching of the wall by water in the formation of the crater, as in the case of the crater from the Castle III explosion set off by the Atomic Energy Commission in the Pacific.[46] The explosion took place on the edge of Tare Island, bordering the lagoon, and essentially no rim was formed on the seaward side of the crater.

As contrasted to craters, the maria show a significant peculiarity. Wherever two maria are nearly contiguous or overlap, the rim between them is fragmentary or nonexistent. On the other hand, when two craters overlap, the rim of one (the younger) is essentially perfect, and the rim of the other (the older) is nonexistent (Ref. 623). On the basis of the present theory, this difference is ascribed to the presence of water at the time of formation of the maria. The contiguous rims are destroyed by the action of the water moving out in a tsunami after the explosion which is second in point of time. Examples are the boundary between Mare Serenitatis and Tranquillitatis, with essentially no common rim where they overlap, and Maria Imbrium and Serenitatis, with only a fragmentary rim where they are contiguous. Baldwin ascribes the cause to the destructive effect of an advancing wall of lava but fails to explain why a lava front capable of destroying the enormous rim of a mare has such slight effect on a ghost crater in its path. On the present explanation, the ghost craters in a mare floor were formed *after* the explosion creating the mare, in all cases.

According to these considerations, a large part of the erosion evident for the lowland regions of the Moon must have taken place subaqueously; a significant amount may have been done by turbidity currents. Because of the relatively low surface gravity, small area available for watersheds, and thinness of the atmosphere (composed in later stages primarily of water vapor), erosion by flowing rivers and their tributaries should not have reached the significance observed on the Earth. Thus, drainage patterns of the type (dendritic, pinnate, or other) characteristic of rivers should appear in the highlands but should not be prominent. Pickering (Ref. 272) has shown observationally that such actually seems to be the case. Many of the features in the highlands described by him are suggestive of the drainage pattern from a tarn, or mountain lake. The relative lack of prominence of fluvial drainage patterns can be understood on the basis of telescopic resolving power (1 km for the best photographs and 100 m for best visual observation in a large telescope)[47] and a scaling on physical principles of the dimensions of terrestrial rivers to the case of the Moon.[48] In this connection, it can be noted that the grid system of the Moon, discussed by Fielder (Ref. 223), is reminiscent of a terrestrial drainage pattern of trellis type.

Some mention should be made of the valley systems of the Moon. The most prominent one is associated with Mare Imbrium, and consists of features scattered from the edge of the mare to perhaps 1500 km distant. These valleys are several kilometers wide and up to perhaps 100 km in length, disposed in a direction generally radial to the mare. It has been suggested by Baldwin (Ref. 205) and by Urey[44] that these valleys are grooves cut by the motion of projectiles ejected·in the explosion that created the mare. However, Fielder (Ref. 223) seems to have reservations about this explanation, and Baldwin himself voices definite doubts in his second work.[39]

At least for the longer valleys, it is difficult to maintain this suggested explanation without doing violence to physical principles. The fact that the grooves follow the curvature of the lunar surface implies that the presumptive projectiles must have moved with the circular velocity

$$v_c = \left(\frac{\gamma M}{R}\right)^{1/2} \tag{12}$$

appropriate to the Moon, differing from the surface value of the escape velocity of Eq. (5) by a factor $1/\sqrt{2}$. Moreover, this value of the missile velocity applies at every point of its trajectory as reflected in the superficial groove. Thus, cutting of the groove by the projectile could have entailed no loss of its kinetic energy, since this circular velocity would have had to be maintained in some cases for over 100 km of distance, without a tendency for the meteorite to enter and penetrate the lunar surface by virtue of deceleration. Further, the circular velocity for the Moon is 1.7 km/sec numerically, lying just on the edge of the regime of hypervelocity impact, whose inception is generally taken to correspond to a lower range in velocity of order 2–8 km/sec. In this connection, note that the velocity[5] at which the kinetic energy per unit mass equals the energy release of TNT is about 3 km/sec. Thus, at the first contact with the lunar surface, the projectile would have suffered essentially complete fragmentation in a distance not vastly greater than its dimensions. At the velocities in question, motion of solid missiles intact to create furrows in rock of length exceeding their width by factors up to 50 or 100 conflicts with known experimental results on hypervelocity impact.[49] The difficulty cannot be avoided by postulating missiles of nickel-iron or other alloys of high strength,[44] in view of the experimental evidence.

This situation would seem to leave no satisfactory physical explanation of the valley systems. However, their existence is reasonable on the hypothesis of the presence of water at the time of the explosions creating the maria. At this moment, a tsunami in the form of a circular wave of water would be created, moving out radially from the impact site. Entrained fragments of rock (in the form of boulders, gravel, silt, etc.) in the water would be capable of scouring grooves, just as the traction load of a river or turbidity current does. In this case, the rock fragments are driven along the surface by the kinetic energy of the wave at relatively low velocity, and Eq. (12) is not applicable. At these low speeds, scouring boulders will merely undergo comminution, so that the preceding objections to motion of missiles intact at high velocity do not apply. This interpretation implies correctly that the valleys be disposed radially from the center of a mare. The enormous grooves in the Haemus and Apennine Mountains radial to Mare Imbrium probably were carved in this manner by the tsunami associated with the explosion creating the mare.

It is possible that many of these valleys actually were created by fluvial action. This interpretation is consistent with the orientation of the Imbrian system radial to the mare, since this direction corresponds to the general slope of the neighboring terrain, as shown in a contour map of the lunar surface constructed by Baldwin.[50] This view would explain the preferential and nonrandom appearance of the valleys at the higher altitudes, both locally and on the general scale. Thus, many of the valleys cross the summits of ridges without appearing in the lower area between. These openings in the tops of ridges could be interpreted as former water gaps, where superposed streams cut through the summits. Such features are common in the Alps of Europe, and a well-known example in the United States is the Delaware Water Gap; where the river has disappeared, they are referred to as wind gaps. In view of the slopes of the neighboring terrain shown in Baldwin's map, this interpretation in terms of river valleys explains naturally why Mare Nectaris and Mare Crisium possess associated valley systems but Mare Serenitatis does not, because of the low gradients in its neighborhood.

Features as large as the Alpine Valley are in a class by themselves, since this cleft between Mare Frigoris and Mare Imbrium is about 150 km long, up to 10 km wide, and up to 3 km in depth. It is possible that this valley was formerly a channel draining Mare Frigoris into Mare Imbrium, formed analogously to the gorge of the Niagara River connecting Lakes Erie and Ontario. The difference in elevation of 2 km between its ends shown by Baldwin's map is consistent with this interpretation, as is the general difference in elevation between Mare Frigoris and Mare Imbrium, which is 5 km at the maximum. The variation in width of the valley is consistent with a fluvial origin: it is narrow at the entrance in Mare Frigoris, widening as it enters the lowlands at the base of the Alps, and narrowing as it passes in a gorge through the mountains.[39] This pattern of changing width is precisely what one observes for a terrestrial river over a similar change of terrain. In conformity with this view, a central rill in the bed of the valley has been photographed.[51]

In this body of ancillary evidence, no one fact points unambiguously to the former presence of water on the Moon. However, attention has been called to the existence of a large number of otherwise disconnected facts whose totality can reasonably be understood on this premise. This evidence supplements the strong implications of the correlation of crater dimensions possible on the basis of the hypothesis.

PRISTINE LIFE ON THE MOON

The preceding considerations on the pristine lunar atmosphere and the dimensions of lunar craters and maria have proceeded from definite physical assumptions, whose consequences follow by computation from known physical principles. Intrinsically, the reasoning that life once existed on the Moon must proceed through a less definite chain. In this section, the nature of the argument will be presented, and the very scanty positive clues discussed. Finally, the effects of radiation and meteoritic infall will be examined, as they affect the conditions under which vestiges of the inferred life could be found by future lunar explorers.

The Nature of the Argument

The maria differ from the highland regions in an essential respect – the relatively low reflectivity of the former, as compared to the latter. Moreover, the foregoing argument indicates that the mare basins were blasted out of rock strata of the same type as that forming the highlands. Thus, the dark color of the maria remains to be explained. The assumption that the dark color is due to flows of lava entails too many difficulties, as enumerated, to be credible.

What is needed is a denigrating agent that will act selectively on the sediments of the maria to produce the dark color. One such agent is carbon derived from a biota, since only a small amount (less than 5%) of organic carbon in a sediment is sufficient to yield a dark rock of low reflectivity.[52,53] It is true that there are many dark rocks not owing their color to this mechanism (lava is one). On the basis of the present theory, however, the coloring agent must be specific to an area, the maria, differing from the highlands not in type of underlying rock but only in the former presence of a water cover. Incidentally, Gold's suggestion (Ref. 623) of radiation effects suffers from the limitation that it is not specific as between the maria and the highlands; furthermore, radiation can brighten some materials as well as it can darken others.

With surprising uniformity, the results of determinations of elemental abundances in the stars by spectroscopic methods and in meteorites and the terrestrial crust by direct analysis indicate that the abundance curve is essentially the same throughout the cosmos.[54] Thus, the cloud of gas and dust which furnished the planetesimals to form the Earth and the Moon must have reflected the universal abundance distribution in its elemental composition. Hence, the elements represented in the primary atmosphere of the Moon must have consisted of hydrogen, helium, oxygen, nitrogen, and carbon, which, in this order of rank, are the most abundant in the galaxy.[54] As already noted, loss of the Moon's original atmosphere derived by accretion carries with it the absence of helium in the secondary atmosphere formed by degassing of its interior. Thus, this secondary atmosphere can be expected to have consisted initially of hydrogen, oxygen, nitrogen, and carbon, all of which are capable of forming solid compounds, which survived the process that dissipated the inert gases. Presumably, moderate internal heating by radioactivity was the mechanism that vaporized the condensates to release the secondary atmosphere. Since the abundance of hydrogen exceeds by a factor of at least one hundred that of any of the remaining elements, it is clear that the most abundant molecules in the Moon's secondary atmosphere were the hydrides H_2, H_2O, NH_3, and CH_4. Only a pristine form of life seems adequate to fix the carbon from this reducing protoatmosphere and leave it deposited in sediments preferentially. Thus, decomposition of CH_4 by solar radiation would deposit carbon without selectivity over the lunar surface.

It has been postulated by Oparin (Ref. 1146) that life originated in the seas of the primitive Earth at a time when the atmosphere was reducing. The dominant sources of free energy for biopoesis are presumed to have been ultraviolet radiation from the Sun and lightning or coronal discharges in the atmosphere (Ref. 1285). The initial steps were the formation of fairly complex organic molecules through the action of these agencies, as reproduced to some extent in the laboratory (Ref. 1280). Presumably, coacervates were an intermediate step in the procession toward self-replicating organisms.

Accordingly, it will be postulated that a primitive form of life existed in the lunar hydrosphere. All the requirements for biopoesis were once met on the Moon, in view of the existence for an extended time of an atmosphere and hydrosphere (Ref. 1245). Their presence would reduce the daily range of temperature from the high value observed at present. In fact, if the albedo of the primitive atmosphere of the Moon were comparable with that of the Earth, the mean surface temperatures would be the same, since the two bodies are at the same distance from the sun.[55] The mean temperature in question refers to an average for day and night conditions, but the diurnal variation is affected by the rate of rotation. However, a faster rate of rotation for the Moon in the past is highly reasonable on the basis of the work of Sir George Darwin[56] and this effect would mitigate the daily extremes of temperature. In any event, the greenhouse effect associated with the presence of the molecules H_2O, NH_3, and CH_4 would reduce greatly the extremes of temperature in the pristine lunar atmosphere.

The time scale of several billion years established for the lunar hydrosphere and atmosphere is favorable to the possibility of pristine lunar life, since the oldest known fossil plant is an alga dated by Holmes[57] as at least 2.6×10^9 yr old. This result indicates that life began on the Earth within a period less than 2×10^9 yr of its origin. This maximum span for the occurrence of biopoesis is less by 1×10^9 yr than the minimum lifetime shown for water in Fig. 1. The actual maximum time for biopoesis to occur must be considerably below the figure inferred from algal remains, since an alga is a relatively advanced form of life in the sense that it contains chlorophyll (frequently masked by other pigments) and thus is capable of photosynthesis.

A further fact should be kept in mind. Precambrian fossils do not show skeletal remains of calcareous or other type. What is generally observed is the imprint of the organism as a depression or cavity in the rock (sometimes lined with graphite).[58] Thus, the dating of the specimen is the date of the rock facies in which it lies. However, the oldest known rocks on Earth do not exceed about 3×10^9 yr in age, and these are generally the highly metamorphosed sediments of the continental shields. Hence, the deficiencies of dating methods preclude recognition of fossils of ages greater than this figure. It is completely within the realm of possibility that life on the Earth antedates by far the ages of the surface rocks that can be dated. In fact, the very sanguine estimates that the origin of life occurred $4.0 \pm 0.5 \times 10^9$ or even $4.2 \pm 0.2 \times 10^9$ yr B.P. have been made by Sagan (Ref. 1179).

So simple a plant as an alga is capable of forming vast beds even in the presence of predacious organisms. Thus, the brown alga *Sargassum bacciferum* forms a blanket extending over about 2×10^6 km² of the Earth's surface in the Sargasso Sea. This areal extent exceeds the value 3×10^5 km² for the lavas of the plateau of the Columbia River, and the original area 8×10^5 km² of the Deccan traps of India (Ref. 205). These features are generally taken as terrestrial analogs of the presumptive lava flows of the mare floors. With no predators present, as on the Moon, lush growth of any primitive indigenous life over areas comparable to or greater in extent than corresponds to these figures can be expected.

As the lunar hydrosphere gradually escaped, the waters of the maria necessarily became increasingly saline. Any biota in the waters would be killed when the salinity reached the range of perhaps 5 to possibly 25%, since concentrations of this magnitude are lethal to terrestrial organisms (the precise figure depends on the organism and the dissolved salts). As a consequence, the dead organic matter (with a specific gravity approaching unity) must have tended to rise to the surface of the water as the salinity gradually increased. When the process of thermal dissipation of the hydrosphere was completed, dead organic matter was dispersed over the surfaces of the sediments in the maria as well as throughout their bulk. Because of the low binding energy (a few electron volts) of organic compounds relative to the energies of the corpuscular and electromagnetic radiation from the Sun and of cosmic rays, most of the organic material distributed superficially and at shallow depth must now be in the form of elemental carbon. It should be re-emphasized that the amount of carbon formed in this manner required to darken the rocks of the maria sufficiently is relatively very small.

If this process of dissipation of the hydrosphere proceeded quiescently in its final stages, one should expect a stratification in the mare basins of sediments, salts, and organic matter, in this order upwards, as in the case of a terrestrial playa. However, the process in the case of the Moon could not have been quiescent. As the atmospheric pressure dropped in the terminal phase of loss of the atmosphere and hydrosphere, the remaining liquid water would commence to boil. Vigorous ebullition on a vast scale would induce convection and turbulence, mixing the upper layers of the sediments, the salts, and the dead organic matter intimately. Thus, the salts would remain unobservable because of the dark color of the organic carbon masking their lighter color. Continued churning and mixing of the surface material would result from the pulverizing action of meteoritic infall through the ages after final desiccation (see *Effects of Radiation and Meteoritic Infall* later in this Chapter).

One can consider an imaginary process in which the gravitational constant on the Earth is decreased in magnitude by a factor of one sixth, reducing the gravitational pull of the solid Earth to that of the present Moon. One may then ask what appearance the Earth would present to a hypothetical astronomer on Mars many billion years hence. The answer is that the gross appearance would be much the same as that of the Moon. In this period of time, the atmosphere and hydrosphere would dissipate through thermal escape. The ocean beds would appear as depressed areas relative to the continental highlands. Moreover, the floors of the extinct oceans would be far darker than the continents, as a consequence of the enormously greater abundance of life in the present seas than on land. The processes that produced this pattern of coloration would be precisely those envisaged above. Through the haze of the Martian atmosphere, however, the mythical astronomer could not easily distinguish the desiccated ocean beds from lava flows.

Ideas in some sense similar to those discussed here have been presented by Sagan. Primarily, he considers the production of complex organic compounds by solar ultraviolet light (and lightning discharges) in a primordial reducing atmosphere of secondary origin on the Moon (Ref. 280). Only in passing does he refer to the possibility of an actual biota on the Moon (Ref. 282).

Positive Clues to Lunar Life

As noted, the positive clues to the former presence of lunar life are meager indeed. In this section, the evidence will be reviewed, as adduced from direct observation of the lunar surface. Clues inferred from the data on the organic constituents of meteorites, the parent bodies of the meteorites, and the nature of the tektites will also be discussed.

1. Direct Lunar Observations

At least two positive clues exist on the former presence of lunar life, as derived from direct observation of the Moon's surface.

As the lunar hydrosphere dissipated, the dark coloration of the maria of Imbrian type tended to recede from the bases of the encircling mountains, as is evident in the pattern of light and dark color in the mare basins. The extent of regression is shown by stippling within the heavy outlines of the rims for four maria in Fig. 4, as constructed from data of Baldwin (Ref. 205). The retreat is most prominent in the case of Mare Nectaris, where the dark material has regressed about 100 km from the

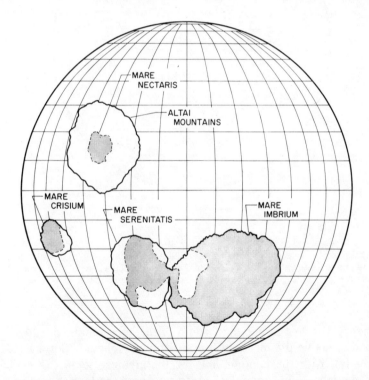

Fig. 4. Outlines of rims (solid) of four maria, for comparison with extent of dark material (stippled) on floor. (Areas of lighter color between rims and dark material are interpreted as recession of latter. North is at bottom.)

ring defined by the arc of the Altai Mountains (which are assumed to re-present the rim of the mare proper, as urged by Baldwin). The phenome-non appears also for Mare Crisium and Mare Serenitatis, and to a lesser extent for Mare Imbrium. It is characteristic of living matter to follow the retreat of its habitat in this manner.

This interpretation of the regression indicated by Fig. 4 is consistent with the variations of the height of the lunar surface above and below a mean sphere, as shown in the lunar contour map constructed by Bald-win.[50] A simplified version of this chart appears in Fig. 5. The contour

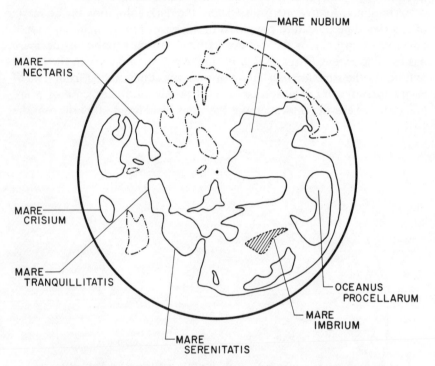

Fig. 5. Simplified version of lunar contour map of Baldwin, constructed from his data. (Contour lines corresponding to 1/1000 lunar radius [roughly 2 km] below and above mean sphere are shown [solid and dot-dashed, respectively]. Contour line for greatest depth [6 km] below mean sphere appears dashed, with interior cross-hatched. North is at bottom and east on right.)

lines corresponding to one thousandth of the lunar radius (roughly 2 km) below and above the mean sphere are shown (solid and dot-dashed, re-spectively), with the contour line for the greatest depth (6 km) below the mean sphere appearing dashed. In this map, the lowest area appears (cross-hatched) in the north-east corner of Mare Imbrium, consistent with the implication in Fig. 4 that the dwindling waters finally pocketed in this region. Mare Serenitatis is higher in elevation than Mare Imbrium, in accordance with the suggestion in Fig. 4 that the former drained into the latter. Further, a channel of the correct depth connects these two maria where they are contiguous. In the general neighborhood of Mare Nectaris, the lowest area is the floor of the mare, in agreement with the appearance of the dark area as a region cut off from drainage into the adjacent Mare Tranquillitatis. Moreover, the intensity of the dark coloration increases along an arcuate locus extending from Mare Nectaris through Mare Tranquillitatis and Serenitatis, to Mare Imbrium.

On the basis of the lava hypothesis, the gaps apparent in Fig. 4 between the edges of the dark material and the bases of the mare rims must be interpreted as a failure of the flowing lava to reach these regions. This behavior is difficult to understand, in view of the extreme fluidity that must be postulated for the lava and the fact that it must have emerged under great dynamic pressure. Thus, the depth of the deepest part of the dark floor of Mare Imbrium is about 5 km relative to its edges, from Baldwin's map, and a driving pressure on the lava sufficient to raise it through this height must be assumed. In view of the great dynamic pressure, it is difficult to see why the lava would not reach the bases of the mare rims in all cases. Further, Baldwin presumes that the lava emerged from Mare Imbrium to flood the visible face of the Moon. Thus, the pressure head must have been sufficient to drive lava against the slope of the terrain over some 1 000 km to flood Mare Nubium and Oceanus Procellarum, whereas it was insufficient to flood completely the adjacent Mare Serenitatis.

The possibility might be raised that the dark color of the mare floors is due merely to solution in the water of complex organic compounds formed in the reducing atmosphere, and not to a biota. In such a case, however, the compounds would have been spread uniformly over the lunar surface, at least initially, as Sagan argues (Ref. 280). The intervention of a biota would seem necessary to concentrate the organic compounds in the hydrosphere to the point where they can affect the reflectivity of the sediments, and to bring about the regression of the coloration.

As noted, the former existence of a biota would imply the occurrence of carbon in the floors of the maria and adjacent craters. The inferred presence of this element in a significant amount would explain in a natural way the observations of Kozyrev[59] (Ref. 252), which he interprets as implying a volcanic eruption on the Moon. With his telescope trained on the crater Alphonsus, Kozyrev noted a sudden emission of reddish light. On spectrograms taken over the succeeding few hours, the Swan bands of C_2 and bands arising from the linear molecule C_3 appeared. Kozyrev interpreted the emission as produced in a volcanic eruption, since it arose from a point near the central peak of Alphonsus.

However, the observations can be explained in a manner consistent with the observed general lack of volcanic features on the Moon (Ref. 233). Through some quirk of chance, Kozyrev observed the aftermath of an event which is now rare on the Moon—the fall of a relatively large meteorite. The impact produced high temperatures to yield the observed light and sublimed carbon to form the spectral bands. One can note that Alphonsus is on the edge of Mare Nubium, and its floor shows the presence of the same dark material appearing in the adjacent mare. Furthermore, the emission observed on the spectra did not arise from the central peak of Alphonsus, but from a point displaced about $1\frac{1}{2}$ km away.

This interpretation would explain naturally the fact that the lines in Kozyrev's spectrogram appeared in *emission* and not in absorption. As pointed out by Kuiper (Ref. 253), the relatively low temperatures associated with a volcanic eruption imply that when viewed against the sunlit surface of the Moon (of known reflectivity in this range of wavelength), it should show an absorption spectrum. In reply, Kozyrev (Ref. 252) seems to say that the lines appeared in emission because the effusing gas was too rarefied to absorb; however, a gas too dilute to absorb is too dilute to emit. The hypothesis of fluorescence under solar radiation of gas molecules effusing from the lunar surface, as made by Urey,[60] entails a large loss in intensity by virtue of the spherically symmetric distribution of the radiation, and thus one would expect the lines to appear in absorption against the sunlit Moon. However, the temperatures attained in the impact of a meteorite on the Moon can reach large values (intermediate between those corresponding to a chemical and a nuclear explosion),[4,5] and emission lines appear automatically. This suggested resolution of the problem could be checked on the basis of temperature, since high temperature favors population of states with large quantum numbers, but Kozyrev does not seem to have inferred a rotational temperature (possibly because of difficulties associated with substraction of the background).

However, Kozyrev's observations are subject to a further difficulty noted by Kuiper.[61] The relevant transition probabilities for the Swan bands are such that, besides the line $\lambda 4737$ observed, the line $\lambda 5129$ should appear also and in comparable strength. In fact, it seems to appear only weakly. On the other hand, Calder[62] reports that the spectroscopist A. A. Kalinyak supports the reliability of Kozyrev's observations, on the basis of an examination of the plate. It is necessary to conclude that, beyond cavil, Kozyrev observed some very significant event in the crater Alphonsus, even though clarification of the precise details is elusive.

As determined by direct observation of the Moon, there thus exist only two circumstances favorable to the hypothesis of a pristine lunar life.

These circumstances represent clues rather than evidence. One is a peculiarity in the distribution of coloration in the mare floors, for which other explanations besides that given admittedly can be proposed. The other represents observations implying the presence of carbon in a crater adjacent to a mare, with which some difficulty as to self-consistency exists. However, regardless of the precise interpretation of Kozyrev's observations, they do represent a positive identification of carbon on the lunar surface, as demanded by the present thesis. Moreover, the inferences drawn from these two clues have the merit that they fit consistently the evidence adduced from the dimensional correlation of lunar craters and maria. Further, they entail no conflict with known properties of the physical and biological world as observed on the Earth.

2. Ancillary Clues

The ancillary evidence available consists of the data on the organic constituents of meteorites, on the parent bodies of the meteorites, and on the nature of the tektites which can be interpreted as consistent with the possibility of a lunar hydrosphere and atmosphere lasting for an astronomically long time. As such, these data do not yield substantive evidence for the existence of a former lunar life but provide clues on the probability of the conditions requisite for such life on the Moon in times past.

a. *Organic constituents of meteorites.* Most meteorites show the presence of traces of carbon in the form of graphite, cohenite, moissanite, or diamond. However, a class of meteorites, the carbonaceous chondrites (consisting of some 29 falls), exists, in which the carbon is not present in these inorganic forms but appears mainly as organic carbon with some carbonates). Although this fact has been known for well over a century (Refs. 854, 969), it recently has prompted great interest and attention, primarily because of the impetus of the work of Nagy et al. (Ref. 929).

Nagy et al. (Ref. 929) and Meinschein et al. (Ref. 922) have studied the hydrocarbon fraction obtained by distillation and extraction from two carbonaceous chondrites, Orgueil and Murray. They state that saturated hydrocarbons isolated from these two meteorites show ranges of molecular weight, infrared spectra, and cracking patterns in the mass spectrometer that resemble those of saturated hydrocarbons formed biogenically on the Earth. As terrestrial reference materials, they used hydrocarbons from recent marine sediments and from butter. In their view, the organic compounds in carbonaceous chondrites are similar to those found in marine sediments. They proposed that these findings represent evidence for biological activity in the parent bodies of the meteorites.

Anders (Refs. 835, 837) has objected strongly to this interpretation. In his opinion, the similarity of the cracking patterns obtained in the mass spectrometer between terrestrial and meteoritic hydrocarbons is by no means so great as claimed. In any event, he notes, a close resemblance does not necessarily imply a common biogenic origin; organisms would be expected to manufacture and utilize to this date organic compounds similar to those made primordially by abiogenic reactions, such as those of Miller–Urey type.

Lately, Briggs (Ref. 864) has studied the organic compounds in Orgueil, Murray, Mokoia, and Haripura. He finds strong indications that the organic compounds were formed indigenously and do not represent a terrestrial contaminant. Thus, they show an enrichment of deuterium and a depletion of C^{13} relative to the values found for terrestrial biogenic material. Further, the small enrichment of S^{34} represents a fractionation opposite to that produced by sulphur bacteria or terrestrial inorganic processes. Thus, the isotopic composition of meteoritic organic matter is quite unlike that of any terrestrial substance.

The organic constituents identified to date in carbonaceous chondrites include fatty acids, aromatic acids and phenols of low molecular weight, urea, acetamides, sugars, and amino acids (Ref. 866). The relative amounts of fatty acids with particular numbers of carbon atoms found chromatographically by Nagy and Bitz (Ref. 933) in Orgueil compare favorably with the corresponding amounts in soil extract. Urea, acetamides and sugars (primarily mannose and glucose) occur in trace amounts. Greater concentrations have been detected for amino acids by Kaplan et al. (Ref. 901); seventeen of these have been found. The amino acids are not as complex as those found in terrestrial rocks; further, glucose and mannose, the dominant sugars identified, are the most common sugars in terrestrial soils, sediments, and natural waters. It should be emphasized that of the organic fraction of carbonaceous chondrites, the predominant portion (some 95%) has not been identified as to constituents. As Briggs and Mamikunian (Ref. 866) note, much of the organic matter present in terrestrial marine sediments similarly is unidentified.

Arguments can be given against a possible origin of these organic constituents of meteorites in biological processes similar to those observed terrestrially. The most persuasive one is the failure of Kaplan et al. (Ref. 901) to detect optical rotation in extracts of either the amino acids or the sugars, indicating that the mixtures are racemic. Further, these authors observed no absorption peaks in the infrared spectra in the region of 260 mμ and 275 mμ, implying the absence of purines and pyrimidines. Finally, they found no peaks in the infrared spectra characteristic of a pigment such as chlorophyll. Thus, the available evidence seems to imply that these constituents were formed by purely chemical or physico-chemical processes.

Recently, Claus and Nagy (Ref. 871) have reported the possible presence of life forms ("organized elements") in carbonaceous chondrites. Because of the far-reaching implications of such a result, the reports have aroused considerable interest and discussion. Apparently, other investigators have failed to confirm the findings of Claus and Nagy, in general (Ref. 839). However, the question is still an open one.

The data obtained over the last few years on the carbonaceous chondrites carry significant implications on the thesis of the present discussion. If indigenous forms of life or compounds of definitely extraterrestrial and biological genesis could be identified in meteorites, it would imply that Oparin's view is correct, that life starts wherever the physical and chemical milieu is appropriate, given sufficient time. The facts on the carbonaceous chondrites do not warrant such a conclusion, and hence, Oparin's theory remains a hypothesis. However, an essential element in the hypothesis is that the organic compounds which are the precursors of life be formed abiogenically. Thus, the carbonaceous chondrites yield relatively unequivocal evidence that precursors of life such as amino acids are formed extraterrestrially, at the very least by purely physico-chemical processes.

This testimony of the meteoritic evidence is by no means trivial, since it removes an inferential element in Oparin's argument. As regards former lunar life, one is again presented with a clue, and not substantive evidence.

b. *Parent bodies of the meteorites.* The possibility of an atmosphere and hydrosphere of the Moon lasting for a time which is long astronomically has a relevance to the problem of the parent bodies of the meteorites, as first noted by Briggs.[63] Conversely, the available information on the parent bodies of the meteorites has a bearing indirectly on the possibility of lunar life. This evidence will be reviewed briefly.

The salient hypothesis on the origin of meteorites postulates a body or bodies in the asteroidal belt, which broke up to yield fragments that reach the Earth via eccentric orbits. While this general view is widely held, Mason has objected that the chondrites at least always have been independent and individual objects, formed from material now represented by the carbonaceous chondrites (Ref. 914). Further, Urey maintained on the basis of data available up to 1959 that only siderites have a direct asteroidal origin, and that aerolites represent fragments spalled from the Moon's surface by impact of bodies from the asteroidal belt.[64] A revision by Fisher[65] of the data upon which the argument was based, and further considerations by Goles, Fish, and Anders,[66] render Urey's hypothesis of lunar origin unlikely. Since that time, furthermore, the orbit of a falling meteorite (the Pribram chondrite) has been determined photographically and its aphelion found to lie in the asteroidal belt.[67]

If an origin of meteorites in the asteroidal region is assumed as a working hypothesis, the question arises whether breakup of a single body at a definite time or of many bodies over an extended period of time was involved primarily. In the former case, the spectrum of ages corresponding to exposure to cosmic rays should display a peak at some maximum value, with a continuum extending to lower values representing the effect of secondary collisions of larger fragments. Anders concludes that the data do not support the idea of fragmentation of a single body (Ref. 836). The alternative hypothesis of fragmentation by collision of asteroids should yield an age spectrum consisting of a continuum on which only minor fluctuations are superimposed. Of the two theories, this one is the more nearly in accord with the data reviewed by Anders, but difficulties remain.

While neither hypothesized type of age spectrum is unambiguously indicated by the data, the fact that the ages for exposure to cosmic rays run from several million to a few billion years, while solidification ages are about 4.5×10^9 yr, necessarily implies that meteorites are fragments of a larger body or bodies that have disintegrated (Ref. 836). From the standpoint of the present discussion, the salient question is the size of the parent body or bodies.

A single parent body somewhat smaller that the Earth has been suggested by Ringwood (Ref. 1459) and Lovering[68] (Ref. 910). However, strong arguments can be presented against the hypothesis of such a large size for the parent body. In this case, one expects the total mass of the asteroids to approximate that of the Earth, whereas it actually is only a few percent of the Moon's mass (Ref. 1438). Thus, in spite of the concentration of the asteroids in a belt, a very effective and preponderant loss mechanism (to the Sun or to outer space) would have to be invoked. Further, solidification ages of meteorites inferred by the K^{40}–Ar^{40} method agree in general with those determined by means of lead isotopes, and retention of argon requires a relatively low temperature.[66] Since such temperatures could exist only in the outer layers of a planet of the size of the Earth, this region alone of the body could yield the observed stony meteorites. Some selective mechanism must be postulated to explain the lack of stony meteorites from the deeper regions of the mantle of the hypothetical planet. Further, one might reasonably expect a larger proportion of siderites among meteorites, arising from the metallic core such a planet presumably would possess. A further difficulty occurs in explaining the existence of the Widmanstätten patterns in siderites (Ref. 840). Finally, it can be noted that the data on the diffusion of argon in meteorites would seem to restrict the parent bodies to radii no greater than several hundred kilometers.[66]

Prior to the work of Ringwood and Lovering, an origin of meteorites in bodies of the size of the Moon had been proposed by Urey (Ref. 103).

He postulated an origin of the solar system in a cold nebula in the shape of a disk. As an intermediate phase in the condensations to the planets, planetesimals of mass approximately that of the Moon were formed. The asteroids and meteorites owe their origin to fragmentation of these bodies of lunar size by collisions. It is obvious that Urey's hypothesis escapes many of the difficulties inherent in the assumption of a large parent body for the meteorites.

Urey assumed that the time scale for breakup of the bodies postulated was relatively short (of the order of 10^8 yr). It is of interest to determine the time for initial breakup of the parent bodies, as implied by the difference between the solidification ages and the maximum cosmic-ray exposure age. One must use the maximum value of the latter ages, because lower values may be the result of secondary fragmentation of bodies derived from a primary one. In Anders' tabulation (Ref. 836) of cosmic-ray exposure ages for iron and stony-iron meteorites, the maximum age appearing is 4.8 Gyr for Clark County, as determined by Bauer;[69] Anders notes that this age is too high, because it is based on the He^3/He^4 ratio in a single sample and was calculated relative to an age for Williamstown now known to be too large. He gives 1.2 Gyr as his estimate of the age. The next largest age appearing is 2.9 Gyr for Deep Springs, also determined by Bauer, and viewed by Anders as too high relative to his own estimate of 1.5 Gyr, for the same reasons as in the case of Clark County. Taking the last figure as the most reliable estimate of the maximum, and using a solidification age of 4.5 Gyr, one finds an age before breakup of 3 Gyr for the parent body.

However, the foregoing argument to determine the time of breakup suffers from a limitation fixed by statistics, since cosmic-ray exposure ages are available for only a few percent of the known meteorites. The argument has other limitations. In the first place, exposure ages of the order of billions of years, as used in the computation above, characteristically appear only for iron and stony-iron meteorites (and not for all of these). In general, stones show much shorter ages, and ages of the chondrites show a tendency to cluster in the neighborhood of some tens of millions of years[70] (Ref. 836). The ages of the carbonaceous chondrites run from about one to some tens of millions of years, with the notable exception of Cold Bokkeveld, with an age[71,72] less than 5×10^4 yr. The difficulty in ascribing this large spread in ages to the effect of secondary fragmentation of parent bodies lies in the variation of the upper limit on age with the type of meteorite, which would seem to imply that the meteorites observed on the Earth do not represent a random sample from the parent population in interplanetary space.

It is clear that the available data allow a much longer time for breakup of the initial parent bodies than Urey assumed. If the time scale for breakup in this model is lengthened accordingly, retention for an astronomically significant time of secondary atmospheres exuded from their interiors could be invoked for these bodies. Thus, the presence of complex organic compounds in meteorites would receive a natural explanation, as a direct result of the presence of a reducing atmosphere for a sufficient period of time. The existence of the parent bodies in the asteroidal zone would lower the mean temperature relative to that of the pristine Moon and favor retention of an atmosphere. It should be emphasized that the phase of moderate internal heating by radioactivity, presumably necessary to exude the protoatmosphere, must have been very short to maintain agreement between solidification ages of meteorites inferred by the K^{40}–Ar^{40} method and those determined by means of lead isotopes. In this connection, it may be noted that Titan, a satellite of Saturn, has a mass comparable to that of the Moon and has a reducing atmosphere (Ref. 54).

There exist arguments in favor of this view of the origin of the organic constituents of the carbonaceous chondrites. Thus, Nagy et al. (Ref. 929) note that the mineral suite observed in Orgueil prescribes an aqueous environment in the parent body. The evidence consists in the presence of hydrous minerals with a lattice of layer type (probably chlorite or, less likely, montmorillonite), which can form only in the presence of water (liquid or vapor). Further, study of phase equilibria (based on the oxidation–reduction potentials and pH) indicates that certain characteristic minerals absent in Orgueil should form at temperatures of a few hundreds of degrees Centigrade. Thus, the evidence implies a temperature of the parent body which was low to moderate. Finally, Nagy et al. speculate that the environment on the parent body was slightly reducing and that the pH was slightly alkaline. The conclusions of Anders (Ref. 837) from the observational evidence do not differ significantly, although he notes that some, at least, of the material of Orgueil must have passed through an early stage of high temperature. As Anders comments, the assumption of a relatively large parent body of the meteorites has an advantage over all others in the explanation of these observed features of Orgueil.

Numerical considerations pertinent to this question have been presented by Sagan.[73] On the basis of the mass fraction of organics in carbonaceous chondrites and the prevalence of this type among the meteorites, he estimates that the asteroids contain the enormous amount of 10^{20} g of organic matter. Assuming that this matter was formed by ultraviolet light in a reducing atmosphere surrounding a meteorite parent body, he computes the time to produce it on the basis of assumptions on the primordial solar flux of ultraviolet photons, the quantum yield, and the probability of a synthesized molecule surviving subsequent dissociation. His figure for this time is about 1 Gyr. He then computes the radius of a single parent body required to retain the atmosphere for this time, and obtains a figure in excess of 4×10^3 km. This number exceeds the radius of 10^3 km, corresponding to coalescence in one sphere of all the matter currently in the asteroidal zone. He concludes that the hypothesis of formation of meteoritic organics in the reducing atmosphere of an asteroidal parent body can be maintained only if some 99% of the matter in the original body were somehow lost.

However, Sagan did not consider the possibility of an exuded atmosphere and hydrosphere, and from this standpoint his results are not necessarily conclusive. As was shown in an earlier Section, this factor in the case of the Moon carries with it the difference between an astronomically significant and an inappreciable time of retention of a hydrosphere and an atmosphere. Conceivably, inclusion of this possibility might eliminate the discrepancy by a factor of at least 4 between the computed radius of the parent body and that permitted by the present mass of the asteroids. Sagan does not state what, if any, steps he took to include the effect of the correction factor B of Spitzer[20] or A_i of Gilvarry;[19] inclusion of such a factor is essential for an approximation of the true answer.

For a parent body in the asteroidal belt of sufficient size, the hydrosphere would consist mainly of ice, in general, since the surface temperature would be of the order of $-50°C$ at most. It is hard to conceive of extensive photosynthesis proceeding while the surface of the parent body remained frozen in a primordial state. This inhospitable condition would be relieved for a large fraction of the corresponding year if the body's orbit were sufficiently eccentric. Although they are of relatively small size, many asteroids with high eccentricity are known:[74] Examples are (1566) Icarus and (1221) Amor among the numbered minor planets, as well as the lost ones, Hermes, Apollo, and Adonis. However, bodies in eccentric orbit of this type have very short lifetimes against collision, as Öpik[75] and Arnold[76] have shown. Thus, one can expect such bodies to be captured by the Earth or Mars within 10^7 to 10^8 years. This fact represents an obvious difficulty in any argument appealing to orbital eccentricity to raise the mean surface temperature.

Other difficulties remain. As Anders (Ref. 837) has pointed out, the carbonaceous chondrites show an exceedingly primitive composition, and the curve of their elemental distribution lies very close to the cosmic abundance curve. Thus, if the carbonaceous chondrites contained the products of prolonged photosynthesis on a parent body, it would be necessary for them to escape geological processes on the surface to retain their primordial composition, as Anders notes.[77] Further, Barghoorn[78] has stressed that the carbonaceous chondrites do not show the slightest evidence of sedimentary structure, contrary to what one would expect for a long residence time on the surface of a body possessing an atmosphere and hydrosphere.

Furthermore, Anders (Ref. 837) has pointed out a possibility of producing the carbonaceous chondrites in a parent body not possessing a hydrosphere in the usual sense. The exposure to liquid water inferred for Orgueil may have taken place in subsurface regions of an asteroid heated by extinct radioactivity. Another possible source of the requisite free energy lies in the conversion of olivine to hydrated silicates. As Anders (Ref. 837) notes, this source of energy is finite but may have served as the basis for a nonphotosynthetic form of life, doomed to eventual extinction when the source of energy vanished.

The possibility remains that the carbonaceous chondrites represent samples of the primordial matter from which the solar system was formed (Ref. 842). In this case, the most likely source of free energy to produce the organic matter was irradiation by charged particles in the solar nebula. Fowler, Greenstein, and Hoyle (Ref. 36) recently have advanced a detailed theory of the early solar system in which such irradiation is a cardinal feature. They invoke it in order to explain the observed elemental and isotopic abundances of Li, Be, and B, as well as numerous other data. To explain some of the isotopic data (such as the abundance anomalies of the light isotopes of Xe), integrated particle fluxes of 10^{17} to 10^{19} cm^{-2} are needed, and energies in the range 10 to 100 Mev. Processes of radiation chemistry should yield a wide diversity of complex organic compounds in such a particle flux, by bombardment of either the gaseous or solid phase. Accretion and condensation would continuously remove some of the newly synthesized compounds from the nebula and protect them from further dissociation by charged particles. In this connection, note that Berger (Ref. 1230) recently has produced urea, acetamides, and acetone by proton bombardment in a cyclotron of a solid mixture of methane, ammonia, and water at a temperature of 77°K.

It may be noted that this process may have been responsible for the organic compounds not only in carbonaceous chondrites but also in comets. From their spectra, it is known that comets contain carbon chains up to C_3, and from the persistence of the lines, it seems likely that at least some of these molecules are derived from parent molecules of higher molecular weight. The era of intense irradiation by charged particles in the early history of the solar system would be sufficient to produce such complex organic molecules by radiation chemistry. Parkin, Hunter, and Brownlow (Ref. 952) have shown recently that some nickel–iron flakes found in association with meteor showers, and thus with comets, contain amorphous organic attachments of high molecular weight. If this observation is correct, it constitutes evidence for the presence of organic matter of high molecular weight (containing C_n, with n equal to 20 and higher) in comets.

Finally, mention should be made of the recent determination of a very short age for exposure to cosmic rays of Cold Bokkeveld[71,72] — less than 5×10^4 yr. This age is far less than the mean lifetime against collision with the Earth of bodies arising in the asteroidal belt, computed by Öpik[75] to be of the order of 10^7 to 10^8 yr, and also is considerably less than the mean lifetime against collision for bodies in the Earth–Moon system, calculated by Öpik to be of the order of 10^6 to 10^7 yr. Thus, one can seriously entertain the possibility of a lunar origin for this carbonaceous chondrite, as Anders notes.[71] In such a case, one should expect the meteorite to come from a mare surface on the basis of the present discussion, in view of the hypothesized presence of organic matter.

Obviously, the thesis of a pristine lunar life would be buttressed if one could demonstrate an origin of the organic matter of the carbonaceous chondrites in a former reducing atmosphere exuded from a meteoritic parent body. The possibility cannot be ruled out completely but would seem to depend on several rather optimistic assumptions. If these are granted, one is faced with the paradoxes associated with relatively large parent bodies — how to break them up, how to get rid of the major part of the mass, etc. However, the discussion has pointed up the probable ubiquity in the solar system of the physico-chemical processes able to form the precursive conditions of life.

c. *The nature of the tektites.* The present considerations have a direct bearing on the problem of the origin of tektites. Conversely, their possible mode of origin has a significance to the thesis of the present discussion. The data and hypotheses on the provenance of these glassy objects found strewn over the Earth's surface have been ably reviewed by Barnes[79,80] and by O'Keefe.[81]

Since the chemical composition of tektites can be matched by terrestrial rocks, many origins for these bodies from the Earth have been proposed over the years. These include an origin from volcanoes on the Earth, from the striking of lightning, from the impact on the Earth of a meteorite[82] or a comet,[83] or from impact of a planetesimal large enough to vent the atmosphere in its explosion.[84] However, in a comparison of hypotheses against eight characteristics of tektites that must be explained, Barnes[80] finds that no one of the explanations cited is in accord with more than six. For this reason, in what follows, extraterrestrial origins of the tektites will be considered primarily, and discussion of a terrestrial origin will be confined largely to answering objections based on such a possibility. The salient difficulty in terrestrial provenience, as stressed by O'Keefe,[81] is the need for prescribing a physical mechanism to maintain a molten globule intact as it is ejected upwards through the lower atmosphere.

Nininger[85] has proposed that the tektites are fragments of rock fused initially by meteorite impact on the Moon and ejected from the lunar surface by the force of the explosion. This suggestion is in accordance with the theoretical and experimental data on ejection velocites of fragments in hypervelocity impact (see next Section). The second melting phase displayed by these objects then occurred during supersonic passage through the Earth's atmosphere. Objections to the possibility of a swarm of bodies from the Moon falling on the Earth in a compact cluster seem to have been disposed of by the recent work of Varsavsky[86] on the possible trajectories, and of Baker,[87] Chapman,[88] and O'Keefe,[89,90] on the effects of atmospheric entry. Chapman believes that the tektites left the Moon as clusters of small objects of approximately their present size. On the other hand, Baker and O'Keefe propose a theory in which the tektites formed by ablation of a relatively large prototektite body during entry into the Earth's upper atmosphere in a grazing orbit of low velocity. For reasons noted later, this version of the theory seems required. Thus, the theory yields properly two periods of fusion, the observed flow structure on the surface and the shape of these objects, as well as the distribution over the Earth's surface.

However, the chemical composition of most tektites is similar to that of argillaceous sedimentary rocks,[79,80] and the view that such rocks could not be present on the Moon has precluded general acceptance of Nininger's idea. This particular objection is met fully by the present considerations, which imply the presence of lunar sedimentary rocks. Erosion would explain the presence of quartz particles in the lunar sediments, required to yield the lechatelierite observed in tektites. On this basis, the theory in question satisfies all the requirements laid down by Barnes.

Barnes[80] has considered also the formation of tektites by collision of asteroids with each other or by destruction of a planet similar to the Earth. The latter hypothesis meets all eight of the criteria he lays down for an acceptable explanation, since such a body would be expected to show the presence of sedimentary rock and superficial quartz particles (to yield lechatelierite). On the other hand, these essential prerequisites would not be expected on asteroids of sizes as they are observed today.

As summarized here, however, the information on the parent bodies of the meteorites admits as a possibility (although not a very likely one), the former existence in the asteriodal belt of bodies approximately of lunar size possessing a hydrosphere and atmosphere. On such bodies, sedimentation and creation of quartz particles by erosion would occur. Thus, another possibility should be added to those in Barnes's list — destruction of a body of approximately lunar size in the asteroidal belt, of the nature of a parent body of the meteorites. Hence, the intriguing possibility arises of a common parent body or bodies of the tektites and meteorites. Necessarily, the tektites would have to arise mainly from the initial breakup of the parent body, since their characteristics reflect surface features of a planetesimal.

However, there exists a very strong objection to the possibility of any astronomical body more remote in space than the Moon serving as an origin of the tektites. The argument is based on the results of Viste and Anders,[91] who determined the amount of the radioactive nuclide Al^{26} present in various tektites. They found an amount of this nuclide which would be formed by the action of cosmic rays over a period of about 10^4 yr. On the other hand, the results of Öpik[75] and of Arnold[76] imply that the mean time of transit of a body from the asteroidal zone to the Earth is of the order of at least 10^7 yr. Since the half-life of Al^{26} is about 8×10^5 yr, one accordingly should expect the concentration of this nuclide in any body arising in the asteroidal zone to reach the interplanetary saturation value actually found in chondrites. Thus, the low concentration of Al^{26} implies an origin of tektites much closer than the asteroidal zone. As Viste and Anders point out, the argument can be invalidated only if the tektite is shielded by a sufficiently large parent body. Independently of the duration of the orbit of a prototektite from the Moon, the possibility of sufficient shielding exists in the models of Baker[87] and O'Keefe,[89,90] if the body is massive enough, although a rather special entry trajectory into the upper atmosphere is called for. On the other hand, no mechanism for shielding is present in the theory of Chapman,[88] and the low exposure of the tektites to cosmic rays demands special orbits of short duration from the Moon, at sharp variance with Öpik's figure of about 10^6 to 10^7 yr for the mean lifetime of a body in the Earth–Moon system against collision with the Earth.[75] Thus, the evidence from cosmic-ray exposure ages would seem to imply strongly that any acceptable theory of a lunar origin of tektites must be very similar to those of Baker and O'Keefe.

In Table 4, possible modes of origin of tektites are considered in a summary similar to that of Barnes of the characteristics of tektites as compared to the probability of various extraterrestrial origins. (An origin from lunar volcanoes is ignored.) "Yes" or "No" entries different from those of Barnes are indicated by italics. As compared to Barnes's tabulation, an additional column corresponding to destruction of a Moon-sized asteroid has been added. Also, an additional row representing the possibility of satisfying the requirements on cosmic-ray exposure has been included. It is assumed that a lunar origin can yield the proper distribution of tektites over the Earth's surface, in view of the work of Varsavsky, Baker, Chapman, and O'Keefe. The only origin shown as definitely excluded is collision of asteroids of present size, since no mechanism for sedimentary composition of tektites or the presence of lechatelierite exists in this case. The import of the Table is that three extraterrestrial origins of tektites are possible – meteoritic impact on the Moon, destruction

TABLE 4. Characteristics of tektites compared to the probability of various extraterrestrial origins[a]

Characteristic	Meteorite impact on Moon	Collision of asteroids (present size)	Destruction of Earth-sized planet	Destruction of Moon-sized asteroid
Two periods of melting	Yes	Yes	Yes	Yes
Lechatelierite particles	*Yes*	No	Yes	Yes?
Flow structure	Yes	Yes	Yes	Yes
Chemical composition	*Yes*	No	Yes	Yes?
Shape	Yes	Yes	Yes	Yes
Size	Yes	Yes?	Yes	Yes
Distribution on Earth	*Yes*	*No?*	*No?*	No?
Ages of strewn fields	Yes	Yes	Yes	Yes
Cosmic-ray exposure	Yes	No?	No?	No?

[a]Entries in italics represent a change from Barnes's tabulation.

of an Earth-sized planet, or breakup of a Moon-sized asteroid. The basic uncertainties associated with the last two origins are whether they can yield the observed distribution of tektites in strewn fields over the Earth and whether they are compatible with the cosmic-ray exposure inferred from the amount of Al^{26}. As regards the first question, the author views the possibility as highly unlikely, since the results of Varsavsky, Baker, Chapman, and O'Keefe do not necessarily apply in this case; concerning the second, the author feels that the probability of satisfying the requirements is very low in view of the necessarily remote origin of the tektites in the solar system. Thus, qualified "No" entries are shown under the corresponding headings in Table 4. The only provenance shown as definitely admitted is meteoritic impact on the Moon.

Clearly, if an origin of the tektites in impact of meteorites on the Moon could be established, the demonstration would be strongly favorable to the present thesis, since it would imply the existence of sedimentary rock in the lunar maria. The data available are insufficient to draw such a conclusion, although certain features point to it. For example, the variability in composition of tektites is very much smaller than the variation in terrestrial sedimentary rocks, as has been emphasized by Lowman.[92] The relative lack of variance for an origin in the lunar maria is understandable because of the absence of diastrophic, metamorphic, and tectonic processes on the Moon's surface. On the other hand, the operation of these processes on the Earth throughout the ages has led to a variety of rocks, so that a terrestrial origin of tektites should imply a correspondingly wide range of composition. On the Moon, only the difference between the rocks of the maria and the highlands should be reflected in the composition of tektites. In this connection, note that a class of presumptive tektites (the americanites, such as Colombia or Peru glass) exists whose composition approaches that of terrestrial igneous rocks; this group might be interpreted as arising from the lunar highlands.

Anders[77] has pointed out that this argument based on the lack of variability of tektite composition may be fallacious. Recent results[93] have confirmed earlier indications[94] that the K–Ar ages of tektites imply the existence of three distinct groups, the North American, Moldavian, and Indo-Chinese–Australian tektites, with ages of 34, 15, and 0.6 Myr, respectively. For an origin in a terrestrial impact, the tektites would represent samples of sedimentary rock drawn at random from three localities on the Earth, although the resulting falls obviously are of wide geographic distribution. In such a case, it would be irrelevant that all tektites from the area of the Pacific show essentially the same chemical composition, since it would be a natural consequence of origin in the same crater. On the other hand, the differences among the three major families of tektites are not inappreciable, since the silica content of tektites from the area of the Pacific is about 70% as contrasted with 80 to 85% for the moldavites and bediasites. Anders[77] feels that this degree of variability is entirely consistent with that for three sedimentary rocks picked at random from the Earth's surface, in opposition to the views of Lowman.[92]

In connection with the foregoing argument, it may be noted that there seems to be a discrepancy between the K–Ar dates and the stratigraphic dating of the australites. The latter date as inferred by Baker[87] is only about 3000 B.C., a conclusion concurred in by Barnes.[95] This figure is in contrast to the measured K–Ar age[93] of 0.6 Myr, determining the time since the last complete degassing. One can note that this figure is of the order of the transit time from the Moon fixed by the mean lifetime against collision, calculated by Öpik[75] to be about 10^6 to 10^7 yr. Thus, if the stratigraphic date is correct, the results are consistent with the formation of a large molten prototektite on the Moon about 0.6 Myr B.P., shielding of its interior from the action of cosmic rays in its transit from the Moon during a period consistent with Öpik's calculation, and production of tektites in its passage through the atmosphere about 3000 B.C.

It has been suggested[94,96] that the strewn field of the moldavites may have been produced by the same impact that formed the Ries crater in Germany. The argument consists in the close similarity of the K–Ar ages of these tektites to those inferred for the glass of impact origin found in the crater. Again, however, a difficulty based on stratigraphy enters, militating against the identification of the moldavites with ejecta from the Rieskessel.[81]

Recently, two fragments of a glassy object resembling a tektite have been found in the Rieskessel under the surface, at a depth of 6 m under the Süsswasserkalk and at the upper boundary of the suevite.[97] The circumstances of the find suggest that the glass might date from the formation of the Ries crater. The fragments are now in the possession of W. Weiskirchner and E. Preuss, but apparently they have not conclusively been identified as tektites. Further, Vand[97] has found twelve glassy objects on the surface in the Rieskessel which resemble tektites. However, some of their characteristics (the index of refraction and the content of CaO) are outside the range for known tektites, and they almost definitely are not moldavites. Thus, the evidence from this source is not conclusive to date.

A very important piece of evidence has been brought out recently by Thorpe et al.[98] They find that the ratio Fe^{3+}/Fe^{2+} of iron in the ferric and ferrous states in the bediasites is constant within relatively narrow limits. Moreover, the mean value of the ratio is only 0.05. This low value implies that the bediasites were derived from precursive materials which were under an atmosphere with a very low partial pressure of oxygen, prior to or at initial melting. Thus, this evidence accords with the demand of the present thesis that the primeval lunar atmosphere was reducing. The results of Thorpe et al. also suggest that the Fe^{3+}/Fe^{2+} ratio is approximately the same for all the tektite families, indicating a uniform reducing atmosphere prior to or at initial melting for the tektites in general.

As Anders[77] points out, the argument based on Fe^{3+}/Fe^{2+} ratios is not incontrovertible. He asserts that it is based tacitly on the assumption that the tektites have remained a closed system since their formation, which is contradicted by the presence of nickel–iron spherules found in philippinites. Moreover, on the assumption that tektites originated in an impact, one should take into account the experimental evidence that considerable chemical fractionation can be caused by shock. Thus, the low K–Ar ages of many tektites imply that argon was quantitatively swept out during either the first or the second period of melting. This assumption must be made in many cases, independently of a lunar or terrestrial origin. The possibility that the argon was swept out raises the possibility of a similar depletion of oxygen. Moreover, there is evidence for partial volatilization of certain elements,[99] such as the alkali metals and germanium. Such processes might be adequate to explain the state of oxidation of the iron, in the opinion of Anders.[77]

Another point important in this connection is the low content of water in tektites, which varies from about 0.02 to 0.0003% by weight.[100] In contrast, fused glass from the site of the first explosion of an atom bomb (the Trinity shot at Alamogordo, New Mexico) shows a higher content (0.03%). These facts could be interpreted as implying that tektites arise in sedimentary rocks low in occluded moisture and water of hydration, which the maria would represent after several billion years of desiccation. Consistently, the amount of occluded gas in tektites is very low (less than 1 ppm by weight).[100] Further, the interiors of the bubbles in them generally,[101] but not invariably,[102] represent good vacua. Note that the geological eras of the strewn fields of the tektites postdate the time of dissipation of the lunar atmosphere and hydrosphere, as computed in an earlier Section.

If the tektites were formed in collisions of meteorites on the mare floors, and if these sites consist of sediments with a slight admixture of carbon, one should expect this element to appear at least as a trace in chemical analyses of tektites. There seems to be no evidence in the literature that carbon has been sought in this connection,[103] in spite of the fact that it is hardly a rare constituent of sedimentary rock. Thus, Taylor[103] concludes that the elemental composition of the australites is consistent with derivation from a mixture of shale and quartz, and organic constituents are common in shales. An effort to detect carbon in tektites should be made, if necessary by use of activation analysis (preferably with He^3 particles).

Moreover, the presence of carbon in the collision sites should be reflected in the composition of any occluded gas in tektites. The heat of the impact would sublime carbon, which would undergo the very fast reaction

$$C + O \rightarrow CO$$

to the highly stable product CO, followed by the slower reaction

$$CO + O \rightarrow CO_2$$

at the high temperatures and pressures in question. The freezing of the partial equilibrium corresponding to these conditions would be reflected in the final relative composition of CO and CO_2. Thus, any occluded gas in tektites should be rich in CO and CO_2. In view of the low content of such gas in tektites, refined methods (such as activation analysis) would be required to detect it and analyze its components. The older literature on the analysis of tektites contains reports of gas contents of the composition suggested here,[79] but the results apparently were affected by contamination.[100]

Although the interiors of tektite bubbles generally represent good vacua, significant amounts of gas have been found in such bubbles by O'Keefe et al.[102] and by Zähringer.[93] The latter studied specimens primarily from the region forming the boundary of the Indo-Chinese and Australian fields, which were rich in bubbles. In the trapped gas, the Ar^{40}/Ar^{36} ratios as well as the $Ar/Kr/Xe$ ratios agree very closely with the atmospheric values, yielding conclusive evidence of its terrestrial origin. Because of the radiogenic origin of Ar^{40}, the Ar^{40}/Ar^{36} ratio should vary from one celestial body to the next and should be highly characteristic of each such body. Thus, one cannot argue that the isotopic ratios permit other than a terrestrial origin of the *gas*.

In one specimen, Zähringer found a gas pressure in the tektite bubbles of 40 mm Hg. As he notes, this pressure occurs in the terrestrial atmosphere at an altitude of 20 km. Further, he points out that the high temperatures present in the tektite melt at the time of bubble formation imply a higher pressure in the gas initially. He concludes that incorporation of the gas in the bubbles must have taken place close to the Earth's surface.

At first blush, Zähringer's results obviously point strongly to a terrestrial origin of tektites. However, this type of tektite, rich in bubbles, is quite rare, found in a restricted geographic locality. Further, the fact that the bubbles are homogeneously distributed throughout the tektite implies that the material of the melt was in turbulent motion through the atmosphere, whether the ultimate origin was lunar or terrestrial. There is no reason to suppose that some of the fine liquid droplets from the ablating surface of a prototektite body might not coalesce in turbulent interaction with the air in their descent, as on the models of Baker and O'Keefe. In any event, models of this type seem necessary to yield the low exposure of the tektites to cosmic rays, on the supposition of a lunar origin. This consideration reinforces the conclusion drawn previously that theories of a lunar origin of tektites which are similar to those of Baker and O'Keefe are the only ones acceptable.

The hypothesis of a lunar origin of tektites is far more vulnerable on another count—that the tektite problem is not solved merely by postulating the presence of sedimentary rocks on the Moon. Not only must the rocks be sedimentary, but they must have undergone major chemical fractionation[104,105] within about the last 100 Myr. This requirement is dictated by the isotopic composition of Sr and Pb in tektites, since the ratios Rb/Sr and U,Th/Pb are high in these bodies. If these elements had coexisted in their present proportions for geologically appreciable periods (more than about 100 Myr), they should contain much more radiogenic Sr^{87}, Pb^{206}, Pb^{207}, and Pb^{208} than they do. The implication seems to be that these ratios were greatly increased rather recently on a geological scale. Mere volatilization seems insufficient. Thus, Pb is more volatile than U or Th, but Rb, the parent element, is more volatile than Sr, the daughter element.

To interpret these anomalies of isotopic abundance, it seems necessary to postulate geochemical processes of differential solubility, that is, processes occurring in the presence of water, as Anders notes.[77] In the light of the model of a lunar hydrosphere exuded from the interior and lasting several billion years, however, the presence of a small concentration of water under the lunar maria is not unreasonable. The eventual and complete loss of the subsurface water to space would depend on a very slow process of diffusion through the overburden, conceivably requiring many billions of years. The water retained in this manner to the present time necessarily must have a very low concentration to accord with the data on the water content of tektites. Otherwise, this type of subsurface zone of water is precisely the same as that postulated by Anders (Ref. 837) in a meteorite parent body as a possible milieu for the synthesis of the organic constituents of carbonaceous chondrites. In such an aqueous medium, diffusion of chemicals preferentially dissolved out of the sediments can be expected, driven by gravitation or thermal gradients. Neither driving force yields a fast rate of diffusion in the necessarily low concentration of water, but one must keep in mind the long span of time available corresponding to the last hundred million years.

In this connection, the limited data on the subsurface temperature of the Moon are pertinent. The surface temperature of the Moon varies from about 100 to −150°C throughout a lunation, as determined by infrared observations.[8] However, this diurnal temperature variation is attenuated with depth. Thus, temperatures at estimated depths of about $\frac{1}{2}$ m below the surface vary from about 30 to −70°C during a lunar day and night, as inferred from microwave observations (the surface is partially transparent to this radiation of sufficiently long wavelength).[106] Sagan (Refs. 280, 282) calculates that the temperature at about 10 m below the surface never rises more than a few degrees above 0°C. At depths somewhat greater, one does not expect the temperature to exceed the estimated figure, until one reaches the level at which the temperature starts to rise toward the center of the Moon, as required by the presence of radioactivity (and gravitational compression) (Ref. 60). This range of temperature would permit the presence of a shallow zone of subsurface moisture below the mare surfaces, in which significant thermal gradients exist throughout a lunation.

O'Keefe[81] also has recognized the importance of the problem raised here and has attempted to resolve it by postulating the presence of continued volcanic activity on the Moon to the present time. However, this hypothesis flies in the face of the lack of visible evidence of obvious vulcanism on the Moon.

In this connection, a very important paper by Chapman and Larson[107] has appeared recently. These authors have applied the analytical tools and experimental methods of the aerodynamics of atmospheric entry to the study of tektites. They show that laboratory experiments on hypervelocity ablation of glass specimens reproduce the surface sculpture, stria distortions, and circumferential flanges found on the australites.

Furthermore, they demonstrate by experiments on ejection of molten glass into an atmosphere that the primary australites were formed by melting in an environment in which the atmospheric density was many orders of magnitude less than that at the Earth's surface, which would rule out a terrestrial origin. Analytical methods have been used to infer the entry trajectories from the amount of ablation, the distortion of the striae, and the spacing between the ring waves on australites. The Moon is the only known celestial body compatible with the computed trajectories. The results of these authors are overwhelming in their completeness and detail.

As Chapman and Larson note, demonstration of a lunar origin for tektites would imply a very significant corollary. Since the specific gravity of tektites (2.3–2.5) is considerably less than that for the Moon's average (3.3), the lunar interior could not be homogeneous, and the crust must be lighter than the core. It follows that some time in its past, the Moon would have had to become a chemically differentiated body, as the result of the sedimentary processes inherent in the present thesis or as a consequence of the process which released volatiles from the Moon's interior to form a hydrosphere and secondary reducing atmosphere. Thus, it would be ineluctable that the selenology of the Moon differ only in degree from the geology of the Earth, and not in kind. As a consequence, the geological doctrine of uniformitarianism would have to be extended from the Earth to the Moon, in a certain sense.

It is clear that the origin of the tektites is a contentious subject. However, many, including the author, believe that the weight of the evidence favors a lunar origin. Perhaps the most apposite remark in this connection has been made by O'Keefe,[81] who asks why 175 yr of a search beginning with Mayer in 1787 have failed to disclose the terrestrial source. To this restricted extent, the nature of the tektites represents a clue that conditions hospitable to life once existed on the Moon.

Effects of Radiation and Meteoritic Infall

When the lunar hydrosphere and atmosphere finally dissipated, the organic remains in the surfaces of the maria necessarily were exposed to the full effect of solar and cosmic radiation, without atmospheric shielding.

Over the course of time, penetration of this radiation to shallow depths would char the organic material to elemental carbon. Disruption, spreading, and mixing of the surface material by the innumerable impacts of small meteorites must have left a thin layer of dust mixed with carbon over the surfaces of the maria. Explorers on the Moon must go to depths providing sufficient shielding to find fossils of the inferred life in which the organic remains are not grossly damaged by radiation.

In order of intensity the significant radiations are the solar ultraviolet, the particles (mainly protons) from the solar wind and flares, the soft X-rays from the Sun, and cosmic rays. In depolymerizing and dissociating organic molecules, ionizing radiation is very much more efficient than nonionizing. Sagan calculates that in the space of a few months to years, essentially all molecular bonds would be broken and complete charring would occur in any organism exposed to the full intensity of the solar wind on the lunar surface (Ref. 282). Thus, the figure presupposes a lunar magnetic field not exceeding 10^{-2} Oe, which otherwise would shield most of the surface from all but the most energetic of the protons. In the contrary case, charring would be induced mainly by solar X-rays, and the process would require some hundred thousand years.

However, the lunar magnetic field does not exceed 6×10^{-4} Oe near the surface, as measured by scientists of the U.S.S.R. by means of a magnetometer in impact of a rocket on the Moon.[108] Thus, the solar wind and the particles from solar flares should readily penetrate to the lunar surface on the side facing the Sun, as emphasized by Neugebauer,[108] although the Russian measurement may be consistent with a somewhat higher actual figure because of confinement of the field within a cavity by the solar wind. It follows that the solar wind and flares should be the dominant factor in charring, and the time period involved is measured in years, at most.

In any event, it is clear that most of the carbon on the surface is necessarily in elemental form. Further, any organic remains initially at depth in the sediments and brought to the surface by a meteoritic impact would rapidly be charred to carbon. Thus, the superficial dark color of the maria has a regenerative capacity in that it cannot be destroyed by meteoritic impacts.

Clearly, the depth at which charring ceases to be significant is fixed by the most penetrating radiation, the cosmic rays, in view of the long span of time available. To estimate this depth, note that the cosmic-ray flux on the Moon is reduced to one tenth the surface value at a depth of about 1 m, and is attenuated to the terrestrial surface value at a depth of a few meters, according to figures given by Sagan (Ref. 282). Further, in determinations of the ages of meteorites corresponding to exposure to cosmic rays in space, a thickness of some meters is usually taken for opacity to the rays (Ref. 836). Thus, one expects a limiting depth of the order of 3 to 5 m in the lunar surface, below which the organic remains in the fossils are essentially undamaged by radiation. These considerations presume a flux of cosmic rays constant throughout past aeons. A closer determination of the limiting depth must depend on a more detailed analysis, which takes into account the actual cross-sections for damage of the different components of the cosmic rays. Because of the presence of different secondary components (such as μ-mesons) varying with extent of absorption of the primaries, the assumption of a mean absorption cross-section for cosmic rays is an approximate one. On the assumption of an exponential decay, the mean free path for absorption is about 150 g/cm^2. Note that even a fairly substantial degree of radiation damage need not destroy the shape of a fossil.

The preceding considerations have neglected the possible effect of meteoritic infall in blanketing the surface of the Moon or possible loss of superficial material from the Moon as a consequence of the numerous meteoritic impacts, over a long span of time. A significant effect of either factor would affect the estimate of the depth at which undamaged fossils could be found. This problem has been discussed by Gilvarry.[109]

To treat this question, attention will be restricted in the first instance to the period of time after the Moon lost its atmosphere. Then, an impinging meteorite suffers no atmospheric deceleration, and the minimum impact velocity on the surface is the Moon's escape velocity[4,5] – 2.4 km/sec. The maximum velocity is the sum of the heliocentric parabolic limit (42.2 km/sec), corresponding to the mean distance from the Sun of the Earth–Moon system, and the orbital velocity (29.7 km/sec) of the Earth–Moon system about the Sun, or about 72 km/sec. This upper limit neglects the small effects of the Moon's gravitational field and its orbital velocity about the Earth. The limits in question are in agreement with the general results of measurements of meteor velocities in the Earth's upper atmosphere by photographic and radio techniques.[110] The distribution function for the velocities between these limits is not known precisely but is bimodal about two maxima.[100] The mean atmospheric velocity of meteorite falls on the Earth has been estimated by Whipple and Hughes[111] as 16.5 (from their own data) and as 21.3 km/sec (from data of Astapovitch).

For the sake of discussion, the one-dimensional model of the impact of a meteorite treated by Gilvarry and Hill[4,5] will be adopted. It is estimated that the lower limit on impact velocity for approximate validity of this treatment may lie between 1 and 10 km/sec. The limit on validity arises from use of an equation of state for the shocked material based on the Thomas–Fermi statistical model of the atom.[112,113,114] In this one-dimensional approach, collision of a meteorite with the lunar surface at an impact velocity V results in two plane shock waves, one racing back into the meteorite to arrest its motion and one running forward into the lunar surface. Between the two shocks, the material velocity V is directed into the lunar surface (independently of the equation of state but on the assumption that the meteorite and impact surface consist of the same material). The model loses validity when the shock in the meteorite reaches the rear surface, from which a rarefaction wave arises.

However, the model is sufficiently reliable to justify the statement that in the explosion resulting from impact of a meteorite with velocity V on the lunar surface, the order of the resulting flow velocities tangent to and directed away from the lunar surface ranges up to V, even in the three-dimensional case. Comparison with the flow fields calculated by Bjork in the two-dimensional case bears out this contention.[115] Thus, impact of a meteorite on the Moon with the lowest possible velocity, the escape value, yields fragments traveling with velocities of the same magnitude into space, and these fragments are derived both from the body of the meteorite and the lunar surface. Moreover, it is known that the volume of an exploding meteorite is far less than the volume of the crater produced.[116] Hence, the conclusion follows that the net effect of meteoritic infall on the Moon is to produce an over-all loss of matter from this body (except perhaps in the case of the lowest possible impact velocities). This deduction is supported by the results of impact experiments carried out by Gault, Shoemaker, and Moore [117] by means of a light-gas gun. They find that the ejection velocities of fragments range up to the same order as the incident velocity, for impact of pellets at speeds up to 10 km/sec. Hence, the layer of dust over the Moon's surface, inferred from infrared and radio observation, arises primarily from the mechanical action of the numerous meteorite impacts over the ages in pulverizing the superficial rocks of the Moon itself and only secondarily as a consequence of direct transfer of meteorite mass.

Note that the argument given does not hold in the presence of an atmosphere, as in the case of the Earth. The presence of the air causes melting, volatilization, and ablation of entering meteoroids, which transfer mass to the atmosphere and eventually to the Earth. As a consequence, only large meteorites moving at high velocity can reach the Earth's surface.[4,5] Subsequent to impact at the surface, atmospheric deceleration prevents the large majority of the fragments from maintaining escape velocity.

The preceding argument fixes the sign involved in the matter of loss or gain of mass by the Moon in meteorite impacts but not the magnitude of the effect. That the mass loss cannot be very large can be shown from an empirical argument. It is known that, on the average, lunar craters satisfy Schröter's Rule, which states that the material in the rim of a crater represents roughly the amount required to fill the volume to the level of the surrounding plain (Ref. 205). In spite of its approximate validity, the existence of this correlation is sufficient to rule out any large loss of lunar mass, proportionately, in a meteorite impact on the Moon. Note that the volume in the rim generally tends to be less than the value required to fill the crater,[39] consistently with the argument presented here.

Independent evidence can be adduced to show that the net effect of meteoritic infall on an atmosphereless Moon cannot correspond to a substantial gain of mass. Consider the ray system of a crater such as Copernicus, Tycho, Aristarchus, or Kepler. These rays seem to be essentially flat, since no shadow cast by them has ever been detected. Thus, only a trifling gain of mass by the Moon from meteoritic infall would be sufficient to obliterate them. The sharp boundary of the dark material in a mare such as Imbrium yields the same conclusion. Any significant rate of deposition of meteoritic material on the Moon after its atmosphere vanished would reduce the maria and highlands to the same color and reflectivity characteristic of the infall. The indications found recently by Hibbs[118] and Whipple[119] of a dustbelt around the Earth, consisting of micrometeoroids not on collision courses but in closed orbits, represents a further argument in this connection. The only reasonable source of this dust is meteoritic impact on the Moon. In this connection, one can note the low counts of interplanetary dust obtained by *Mariner II* far away from the Earth–Moon system.[120]

Gault, Shoemaker, and Moore[117] independently have come to the same conclusion drawn by Gilvarry,[109] that the Moon currently loses mass by virtue of meteoritic impact. Their method was experimental, based on observation of ejecta from craters formed by impact of projectiles fired from a light-gas gun. Dependent on the impact velocity, they estimate that in a meteoritic impact on the Moon, a mass of fragments equivalent to several projectile masses is ejected at velocities in excess of the lunar escape value and is lost to the lunar gravitational field. Using the data of Bjork,[115] Anders[71] estimates from the numerical analysis of the impact at Meteor Crater that a mass about 14 times that of the projectile was ejected at more than the lunar escape value in this event.

The foregoing arguments tending to show no appreciable gain of mass by the Moon from meteoritic impacts imply that the level at which remains of organisms essentially undamaged by radiation could exist is fixed at a depth of roughly 3 to 5 m by the effect of cosmic-ray bombardment. At such a depth and lower, the state of chemical preservation of the remains is fixed by the stability of the constituent compounds relative to the ambient temperature existing since the hydrosphere and atmosphere dissipated. The data on the subsurface temperature of the Moon have been noted already. The surface temperature varies from about 100 to −150°C throughout a lunation,[8] but this diurnal temperature variation is attenuated with depth. Temperatures at estimated depths of about ½ m below the surface vary from about 30 to −70°C during a lunar day and night.[106] However, Sagan (Refs. 280, 282) calculates that the temperature at about 10 m below the surface never rises more than a few degrees above 0°C. If the temperature at this depth below the lunar surface never fluctuated more than mildly above this upper limit since the organic fossils were laid down, they may be chemically intact at the present time, at least to large extent. This conclusion follows because the half-lives with respect to thermal stability approach the order of the age of the Earth for many organic molecules, provided the temperature is restricted to the low values in question (Ref. 114). Note that diastrophic, metamorphic, and tectonic processes, which operate to induce profound changes in fossils in terrestrial rocks over geological periods of time, should be absent on the Moon.

These considerations have a relevance to the discussion of the presence of indigenous organic matter on the Moon by Sagan (Refs. 280, 282). He assumes that complex organic molecules formed in the primordial reducing atmosphere of the Moon and deposited on its surface have been buried throughout the aeons by meteoritic infall to preserve them. Using Whipple's figures for the rate of infall (Ref. 293), he computes a depth of burial of the order of some tens of meters. On the basis of the present discussion, a depth of burial even approaching this value seems highly unlikely, since accretion could have taken place only while the Moon retained its atmosphere, during which time other effects would have operated.

The salient differences between the present conclusions and those of Sagan should be noted. The present theory implies a former biota on the Moon, restricted primarily to the maria. Its traces today should be free carbon distributed superficially and at shallow depth in the maria, with organic remains essentially undamaged by radiation possibly occurring at depths of the order of 3 to 5 m or more below their surfaces. Sagan considers primarily the former presence of complex organic molecules on the Moon, now buried under debris from meteoritic infall. Specifically, he asserts that these vestiges of the former pristine atmosphere should be found only in the highlands, since he apparently subscribes to the lava hypothesis.

POSSIBLE ROLE OF METEORITES IN BIOPOESIS

The sources of free energy suggested as the primary agents in biopoesis are ultraviolet radiation from the Sun, lightning and coronal discharges in the atmosphere, cosmic rays, radioactivity in the superficial crust of the Earth, and volcanic activity (Ref. 1285). This listing is in order of total free energy available at the Earth's surface. By far the greatest source of free energy is ultraviolet radiation, but laboratory experiments to synthesize complex compounds by this agent have been consistently less successful than by means of electric discharges (Ref. 1285). Thus, it is obvious that the correct figure of merit in this connection is not the free energy alone but the product of the free energy by a biopoetic efficiency. Unfortunately, the latter factor is difficult to evaluate. Obviously, a salient element affecting it is the height of deposition of compounds in the atmosphere, since low height favors the necessary transit to the oceans.

An argument against the effectiveness of ultraviolet radiation as a dominant agent in biopoesis has been given by Pringle (Ref. 1169). He notes that molecules which could be synthesized by the ultraviolet rays often absorb at longer wavelengths than their precursors. Since more energy is available at longer wavelengths, one might expect the molecules to be destroyed faster than they are synthesized, to yield a vanishing net rate of production. It is obvious that the conclusion can be avoided if a molecule, after its formation, can be transported rapidly to a lower depth in the atmosphere, where the photolytic ultraviolet is sufficiently attenuated. In this connection, Sagan has presented computations indicating that gravitational diffusion is a sufficiently rapid mechanism for this purpose (Ref. 282). However, the computations neglect convection and advection. In view of this fact, it is not obvious that diffusion is a mechanism capable of transporting the molecules with sufficient rapidity through the convective homosphere (the mesosphere, stratosphere, and troposphere) to solution in the primitive seas where life first formed. One can note the long time (of the order of years) required for the dust from the explosion of Krakatoa eventually to settle.

Of the agents mentioned, none tend to deposit organic compounds directly in the seas. Thus, for ultraviolet light, lightning discharges, and cosmic rays, the deposition is relatively high in the atmosphere. Advection, convection, and diffusion must be invoked as the mechanisms depositing the reaction products in the hydrosphere. Similarly, superficial radioactivity should be operative mainly on land, and fluvial transport must be invoked for the products to reach the oceans. In the case of volcanoes, only those on the ocean floor with their summits above the water could be biopoetically efficient. For these reasons, Gilvarry and Hochstim suggested meteoritic infall as a physical process capable of yielding organic compounds of high complexity in the primitive atmosphere and providing a relatively high efficiency of transfer to the hydrosphere.[121]

When a large meteoroid enters the atmosphere, its minimum speed (11.3 and 2.4 km/sec for the Earth and Moon, respectively)[4,5] corresponds to hypersonic conditions, and a detached shockwave forms ahead which accompanies it in flight. The temperatures behind the shock are greatest in the stagnation region and fall off gradually with distance behind the meteoroid and away from the roughly hyperboloidal envelope of the shock. Computations have been carried out by Hochstim[122] for the concentrations of atomic, molecular, and free-radical species at various points behind such a shock front in a standard atmosphere. The calculated concentrations presume local thermodynamic and chemical equilibrium. As such, they cannot yield final concentrations of neutral species after passage of the shock, since these depend on the various rates of reaction involved (which are generally not well known).

Direct computations for an ambient reducing atmosphere have not been made. However, the results for normal air are very suggestive. So long as the velocity of a body impinging on the top of the terrestrial atmosphere exceeds about 7 km/sec, the corresponding stagnation temperature at equilibrium behind the shock varies from 5000 to 10,000°K for altitudes ranging from 100 km to sea level, respectively. These temperatures are sufficient to yield dissociation, essentially complete for oxygen and partial for nitrogen, with some ionization of the products to O^+ and N^+. For higher velocities, double ionization and other processes occur. The equilibrium concentration of a particular species (not present in the ambient atmosphere) rises with the distance behind the meteoroid and then falls off.

Qualitative extrapolation of these results to a reducing atmosphere containing hydrogen, methane, ammonia, and water is easily made. Passage of a hypersonic meteoroid should yield a wake containing the monatomic species H, C, N, and O, the diatomic species CH, CN, CO, NH, OH, and NO (charged and uncharged in these cases), triatomic species, electrons, etc. As the temperature downstream of the meteoroid drops, the original ambient composition will be approached asymptotically, possibly with a small amount of complex compounds residual in the wake, as permitted by the kinetics of the situation.

However, the process of reversion to the original composition can be arrested, at least partially, if the meteoroid (and its initial velocity) is sufficiently large for it to survive passage through the atmosphere and to impinge explosively in the sea. In this case, the phenomena occurring should be similar to those in the near-surface explosion of a nuclear bomb in water,[4,5] as in the Baker series of tests by the Atomic Energy Commission at the atoll of Bikini.[35] A hollow column of water and spray should shoot up into the atmosphere. Afterward, a dome-shaped cloud of droplets of water (the condensation cloud) should form, and finally, the characteristic mushroom-shaped cloud above the water should appear. Thus, hot water mixed with steam will engulf the hot descending remnants of the wake, preventing reversion to the original composition of the ambient atmosphere and providing the possibility of further reactions in a gaseous and aqueous medium to form complex compounds. The fallout of the water from these clouds should provide an efficient mechanism for direct transfer of complex organic compounds to solution in the hydrosphere. For infall on the primitive atmosphere of meteorites able to reach the terrestrial surface, the process should be operative in at least two-thirds of the cases, since this fraction represents the present ratio of sea to total surface of the Earth.

Anders[77] has pointed out a further possibility. The free radicals will be present in the wake in low concentration relative to the neutral molecules. Hence, they are likely to react with neutral species, possibly in several consecutive steps, leading to the formation of molecules of higher molecular weight than the initial ones. These compounds will be deposited in the water on impact of the meteorite in the ocean.

It might be argued that the complexity of the compounds involved in the origin of life would imply a concentration, after passage of the shock, so low that it would be unimportant in biopoesis. However, consider a meteorite with a diameter of 1 km impinging on the Earth. Viewing the wake in the atmosphere as cylindrical with a diameter at least equal to that of the meteoroid, one computes that a minimum of 10^{10} kg of air would have passed through the wake in the shock. From results for normal air,[122] the yields of NO, O, CO_2, CO, NO_2, and N_2O in the wake, where the temperature is 2000°K, correspond to approximate molar fractions 10^{-2}, 10^{-3}, 10^{-4}, 10^{-5}, 10^{-6}, and 10^{-8}, respectively; hence, passage of the meteoroid creates at least 10^8 kg of NO, 10^7 kg of O, 10^6 kg of CO_2, 10^5 kg of CO, 10^4 kg of NO_2, and 10^2 kg of N_2O in the atmosphere at this temperature. These numbers hold only for air in equilibrium but suggest strongly that formation of complex compounds by reactions following passage of the shock may be quantitatively significant. Note that the meteorite diameter selected corresponds closely to that of the minor planet (1556) Icarus. which would have an atmospheric velocity of 32 km/sec if it encountered the Earth.[111]

A direct experimental check on the production of organic compounds in this manner has been undertaken by Dr. W. J. Hooker[123] of this Laboratory, in collaboration with Dr. C. A. Ponnamperuma[124] of Ames Research Center. Hooker has fired hypersonic projectiles into a tank of water, through a reducing atmosphere of composition equivalent to that used by Miller (Ref. 1280). Preliminary analysis of the samples has indicated the presence of materials absorbing ultraviolet light of wavelength 260 mμ and appearing to have chromatographic characteristics similar to some of the known biological purines. There are indications of amino acids, also. It must be emphasized that these findings represent merely preliminary results, which require confirmation.

Using the figures of Brown[125,126] for the rate of fall of meteoritic mass on the Earth and taking 20 km/sec as a mean impact velocity, one computes the free energy available from this source as about 10^{-5} cal/cm^2 yr on the Earth *at the present time*. This figure is far lower than the free energy, about 4 cal/cm^2 yr, available from electric discharges (Ref. 1285). However, the comparison can be misleading, since it neglects the effect of the difference between the biopoetic efficiency of meteoritic falls in the ocean and electric discharges in the atmosphere, which might be significant. A further point that should be kept in mind is the much higher intensity of the rain of meteorites on the primitive Moon and Earth that must be inferred from their genesis in accretion of planetesimals.

In view of the uncertainties, it is entirely possible that a primary agent in biopoesis on the Earth and Moon was meteoritic infall. If this is true, it would go far to justify Sagan's estimate of a very short interval of time after the Earth's formation for biopoesis to occur.

CONCLUSIONS

This review has brought out the fact that essentially all the features of the lunar surface which the lava hypothesis purports to explain can be understood on the basis of the former presence of a hydrosphere and atmosphere, with essentially complete internal consistency. Moreover, the present theory goes far beyond the lava hypothesis in that it predicts a dimensional correlation for craters and maria, which is found to exist in fact. Not only does the lava hypothesis have no predictive capability but its postulates must be strained to explain many obvious features of the lunar surface, such as the existence of ghost craters and the low frequency of craters in the mare floors.

If the hypothesis of a former hydrosphere and reducing atmosphere for an extended time is true, one is almost forced into the position of assuming a pristine lunar life, since one is postulating the conditions which must have held at the inception of terrestrial life. Under these circumstances, life has a certain inevitability. No other mechanism seems capable of selectively darkening the mare surfaces. As has been discussed, some positive clues exist for this possibility. However, the case remains circumstantial. If future lunar explorers do not find signs of a pristine life on the Moon, it follows that at least one link in the chain of argument of the Section on Pristine Life on the Moon is invalid. Such a negative finding would almost imply that the Moon is a body captured by the Earth, since the reasoning leans heavily on the assumption that the Moon and Earth were formed at essentially the same distance from the Sun, at approximately the same time, and under roughly the same conditions.

Both in the past and currently, speculation on the possibility of life outside of the Earth has been centered on Mars and Venus, the Earth's nearest planetary neighbors[127] (Ref. 692). The basis of such discussion has been, of course, the feeling among investigators that life can hardly be peculiar to one particular planet of one lone star in a solitary galaxy. However, sight seems to have been lost, or at least little notice seems to have been taken, of the fact that preeminent grounds exist for suspecting the Moon as a former abode of life — it lies at the same mean distance from a star as the only other astronomical body known to support life. In some measure, the present discussion should serve to redress this imbalance of thinking in the field of exobiology.

In conclusion, it should be emphasized that the deductions drawn here are speculative. However, they do not represent idle speculation and should be subject to observational confirmation in the relatively near future. If these ideas are correct, one photograph of the lunar highlands at short range from a space vehicle should reveal the presence of the characteristic drainage patterns (dendritic or otherwise) associated with rivers. The elemental composition of the rock of a mare floor could be determined remotely in an unmanned lunar station by an analysis of neutron or He^3 activation and relayed to the Earth by telemetry. If the views stated here are correct, the distribution of elements should be characteristic of sedimentary rock and should show the presence of carbon. A hand specimen of rock from the floor of a mare would settle many questions if it could be obtained successfully on the Earth. Finally, a trained geologist landed on the Moon, with locomotive or ambulatory equipment available, should have little difficulty in detecting visually signs of the former presence of water and life if they actually exist.

With specimens of rock from the lunar surface available for analysis on the Earth, it should be possible to separate and identify samples of coesite and stishovite, the allomorphs of quartz, at high pressure. In this manner, the moot question of whether the maria and craters of the Moon are in fact of impact origin can be settled beyond the shadow of a doubt, after more than a century of controversy. Further evidence of the origin of the maria and craters in processes of explosive violence should be found in the form of shatter cones in the pits. In view of the fact that meteorites containing graphite yield diamonds on impact, as observed in Barringer Crater in Arizona, such gems should be found in the surfaces of the maria, on the present thesis that these features owe their superficial dark color to organic carbon.

The attainment of goals such as those mentioned is, of course, an issue in a current technological race between two great powers, the United States of America and the Union of Socialist Soviet Republics.

ACKNOWLEDGMENTS

The preparation of this review has entailed help from a number of the author's colleagues, particularly Drs. D. H. Sowle, R. W. Lowen, A. L. Berlad, and F. G. Casal. Discussions with Drs. M. H. Briggs and G. Mamikunian of the Jet Propulsion Laboratory, Professor E. S. Barghoorn of Harvard University, and Professor G. P. Kuiper of the University of Arizona are acknowledged. The author thanks Drs. W. J. Hooker and C. A. Ponnamperuma for the privilege of mentioning results prior to publication. Thanks are due Dr. F. G. Casal for reading and discussing the manuscript. Finally, special gratitude is owed Professor E. Anders of the University of Chicago, for his careful study and incisive criticism of the manuscript. These colleagues bear no responsibility for any views expressed here.

REFERENCES

1. GILBERT, G. K.,The Moon's Face; A Study of the Origin of Its Features, *Philosophical Society of Washington, Bulletin,* Washington, D.C., vol. 12 (1893), pp. 241–92.
2. GIFFORD, A. C., Mountains of the Moon, *The New Zealand Journal of Science and Technology,* vol. 7, No. 3 (1924), pp. 129–42.
3. GIFFORD, A. C., Origin of the Surface Features of the Moon, *The New Zealand Journal of Science and Technology,* vol. 11, No. 2 (1930), pp. 319–27.
4. GILVARRY, J. J., and HILL, J. E., The Impact Theory of the Origin of Lunar Craters, *Publications of the Astronomical Society of the Pacific,* vol. 68 (1956), pp. 223–9.
5. GILVARRY, J. J., and HILL, J. E., The Impact of Large Meteorites, *The Astrophysical Journal,* vol. 124 (1956), pp. 610–22.
6. KUIPER, G. P., On the Origin of the Lunar Surface Features, *Proceedings of the National Academy of Sciences of the United States of America,* vol. 40 (1954), pp. 1096–112.
7. GILVARRY, J. J., Nature of the Lunar Surface, *Nature,* vol. 180 (1957), pp. 911–5.
8. GILVARRY, J. J., The Nature of the Lunar Maria, *The Astrophysical Journal,* vol. 127 (1958), pp. 751–62.
9. PETTIT, E., Radiation Measurements on the Eclipsed Moon, *The Astrophysical Journal,* vol. 91 (1940), pp. 408–20.
10. JEANS, J. H., *The Dynamical Theory of Gases,* third edition, Cambridge: Cambridge University Press (1921), p. 342.
11. GILVARRY, J. J., The Origin of Ocean Basins and Continents, *Nature,* vol. 190 (1961), pp. 1048–53.
12. DIETZ, R. S., Point d'impact des astéroides comme origine des bassins océaniques: une hypothèse, *Colloques Internationaux du Centre National de la Recherche, Nice, France, Mai 5–12, 1958,* LXXXIII (1959), pp. 265–75.
13. HARRISON, E. R., Origin of the Pacific Basin: A Meteorite Impact Hypothesis, *Nature,* vol. 188 (1960), pp. 1064–7.
14. GILVARRY, J. J., The Possibility of a Pristine Lunar Life, *Journal of Theoretical Biology,* vol. 6 (1946), pp. 325–46.
15. BROWN, H., Rare Gases and the Formation of the Earth's Atmosphere, *Atmospheres of the Earth and Planets,* ed. by G. P. KUIPER, second edition, Chicago: University of Chicago Press (1952), pp. 258–66.

16. SUESS, H. E., Die Häufigkeit der Edelgase auf der Erde und im Kosmos, *The Journal of Geology*, vol. 57 (1949), pp. 600–7.

17. RUBEY, W. W., Development of the Hydrosphere and Atmosphere, *Crust of the Earth*, ed. by A. POLDERVAART, New York: Geological Society of America (1955), pp. 631–50.

18. GILVARRY, J. J., Escape of Planetary Atmospheres, I. Escape Layer, *The Physics of Fluids*, vol. 4 (1961), pp. 2–7.

19. GILVARRY, J. J., Escape of Planetary Atmospheres, II. Lifetimes of Minor Constituents, *The Physics of Fluids*, vol. 4 (1961), pp. 8–12.

20. SPITZER, L., The Terrestrial Atmosphere Above 300 km. *The Atmospheres of the Earth and Planets*, ed. by G. P. KUIPER, second edition, Chicago: University of Chicago Press (1952), pp. 211–47.

21. GILVARRY, J. J., Physical Parameters of the Atmospheric Escape Layer, *Nature*, vol. 188 (1960), pp. 804–5.

22. BREWER, A. W., Evidence for a World Circulation Provided by the Measurements of Helium and Water Vapour Distribution in the Stratosphere, *Journal of the Royal Meteorological Society*, vol. 75 (1949), pp. 351–63.

23. SVERDRUP, H. U., Oceanography, *Handbuch der Physik*, ed. by S. FLÜGGE, vol. 48, Berlin: Springer-Verlag (1957), pp. 608–70.

24. *The Other Side of the Moon*, tr. by J. B. SYKES, London: Pergamon Press, Ltd. (1960).

25. WATSON, K., MURRAY, B. C., and BROWN, H., The Behavior of Volatiles on the Lunar Surface, *Journal of Geophysical Research*, vol. 66 (1961), pp. 3033–45.

26. DARLING, T. A., Isthmian Canal Study Memoranda 283-P, 284-P, 286-P, 287-P, Department of Operation and Maintenance, Panama Canal, Canal Zone, 1948.

27. VORTMAN, L. J., *Relative Cratering Efficiency of Nuclear Explosives*, Report SCTM 114-59(51), Sandia Corporation, Albuquerque, New Mexico (Available from U.S. Dept. of Commerce, Office of Technical Services, Washington, D.C.), April 1959.

28. BEALS, C. S., FERGUSON, G. M., and LANDAU, A., II. Search for Analogies Between Lunar and Terrestrial Topography on Photographs of the Canadian Shield, Part I, *The Journal of the Royal Astronomical Society of Canada*, vol. 50 (1956), pp. 203–11.

29. MILLMAN, P. M., A Profile Study of the New Quebec Crater, *Publications of the Dominion Astrophysical Observatory*, Victoria, B.C., vol. 18 (1955), pp. 61–82.

30. BEALS, C. S., A Probable Meteorite Crater of Great Age, *Sky and Telescope*, vol. 16 (1957), pp. 526–8.

31. KRAUS, E., MEYER, R., and WEGENER, A., Untersuchungen über den Krater von Sall auf Ösel, *Gerlands Beitraege zur Geophysik*, vol. 20 (1928), pp. 312–78.

32. NININGER, H. H., Another Meteorite Crater Studied, *Science*, vol. 130 (1959), pp. 1251–2.

33. JANSSEN, C. L., Meteor Craters in Hérault, France, *The Journal of the Royal Astronomical Society of Canada*, vol. 45 (1951), pp. 190–8.

34. MEEN, V. B., Merewether Crater–A Possible Meteor Crater, *Proceedings of the Geological Association of Canada*, vol. 9 (1951), pp. 49–67.

35. *The Effects of Nuclear Weapons*, ed. by S. GLASSTONE, Washington, D.C.: U.S. Atomic Energy Commission (1957), pp. 41–226.

36. SCHMIDT, J. F. J., *Charte der Gebirge des Mondes*, Berlin: Dietrich Reimer (1878); *Kurze Erläuterung zu J. Schmidts Mondcharte*, Berlin: Dietrich Reimer (1878).

37. SPENCER, L. J., Meteorite Craters as Topographical Features on the Earth's Surface, *Geographical Journal*, vol. 81 (1933), pp. 227–48.

38. GILVARRY, J. J., Dimensional Correlation of Lunar Maria and Terrestrial Ocean Basins, *Nature*, vol. 1961 (1962), pp. 975–6.

39. BALDWIN, R. B., *The Measure of the Moon*, Chicago: University of Chicago Press (1963), pp. 148, 309, 317, 322, 331, 338.

40. ÖPIK, E. J., The Lunar Surface as an Impact Counter, *Monthly Notices of the Royal Astronomical Society*, vol. 120 (1960), pp. 404–11.

41. KREITER, T. J., Dating Lunar Surface Features by Using Crater Frequencies, *Publications of the Astronomical Society of the Pacific*, vol. 72 (1960), pp. 393–8.

42. SHOEMAKER, E. M., HACKMAN, R. J., and EGGLETON, R. E., Interplanetary Correla-

tion of Geologic Time *Advances in the Astronautical Sciences*, vol. 8, New York: Plenum Press (1963), pp. 70–89.
43. McGILLEM, C. D., and MILLER, B. P., Lunar Surface Roughness from Crater Statistics, *Journal of Geophysical Research*, vol. 67 (1962), pp. 4787–94.
44. UREY, H. C., Origin of the Moon's Surface Features, Part I; Origin of the Moon's Surface Features, Part II, *Sky and Telescope*, vol. 15 (1956), pp. 108–11; 161–3.
45. UREY, H. C., The Duration of Intense Bombardment Processes on the Moon, *The Astrophysical Journal*, vol. 132 (1960), pp. 502–3.
46. VAILE, R. B., Pacific Craters and Scaling Laws, *Journal of Geophysical Research*, vol. 66 (1961), pp. 3413–38.
47. KUIPER, G. P., The Moon, *Journal of Geophysical Research*, vol. 64 (1959), pp. 1713–19.
48. GILVARRY, J. J., Unpublished data.
49. ALLEN, W. A., RINEHART, J. S., and WHITE, W. C., Phenomena Associated with the Flight of Ultra-Speed Pellets. Part I, Ballistics, *Journal of Applied Physics*, vol. 23 (1952), pp. 132–7.
50. BALDWIN, R. B, A Lunar Contour Map, *Sky and Telescope*, vol. 21 (1961), pp. 84–85.
51. *Sky and Telescope*, vol. 25 (1963), pp. 20, 32–3.
52. PETTIJOHN, F. J., *Sedimentary Rocks*, New York: Harper and Brothers (1949), p. 175.
53. PATNODE, H. W., Relation of Organic Matter to Color of Sedimentary Rocks, *Bulletin of the American Association of Petroleum Geologists*, vol. 25 (1941), pp. 1921–33.
54. BROWN, H., A Table of Relative Abundances of Nuclear Species, *Reviews of Modern Physics*, vol. 21 (1949), pp. 625–34.
55. MÖLLER, F., Strahlung in der unteren Atmosphäre, *Handbuch der Physik*, vol. 48, ed. by S. FLÜGGE, Berlin: Springer-Verlag (1957), pp. 155–253.
56. DARWIN, G. H., *The Tides*, Boston: Houghton Mifflin Co. (1898).
57. HOLMES, A., The Oldest Dated Minerals of the Rhodesian Shield, *Nature*, vol. 173 (1954), pp. 612–14.
58. TYLER, S. A, and BARGHOORN, E S., Occurrence of Structurally Preserved Plants in the Pre-Cambrian Rocks of the Canadian Shield, *Science* vol. 119 (1954), pp. 606–8.
59. KOZYREV, N. A., Vulkanicheskaia deiatel'nost' na Lune, *Priroda*, vol. 3 (1959), pp. 84–7.
60. UREY, H. C., On Possible Parent Substances for the C_2 Molecules Observed in the Alphonsus Crater, *The Astrophysical Journal*, vol. 134 (1961), pp. 268–9.
61. KUIPER, G. P., The Exploration of the Moon, *Vistas in Astronautics*, vol. II, ed. by M. ALPERIN and H. F. GREGORY, New York: Pergamon Press, Inc. (1959), pp. 273–313.
62. CALDER, N., What Will Man Find on the Moon? *New Scientist*, vol. 8 (1960), pp. 1636–8.
63. BRIGGS, M. H., Recent Advances in the Investigation of Meteorites, *Science Progress*, vol. 50 (1962), pp. 376–87.
64. UREY, H. C., Primary and Secondary Objects, *Journal of Geophysical Research*, vol. 64 (1959), pp. 1721–37.
65. FISHER, D. E., Origin of Stone and Iron Meteorites, *Nature*, vol. 190 (1961), pp. 244–5.
66. GOLES, G. G., FISH, R. A., and ANDERS, E., The Record in the Meteorites—I. The Former Environment of Stone Meteorites as Deduced from K^{40}–Ar^{40} Ages, *Geochimica et Cosmochimica Acta*, vol. 19 (1960), pp. 177–95.
67. CEPLECHA, Z., RAJCHL, J., and SEHNAL, L., New Czechoslovak Meteorite 'Luhy', *Ceskoslovenska Akademie ved. Prague, Astronomicky Ustav*, vol. 10 (1959), pp. 147–8.
68. LOVERING, J. F., A Typical Parent Meteorite Body, *Geochimica et Cosmochimica Acta*, vol. 14 (1958), pp. 174–7.
69. BAUER, C. A., New Measurements of the Helium-3 and Helium-4 Contents of Meteorites, *The Astronomical Journal*, vol. 65 (1960), pp. 340–1.
70. STOENNER, R. W., SCHAEFFER, O. A., and DAVIS, R., Meteorites as Space Probes for Testing the Spatial Constancy of Cosmic Radiation, *Journal of Geophysical Research*, vol. 65 (1960), pp. 3025–34.

71. ANDERS, E., Two Meteorites of Unusually Short Cosmic-Ray Exposure Age, *Science*, vol. 138 (1962), pp. 431–3.
72. FIREMAN, E. L., Private communication from E. Anders.
73. SAGAN, C., Organic Matter and Life in Meteorites, *Proceedings of Lunar and Planetary Exploration Colloquium*, vol. 2, No. 4, Aerospace Laboratories. North American Aviation, Inc., Downey, California (1961), pp. 49–54.
74. GILVARRY, J. J., Relativity Advances of the Periphelia of Minor Planets, *Publications of the Astronomical Society of the Pacific*, vol. 65 (1953), pp. 173–8.
75. ÖPIK, E. J., Collision Probabilities With the Planets and the Distribution of Interplanetary Matter, *Proceedings of the Royal Irish Academy*, vol. 54A (1951), pp. 165–99.
76. ARNOLD, J. R., The Origin of Meteorites as Small Bodies, *Isotopic and Cosmic Chemistry*, ed. by H. CRAIG, S. MILLER, and G. J. WASSERBURG, Amsterdam: North-Holland Publishing Co. (1964), pp. 347–64.
77. ANDERS, E., Private communication.
78. BARGHOORN, E. S., Private communication.
79. BARNES, V. E., *North American Tektites*, Publication 3945, University of Texas, Austin, Texas, 1940, pp. 477–582.
80. BARNES, V. E., Properties of Tektites Pertinent to Their Origin, *Geochimica et Cosmochimica Acta*, vol. 14 (1958), pp. 267–78.
81. O'KEEFE, J. A., The Origin of Tektites, *Tektites*, ed. by J. A. O'KEEFE, Chicago: University of Chicago Press (1963), pp. 167–88.
82. SPENCER, L. J., Origin of Tektites, *Nature*, vol. 131 (1933), pp. 117–18.
83. UREY, H. C., Origin of Tektites, *Nature*, vol. 179 (1957), pp. 556–7.
84. UREY, H. C., On the Origin of Tektites, *Proceedings of the National Academy of Sciences of the United States of America*, vol. 41 (1955), pp. 27–31.
85. NININGER, H. H., *Chips From the Moon*, El Centro, California: Desert Press (1947).
86. VARSAVSKY, C. M., Dynamical Limits on a Lunar Origin for Tektites, *Geochimica et Cosmochimica Acta*, vol. 14 (1958), pp. 291–303.
87. BAKER, G., Origin of Tektites, *Nature*, vol. 185 (1960), pp. 291–4.
88. CHAPMAN, D. R., Recent Re-Entry Research and the Cosmic Origin of Tektites, *Nature*, vol. 188 (1960), pp. 353–5.
89. O'KEEFE, J. A., Origin of Tektites. *Science*, vol. 130 (1959), pp. 97–8.
90. O'KEEFE, J. A., Tektites as Natural Earth Satellites, *Science*, vol. 133 (1961), pp. 562–6.
91. VISTE, E., and ANDERS, E., Cosmic-Ray Exposure History of Tektites, *Journal of Geophysical Research*, vol. 67 (1962), pp. 2913–19.
92. LOWMAN, P. D., Tektites vs. Terrestrial Rocks: A Comparison of Variance in Compositions, *Geochimica et Cosmochimica Acta*, vol. 26 (1962), pp. 561–79.
93. ZÄHRINGER, J., K–Ar Measurements of Tektites, *Radioactive Dating*, Vienna: International Atomic Energy (1963), pp. 289–305.
94. GENTNER, W., LIPPOLT, H. J., and SCHAEFFER, O. A., Das Kalium-Argon-Alter einer Glasprobe vom Nördlinger Ries, *Zeitschrift für Naturforschung*, vol. 16a (1961), p. 1240.
95. BARNES, V. E., Tektites, *Scientific American*, vol. 205, No. 5 (1961), pp. 58–65.
96. GENTNER, W., LIPPOLT, H. J., and SCHAEFFER, O. A., Argonbestimmungen an Kaliummineralien—XI. Die Kalium-Argon-Alter der Gläser des Nördlinger Rieses und der böhmisch–mährischen Tektite, *Geochimica et Cosmochimica Acta*, vol. 27, No. 2 (1963), pp. 191–200.
97. VAND, V., Private communication.
98. THORPE, A. N., SENFTLE, F. E., and CUTTITTA, F., Magnetic and Chemical Investigations of Iron in Tektites, *Nature*, vol. 197 (1963), pp. 836–40.
99. GREENLAND, L., and LOVERING, J. F., The Evolution of Tektites: Elemental Volatilization in Tektites, *Geochimica et Cosmochimica Acta*, vol. 27, No. 3 (1963), pp. 249–59.
100. FRIEDMAN, I., The Water, Deuterium, Gas and Uranium Content of Tektites, *Geo-*

chimica et Cosmochimica Acta, vol. 14 (1958), pp. 316–22.

101. SUESS, H. E., Gas Content and Age of Tektites, *Geochimica et Cosmochimica Acta*, vol. 2 (1951). pp. 76–9.

102. O'KEEFE, J. A., LOWMAN, P. D., and DUNNING, K. L., Gases in Tektite Bubbles, *Science*, vol. 137 (1962), p. 228.

103. TAYLOR, S. R., The Chemical Composition of Australites, *Geochimica et Cosmochimica Acta*, vol. 26 (1962), pp. 685–722.

104. PINSON, W. H., and SCHNETZLER, C. C., Rb–Sr Correlation Studies of Tektites, *Journal of Geophysical Research*, vol. 66 (1961), p. 2553.

105. TILTON, G. R., Isotopic Composition of Lead From Tektites, *Geochimica et Cosmochimica Acta*, vol. 14 (1958), pp. 323–30.

106. PIDDINGTON, J. H., and MINNETT, H. C., Microwave Thermal Radiation From the Moon, *Australian Journal of Scientific Research*, Series A, vol. 2 (1949), pp. 63–77.

107. CHAPMAN, D. R., and LARSON, H. K., On the Lunar Origin of Tektites, *Journal of Geophysical Research*, vol. 68 (1963), pp. 4305–58.

108. NEUGEBAUER, M., Question of the Existence of a Lunar Magnetic Field, *Physical Review Letters*, vol. 4, No. 1 (1960), pp. 6–8.

109. GILVARRY, J. J., Effects of Loss of Lunar Mass by Meteoritic Impact, *Icarus*, vol. 3 (1964), pp. 121–9.

110. LOVELL, A. C. B., *Meteor Astronomy*, Oxford: Clarendon Press (1954), Chapters 11, 12.

111. WHIPPLE, F. L., and HUGHES, R. F., On the Velocities and Orbits of Meteors, Fireballs and Meteorites, *Meteors*, èd. by T. R. KAISER, London: Pergamon Press, Ltd. (1955), pp. 149–56.

112. GILVARRY, J. J., Thermodynamics of the Thomas–Fermi Atom at Low Temperatures, *The Physical Review*, vol. 96 (1954), pp. 934–43.

113. GILVARRY, J. J., Solution of the Temperature- Perturbed Thomas–Fermi Equation, *The Physical Review*, vol. 96 (1954), pp. 934–43.

114. GILVARRY, J. J., and PEEBLES, G. H., Solutions of the Temperature-Perturbed Thomas-Fermi Equation, *The Physical Review*, vol. 99 (1955), pp. 550–2.

115. BJORK, R. L., Analysis of the Formation of Meteor Crater, Arizona: A Preliminary Report, *Journal of Geophysical Research*, vol. 66 (1961), pp. 3379–87.

116. HILL, J. E., and GILVARRY, J. J., Application of the Baldwin Crater Relation to the Scaling of Explosion Craters, *Journal of Geophysical Research*, vol. 61 (1956), pp. 501–11.

117. GAULT, D. E., SHOEMAKER, E. M., and MOORE, H. J., *Spray Ejected From the Lunar Surface by Meteoroid Impact*, Technical Note D-1767, National Aeronautics and Space Administration, Washington, D.C., April 1963.

118. HIBBS, A. R., The Distribution of Micrometeorites Near the Earth, *Journal of Geophysical Research*, vol. 66 (1961), pp. 371–7.

119. WHIPPLE, F. L., The Dust Cloud About the Earth, *Nature*, vol. 189 (1961), pp. 127–8.

120. ALEXANDER, W. M., Cosmic Dust, *Science*, vol. 138 (1962), pp. 1098–9.

121. GILVARRY, J. J., and HOCHSTIM, A. R., Possible Role of Meteorities in the Origin of Life, *Nature*, vol. 197 (1963), pp. 624–5 (Note added in proof, p. 626.)

122. HOCHSTIM, A. R., *Equilibrium Compositions, Thermodynamic and Normal Shock Properties of Air with Additives*, Report ZPh-122, General Dynamics/Convair, San Diego, California, December 1, 1961.

123. HOOKER, W. J., Private communication.

124. PONNAMPERUMA, C. A., Private communication.

125. BROWN, H., The Density and Mass Distribution of Meteoritic Bodies in the neighborhood of the Earth's Orbit, *Journal of Geophysical Research*, vol. 65 (1960), pp. 1679–83.

126. BROWN, H., *Addendum:* The Density and Mass Distribution of Meteoritic Bodies in the Neighborhood of the Earth's Orbit, *Journal of Geophysical Research*, vol. 66 (1961), pp. 1316–17.

127. OVENDEN, M. W., *Life in the Universe*, Garden City, New York: Doubleday and Co., Inc. (1962).

CHAPTER VI

POSSIBILITIES OF LIFE ON MARS

F. JACKSON* AND P. MOORE†

INTRODUCTION

THE planet Mars has for a long time received a great deal of attention, largely because in important respects it is more "Earthlike" than the other planets of the solar system. Until recently, it seemed possible that Venus was more likely to harbor life of a relatively high order, but the results obtained from the probe *Mariner II* indicated that Venus is much too hot to support organisms of the type we know on Earth. If this conclusion is confirmed, Mars is perhaps the only planet in the solar system left for biological explorations; if it, too, should prove to be sterile, further developments in exobiology are unlikely without recourse to the exploration of other planetary systems, and this will not become practicable in the foreseeable future, if at all.

PRELIMINARY CONSIDERATIONS

It is probably fair to say that, at the present time, there is a considerable amount of evidence in favor of the view that organisms of some sort are present on Mars; this evidence has been reviewed in numerous publications, but it is certainly not conclusive. Life as we know it depends on the availability of water, among other things, and it is only recently that the presence of water vapor in the Martian atmosphere has been conclusively demonstrated. At the time of writing, no official report of the detection of water vapor, achieved by infrared spectroscopy in the American Stratoscope II experiment, has been published, but preliminary reports suggest that the amount present in the planet's atmosphere is a fraction of 1%. However, Spinrad, Münch, and Kaplan[1] have found eleven weak lines of water vapor on a high-dispersion near-infrared spectrogram of Mars. The Martian H_2O lines in the $\lambda8200$ water-vapor band are displaced 0.42 Å longward of their telluric counterparts as a result of the relative velocities of Earth and Mars. The Martian lines are strongest over the poles of the planet. This apparent polar strengthening of the Martian H_2O lines is at least partially due to the increased air mass

*University of London, London, England.
†British Astronomical Association, East Grinstead, Sussex, England.

through the line of sight to high latitudes. The Martian H_2O lines have strengths of approximately 3–5 mA. In their preliminary examination of data, Spinrad et al. indicate that the H_2O abundance on Mars is probably near 5–10 μ precipitable water over the Martian poles. It has been suspected for more than a decade (Ref. 54) that the polar caps consist of some sort of frosty or icy deposit, and this now seems almost certainly true.

ATMOSPHERE

Mars has an atmosphere, but it is much more tenuous than that of the Earth, and of different composition. The current views on the composition of the Martian atmosphere are based on inadequate observational data and may not be reliable, but the estimates given by de Vaucouleurs (Ref. 369) are likely to be approximately correct. His figures are as follows:

	Thickness meters STP	Volume %
N_2	1650	93.8
O_2	< 2	< 0.1
A	70(?)	4.0(?)
CO_2	40	2.2

Very recently (1963), Russian work has indicated that the amount of CO_2 may be only about one-fifth of the amount given here, but this, even if correct, would not materially affect the possibility of finding living organisms on Mars. The pressure of the atmosphere at the Martian surface is believed to be about 83 millibars (Ref. 347), an estimate which is likely to be inaccurate by more than two orders of magnitude.

Kaplan et al.[2] recently detected the rotational lines of H_2O near λ8300 and of CO_2 near λ8700 on a high-dispersion spectrogram of Mars taken at Mount Wilson. The amounts of H_2O and CO_2 found in the Martian atmosphere were $14 \pm 7 \mu$ precipitable water and 55 ± 20 m atm CO_2. On the basis of the absence of O_2 in the Martian spectra, they set an upper limit of 70 cm atm for the O_2 content. Combining the amount of CO_2 with the strongly saturated bands in the 2 μ region, a surface pressure of 25 ± 15 millibars was derived by the authors. The surface pressures for the possible major constituents of the Martian atmosphere are tabulated below (after Kaplan et al.[2]):

Pressure	Low, mb	Mean, mb	High, mb
Total	10	25	40
CO_2	6	4	3
A^{40}: a	–	19	19
b	2	2	2
N_2: a	–	2	18
b	2	19	38

There is no direct evidence for the presence of nitrogen, but by analogy with the Earth, it would seem to be the most likely major constituent. It must be admitted that our positive knowledge of the Martian atmosphere is slight, so that here, as in many fields of concern to exobiologists, the ratio of speculation to fact remains uncomfortably high.

A new theory was advanced in 1960 by Kiess et al.,[3] who suggested that the atmosphere of Mars might contain several different oxides of nitrogen, the polar caps being solid nitrogen tetroxide and the whole planet "the locale of a gigantic photochemical nitrogen fixation process". This, however, would require an atmospheric pressure twice Dollfus's estimate, and Sinton (Ref. 524) has given reasons for supposing that the oxides could not exist on Mars in the postulated amounts. The demonstration of free water vapor would also seem to militate against the correctness of this theory. It is probably safe to conclude that the atmosphere of Mars is not likely to be actively toxic to terrestrial-type organisms at the present time.

CLOUDS

Clouds are often observed in the Martian atmosphere. They have been studied extensively, the series of photographs taken at the Lowell observatory by Slipher being particularly notable (Ref. 534). Some, the so-called "blue" clouds, may be caused by high-altitude crystals, analogous to terrestrial cirrus; there are also lower-level "white" clouds, visible in moderate telescopes, and finally, the "yellow" clouds, which may sometimes cover large areas of Mars—an important example being the great yellow cloud of 1911 (Ref. 300). These yellow clouds are usually regarded as dust storms, the material having been whipped up from the surface by winds. Definite indications of nitrogen dioxide have recently been reported by Karrer and Kiess[4] with respect to the yellow clouds. This was particularly apparent when Mars was still thinly veiled by remnants of the great yellow cloud that obscured the surface features of the planet for several weeks in 1956. The authors suspect that perhaps a versatile group of oxides of nitrogen—NO, NO_2, N_2O_3, and N_2O_4—might be responsible for other features of Mars as well as the yellow clouds. An alternative suggestion by Öpik (Ref. 462) that the clouds are produced by minor planets striking Mars has met with little support and appears to be most improbable.

There can be little doubt that rainfall never takes place on Mars, although we cannot say that precipitation has always been unknown. In past ages, Mars may have had a denser, moister atmosphere than at present, so that the conditions on the planet could have been more favorable to biopoesis than they would have been if Mars had always been extremely dry. Unfortunately, it is extremely difficult to judge whether or not liquid water exists at the Martian surface, and some sort of direct exploration of the planetary surface by automated probes may be necessary to solve this problem.

The Violet Layer

The "violet layer", alternatively termed the "blue haze", appears to be a layer in the Martian atmosphere which is remarkably opaque to light of short wavelength. This was noted by Slipher many years ago (Ref. 532). He also pointed out that there are occasions on which the layer is temporarily withdrawn, so that photographs taken in the ultraviolet range reveal the surface detail in the same way that infrared pictures normally do. Slipher held that the layer was made up of finely divided matter capable of scattering short wavelengths and dissipating at irregular intervals, though always reforming later. Nothing has been found to cast doubt on the basic accuracy of these conclusions, but the precise nature of the layer is still uncertain. Ice crystals have been suggested[5] (Ref. 420), but this has been questioned by de Vaucouleurs[6] (Ref. 366), since, in the ultraviolet, Mars appears almost as "black as soot".

The clearings may be fairly localized, but, as has been pointed out by Wilson (Ref. 585), the greater the area affected, the greater the transparency. During the major clearing of 1939, Hess (Ref. 420) noticed that while the layer was absent, the seasonal cycle of the dark areas was halted. He suggested that this was because Martian organisms were inhibited by exposure to ultraviolet radiations from which they are normally protected.

It may be added here that Kozyrev has suggested that the red color of Mars is not due to the surface but to the spectral properties of the atmosphere (Ref. 433); however, this theory has not been well received.

A possible alternative explanation has been suggested by Briggs (Ref. 327), who considers that the blue haze of Mars is similar to the hazes of Earth due to volatile plant products. Terrestrial hazes are blue because of their very small particle size (less than 0.1 μ), and they appear to be composed of terpenes, a group of derivatives of hydrocarbons containing 10 carbon atoms per molecule. Terrestrial plants, almost without exception, release terpenes and related isoprene compounds, and it seems not unreasonable to suppose that Martian "plants" might produce similar compounds, even if in much smaller amounts. The lack of oxygen in the Martian atmosphere would mean that the terpenes would not be oxidized. A terpene layer would filter off ultraviolet radiations and so perform a function analogous to that of the ozone layer of the Earth's atmosphere.

Along similar lines, Guerin's spectrophotometric studies in the

3100–3850 Å region showed the reflectivity curve to have undulations.[7] He suggests that, if these are real, they may be due to pockets of absorption bands produced by some organic compounds ejected by Martian "vegetation". Briggs further suggests that weak absorptions detected in infrared spectra of the desert regions of Mars (Ref. 523) could be given by terpenes in the atmosphere and points out that if an infrared spectrum of the Martian deserts could be obtained during one of the rare "blue clearances", there should be no absorptions at 3.5 μ.

Temperatures

There is no doubt that temperature changes of extreme range, judged by terrestrial standards, occur in the course of every Martian day and night. At noon on the Equator the temperature may reach 30°C, but during the night it falls as low as $-80°C$ (Ref. 369). It is probable that the temperature of the subsoil remains for most of the time below the freezing point of water, and only the surface itself, to a depth of a few centimeters, reaches, even for short periods, a temperature at which liquid water could exist.

It is not impossible that there are certain spots on the surface which are relatively warm and wet because of the discharge of hot springs, fumaroles, and volcanoes (Ref. 996). These "hot spots", if they exist, might be particularly suitable for the support of living organisms, but there is as yet no certain evidence for their existence.

There is, of course, no reason to rule out the presence of subsurface water. V. V. Davidov has put forward the theory that Mars possesses an extensive underground hydrosphere, but serious objections to this theory have been raised by others. Davidov's paper has not appeared in full English translation, but it has been summarized by Moore (Ref. 459).

The Bright Regions

The reddish-ochre regions which cover much of Mars are commonly called "deserts". To establish the chemical nature of the prominent surface features of Mars without a fairly exact knowledge of the prevailing physical conditions is obviously a hopeless task. The current physical theory is that the Martian surface consists of crumbled rocks exposed to wide temperature variations and ultraviolet flux. The chemical composition of these rocks remains an unsolved problem. Polarization studies by Dollfus (Ref. 30) of the deserts led to the conclusion that they have properties similar to terrestrial limonite ($Fe_2O_3 \cdot n\,H_2O$), a fairly common mineral on Earth. The possibility of the presence of an oxidized compound of this type on a large scale on Mars is worthy of note, since studies of the early rocks of the Earth[8] have shown them to contain iron in the reduced ferrous state, as does limonite. It is only in geologically recent rocks that ferric iron can be found. These observations of terrestrial minerals are used as evidence that the primitive atmosphere must have been reducing and only fairly recently changed to its present oxidizing form. On Mars, however, which has very little free oxygen in its atmosphere, the presence of limonite would indicate that at some time in the past, an oxidizing atmosphere was present.

In order to account for the widespread presence of oxidized materials, it has been suggested that Mars may once have possessed atmospheric oxygen. However, it cannot be definitely concluded that the deserts are limonite. Other studies of the bright regions have indicated that the reflected light of the spectral distribution resembles that of felsitic rhyolite, a mineral mixture of quartz and alkaline silicates (e.g. $KAlSi_3O_8$). Such minerals provide no insight into the nature of the past history of the atmosphere. The supporting evidence for the silicate hypothesis of the deserts comes from studies of a different phenomenon.[9] Radiations from the deserts do not conform to the Stefan–Boltzmann law, but the deviations can be partially explained if the areas are selectively reflecting silicates. It should be noted that the bright regions are slightly but detectably cooler than the dark areas.

The Dark Areas

The celebrated dark areas of Mars have for long been considered a possible abode of living organisms of some kind. They have been under telescopic observation for more than three centuries and are basically permanent. They show seasonal changes, associated with the growth and shrinkage of the polar caps, as well as irregular alterations in form and intensity.

The problem of the evolution of the fine structure of the dark areas of Mars introduces several questions in connection with the seasonal variations and their intensity. These have been specified by Focas[10] as follows:

1. Water vapor in the form of ice crystals is considered responsible for the seasonal phenomena of the dark areas of Mars. On which time scale are the clouds covering the polar areas and the resulting snow deposits produced?

2. The seasonal darkening of the Martian dusky areas is attributed to the action of water vapor scattered from the polar areas toward the Equator. Is this vapor scattered when the polar cloud is in regression or the polar snow deposit in sublimation, or both?

3. What is the aspect of the fine structure of the dark areas during the seasonal cycle?

4. Do the position and size of the spots appearing in the dark areas vary during the seasonal cycle?

5. Are the aerographic distribution by sizes and the frequency of the

individual spots in the dark areas connected with the duration of
the action in aerographic latitude of the darkness-generating
element?

6. Do only the individual spots, or the interstices between them, or
   both, vary in intensity during the seasonal darkening of the dusky
   areas?

7. What is the nature of the fine structure in areas resulting from accidental variations?

8. Does the fine structure of the "canals" change during their seasonal
   variation in intensity?

Various inorganic theories of the dark areas have been proposed.
Arrhenius[11] suggested that they might be deposits of hygroscopic salts,
but it now seems probable that the available water is insufficient to
account for the seasonal darkening which is observed. McLaughlin (Ref.
450) maintains that the areas are made up of volcanic ash, ejected at irregular intervals by surface volcanoes; but this would not explain the
seasonal cycle, and there are other objections to McLaughlin's theory.
Sharonov[12] has advanced a theory suggesting that the processes of weathering and denudation on Mars give rise to large quantities of fine dust;
dark areas are considered to be regions of formation and deflation of the
dust, the bright zones being areas of its accumulation. The weight
of evidence, however, would still seem to favor the view that the changes
in the dark areas are signs of biological activity.

Polarimetric studies by Dollfus (Ref. 30) have given results more
compatible with a biological than with a nonbiological explanation of the
changes in the dark areas, [13,14] but it is true that this conclusion might easily
be upset by a few new facts. Dollfus's work does not support the view
that the dark areas are a crystalline deposit; they more probably consist
of very small opaque granules which change in size and shape during
the Martian seasons, a property that would be exhibited by no known mineral but is compatible with a covering of some sort of "microflora" (using
that term in a general sense). Dollfus suggested that the polarimetric
measurements are those of the microscopic structures making up
Martian organisms. It is, indeed, quite possible that Mars supports
microscopic rather than macroscopic life forms.

Spectroscopic studies of the dark areas have never revealed evidence
of the presence of chlorophyll (Ref. 550). Unlike regions covered by
terrestrial green plants, the dark areas of Mars appear darker in infrared
photographs than in photographs taken with visible light. Tikhov has,
however, drawn attention to similarities between the spectra of the dark
areas and those of terrestrial plants adapted to life under cold, rigorous
conditions on the Earth. In these, the presence of cholorophyll may be
masked by other pigments. Kuiper (Ref. 54) has found certain similar-

ities between the infrared spectrum of the dark areas and that of terrestrial lichens. This is of some interest in relation to Strughold's theory (Ref. 542) that Mars might support organisms resembling lichens, for we know that these are suited to life under harsh conditions.

Recently, observations of the infrared spectra of the Martian dark areas have been made by Sinton (Refs. 522, 523), who considers that he has found evidence for the presence of molecules containing the C–H bond, found in organic molecules. Infrared spectrograms of the dark areas showed pronounced absorption peaks at 3.43, 3.56, and 3.67 μ. The band at 3.43 μ is present in the spectra of all terrestrial plants that have been examined, but that at 3.67 μ was at first something of a mystery. A similar absorption band has since been found in the spectrum of algae belonging to the genus *Cladophora,* and is probably produced by a carbohydrate present in the organisms. Sinton tentatively suggested that Martian organisms with large carbohydrate reserves might be present in the dark areas. It is, however, not quite certain that similar bands could not be produced by other compounds, even perhaps by inorganic materials of some kinds. The presence of the bands in the Martian spectrum has been fully confirmed by Sinton in a study made in 1958 with a new and improved spectrophotometer attached to the coudé focus of the 200-in. Hale reflector (Ref. 369).

The famous "canals" of Mars were first clearly indicated by Schiaparelli, although some of the seemingly linear markings were depicted in the drawings of other observers, active around the middle of the nineteenth century. The view that the canals might be the work of intelligent beings is of uncertain origin. Schiaparelli referred to it, and did not dismiss it, but kept an open mind. As is well known, the American astronomer, Percival Lowell, became convinced that the canals were artificial and depicted large numbers of canals as narrow features running across the surface of the planet.

The present view is that the canals have a firm basis in reality, and that roughly linear features do exist. They have not, however, the artificial aspect shown in Lowell's drawings. Tombaugh[15] has suggested that they are cracks, produced by the impact of large bodies of asteroidal dimensions, and that Martian organisms have developed in the cracks. Davidov (Ref. 459), on the other hand, would regard them as large cracks in the ice which he believes covers the planet, and perhaps the site of biological activity.

The appearance of canals probably arises from the tendency of the eye to see discontinuous features arranged roughly as a continuous line. Under conditions of good visibility, the canals may be resolved into discontinuous streaks and patches.[16] We may conclude that, from the point of view of exobiologists, the seasonal evolution of the dark areas and perhaps the canals have the same significance as pointed out by Focas[10] in that:

1. Polarization shows that the cycle of water vapor in the circumpolar and polar areas of Mars covers approximately the whole year.
2. The dark areas of Mars show periodic variation of intensity, following the cycle of water vapor.
3. The average intensity of the dark areas, not including the action of the darkening waves, increases from the poles toward the equator.
4. The action of each one of the darkening waves decreases from the poles toward the equator. This decrease is balanced in the equatorial zone by the combined action of the two darkening waves alternately originating at the two poles. The action of the darkness-generating element seems to be constant for all latitudes during the Martian year.
5. Blocks and nuclei of dark matter on a dusky background constitute the fine structure of the dark areas of Mars during their maximum intensity.
6. At minimum intensity, areas affected by one darkening wave fade and have a half-tone appearance with no details. Areas affected by two darkening waves show dark blocks of minor intensity of the largest sizes.
7. The sizes of the dark blocks and the density of the nuclei in the dark areas seem to depend on the duration of the action of the darkening element. Areas affected by two darkening waves contain blocks of the largest sizes.

The problem is to demonstrate in some convincing way the presence or absence of living organisms in association with these features.

The evidence for the existence of life on Mars has been critically reviewed by D. G. Rea,[17] who concludes that the biological interpretation of Martian phenomena is very tenuous and that inorganic interpretations should be given greater credence. The infrared reflection spectra for a large number of inorganic and organic samples, including minerals and biological specimens, were recently recorded by Rea, Belsky, and Calvin.[18] The data were analyzed for the purpose of interpreting the 3–4 μ spectrum of Mars. The results cast serious doubt on Sinton's interpretation of absorption bands, attributed to organic molecules. Rea points out that the summer temperature of Depressio Hellespontica may not reach 0°C, being perhaps always lower. Nevertheless, this area shows one of the greatest seasonal changes in visual albedo, in spite of the fact that its temperature seems so low as to make the existence of active water-based life improbable. Rea concludes that if a non-life mechanism must be invoked to explain seasonal changes in one dark area, it is reasonable to assume that it is applicable to others, even those nearer the equator.

Rea also seems to favor a nonbiological interpretation of Dollfus's polarimetric findings. The polarization variations might be caused by roughen-
ing of the surface by the removal of small loose particles by winds, leaving
larger particles. This could account for the observed changes in the
Martian spring. Rea prefers the volcanic ash and wind circulation theories
of McLaughlin (Ref. 450) and Kuiper (Ref. 54), respectively, to account
for variations in brightness of parts of the surface, and "regeneration" of
dark areas. Rea also doubts the reliability of reports of colors and color
changes in the dark areas. In spite of all these reasonable comments, Rea
is not prepared to exclude the possibility of Martian life, although he
favors the inorganic interpretation of Martian phenomena. His arguments
should serve to sharpen our realization of the urgent need for more factual
knowledge of conditions on Mars.

Biological Considerations

Starting from the supposition that conditions on Mars are not greatly
different from those which seem to be indicated by the most recent astronomical observations, we can proceed to speculate on the nature of
indigenous Martian life. It must be stressed that far-reaching reorientation
of ideas on Martian conditions may become necessary as new observational data are collected, so that radical rethinking on this problem may be
required in the not too distant future.

It is fairly safe to assume two things. If there are organisms on Mars,
all that we know about life on the Earth would lead us to suppose that
there will be microscopic Martian life, whether or not macroscopic forms
are present. Secondly, it is reasonable to postulate that Martian life, like
terrestrial life, will depend ultimately on solar energy for its continuation,
so that at least some Martian organisms must be photosynthetic.

We have already mentioned that the polarimetric observations of
Dollfus[13] are consistent, at the moment, with the presence of microscopic
biological units on the dark areas of Mars. More we cannot say at present.
There is little doubt that a hardy microbiological population would have
a reasonable chance of survival under Martian conditions. Experiments[19]
(Refs. 399, 1433, 431) carried out to test the ability of terrestrial microorganisms to survive under simulated Martian conditions, including some
undertaken by the present authors, have shown that many bacteria can
survive the temperature cycling and atmospheric conditions and can grow
if suitable nutrients are present and sufficient water is available. We can
hardly doubt that if life ever began on Mars, perhaps under more favorable conditions in the past, the course of Martian biological evolution
could have led to the production of organisms well adapted to the rigorous
conditions, and we might expect Martian organisms to survive terrestrial
organisms on their home ground.

The possibilities for photosynthesis under Martian conditions have been extensively discussed by Salisbury (Ref. 498), who has pointed out that the equation for photosynthesis can be written in a generalized form, showing the process as a transfer of electrons between carbon and oxygen, or between any two atoms which differ in such a way that the energy transfer is significant (Figs. 1 and 2). Respiration may similarly

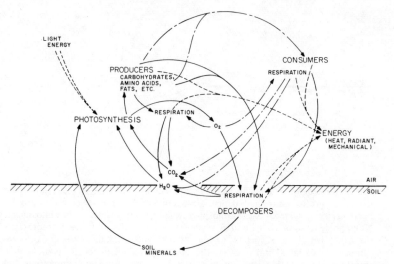

Fig. 1. Biogeochemical cycles on Earth. (Cycles of carbon, oxygen, hydrogen, soil minerals, and energy through the living organisms of the Earth's biotic communities are indicated [nonbiological transformations are not shown]. Dot-dash lines show essential transformations between producers and decomposers. Broken lines indicate that consumers are not theoretically essential to a cycling of elements. Dashed lines show energy transfer from input as light energy to expenditure. Forked lines indicate that not all energy is lost through respiratory processes, but that some may enter the external environment via other metabolic and physical functions of the organism. Producers on Earth are the photosynthesizers – the chlorophyll-containing plants. Consumers include the animals and many parasitic and saprophytic plants. Decomposers are primarily microorganisms, although it is sometimes technically difficult to draw a line between them and certain consumers. Water is indicated at the soil–air boundary because it usually enters metabolic reactions by first being taken up through plant-root systems. Redrawn from Ref. 498.)

be represented as electron transfer, but in the opposite direction. One possibility suggested by Salisbury is that nitrogen, which has many oxidation states, might replace oxygen in a photosynthetic system. Alternatively, Martian organisms might split off oxygen from iron oxides in the soil by a photochemical mechanism, in a manner analogous to the splitting of oxygen from the water molecule in our green plant photosynthesis. After use in metabolism, the oxygen could return to its original combination with iron.

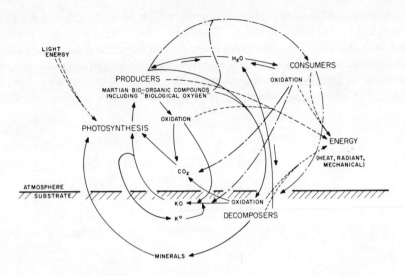

FIG. 2. Biogeochemical cycles as they might occur on Mars. (An attempt is made in this Figure to apply the balances shown in Fig. 1 to the Martian situation by keeping free oxygen out of the atmosphere and restricting water to the atmosphere. KO represents some compound of oxygen occurring in the substrate. K° represents the free form of the K in KO, or K combined with something besides oxygen. "Biological oxygen" implies that the energy received in the form of light is transferred to the chemical energy of the Martian bio-organic compounds and to oxygen in some nongaseous form. Thus, it may later be combined with bio-organic compounds and K° to produce KO and CO_2, releasing energy which might be used in life processes. "Biological oxygen" would thus be transferred from producer to consumer or decomposer as part of food. Such a scheme has many obvious deficiencies, and other schemes might be proposed [such as substituting nitrogen for the oxygen of Fig. 1], but the diagram indicates some of the problems and one possible approach to their solution. Redrawn from Ref. 498.)

Mention has been made that chlorophyll has not been detected on Mars, and that this does not necessarily mean that it is absent, as its presence might be masked. It is possible that Martian organisms use chlorophyll, or some related pigment, together with other pigments. The type of photosynthesis found in certain terrestrial sulfur bacteria, in which free oxygen is not released, might also be suited to Martian conditions.

The photosynthetic organisms we have postulated can be termed "plant-like" in a general sense, but would there be "animals" on Mars? There is no reason why nonphotosynthetic organisms should not exist mingled with the photosynthetic ones, so that a cycling of materials could occur between plant-like and animal-like organisms. Mutational loss of photosynthetic ability in Martian organisms would almost certainly have occurred and might not necessarily have been lethal.

Macroscopic Martian Organisms?

Here we are concerned not so much with "Martians" as with the possibility that Martian organisms analogous to our many-celled organisms might exist. Some years ago, Strughold (Ref. 542) put forward the suggestion that organisms resembling our lichens might be particularly suited to survive Martian conditions. These organisms are a symbiotic combination of algae and a fungus. In their internal spaces, in the interstices of the fungus threads, oxygen produced by photosynthetic activities of the algae can be stored. In this way, the organisms can conserve a private, internal atmosphere. A plan of this kind obviously has possibilities when existence under rigorous conditions is necessary. Selection would also have to favor cold-resistance and drought-resistance. Biological water conservation mechanisms would probably have to be more highly developed on Mars than on the Earth.

Salisbury is almost alone among present-day biologists in seriously maintaining the possibility that advanced life might exist on Mars. His arguments are thoughtful and demand respect. He believes that the observational evidence, particularly the rapid reappéarance of dark areas after they have been covered by dust deposits from storms, points to the presence of rapidly growing organisms and not merely to "struggling lichens". Rather, he thinks, there must be a "thriving vegetal cover". Salisbury does not rule out the existence of intelligent life on Mars, as novel, efficient metabolic systems might make this possible. Discussing the implications of this possibility for the collection of data by instrumented probes landed on the surface of Mars, he says that the results could be surprising: "At least I can imagine how I might react if such an apparatus landed in my back-yard and started grabbing for my apple tree, the cat, and maybe me!"

Terrestrial animals could not exist unaided on Mars. It is true that some microscopic animals can survive under anaerobic conditions, and that cold-blooded animals can withstand long exposure to conditions of oxygen lack, but none of our advanced animals could tolerate such conditions.

Diurnal Temperature Variation and Life

It has already been mentioned that even at the Martian equator, the temperature may vary from $+30$ to $-80°C$ between noon and midnight. It is obvious, therefore, that organisms exposed at the surface would be frozen and thawed repeatedly. We know that under suitable conditions, some bacteria can withstand treatment of this sort, but it is less well known that remarkable degrees of resistance to cold have been found among quite complicated animals. Certain insect larvae, for instance, may survive exposure to temperatures as low as $-47°C$. In the middle of the winter, these larvae were found to contain 20–27% glycerol in their tissues. Here was a biological antifreeze system! Some molluscs, on exposed shores, may withstand freezing and thawing twice daily as the tide falls and rises in winter, and as much as 70% of their body water may be in the form of ice. They too, have some sort of antifreeze system. These examples show us that there is no reason to doubt that biological adaptation, even to extreme cold, could probably occur.[20]

If the "hotspots" mentioned earlier exist, some parts of the Martian surface might possibly support less hardy forms of life.

In laboratory experiments by Siegel *et al.* (see Chapter IV and Ref. 516) it was found that complex terrestrial organisms can grow under conditions that constitute an extreme departure in one or more respects from the normal terrestrial environment. Moreover, the tolerance of plants to low temperatures was favorably influenced by atmospheres low in oxygen. These authors concluded that Mars might easily support recognizable life forms and that the plasticity of organisms we know may be far greater than is generally believed.

One clear possibility emerges from these considerations. Even if Mars has no biosphere of its own, if, in the course of time, man should feel so inclined and has the necessary space vehicles, an enormous biological experiment, the colonization of Mars by terrestrial organisms, could be attempted. This is the sort of experiment man might reasonably undertake when he has put his own planet and way of life in order.

The Search for Life on Mars

The dawn of the space age presents us with the real possibility of seeking life on other planets by direct means, including instrumented probes, automatic equipment landed on the planetary surface, and even manned expeditions. There is little doubt that much further information about Martian conditions will be collected by automatic equipment long before the first landing of man on Mars (see Chapter VII). Much energy and ingenuity are at present being directed toward the design of instruments suitable for inclusion in Mars probes. The simplest of these instruments will seek indirect evidence of the presence of living things, whereas more advanced apparatus is planned for the transmission of pictures of both macroscopic and microscopic structures that may be present.

The earliest advances may come from an extension of observations of infrared spectra by means of apparatus carried to high altitudes by balloons. Later, observatories will probably be established on orbiting space stations and on the Moon's surface. This will be a logical extension of Sinton's work, described earlier.

Detection of enzyme activities by what may be termed "microlaboratories", fully automatic, will probably be the next aim. The design of suitable equipment is already quite advanced. The "multivator", contained in a tube about $2\frac{1}{2}$ in. in diameter and 10 in. long, is capable of carrying out several experiments. A typical experiment might be the detection of splitting of phosphate from organic compounds, for phosphatases are known to be widely distributed in living organisms of the type known to us on Earth. Information of this kind can be coded in a simple way, so that only a small amount of power is necessary for its transmission.

Apparatus to detect the growth of microscopic organisms as well as some of their activities has been designed by various workers (Refs. 994–1000). Vishniac's apparatus, the "wolf trap", will provide a medium which, inoculated with Martian soil, will detect changes in turbidity and reaction. Levin and his colleagues (Ref. 993) have developed the instrument they appropriately term "Gulliver" to seek the microscopic inhabitants of Mars. Gulliver will detect the ability of organisms to release radioactive CO_2 from combination. The measurements will be made at intervals, so that if growth is occurring, a curve of the amount of CO_2 released will indicate the increase of the population, or at least give evidence of an autocatalytic process.

The design of a microscope, fitted with a vidicon camera, to be landed on Mars and carry out a survey aimed at detection of organisms and visualization of their morphology presents great difficulties[21] (Ref. 154). The problems of collection and treatment of samples, selection of a suitable optical-vidicon system, and interpretation of any pictures obtained all seem formidable on first consideration. Nevertheless, the apparatus remains a possibility, and some preliminary experimental work has been done.[21] The transmission of good pictures, containing enough information to permit interpretation, would require a considerable power supply; this, at present, is a limiting factor.

All schemes to land instruments on Mars raise, in acute form, the problem of sterilization of space probes (see Chapter VIII). It would be most unfortunate if an indigenous Martian biosphere were to be interfered with and perhaps grossly modified by the wanton introduction of terrestrial microorganisms. The sterilization of space vehicles can be neglected only at the risk of sacrificing much valuable knowledge.

Mars is at such a distance from the Sun that it receives only about 45% of the radiant energy received by the Earth. It is possible that life on Mars has never progressed beyond a simple stage of organization because sufficient evolution had not occurred before conditions became too rigorous. Mars may therefore contain clues to early stages of life's evolution, at the biochemical level, and would be of particular interest to those concerned with the mechanisms of biopoesis. These features might be rapidly obscured by the spread of terrestrial microorganisms.

CONCLUSION

There is a real possibility that Mars bears indigenous organisms of some kind, based on the following observational arguments (as summarized by Rea):[17]

1. The various colors, including green, exhibited by the dark areas.
2. The seasonal changes in the visual albedo and polarization of the dark areas.
3. The ability of the dark areas to regenerate after an extensive "dust storm".
4. The presence of 2700–3000 cm⁻¹ absorption bands, attributed to organic molecules.

The biological interpretation of changes in the dark areas still seems to be more in accord with the facts than the various nonbiological theories. There is, however, a grave lack of observational material of a kind that would enable us to be more positive in our conclusions. We have every reason to suppose that this defect will be remedied in the next one or two decades. What is now needed is a new supply of facts, rather than a new spate of speculation.

REFERENCES

1. SPINRAD, H., MÜNCH, G., and KAPLAN, L. D., The Detection of Water Vapor on Mars, *The Astrophysical Journal,* vol. 137 (1963), pp. 1319–21.
2. KAPLAN, L., D., MÜNCH, G., and SPINRAD, H., An Analysis of the Spectrum of Mars, *The Astrophysical Journal,* vol. 139 (1964), pp. 1–15.
3. KIESS, C. C., KARRER, S., and KIESS, H. K., A New Interpretation of Martian Phenomena, *Publications of the Astronomical Society of the Pacific,* vol. 72 (1960), p. 256–67.
4. KARRER, S., and KIESS, C. C., *A Laboratory Demonstration of Martian Phenomena,* Preprint of paper presented at the Meeting of the American Astronomical Society, December 27, 1963.
5. SHARONOV, V. V., A New Physical Interpretation of Colour Phenomena of Jupiter's Disk, *Astronomicheskii Tsirkulyar, SSSR,* No. 42 (1945), pp. 2–4.
6. DE VAUCOULEURS, G., Problems of Mars, *1963 Yearbook of Astronomy,* New York: W. W. Norton and Co., Inc. (1963), pp. 91–102.
7. GUERIN, P., Spectrophotometric Study of the Reflectivity of the Center of the Martian Disk at Opposition, and the Nature of the Violet Layer, *Planetary and Space Science,* vol. 9 (1962), pp. 81–7.
8. WILDT, R., Ozon und Saurestoff in den Planeten-Atmosphären, *Nachrichten der Akademie der Wissenschaften, Göttingen, Mathematisch-physikalische Klasse II,* vol. 1 (1934), pp. 1–9.
9. COBLENTZ, W. W., Temperature estimates of the Planet Mars, 1924 and 1926, *Journal of Research, National Bureau of Standards,* vol. 28 (1942), pp. 297–309.
10. FOCAS, J. H., Seasonal Evolution of the Fine Structure of the Dark Areas of Mars, *Planetary Space Science,* vol. 9 (1962), pp. 371–81.

11. ARRHENIUS, S., Les conditions physiques sur la planète Mars, *Journal de Physique et le Radium*, vol. 1 (1912), pp. 81–97.

12. SHARONOV, V. V., Visueller Vergleich von Helligkeit und Farbe der Marsscheibe mit Gebilden terrestrischer Wüstendecken. *Abhandlungen der Staatsuniversität Leningrad*, No. 273, pp. 120–43.

13. DOLLFUS, A., Étude des planètes par la polarization de leur lumière, *Annales d'Astrophysique*, Supplement 4 (1956), pp. 70–110.

14. DOLLFUS, A., Planetary Studies, *Proceedings of Lunar and Planetary Exploration Colloquium*, vol. 2, No. 3 (1961), pp. 17–41.

15. TOMBAUGH, C., Comparison of Lunar and Martian Features, *Proceedings of Lunar and Planetary Exploration Colloquium*, vol. 1, No. 4 (1959), pp. 38–41.

16. DOLLFUS, A., Étude visuelle de la surface de la planète Mars avec un pouvoir séparateur 0.2, *l'Astronomie*, vol. 67 (1953), pp. 85–106.

17. REA, D. G., Evidence for Life on Mars, *Nature*, vol. 200 (1963), pp. 114–16.

18. REA, D. G., BELSKY, T., and CALVIN, M., Interpretation of the 3- to 4-micron Infrared Spectrum of Mars, *Science*, vol. 141 (1963), pp. 923–7.

19. SIEGEL, S. M., HALPERN, L. A., GIUMARRO, C., RENWICK, G., and Davis, G., Martian Biology: The Experimentalist's Approach, *Nature*, vol. 197 (1963), pp. 329–31.

20. SMITH, A. V., *Biological Effects of Freezing and Supercooling*, London: E. Arnold and Co., Ltd. (1961).

21. SOFFEN, G. A., Simple Vidicon Microscopy, *Proceedings of Lunar and Planetary Exploration Colloquium*, vol. 3, No. 2 (1963), pp. 47–8.

CHAPTER VII

LIFE-DETECTION EXPERIMENTS

G. L. HOBBY

Jet Propulsion Laboratory
Pasadena, California

INTRODUCTION

WITHIN the next decade, it will be possible to transport small, unmanned biological laboratories to the surfaces of the planets, where tests can be performed for the existence of extraterrestrial life. Through the use of these new tools, the biologist may be able to obtain answers to important fundamental questions on the origin and nature of life which could never be answered by terrestrial studies alone. In fact, the information obtained from these ventures may prove to contribute more to our basic understanding of life than the experiments of the physical scientists will contribute to the understanding of the solar system. A model of a typical space probe or unmanned spacecraft is shown in Fig. 1. This spacecraft is being constructed to soft-land on the lunar surface, where

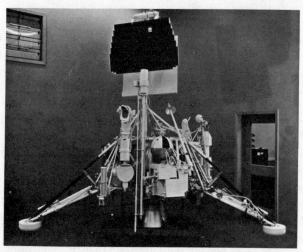

FIG. 1. Full-scale model of *Surveyor* spacecraft with complement of scientific instruments (including gas chromatograph for analysis of lunar crust. Courtesy Jet Propulsion Laboratory, Pasadena, California.)

its automatic instruments will collect chemical and physical data on the lunar environment and telemeter the results to scientists on the Earth. Similar spacecraft may be used to obtain biological and other scientific information about the planets.

While the use of the soft-landed space probe is perhaps the only approach to establishing the existence of extraterrestrial life, remote observations already made from Earth have provided preliminary information on the possibility of a Martian biology. At the same time, terrestrially based observations have practically eliminated Venus as a potential bearer of life because the data indicate that surface temperatures are higher than 600°K.[1,2] Because Mars appears to be the only planet in the solar system, other than Earth, that has any reasonable chance of supporting a biosphere, the following discussions will deal only with that planet.

BIOLOGICAL CRITERIA FOR THE DETECTION OF EXTRATERRESTRIAL LIFE

In planning an experimental program for the detection of extraterrestrial life, the most obvious assumption to make is that Martian life must have properties similar to those of terrestrial life. Nevertheless, it is sometimes tempting to postulate the existence of bizarre or exotic forms differing markedly from any known Earth organisms because the physical and chemical environments of all planets in the solar system, including Mars, are quite different from those of the Earth. However, if life differed so radically that it exhibited none of the properties with which we are familiar, it would not be detectable.

Good arguments can be made for the premise that the origin and evolution of life are dependent upon specific physical and chemical conditions (Refs. 1096, 1144). Life would then arise wherever these conditions occurred in the universe, as a result of a specific kind of chemical evolution. Therefore, the basic chemical form of life, wherever it arose, might always be the same, although differences in its detailed chemistry could occur within certain limits. Essentially, these conditions would require (1) the formation of a planet at relatively low temperatures, as postulated by Urey (Ref. 103); (2) the persistence of reducing conditions for an adequate period of time, with the presence of a reducing atmosphere; (3) the accumulation of sufficient planetary mass to provide a gravitational field strong enough to prevent loss of the atmosphere; and (4) solar energy to provide suitable supplies of radiation (Ref. 1474). On the basis of a chemical evolutionary theory, it is implicit that life originating from these processes would be based upon carbon chemistry. Although the possibility of life based on silicon has been discussed extensively (though casually), no serious theoretical chemical arguments have been proposed to support this presumption.

If the above arguments are acceptable, it is implied that the kind of life to be searched for on Mars would be forms whose general properties must be similar to terrestrial organisms but whose chemistry and structure may differ in details. Therefore, the attributes to be looked for in identifying extraterrestrial organisms are those properties which define terrestrial life in a general sense. These are (1) the ability to achieve decreases in entropy in a system comprising the organism and its immediate environment, i.e. as possibly expressed by structural organization; (2) evidence of metabolic activity; (3) reproductive and growth capacity; (4) a chemistry which is basically organic and involves macromolecular polymerized structures, metabolic reactions which are catalyzed by enzymes, and has optical activity; (5) a system of information storage and transmission based on macromolecular structures; (6) the presence of water as a solvent and metabolic reagent; (7) mutability; (8) adaptability; (9) irritability. The demonstration of several of these characteristics in a sample would be adequate to identify a living organism, although a single observed property might be inconclusive. For life-detection experiments, the first four characteristics would probably be the easiest to demonstrate.

In addition to postulations about the individual characteristics of Martian organisms, further presumptions can be made about the biosphere. If the biosphere is extensive, significant and probably detectable interactions with the lithosphere, atmosphere, and hydrosphere (if it exists) must occur. Depositions of metabolic products may accumulate on or beneath the surface; the atmosphere may be in a dynamic steady state with the biosphere, thereby affecting its composition; the radiative properties of the surface may be altered by the presence of absorbing pigments; and alteration of surface minerals and the formation of soils may occur. Obviously, if life exists, it must be dependent upon solar energy. An extensive population of chemosynthetic organisms would exhaust their supply of energy in a relatively short time. If decreases in entropy are to occur for prolonged periods, sunlight must be utilizable as a source of free energy in one half of an energy cycle. Since a dynamic steady state in a biosphere is required to prevent complete reduction or complete oxidation of all available carbon, a cycling of this element must occur between the biosphere, atmosphere, lithosphere, and whatever hydrosphere is available. Therefore, the chance seems high that life on Mars must involve a reductive photochemistry as well as an oxidative chemistry.

Current thinking on life-detection experiments has emphasized the supposition that a Martian microflora should be abundant if life exists at all (Ref. 1443). On the basis of our conviction that life evolved from simple to more complex structures, microorganisms or cell structures must have been the first entity satisfying our definition of life. Whether cell-like structures evolved by mechanisms analogous to the cell models of Fox (Ref. 1069) or Perti[3] in relatively short periods, or developed through a long period of chemical evolution, the necessary appearance of microorganisms in the evolutionary sequence, before higher forms, is an essential concept. If microorganisms once occurred during evolution, the chances are good that they would persist as they have on Earth. They can subsist on a minimum of available substrate, an important consideration when environmental conditions are harsh. They are readily distributed to all parts of a planetary surface by wind circulation, thereby increasing their chances of finding suitable niches for their growth and activity. Because of their relative structural simplicity, they seem less susceptible to environmental damage, such as freeze–thaw cycles and mechanical disruption; and, under favorable conditions, their numbers increase at very rapid rates so that they normally exist in exceedingly large numbers, which increases the probability of their survival under unfavorable conditions. For these reasons, evolution should tend to select microorganisms as one of the predominant forms of life on any planet, and hence, it is quite probable that microorganisms constitute a significant portion of the Martian biosphere.

The arguments presented support the thesis that if Martian life exists, it is fundamentally similar to terrestrial life. Nevertheless, details of its structure and function must be different because the environmental constraints on Mars seem too severe to permit terrestrial life to thrive. As far as we know, the major factors against which organisms must contend are very low water abundance, exposure to extreme diurnal temperature variations, low partial pressures of atmospheric gases, and possible exposure to ultraviolet radiation. Recent data obtained from spectroscopic observations of the Martian atmosphere[4] estimate the abundance of precipitable water vapor over the poles to be 14 μ or about 1/1000 of the mean water vapor in the Earth's atmosphere. Measurements of surface temperatures have been made by various workers. Diurnal variations between $+36°C$ at noon and less than $-36°C$ at 5 hr 45 min past noon have been recorded near the equator during the summer season (Ref. 347). The effect of such cycles is probably not critical in view of the results obtained from studies of terrestrial organisms (Ref. 409).[5,6] The total surface pressure of the atmosphere, as recently estimated by Kaplan et al.,[4] is about 25 mb, or 2.5% of the Earth's atmospheric pressure, and carbon dioxide was estimated to be 55 M-atmosphere. — If oxygen occurs in the atmosphere, its abundance must be very low (Ref. 361). The thin atmosphere and low abundance of oxygen might permit the penetration of solar ultraviolet radiation to the surface, thus requiring living organisms to develop special adaptations against radiation damage. However, the possibility that ultraviolet radiation does penetrate the atmosphere has not yet been established. Of the environmental factors affecting life on Mars, the low abundance of water seems the most critical.

Whether living systems based on carbon, hydrogen, oxygen, and nitrogen could evolve and survive under these conditions is one of the questions that life-detection experiments may answer. However, consideration must also be given to the fact that astronomical measurements so far taken represent averages over large areas of the planet. Since we know nothing about the microclimate we cannot be certain that less harsh environments do not exist in many local areas (Ref. 996). Currently available data suggest that only the solid and vapor water phases exist (Ref. 30). In order for liquid water to be present at any time, conditions departing from those now understood to exist would be necessary. If a biology exists which is not dependent upon liquid water, it must be very unusual indeed.

RESULTS OF REMOTE OBSERVATIONS

Telescopic observations of Mars have revealed phenomena explainable as biological activity; however, alternative explanations have been proposed in every case.

The surface of Mars is characteristically divided into three types of zones. About three-quarters of the surface consists of bright reddish or yellowish regions which are thought to be deserts. Much of the remaining area is covered by surface material of considerably lower reflectivity, marking the planet with distinct geographical features. The third region consists of the polar caps, which disappear during the summer season and re-form in the autumn and winter. The evidence for life involves essentially the dark regions, or maria, and the polar caps.

Extensive studies have been made by A. Dollfus at the Pic du Midi Observatory on the optical polarization characteristics of the Martian atmosphere and surface (Ref. 303). These observations demonstrated that seasonal changes in polarization occur in the dark maria but not in the bright regions. Changes in the polarization curves are suggestive of changes in the shape or size of very small, opaque particles on the surface.[7] The phenomenon is therefore suggestive of growth, and possible reproduction, during the Martian spring, when water vapor is presumably more plentiful in the atmosphere.

Another observation in support of this interpretation is due to Öpik (Ref. 462). When clouds of yellow dust are blown across the dark maria, the albedo of these areas is increased. However, after such storms, the dark regions reappear relatively rapidly, suggesting that something with a vigorous capacity to grow and reproduce may exist in these regions.

One of the most controversial phenomena suggestive of reproduction and growth as well as the formation of biological pigments is the seasonal change in contrast of the dark maria. Focas has described this seasonal darkening in considerable detail.[8] As the Martian spring arrives, the polar cap recedes, and a narrow band of darkening appears at the periphery of the cap. The band broadens and radiates from the polar regions across the respective hemisphere, producing a decrease in the albedo of already visible dark areas. The rate of transit across the surface is about 35 km per day and seems to correspond to the expected rate of transport of water vapor by the atmosphere from the subliming ice caps. The intensity of the darkening varies among different maria at the same latitude during passage of the wave, and even the same maria may show differences in the degree of darkening in different Martian years. In general, the features which exhibit the most intense darkening are located in the higher latitudes, and the zone immediately adjacent to the polar cap displays very strong intensification during the polar recession. If this phenomenon is due to the influence of free water vapor on biological organisms, it suggests that temperature is a minor constraint on their activity as compared with available water. The temperatures in the higher latitudes, even during the summer, never exceed a few degrees above zero. However, terrestrial antarctic microflora has been found which is presumably active within a temperature range between -24 to $-4°C$ in saline lakes,[9] demonstrating that temperature need not be a constraining factor.

Some data also exist which are indicative of possible photosynthetic pigments on Mars. Both Kuiper (Ref. 54) and Tikhoff (Ref. 549) compared the visible reflection spectra of the maria with spectra of laboratory preparations of lichens. The lichens found in cold regions on the Earth absorb energy in the near-infrared, as distinct from higher plants and those found in warmer regions, which resembles the absorption characteristics of the dark features of Mars.

Infrared reflection spectra have been obtained of the maria that suggest the presence of organic matter (Ref. 523).[10] Absorption peaks were obtained at 3.45, 3.58, and 3.69 μ. Colthup (Ref. 348) believes that acetaldehyde or higher aldehydes may be representatives of this band. Since spectra obtained on the desert regions had no absorption lines at these positions, association of the dark geographical features with biological phenomena is given further support.

Although the phenomena occurring on the Martian surface can readily be interpreted as evidence for the existence of life, this interpretation is speculative. In every case, alternative hypotheses have been proposed to explain the mysterious changes that take place. It has been suggested that the seasonal variations in the darkening of the maria can be explained by changes in color due to hydration.[11] However, no one has yet proposed a type of mineral in which this might occur. Rea[12] suggests two alternative explanations for the polarization data of Dollfus: (1) The seasonal shift in the polarization curves could also be explained by the increasing absorbency of the dark regions, even if no change in surface texture occurred. (2) Changes in surface texture might be the result of the action of seasonal winds.

Infrared reflection spectra obtained by Sinton have been explained alternatively by the presence of carbonates or of other inorganic material on the surface (Ref. 1041). However, according to Kiess, Karrar, and Kiess,[13] all Martian surface phenomena, including the data of Sinton, are explainable if the atmosphere is assumed to be composed of nitrogen oxides. The phase changes occurring between N_2O_4, NO_2, and N_2O_3 as a result of seasonal temperature variations would account for the increase and decrease in the albedo of the dark regions, regeneration of dark areas after dust storms, and the observed infrared spectra. Rea favors the volcanic hypothesis of McLaughlin (Ref. 450) and Kuiper (Ref. 435), which explains the changing surface features as the result of the deposition and removal of volcanic ash by seasonal wind circulation.

The information obtained from remote observations of the planet is intriguing and suggestive but probably can make few further significant contributions to the question of life on Mars other than slight additional refinements on the composition and mass of the atmosphere. Remote observations must be replaced with attempts to perform tests and measurements directly on the surface. Even direct measurements with space probes may, in the early attempts, provide no more than intriguing but not necessarily definite answers. However, it seems obvious that the technology and technique of space flight are the only approaches capable of solving this riddle.

EXPERIMENTAL APPROACH TO ON-SITE INVESTIGATIONS

On the basis of the criteria suggested earlier, the investigations of the planet's surface for life would involve observations or tests which would reveal the presence of properties similar enough to terrestrial life to be recognizable. The objective of the first biological studies of Mars would be to establish the existence of life. If it is found, further studies would elucidate its chemical and physical nature. Ideally, the first payloads of life-detection experiments designed for space-probe missions to Mars should be selected to maximize the chance of detecting life. This would be desirable for a number of reasons. Establishing the existence of extraterrestrial life would be one of the most important events in human history, and the desire to satisfy our curiosity as soon as possible is very strong. Also, the cost of each mission will be large, and the waiting period to repeat experiments is about two years. Finally, the risk of altering an indigenous Martian biology before biological data can be obtained by inadvertently contaminating the planet with terrestrial microorganisms carried by the space probe would be reduced if maximum information were obtained in the fewest possible missions. In addition, the chances of detecting previously deposited biological terrestrial contaminants during later missions would also be lessened. Considerable concern over possible contamination of the planet has been expressed by conscientious biologists (Ref. 281).[14, 15, 16] Unfortunately, the limitations of the first rocket booster systems available for the early Mars landings will probably not permit the performance of the ideal number and kinds of biological experiments per mission. The answer to the question of whether life exists on Mars therefore may require many missions and an extended period of time.

Life Detection by Visual Examination

One of the most appealing methods of life detection would be a thorough examination of the landscape near the landing site of the spacecraft by vidicon photography. Our system of taxonomy relies heavily on morphology, and we have an intuitive confidence in our ability to interpret visual data. Although misinterpretation of photographic data is possible, the chances do not appear very great. The more complex forms of life generally have structural characteristics which are not typical of inorganic material. Provided the photographic system has sufficient resolution to permit an analysis of structural details of objects, it is highly probable that living forms could be identified beyond reasonable doubt. To increase the probability of success of the visual experiment, a 360-deg scan of the horizon and various intermediate distances up to the immediate vicinity of the landed spacecraft would be desirable. The resolution of the photographs should overlap, ranging from meters on the horizon to fractions of a millimeter on the surface close to the spacecraft. Additional tests could be made for the presence of pigmented objects by the use of appropriate color filters.

Lederberg has proposed microscopy as a life-detection technique (Ref. 154). The examination of particles recovered from the atmosphere or from samples of soil would provide a desirable extension to the macroscopic scan into the microscopic range. A system in which the maximum resolution of the macroscopic photography was overlapped by the minimum resolution of the photomicrography would ensure against missing organisms intermediate in size between the two ranges. The maximum resolution of the microscope system should probably be at least 1 μ in order to distinguish the internal structure of microorganisms in the size range down to 10 μ. Distinguishing microorganisms from soil or dust particles which are smaller than 10 μ is very difficult because of the decrease in obvious internal structure in the smaller particles.

Although, from the biological standpoint, visual techniques are probably the most desirable for the earliest attempts to detect life, the technical difficulties are very great, both because of the difficulties involved in designing a microscope system to be remotely operated and because of the large amount of information that must be acquired and transmitted by the telemetry system of the spacecraft. For this reason, visual techniques may have to be delayed until sufficiently large rocket systems are available to transport the necessary auxiliary equipment to the Martian surface.

Organic Chemical Tests

The chemical evolutionary hypothesis suggests that life will probably arise anywhere in the universe where conditions are favorable. It also implies that even if life never originated on a planetary system, the abiogenic formation of organic compounds is very probable. The experimental synthesis of biochemically important compounds under reducing conditions has been demonstrated sufficiently to ensure confidence in this assumption (Refs. 1234, 1285, 1302).[17] Another source of organic matter may arise from the influx of large quantities of carbon-containing meteorites, which, over periods of millions or billions of years, could deposit significant amounts of carbon compounds on the surface. The estimated annual terrestrial collection of meteoric dust is quite large; for example, Pettersen[18] estimates 3.5×10^{11} g of nickel per year. Comparable amounts of carbon can also be expected based on meteorite studies. The Martian infall could be expected to be just as large. Therefore, one of the first considerations in the organic analysis of the Martian surface would be to determine whether the organic matter is of biogenic or abiogenic origin. If life exists, almost all organic matter will probably have entered into the biological cycle. If chemical experiments can be designed to distinguish between indigenous biogenic and abiogenic organic matter and deposits originating from meteorite material, suggestive evidence for the presence or absence of life may be obtained. Indigenous organic compounds arising from the interaction of a primitive reducing atmosphere with solar ultraviolet radiation early in the planet's history would obviously be transformed during subsequent geological evolution. If remnants of these compounds persisted to the present day, it is difficult to predict what the final product might be. Stable organic products of this chemical evolution might differ from the stable organic residues found in carbonaceous chondrites if they were formed under different conditions. In this respect, the kinds of studies now being performed on the abiogenic synthesis of biologically important organic compounds and the nature and origin of organic material in carbonaceous chondrites may be of inestimable value in supporting life-detection experiments.

In order to establish the possible biogenic origin of organic matter found on Mars, several important properties characteristic of compounds originating from biological organisms could be examined. These would be the identification of one or more major classes of biochemical compounds, tests for macromolecular polymerized molecules, tests for the presence of enzymes, and tests for molecules having optical activity. Qualitative tests should be made for pyrimidine and purine bases, amino acids, polycarboxylic acids, porphyrins, sugars (including ribose), and organic nitrogen, sulphur, and phosphorus. To demonstrate the possible presence of macromolecules, tests for DNA, proteins, and polysaccharides would obviously be included. Further experiments to detect very stable forms of polysaccharides and phenolic polymers, e.g. cellulose and lignin, which are common, known residues from terrestrial plants, could be included. Finally, the presence of hydrocarbons having even numbers of carbon atoms might also provide supporting evidence for biological activity.

The widespread preference by terrestrial organisms for specific enantiomorphs of optically active compounds suggests that this property may be a universal requirement in the origin of living systems. The impossibility of forming a double-stranded DNA molecule from deoxyribose chains having random D and L configurations illustrates the necessity for precise molecular form in systems having the molecular complexity required in living organisms. Whether the particular choice of asymmetry in D-sugars and L-amino acids in life on Earth was accidental or essential is still an unanswered question. If life were discovered on Mars, it would be of interest to learn which stereoisomers were preferred in these systems. This information could be helpful in understanding whether one kind of optical isomer possessed a functional advantage over its antipode. Whether the discovery of optically active organic compounds would be completely definitive for the presence of living organisms is uncertain because their origin by abiogenic processes cannot as yet be completely discounted.

Enzyme activity occurs in terrestrial soils.[19] Tests for enzyme activity in Martian soil would constitute one of the most important life-detection approaches. Catalytic processes which have the efficiency and specificity of enzyme systems probably do not exist apart from biologic material. Therefore, any abiologic catalytic activity discovered in Martian soil could probably be distinguished from biological catalysis. In the first tests, those enzymes having the highest ubiquity in terrestrial organisms would be likely candidates for detection. These might include catalases, phosphatases, and dehydrogenases. The sensitivity of enzyme tests makes them especially attractive for life-detection purposes, although their specificity may prove to be a disadvantage in the selection of substrates for a life-detection experiment.

Metabolic Tests

Interesting speculations have been made on the possible metabolic schemes utilized by Martian organisms (Ref. 498). However, only tests for metabolic systems typical of terrestrial organisms seem reasonable for preliminary life-detection experiments. If we assume that Martian life is a carbon chemistry, and that essential elements are cycled, tests for the fixation or production of carbon dioxide must receive the highest priority in the metabolic approach to life detection. Carbon dioxide is known to exist in the Martian atmosphere, and we would expect it to be reduced by photochemical processes. Because oxygen occurs in the atmosphere in very low abundance, if at all, the photochemical processes might more closely resemble those of terrestrial bacteria.

In order to complete the carbon cycle, it is obviously necessary to postulate a heterotrophic metabolism. Although anaerobic oxidation may be expected, aerobic oxidation cannot be discounted because even if oxygen exists at a very low partial pressure, it may be high enough to support respiration. The existence of carbon dioxide in the atmosphere suggests that the carbon cycle requires oxygen, even though it may not be utilized directly from the atmosphere. However, demonstration of carbon dioxide assimilation and consumption would be a far better test for metabolism.

Tests for Growth and Reproduction

The demonstration of growth and reproduction in Martian samples would be one of the most definitive kinds of evidence for the presence of life. Although it is possible to hypothesize a form of life which does not have these properties, it is almost impossible to conceive how it could persist for very long periods of time. The simplest tests to demonstrate reproducibility and growth are obviously bacteriological culture techniques in an aqueous medium. Although the selection of a correct synthetic growth medium for Martian organisms is a difficult problem, the most promising solution might be the preparation of extract media from Martian soil. It is also possible that Martian microorganisms have an inherently slow growth rate. The life cycle could include long periods in a resting or dormant phase. If this were true, defining exactly the conditions necessary to stimulate them to active growth and reproduction would be difficult. However, despite some of the uncertainties of detecting life by testing for growth and reproducibility in a well-designed experiment, a positive answer would be so convincing that it must be considered one of the best tests.

Measurement of Environmental Parameters

The most obvious environmental factors important to Martian biology are associated with the atmosphere and soil. The composition of the atmosphere and its pressure would suggest possible metabolic constraints on any organisms that might exist and could indicate the type of metabolism possible. The soil temperature, structure, and chemistry would be of particular interest, especially the moisture content. If life is to exist, one must assume that water is somehow made available to the organisms present. If present data on the Martian atmosphere indicate that liquid water is rare or does not occur, it is necessary to postulate mechanisms whereby a liquid phase is possible or some biological mechanism for obtaining atmospheric water vapor and converting it into the liquid phase. Therefore, the amount and phase relations of water in the soil, and especially as related to temperature changes, would be important measurements in order to establish the feasibility of life. The textural properties of the soil would provide information on the nature of soil formation, e.g. whether biology was a significant factor, and chemical assays for ions of known biological significance would provide further supporting data for life detection.

LIFE-DETECTION INSTRUMENTS

Problems and Constraints

The biological laboratory which would be transferred to Mars would consist of a series of instruments designed to operate automatically after the spacecraft had successfully landed on the surface. The technology required to accomplish these missions is extremely difficult and an unusual challenge to the development of engineering techniques. It may be expected that developments in instrumentation design and automation applicable to many other fields will be the final outgrowth of engineering efforts now underway to meet the needs of the unmanned space exploration program.

Stuart[20] and Heacock[21] have summarized the important flight and design constraints demanded of life-detection instruments. These are: minimizing the weight, volume, and power requirement for each instrument; maximizing the information obtained while restricting the demands on the telemetry system; survival in the launch and space environment during transit to the planet; survival during the re-entry maneuvers and landing on the planet; and high reliability.

The need for restricting the weight, volume and power of all components of the payload is obvious upon considering the ratio of gross weight to usable payload weight in modern rocket systems. The payload of instruments for performing scientific experiments is considerably less than 0.1% of the gross weight. In addition, the batteries needed to supply power are a very heavy component, so that the power requirements for all systems must be kept as low as possible in order to reduce weight.

Each instrument will perform the desired test, and the results will appear at the output terminals normally in the form of an analog signal of electrical potential. In order to facilitate the storage of these signals on recorders for subsequent transmission to Earth, they will be digitized in binary code. The code will be telemetered to Earth at a rate dependent upon the telemetry bandwidth, a property which is dependent upon the power of the transmitter, the efficiency of its antenna systems, and the distance from Earth. The data-transmission rate may be of primary concern if information is telemetered in "real-time", or directly, as it is retrieved from the instrument. However, when a data-storage system is utilized, information can be collected at the output rate of the instrument, stored, and telemetered at slower rates at a future time. This is necessary when a relatively large amount of data is to be collected and telemetered by a transmitting system of limited bandwidth. Data systems can also be designed to monitor and cancel out redundant information, limiting the transmission to pertinent information only.

The main environmental stress on the instrument systems during the launch phase of the mission would consist of high-acceleration loadings and rather severe vibrational forces. All structures must be designed to withstand high stresses to ensure their survival under actual launch conditions. After launch, the spacecraft with its payload will be injected into free space, where it may remain for 6 to 8 months. Meanwhile, it will be subjected to high vacuum, radiation, micrometeorite bombardment, and possibly detrimental factors of an unknown nature. During this period, the instruments are in a "stored" condition in which various degenerative processes may be occurring in the materials of the instruments. After the prolonged period of storage, the instrument must undergo the severe stress of deceleration during the atmospheric entry at destination and survive being landed on the surface. Finally, the instrument will be energized and will be expected to perform its experiment 40 million miles and 6 to 8 months from the launching site.

The experiments in the remote life-detection laboratory are unique when compared to physical measurements taken to determine radiation, magnetic or gravitational fields, since life-detection experiments require the acquisition and analysis of a sample. This requirement introduces an additional complication to an already complicated system. The collection of an adequate sample necessitates an additional expenditure of power, weight, and space for the collecting mechanism. If the sample-collection system demands a controlled attitude of the spacecraft after landing, further weight and complexity of the design are necessary. Also, it will not be possible to predict whether the spacecraft will land on hard rock, sand or dust, frozen clay, or even in a patch of vegetation. A landing on rough terrain may completely disorient the sample-collection mechanism so that it may be unable to gather any sample at all. Therefore, a major problem is to design a sample-recovery system which has a very high chance of successfully recovering a sample under all conceivable conditions. Approaches to this problem, under study at the Jet Propulsion Laboratory, include electromechanical devices using rotation brushes and conveyor drives, jet aspiration devices which will agitate surface dust by means of a gas jet and will draw the subsequent aerosol into the experimental device by gas-pressure differential, electrostatic collection devices, and direct aerosol collection systems using vacuum-cleaner techniques.[22]

After sample acquisition, processing may require additional operations involving sorting soil particles according to size and density, chemical extractions with water or organic solvents, acid or alkaline hydrolysis of sample material, chromatographic separations, precipitations, or other operations which will have to be programmed into the instrument and monitored by electronic logic systems. Such requirements dictate a limitation on the degree of simplicity obtainable, even though simplicity and reliability are of primary concern in the design and fabrication of these instruments.

An important consideration which affects exobiological instrumentation as well as the complete spacecraft system is the requirement that spacecraft landed in planetary environments be free of all viable terrestrial microorganisms. Because of the prolific reproductive capacity of microorganisms, their transportability by natural forces, and their capacity for altering biological ecologies on a widespread scale, a single viable microbial spore landed on the Martian surface could theoretically interact with the indigenous biosphere, causing widespread changes. Therefore, in order to minimize this possibility, spacecraft and instrumentation landed on Mars must be exposed to scrupulous sterilization environments such as dry-heat temperatures as high as 135°C for 24 hr. This requirement introduces an additional constraint upon the life-detection instrumentation system because of the perishability of substrates and instrument materials.

Representative Instruments

A number of instruments are presently under development which are intended to perform biological tests in the areas discussed. However, it should be pointed out that a thorough discussion of life-detection instruments is premature, because the present activity is one of preparation and planning and the concepts and instruments described may change in considerable detail before the actual flight missions are accomplished.

Gulliver. A life-detection instrument designed to detect the metabolism and growth of extraterrestrial microorganisms has been proposed by Levin *et al.* (Ref. 997). The instrument employs sensitive radioisotope techniques for detecting the evolution of carbon dioxide which is formed as a product from the metabolism of a tagged carbon substrate. On the basis of the criteria for Martian life that were previously assumed, the experiment is sound in principle, although its success may depend on the specific substrates finally selected for the growth medium. The sensitivity of the technique makes the probability of detecting microorganisms existing in low concentrations relatively high. As the amount of carbon dioxide released per unit of time will depend upon the number of actively metabolizing organisms and their specific metabolic rate, growth and metabolism can be measured by the amount of labeled C^{14} detectable in the gas phase. For a growing culture, plots showing radioactivity from $C^{14}O_2$ in the gas phase vs. time would be exponential. For actively metabolizing but nongrowing organisms, a linear increase in radioactivity in the gas phase would be expected.

Controls are included in the experiment for artifacts which might be produced by spontaneous degradation of the tagged substrate. This might occur as a result of its innate instability to space radiation during the interplanetary transit period, or possibly of nonbiological interaction between the tagged substrate and reactants in the test sample after inoculation.

The results of an actual field trial of this instrument are illustrated in Fig. 2.

The present instrument model consists of four basic systems: (1) a sample-collection system, (2) a culture chamber, (3) a radiation-detection system, and (4) an electronic programmer. The device is also equipped with storage chambers for medium and antimetabolite, and a mechanism which breaks the storage vials. Some of the detailed structures are illustrated by the model in Fig. 3. The final flight instrument is expected to weigh less than 3 lb, with a consumption power of less than 3 w.

The sample-collection system consists of a pair of projectiles, each having a spool of string, explosive charges to launch the projectiles, a drum in the culture chamber to which one end of the string is attached, and a small electric motor for winding the string onto the drum.

The culture chamber has ports for the introduction of the sample, the medium, and the antimetabolite. Part of the structure of the chamber

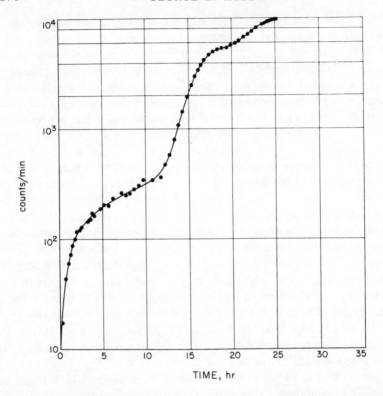

FIG. 2. Curve obtained from field test of Gulliver radioisotope life-detection device. (Character of curve suggests presence of at least three types of organisms. From Annual Progress Report to NASA, Contract No. NASr-10.)

includes a series of baffles to prevent the radiation detector, mounted directly above the chamber, from seeing the radio-labeled substrate so that it will record radioactivity only from the carbon dioxide diffusing to its surface.

Although a final decision on the type of detector to be employed in this instrument has not yet been made, either solid-state or geiger counters will be used.

Finally, the programmer will ensure that the manipulations of the experiment are carried out in proper sequence and the time duration between events meets the experimental requirements.

Mars microscope system. Designs for a Mars microscope are currently being studied.[23]

The primary problems of the system are (1) the difficulty of distinguishing between particles of a nonbiological nature and those which are biological,[24] (2) the collection of a suitable sample for observation under

FIG. 3. Close-up view of advanced breadboard model of Gulliver. (Cannon with projectiles in lower foreground; strings enter through ports and are attached to drum inside culture chamber. Cylindrical structure resting on pedestals encloses geiger tube circuitry and anti-coincidence counter. Courtesy Resources Research, Inc., Washington, D.C.)

the vidicon microscope, (3) the processing and concentration of a sample within a small area beneath the microscope objective, and (4) the reduction of redundant information from the picture in order to reduce the burden on the telecommunications system.

The problem of discrimination between biological particles and other material is increased by the fact that the morphology of Martian microorganisms may be quite unlike that of terrestrial forms. Unless microorganisms are growing in relatively concentrated clusters in the form of rods, spheres, or other familiar groupings, they will be exceedingly difficult to recognize. However, microorganisms large enough to exhibit detailed internal structures will be considerably easier to distinguish. In the case of the Mars microscope system, in which samples will consist of soil or dust particles from aerosols, the ratio of microorganisms to inorganic particles may be very low. Therefore, a system of fractionating and concentrating particles most likely to be biological is a prime requirement.

Despite these problems, the importance of attempting a direct detection of microscopic life on the Martian surface cannot be disputed. There appears to be no area of the Earth's surface from which one could not recover some type of microbial life. If Mars has a biosphere, microorganisms would undoubtedly be widely dispersed, whether they are in an active state in favorable environments or whether they are blown into unfavorable geographical areas by winds and exist in a dormant condition. Therefore, if the problems of sample processing, recognition, and data processing can be solved satisfactorily, the chance of detecting life on Mars by a remote microscope system should be relatively high.

One solution to the problem of sample-acquisition for microscopic examination would be to collect the sample in the form of aerosols. This may be done by direct collection of dust from the atmosphere above the ground or by means of a device which will agitate surface dust and draw the resulting aerosol into the sample-processing system.

One of the most promising methods for fractionating a crude sample, at the same time increasing the chance of isolating biological particles from nonbiological debris, would be to perform a series of mass density fractionations in liquids of different densities. Each fraction could then be examined for particles having morphologically distinguishing characteristics suggestive of cellular structure. Experiments along these lines are being conducted in order to select optimal liquid systems for this fractionation.

Gas chromatography. The Jet Propulsion Laboratory has undertaken the development of several gas chromatographic systems to perform gas analyses of planetary atmospheres as well as lunar and planetary surface and subsurface material.[25,26,27] Solid samples are to be analyzed for occluded gases and crystalline water by heating and collecting the vapors for analysis. Nonvolatile organic matter will be identified by analyzing the volatile decomposition products of pyrolysis or other sample preparation techniques.

The basic system of a gas chromatograph designed for the analysis of organic compounds on lunar missions is illustrated in Fig. 4. It consists essentially of an oven for pyrolyzing the sample, a helium carrier gas-storage tank, a sampling loop for the concentration of the volatile pyrolysis products, three chromatographic columns for the detection of a

FIG. 4. Advanced model of lunar gas chromatograph. (Hopper containing powdered lunar sample is at upper right at rear of instrument. Three concentrically wound chromatographic columns are shown in upper right foreground, and part of programming electronics at left of instrument. Chromatograph was developed by Beckman Instruments Corp. under contract to Jet Propulsion Laboratory, Pasadena, California.)

variety of organic vapors, and three ionization detectors. The system would also include electronics for amplifying the detector signals and programming the sequence of operations. A prototype of this design has been constructed. The physical dimensions are $8 \times 8 \times 10$ in., it weighs 14 lb, and consumes 12 w of power during the pyrolysis cycle and 2 w continuous power during the analytical cycle. The sensitivity is expected to be about 10^{-10} mol of gaseous sample.

The gas chromatograph is attractive from the standpoint of its potential ruggedness and ease of miniaturization for space applications. Its potential use as a life detector as well as an instrument for performing organic analysis has been indicated by preliminary studies, in which "fingerprint" chromatograms of the pyrolysis products of biological material have been obtained.[28]

The wolf trap. Vishniac (Ref. 1000) has proposed an instrument for the detection of reproducibility and growth of microorganisms in culture media. The device would utilize nephelometric techniques to detect the increase in size and number of particles inoculated into a variety of culture broths. At the present time, it is expected that less than 10^5 particles may be detected, although studies to increase the sensitivity of this method are in progress. The experiment would be designed to culture organisms utilizing carbon substrates as well as substrates for chemosynthetic organisms. For verification of the assumption that increases in turbidity are due to biological growth, simultaneous pH measurements would be made during the incubation period.

The four types of life-detection instrumentation described here are examples of approaches to the detection of extraterrestrial life. They do not represent all of the activity in this area. The exobiology program of the Instrumentation Laboratory at Stanford University, under J. Lederberg, is developing miniature instrumentation designed to perform biochemical assays of samples obtained from the Martian surface. Other groups are studying the feasibility of optical rotatory dispersion, J-band analysis techniques for proteins, mass spectrographic analysis, and electrochemical techniques for life-detection application. The exobiology staff at the Jet Propulsion Laboratory is also studying problems of sample acquisition and various chemical assay methods of life detection.[29] Major efforts are required to advance the state-of-the-art of instrument design and construction for the biological exploration of the planets, and the development of life-detection experiments must begin years before scheduled planetary missions because of the great amount of preparation required.

REFERENCES

1. DRAKE, F., Personal communication.
2. BARATH, F. T., BARRETT, A. H., COPELAND, J., JONES, D. E., and LILLEY, A. E., *Mariner II:* Preliminary Reports on Measurements of Venus: Microwave Radiometers, *Science,* vol. 139 (1963), pp. 908–9.
3. PERTI, O. N., The Origin of Life, *Agra University Journal of Research,* vol. XII, Part 2 (1963), pp. 1–48.
4. KAPLAN. L. D., MÜNCH, G., and SPINRAD, H., An Analysis of the Spectrum of Mars, *The Astrophysical Journal,* vol. 139, No. 1 (1964), pp. 1–15.
5. PACKER, E., SCHER, S., and SAGAN, C., Biological Contamination of Mars: II. Cold and Aridity as Constraints on the Survival of Terrestrial Microorganisms in Simulated Martian Environments, *Icarus,* vol. 2 (1963), pp. 293–316.
6. SIEGEL, S. M., Personal communication.
7. DOLLFUS, A., Planetary Studies, *Proceedings of Lunar and Planetary Colloquium,* vol. 2, No. 3 (1961), pp. 17–30.
8. FOCAS, J. H., Seasonal Evolution of the Fine Structure of the Dark Areas of Mars, *Planetary and Space Science,* vol. 9 (1962), pp. 371–81.

9. MEYER, G. H., MORROW, M. B., and WYSS, O., Antarctica: The Microbiology of an Unfrozen Saline Pond, *Science,* vol. 138 (1962), pp. 1103–4.

10. SINTON, W. M., Comments on Identification of Aldehyde in Mars Vegetation Regions, by N. B. COLTHUP (Letter), *Science,* vol. 134 (1961), p. 529.

11. ARRHENIUS, S., *The Destinies of the Stars,* New York: Putnam (1918).

12. REA, D. G., Evidence for Life on Mars, *Nature,* vol. 200 (1963), pp. 114–16.

13. KIESS, C. C., KARRAR, S., and KIESS, H. K., A New Interpretation of Martian Phenomena. *Publications of the Astronomical Society of the Pacific,* vol. 72 (1960), pp. 256–67.

14. Report of CETEX 1959, ICSU Rev. 1100 (1959).

15. LEDERBERG, J., Exobiology: Approaches to Life Beyond the Earth, *Science,* vol. 132 (1960).

16. *Review of Space Research,* NAS-NRC Publication No. 1079, Washington, D.C. (1962).

17. PONNAMPERUMA, C., SAGAN, C., and MARINER, R., Synthesis of Adenosine Triphosphate Under Possible Primitive Earth Conditions, *Nature,* vol. 199 (1963), pp. 222–6.

18. PETTERSON, H., Rate of Accretion of Cosmic Dust on the Earth, *Nature,* vol. 181 (1958), p. 330.

19. McLAREN, A. D., Biochemistry and Soil Science, *Science,* vol. 141 (1963), pp. 1141–7.

20. STUART, J. Extraterrestrial Biological Instrumentation Problems, *Proceedings of San Diego Symposium for Biomedical Engineering* (1963), pp. 246–53.

21. HEACOCK, R. L., Scientific Instruments in Space Exploration, *Science,* vol. 142 (1963), pp. 188–95.

22. ESKIND, N., Sample Collection for Mars Biological Experiments, *Space Programs Summary No. 37-23,* vol. IV, Jet Propulsion Laboratory, Pasadena, California, October 1963.

23. SOFFEN, J., Mars Microscope, *Space Programs Summary No. 37-13,* vol. IV, Jet Propulsion Laboratory, Pasadena, California, March 1962.

24. SOFFEN, J., Implications of Morphology in the Investigation of Extraterrestrial Life, *The American Biology Teacher,* vol. 25, No. 7 (1963), pp. 536–8.

25. BOWMAN, L., JOSIAS, C., and MARSHALL, J. H., Gas Chromatographic Instrumentation Development, *Space Programs Summary No. 37-20,* vol. IV, Jet Propulsion Laboratory, Pasadena, California, April 1963.

26. BOWMAN, L., Gas Chromatography, *Space Programs Summary No. 37-19,* vol. IV, Jet Propulsion Laboratory, Pasadena, California, February 1963.

27. WILHITE, W. F., *Development of the Surveyor Gas Chromatograph,* Technical Report No. 32-425, Jet Propulsion Laboratory, Pasadena, California, May 15, 1963.

28. OYAMA, V. I., Use of Gas Chromatography for the Detection of Life on Mars, *Nature,* vol. 200 (1963), pp. 1058–9.

29. RHO, J., and BEHAR, J., Fluorometric Measurements of Growth. II. The Fluorescence of Proteins as a Measure of Bacterial Growth, *Space Programs Summary No. 37-25,* vol. IV, Jet Propulsion Laboratory, Pasadena, California, February 29, 1964.

CHAPTER VIII
BIOLOGICAL CONTAMINATION OF
THE PLANETS

P. J. GEIGER, L. D. JAFFE, and G. MAMIKUNIAN

Jet Propulsion Laboratory
Pasadena, California

INTRODUCTION

THE accidental introduction of terrestrial microorganisms to other planets during the course of space exploration by unmanned spacecraft is now a very real possibility. If these organisms survive and multiply, recognition of any native extraterrestrial life on that particular planet will be very difficult. The newly immigrant organism(s) may thrive and compete with existing microflora and perhaps become the predominating species on the planet, thus permanently marring the investigations and the possible discovery of an independent origin of life in the solar system. Even if the planet had no indigenous life, the terrestrial microorganisms might degrade or alter irreversibly the indigenous organic matter that might be of recent cosmochemical synthesis or a residue of former but now extinct life. If life was at one time present at a certain stage of evolution but somehow is now extinct, the organic residue would be of great significance and must be considered a part of the biological record of the planet. This organic matter no doubt could easily be utilized by the contaminating microbial species, given the right conditions, and therefore a valuable record of the past history of the planet could be completely falsified or permanently lost. For these reasons, the sterilization of planetary spacecraft and their ancillary vehicles, or alternative methods for avoiding accidental introduction of microorganisms, appears to be imperative.

Despite considerable controversy on the need, degree, and methods of sterilization, there is general agreement, at least among biologists, that to avoid interference with exobiological observations on planets that may contain an active biota, terrestrial organisms should not be inadvertently released there. Studies of terrestrial organisms in natural and simulated environments indicate their survivability and persistence and, hence, the necessity for requiring a degree of assurance against contamination of Mars and Venus, in particular, with these Earth organisms. Thus, steril-

283

ization and other techniques of avoiding man-made biological contamination of the planets should be prerequisite for exobiological exploration.

However, sterilization lowers spacecraft systems' reliability, and it reduces the chance of launching within periods fixed by astronomical constraints. The gain which should be achieved through spacecraft sterilization, in return of significant biological and biochemical information about the planets, must be balanced against these losses. On the other hand, the experimental results of unmanned probes may dictate the level of sterilization required for subsequent missions of manned vehicles and perhaps in the future help to reduce the stringency of the requirement.

In this Chapter, examples of the persistence of terrestrial life are presented, and the probability of achieving and maintaining sterility of spacecraft with various suggested procedures at early stages of unmanned space exploration and alternative techniques for avoiding biological contamination of the planets are discussed. Only unmanned exploration is dealt with, since sterilization of manned spacecraft will require separate consideration. Only contamination of another planet with Earth organisms is discussed; contamination of Earth with organisms from other planets, when samples or spacecraft are brought back, is not considered.

THE PERSISTENCE OF LIFE

In this Section, we shall consider examples, particularly from microbiology, of life found in some of the most forbidding kinds of ecological niches, judged from a purely terrestrial, and perhaps anthropocentric, standpoint. In addition, attention will be drawn to some results of experiments dealing with the survival of microorganisms, but not necessarily their ability to thrive or even to reproduce, under certain other extreme conditions. The purpose is to indicate the seriousness and likelihood of the possibilities raised in the Introduction with regard to contamination. The discussion following is in no sense intended to be a complete review but does seek to point out examples from a wide variety of sources to invite the reader's interest and provide a basis for deeper appreciation of the adaptability and persistence of life.

Natural, Extreme Environments

A concise and informative review has appeared recently on this subject,[1] but many of the facts bear repeating and re-emphasizing for our purposes. In addition, some newer material has been reported more recently which further supports and extends the conclusions that were drawn regarding the amazing adaptability of microbial life.

Temperatures. Microorganisms are found to grow and reproduce over a wide temperature range extending from −24 to 104°C. The lower limit has been observed in Antarctica,[2] where several genera, including *Bacillus megaterium, micrococcus* sp., *corynebacterium* sp., and a single yeast, *Sporobolomyces,* were found. Apparently, no algae were present here, but these have been found in other ponds in the Wright Valley, where they provide food for bacteria and larger microscopic animals. The pond water was of low organic content and high salinity, and its freezing point was −48°C. High adaptability is indicated because these species all grew in common media at room temperatures. High salinity and depressed freezing point of the natural medium have been observed in many other recorded cases of bacteria cultured at subzero temperatures, particularly marine bacteria. ZoBell has been able to culture 76 out of 88 kinds of marine bacteria at subzero temperatures.[3]

Besides the yeast already mentioned above, the mold *Sporotrichum carnis,* as well as other fungi, grows at temperatures as low as −10°C.[4] Zernow has observed swimming *Dunaliella* and *Pyramidomonas* in drops of water from Lake Balpash, Kazakh, U.S.S.R., at temperatures as low as −15°C.[5]

Other cases of low-temperature growth have been observed by Borgstrom, who described some pseudomonads and molds that grow in concentrated sugar solutions and fruit juices at temperatures as low as −18 to −20°C.[6] The same author has indicated that *Aspergillus glaucus* will grow at −18°C in glycerol.

Bacteria of the usual kinds found in other soils occur in certain Antarctic soils as well, including typical bacillary, spiral, coccal, and filamentous forms. Bacteria persist even in the ice and snow of Antarctica, but in sheer mass the algae are the most abundant microbial forms found in ice and snow as well as on open ground and in water.[7] Where regions of Antarctica are sterile, extreme dryness would seem to be the cause but not low temperatures *per se*. Plants best withstanding desiccation and extending farthest south to within about 4° of the pole are the lichens, but how much of their growth occurs at subzero temperatures is not clear, since during the long summer days after the sun "rises", rock temperatures increase from −15 to 27.8°C in a matter of 3 hours.[7] Interestingly enough, the pattern of microbial life follows that found in the Antarctic seas in that the numbers of organisms are as large as those found in temperate regions of the Earth; the numbers of different species, however, are smaller.

In regions of high temperature, it is well known that certain thermophiles, bacteria and blue-green algae, live in hot springs in ranges of 80–88°C. A recent article by Allen, for instance, might be cited on this subject.[8] *Bacillus stearothermophilus,* a spore former, can also be grown at these high temperatures. In fact, besides the blue-green algae, most of the thermophiles found widely distributed are aerobic spore-forming bacteria, although fungi and actinomycetes also exist. The only chlorophyte known that can grow at high temperatures (55°C) is *Cyanidium caldarium*.[8] ZoBell[9] has cultured sulfate-reducing bacteria at temperatures up to 85°C, and by increasing the pressure to 1000 atm, one strain could be grown at 104°C. Under natural conditions, these forms exist at temperatures up to 105°C but are apparently permitted to do so only by the concomitant high pressures of around 400 atm. Extremely high-temperature forms of microorganisms are probably not significant where biological contamination of the planets, particularly Mars, will be our concern, since accompanying pressures must also be very high. Similarly, although deep-sea sediments have the low-temperature conditions of interest, pressures again are very high.[10]

Aridity. It has already been mentioned that only lichens grow in and resist the most arid regions of the south terrestrial pole. But even these have a limit, and there are also dry, sterile valleys to be found in Antarctica.[7]

There are cases, however, in which bacteria and fungi do grow at extremely low water activities. Scott has mentioned the ability of *Aspergillus glaucus* to grow on substrates where the activity of water was as low as 0.65,[11] and Zeuch[12] has stated that *Pleurococcus vulgaris* can grow at relative humidities of 48% at 20°C, 55% at 10°C, and 68% at 1°C.

On a planet like Mars, where the amount of available water is unknown but probably very low, perhaps only very specialized forms that conserve and do not excrete water as an end product of metabolism are prevalent. One might then ask what chance the expected types of contaminants from the Earth would have to mutate to such forms themselves. Simple adaptation under these conditions may not be possible, although survival in a dormant state is likely, as we shall see later.

Radiation. Ultraviolet radiation effects are well documented for short periods of exposure. Sterilization of aerosols, at least, can be accomplished with wavelengths in the range of 2650 to 2900 Å. Photoreactivation phenomena are also known,[13] and shielding by dust particles or by other means can certainly protect organisms from lethal effects. There seems to have been no systematic work done employing continuous doses of ultraviolet light during culturing. Survival of organisms in soil under these artificial conditions will be mentioned later.

In the food industry a highly resistant strain (*Micrococcus radiodurans*) has been isolated and found to withstand doses as high as 6×10^6 rad,[14] an unusually high resistance for a non-spore-forming organism.

In certain lichens, special pigments have been found to develop.[15] Perhaps these help to confer upon them increased resistance to ultraviolet light and might permit them to live at great altitudes in the Himalaya mountains, where lichens are indeed found but apparently do not fare as well as certain grasses. Those lichens whose fungal hyphae are heavily pigmented certainly must reduce harmful light reaching the algal symbiont;[15] any conclusions about protective effects are purely a matter of conjecture at this time, since the mechanisms have by no means been elucidated. With this kind of adaptatability, however, there is no reason not to suspect that microorganisms can adapt to effects of ultraviolet as well as strong visible radiation.

Salinity. A wide range of salt concentrations is apparently easily tolerated by microorganisms. Some heterotrophic bacteria will grow in distilled water containing only 70 μg of organic matter per liter.[16] At the high concentrations of brine in the Dead Sea (salinity 280 to 320/1000) a gram-negative rod, a yeast-like form, and a green filamentous form were found when samples of the water were supplemented with 1% peptone[17] and incubated. Halophilic bacteria, in fact, are quite abundant in nature and may fail to grow if the salt concentration falls below 15 to 16%; many are osmotically injured by solutions that are too dilute.[18] It seems probable that halophilic bacteria, like marine bacteria, are to be regarded as salt-water-adapted forms of common organisms.[19] It should be noted that algae are common in brine pools, too. In natural pools of saturated salt solution concentrated by evaporation, the most prominent of the algae is *Dunaliella salina,* a bright red form.

Perhaps one of the most curious cases is that of *Bacillus circulans,* which has been isolated from solid media, salts of the German zechstein, on three occasions by Dombrowski as well as by others.[20] Probably, these bacteria have been preserved there; it is doubtful that they grow and reproduce under such conditions.

Range of Eh and pH. Baas Becking *et al.* have given the best treatment of these variables as they pertain to natural environments.[21] The graphical representations from their work are redrawn here as Figs. 1–3. The Eh values are given for the prevailing pH values and were found in the range of 850 to −450 mv. The pH values lay between 1.0 and 10.2. There may be more extreme situations, but these authors used only data for Eh and pH measured simultaneously.

Growth and reproduction of *Thiobacilli* can take place in extreme acid media, and pH values as low as 0 are well known. Among the molds, Starkey and Waksman found *Acontium velatum* and fungus D to be most acid resistant.[22] These were originally isolated from an industrial $CuSO_4$ solution and grow well at a pH value as low as 0.4, some growth even being recorded at pH 0.

Allen has shown that the alga, *Cyanidium caldarium,* can grow essentially at pH 0.[23] This algal strain was originally isolated from a hot spring containing 0.1 N H_2SO_4.

At high pH values, many microorganisms can be found to grow and

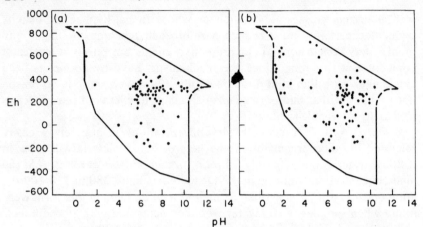

FIG. 1. Eh–pH characteristics. a, Green algae and diatoms. b, Blue-green algae.

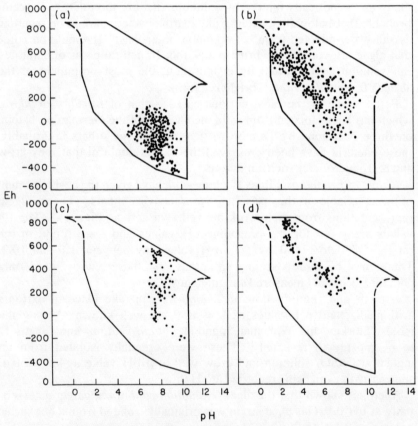

FIG. 2. Eh–pH characteristics. a, Sulfate-reducing bacteria. b, Thiobacteria.
c, Denitrifying bacteria, d, Iron bacteria.

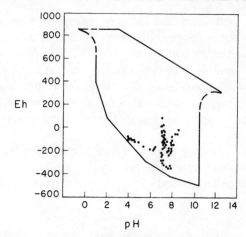

FIG. 3. Eh–pH characteristics of heterotrophic bacteria (*Escherichia coli, Clostridium botulinum,* and *Lactobacillus*).

reproduce; values of 10 or 11 are not uncommon for *Streptococcus fecalis* and *Bacillus circulans*; even values as high as 13 have been claimed, but this observation has not been supported by others.[1,24] "Higher" forms of life than bacteria have been found in the pH range of 9 to 11 in certain alkaline lakes. Among these were algae, rotifers, and copepods.

Summary. The discussion in the foregoing Sections is summarized in Table 1. These indicated limits have so far been found to occur naturally, with a few exceptions, in various terrestrial situations. There is little reason to doubt that more extreme conditions could be produced artificially, in which growth and reproduction would probably be far from optimal. There is no intention to imply that growth and reproduction are anywhere near optimal under the conditions described in Table 1 — merely to indicate that they do occur. With further investigation, perhaps even wider ranges of environment might be discovered.

Artificial, Extreme Conditions

In the following discussion, the emphasis is on the survival of microorganisms under certain extreme conditions in which there may be no possibility of growth and reproduction. This is an important indication of the suitability of microorganisms for space travel and survival at the destination, regardless of whether or not they are present as unwanted companions.

Freeze-drying. A wealth of information has been developed in this area because of its interest for maintaining culture collections. Heckly's review of the subject is recent and valuable.[25] Generally, the best preservation is achieved for an exceedingly wide variety of microbial types by choosing mature, well-nourished cultures which are then suspended in some protecting solution, containing perhaps sucrose or serum, and then frozen in small batches by cooling to −10 to −20°C. A vacuum of about 150 μ is applied and evaporation carried out while maintaining the frozen state. Other authors state that freezing is not necessary, and simple desiccation under vacuum at room temperature is adequate for even the more delicate organisms.[26] Preservation usually lasts from several months to many years.

Vacuum and temperature effects. There seems little doubt now that the ultrahigh vacuum of space will not lead to death of microorganisms. Despite one report to the contrary,[27] most workers have found significant survival rates.

TABLE 1. Environmental limits for growth and reproduction of microorganisms (adapted from Vallentyne[1])

Factor	Lower limit	Upper limit
Temperature	− 24°C (fungi, bacteria)	104°C (sulfate-reducing bacteria under 1000 atm hydrostatic pressure)
Aridity	Double-distilled water	48% relative humidity at 20°C (*Pleurococcus vulgaris*)
Radiation	Essentially 0	6×10^6 rad (*Micrococcus radiodurans*)
Salinity	Double-distilled water (heterotrophic bacteria)	Saturated brines (*Dunaliella*, halophilic bacteria, etc.)
Eh	− 450 mv at pH 9.5 (sulfate-reducing bacteria)	+ 850 mv at pH 3 (iron bacteria)
pH	0 (*Acontium velatum*, fungus D, *Thiobacillus thiooxidans*)	13 (?) (*Plectonema nostocorum*)
Hydrostatic pressure	Essentially 0	1400 atm (deep-sea bacteria)

Portner *et al.* (Ref. 1366) exposed *Bacillus subtilis* var. *niger, Aspergillus fumigatus,* and *Mycobacterium smegmatis* to ultrahigh vacuum, attaining 3.6×10^{-10} torr at 5 days. *M. smegmatis* was the only organism to lose appreciable numbers, but even then, only two-thirds of the control sample were killed. Temperatures in this experiment were ambient.

In a series of studies, Davis and coworkers have sought to determine the combined effects of ultrahigh vacuum and temperatures on the viability of some spores and soil organisms.[28] Considerably fewer spores of *B. stearothermophilus, B. megaterium,* and *Clostridium sporogenes* were recovered than were spores of *B. subtilis* var. *niger* and *A. niger* after 4 to 5 days at 53 and 60°C and 10^{-8} to 5×10^{-9} torr. There were no significant differences in the recoveries of these five organisms after exposure to 25 and −190°C in vacuum. *B. subtilis* spores were killed only after 5 days at these vacuums and 90°C; 10^4 out of 10^6 spores, however, survived at this temperature for 5 days at atmospheric pressure. Molds and actinomycetes were particularly resistant up to 60°C in vacuum, and actinomycetes were recovered even after exposure to 120°C. Geiger *et al.*[29] have found that at 25°C and 10^{-10} torr exposure for 137 days there was considerable survival of *B. subtilis* var. *niger* and *A. niger* spores and *M. phlei* cells after a relatively small initial decrease in numbers no doubt due to drying from the water suspensions.

Survival of many microorganisms after exposure to temperatures near absolute zero has been well documented by Becquerel.[30] At the higher end of the temperature scale, Rodenbeck has observed the survival of some bacterial spores after 5 hours' immersion in nonaqueous media at temperatures approaching 140°C.[31] In another report, Silverman *et al.* state that a soil sample yielded viable bacteria after exposure to 170°C and ultrahigh vacuum.[32]

Radiation. Probably, situations involving strongly ionizing radiations can almost all be classed as artificial; for instance, the passage of spacecraft through the Van Allen belts, the exposure of foods to gamma radiation, or the exposure of other cultures to X-rays or gamma radiation. Nevertheless, populations of many microorganisms will survive single large doses in the range of 10^6 roentgens.[33] The case of *Micrococcus radiodurans* has already been mentioned. Similarly, Schmidt and Nank have reported significant survival of *Clostridium botulinum* spores in a number of representative foodstuffs irradiated with 2.8×10^6 rad dosage of ionizing radiation.[34] Silverman *et al.* have also reported that "a reduction of from one-third to one-ninth of the viability of spores irradiated in vacuum occurred with vacuum-treated spores irradiated in air".[32]

Simulation of extraterrestrial ecologies. There is little information available in this field at the present. Nevertheless, there may be some important results yet to be learned that pertain to the adaptability of microorganisms to specific combinations of conditions. Currently, the conditions of most interest are those of Mars. The ranges of only a few parameters of a simulated Martian ecology are known with any confidence; the rest are estimated for purposes of the experiments. For an excellent treatment of this subject, the reader is referred to Chapter IV of this volume.

Packer *et al.* have also presented some of the more recent evidence from terrestrial experiments simulating Martian conditions and have reviewed much earlier literature for combinations of similar conditions that have been tried. Their paper should be consulted for details,[35] but the main conclusions are clear. All terrestrial soil samples tested contained populations of microorganisms that survived for at least 6 months under the following conditions: (1) a 12-hour freeze–thaw cycle from about $-60°C$ to about $20°C$; (2) atmospheres of 95% nitrogen, 5% carbon dioxide, and low moisture content; (3) less than 0.1 atm pressure; and (4) a total ultraviolet dose at $2537 Å$ of $10^9 erg cm^{-2}$. These conditions effected some selection among the microorganisms tested; conditions were not, however, conducive to growth and reproduction. Nevertheless, the authors state, "The probable existence of organic matter and moisture on Mars, at least in restricted locales and times, makes it possible that terrestrial microorganisms can also reproduce on Mars."

TECHNIQUE AND PROBLEMS OF STERILIZATION

Since terrestrial microorganisms can be extremely hardy, as we have seen, careful consideration and design of sterilization methods and scrupulous application of such methods to all spacecraft destined for biological exploration are required in order to achieve the degrees of confidence that have been indicated. This Section considers the feasibility and usefulness of various techniques suggested for this purpose.

Sterilizing a spacecraft is not a simple matter. Although sterilization procedures are used routinely on surgical instruments and supplies, drugs, food, and other items, sterilizing an entire operating room of a hospital or a complete ward is a problem of a higher order. For an individual spacecraft, the problem is of a similar order, with the profound complication that we wish each of the components to be sterile internally as well. Referring to the example of the hospital, it is as if, in addition, all the furnishings, equipment, instruments, etc., in the hospital had to be externally and internally sterile for fear that accidental breakage might lead to severe and intolerable contamination.

A further complication is the fact that the usual methods of sterilization damage a great many spacecraft components and materials. Also, spacecraft are large, complex devices and are likely to require repair or replacement of parts during fabrication and testing. Again, and most important, standards applied to sterilization for the usual terrestrial purposes are simply not sufficiently rigorous for spacecraft. A surgical instrument should be free of pathogens; a spacecraft should, to a high degree of confidence, be free of all microorganisms. Even if a few pathogens reach a surgical incision, for instance, the defenses of the human body will usually take care of them. Perhaps ultimately during our endeavors, another planet will be assumed to have defenses comparable or somewhat analogous in effectiveness. But for the present and near future at least, current scientific opinion would adhere to the necessity for scrupulous sterilization of spacecraft, however it may be brought about.

The word sterility has sometimes been used somewhat loosely. Important reviews and books on sterilization point this out, and, in addition, contain much valuable information on modern techniques (Ref. 1394).[36,37] As has been stated by the Council on Pharmacy and Chemistry of the American Medical Association, sterility is an absolute term. An object is either sterile or not sterile; a single viable organism within the object or on its surface spells contamination.

Unfortunately, it is not possible by any simple examination of the object to determine whether or not it is sterile. In general, there is no way to determine sterility without destroying either the usefulness or the sterility of the object. All that can be done is to use procedures which, based on past experience, lead us to believe that the chance that the object is not sterile is less than some selected, small value. We must therefore evaluate a probability that sterility has, in fact, been achieved; that this probability can, in general, only be estimated is no argument against the use of procedures for sterilization. When conclusive experimental data are impossible to obtain, the best available data plus sound technical judgment based upon experience must be used. Indeed, much practical science and engineering are based on this approach.

General Considerations

If cells of a given microbial species are exposed to a sterilizing agent under constant conditions, the viable population usually falls exponentially with the period of exposure. In chemistry, this would be the description of a first-order reaction, and, analogously, if we plot the logarithm of the viable count with respect to time, the result is a straight line of negative slope (Fig. 4). Chemical agents, heat, and radiation ordinarily reduce single microbial populations in this way. Sometimes, however, the curve is observed to become less steep after a long period of exposure. This diminishing death rate is ordinarily considered to be caused by the presence of microbial strains with varying resistances to the sterilizing agent, i.e. a lack of homogeneity in the original population.[38,39]

If we accept and make use of the exponential law, the necessary period for completing sterilization depends upon the initial viable microbial count. If an experimental death curve is then extrapolated to negative values of the logarithm of the population, these values may be interpreted as the probabilities that a single viable organism remains after a given period of exposure to sterilant.

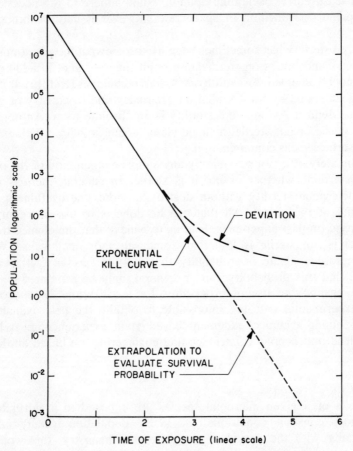

FIG. 4. Effect of exposure to a sterilizing agent upon a homogeneous microbial population (assumed initial population, 10^7 microbes).

Physical Methods

Moist heat. Moist heat, that is steam under pressure, in one of the most commonly used sterilizing agents. A great many spacecraft components, however, would be damaged and perhaps rendered completely useless by heating under pressure with steam, or autoclaving, as the method is called. An even more fundamental difficulty, however, is that many space-craft components, such as vacuum tubes, transistors, or electronic de-vices, are sealed. Steam applied to their exteriors will heat but not moisten their interiors; any effects on microorganisms in the interior will be solely due to dry heating. This is true also of plastics and other structural materials that may contain microorganisms embedded within their matrices. We must conclude that steam under pressure is not satisfactory for sterilizing spacecraft of present design.

Dry heat. Sterilization by dry heat requires considerably greater times and temperatures than does sterilization by moist heat. As far as is known, spore-forming bacteria are the most resistant of all organisms to dry heat. The population of highly resistant bacterial spores has been reported to be lowered by a factor of about 10^{-13} upon subjection to 24 hr of dry heat at 135°C.[40,41] An estimated total of 10^9 organisms on the surfaces and in the interiors of spacecraft has been mentioned as representative.[42] With this starting population, exposure to 135°C dry heat for 24 hr should reduce the probability that a single viable organism remains to about 10^{-4}. There is, however, the possibility that through some error, a portion of an individual spacecraft component might not receive the intended exposure to heat. The probability that such an error may occur, thus jeopardizing attainment of sterility, might be made as low as 10^{-6} by adequate temperature monitoring and other care by well-trained personnel, including careful work by experts on heat-flow problems. Dry-heat sterilization, therefore, might appear to be the method of choice. Unfortunately, many of the components now used in spacecraft are damaged by this severe heating. Components that can withstand strong heating probably can be developed, and considerable effort is now being expended on such development. The number of different types of components is large, however, and a great deal of time and money are required to make this kind of development fruitful for the space program.

Radiation. Ultraviolet radiation, though sometimes useful for sterilization of exposed surfaces and aerosols, does not reach interiors or shadowed surfaces. Ionizing radiation of sufficiently high energy for penetration would eliminate this difficulty. Available data on resistant organisms[43] indicate that on the basis of an exponential death rate, it should be possible to reduce the original microbial count by a factor of 10^{-13} with a dose of 1.2×10^7 rad. Unfortunately, this dose will damage many plastics and elastomers, including solid propellants. It will also damage optical properties of many inorganic materials, including glasses and pigments. A great deal of time, money, and effort will again be needed to develop components with better radiation resistance and, at the same time, suitable in other necessary ways for spacecraft engineering.

Filtration. For certain fluids, it is possible to use heat, radiation, and internal chemical sterilization. Sterilization by passing through a bacteriological filter should also be considered. For gases, fiber-type filters may be used. With a properly designed, prechecked, and postchecked system, the chance of contamination with such filters can be brought to 10^{-3} or lower. Moreover, several filters could be used in series to increase the likelihood that no organisms get through. For liquids, fiber-type filters must be very thick and provide very slow filtration. As an alternative, filters all of whose pores are smaller than the size of the organism may be used; with present technology, this means membrane filters. Such filters are likely to fail because of surface scratching, fracture, or other imperfections. The assurance of sterilization is, therefore, only about 10^{-2}. Several such filters could be used in series to improve assurance, but being of the same type, and particularly if they are from the same batch, there is considerable likelihood that all will show the same imperfections any particular one does. Thus, the probability that all will fail might be greater than the product of the failure probabilities of separate filters.

Ultrasonic methods. Ultrasonic vibrations have been used routinely in the laboratory for some years now for breaking cell walls of various kinds of microorganisms when it is desired to prepare the walls for chemical examination or enzymes for biochemical studies. Generally speaking, the method requires large amounts of energy to be delivered to small volumes of liquid. The method does not usually produce exceptionally good yields of material nor kill microorganisms very effectively (but see Hughes and Nyborg[44]).

For spacecraft, the method would appear to be impractical if not impracticable. Surely certain components would be degraded or damaged by application of such a technique, which might cause heating in conjunction with mechanical effects, and reliability would therefore suffer. In addition, there is some doubt that the kind of rapid compression and decompression or cavitation necessary could be produced in dry materials; hence, the mechanism occurring in fluids would probably not be present in solid spacecraft materials, with the possible exception of certain plastics. Nevertheless, the method might still find some application for those portions of the spacecraft that are fluid — perhaps certain exobiological or life-detecting instruments that may partly rely on aqueous solutions for their mode of operation. In such a case, a sealed package which cannot be exposed to heat might yet be sterilized by judicious use of ultrasonics.

Chemical Methods

Gaseous sterilants. Gas sterilization kills only microbes on exposed surfaces or in materials easily penetrated by the gaseous sterilant. Sealed interiors are usually not reached, nor are interiors of closed screwholes, flanges, gasket seats, electrical connectors, or other closely fitting surfaces.

Ethylene oxide is probably one of the best available sterilizing gases and does not damage most spacecraft components. In appropriate concentrations, it has killed populations of about 10^8 resistant organisms that were dried on paper patches; for this result, an 11-hr exposure period under appropriate conditions of temperature and humidity was required.[45] If we desire a probability of 10^{-4} that a single viable organism remains, then, starting with a surface population of 10^8,[42] it is necessary to reduce the count by a factor of 10^{-12}; on the basis of an exponential death curve, the necessary exposure period would be increased to about 17 hr.

In using a gaseous sterilant, it is necessary to make certain that the gas reaches all surfaces intended. There is also the chance of human or instrumental errors being made in control of concentration, temperature, humidity, etc. It is estimated that there is one chance in a thousand of a serious human error occurring. By a system of multiple checks, duplication of measuring instruments, etc., the probability that a breach in sterility might arise could be reduced to less than 10^{-3}.

Some significant uncertainties remain, however, with regard to the · effects of substrates that might harbor contamination[46-53] and humidity and vacuum conditions[39,54] different from those in the experiments referred to. In particular, for some components, and for some important modifications in humidity or vacuum conditions which might be of practical importance for spacecraft, there is evidence that ethylene oxide death curves are not exponential but level off between 8 and 18 hr, so that longer exposure produces no further reduction in viable population;[39,48] it would appear that there is not yet sufficient evidence that ethylene oxide can be relied upon to produce high probabilities of sterility under conditions necessary for the treatment of spacecraft. Even fewer data are available for other gaseous sterilants of interest. We conclude that, at the present, ethylene oxide can be of some limited value for surface sterilization of spacecraft.

Liquid sterilants. It might be possible to dip components of a spacecraft or its capsule into a sterilizing liquid; formaldehyde in methanol is considered one of the best of these.[55,56,57] As in the case with gaseous sterilants, however, liquids will sterilize only the exposed surfaces that they touch. Moreover, because of higher viscosity and surface tension, liquids will not reach many crevices that would be reached by gaseous sterilants. For those surfaces that are reached, it is possible to achieve a high probability of sterility in a shorter time than with gas. The required periods of exposure are some hours, rather than a few minutes as is sometimes thought.[55,56,57] Moreover, the effectiveness of liquid sterilants may be somewhat erratic, apparently as a result of minor variations in concentration, total quantity, time of storage, temperature, humidity, substrate composition, and cleanliness.[55,56,58]

Experiments with liquid sterilants on simple spacecraft components previously inoculated with bacterial spores[58] have indicated that, at best, viable spores were recovered from the surfaces of 1 to 10% of the components used; for 100 components, therefore, the probability of contamination was essentially unity in these experiments.

With either liquids or gases, plumbing connections to a sterile lander can be made only to the nonsterile side of a sterilization barrier (filter, heater, or pipe full of sporicidal liquid). A suitable design for separation is needed to remove nonsterile parts of the plumbing from the spacecraft without exposing the latter to possible contamination. This might imply remote or automatic separation, with its additional complications, rather than manual separation of the necessary connections.

A further problem is that presently available liquid sterilants damage certain critical spacecraft components; in particular, they degrade the electrical properties of electrical connectors.

It must be concluded that liquid sterilants will probably be useful in helping to solve only a small part of the over-all problem.

Internal chemical sterilization. Some materials used in spacecraft are inherently sterile; for example, fuming nitric acid, a propellant.[59] A microbicidal chemical might be added in the course of the manufacture of some other materials and components. This might be done during normal production or be specified by those concerned with sterilization. The chance that contamination remains depends, of course, upon the item and the procedures used. To obtain quantitative estimates of this chance, it will be necessary to obtain experimental death curves for the particular chemical formulation and the conditions employed. The overwhelming difficulty here is that in order to know that the chance of contamination is 10^{-4}, it will be necessary to make over 10,000 tests and be certain that not more than one of these indicates any microbial growth.

There are other problems too. If addition of the internal chemical sterilant is not an indispensable part of the normal manufacturing procedure, then there remains the chance that human errors may lead to omission of the sterilant. Problems of this sort are different in kind from the technical problems and need to be handled by careful administrative procedures.

One is forced to conclude that the whole problem of internal sterility of various solid parts and elastomers is an extremely difficult one, not only from the standpoint of the sheer number of tests that need to be made but also from the fact that microorganisms must first be mechanically recovered from the various materials in order to make the tests. This very difficulty perhaps suggests a new way of examining the problem, for if internal contaminants can be recovered only with great difficulty, what is the probability that these same contaminants, locked within solids, might be released by inadvertent breakage — a crash landing for instance? Indeed, the probability may be acceptably small for certain materials and components (as discussed in a later Section).

Aseptic Technique

In the previous two Sections, it was more or less implied that whole spacecraft were being considered for treatment by one or another of the methods suggested. In this Section, we consider piecemeal sterilization during fabrication or assembly of a spacecraft in which some of the methods that have already been discussed are applied in definite ways. Specific techniques and ordered sequences of application are needed to allow for various difficulties connected with certain materials and components already mentioned.

Assembly of sterile components. Aseptic procedures similar to those used in surgery or bacteriology have often been suggested for assembly of previously sterilized spacecraft components or subassemblies. If the assembly is done in an ordinary "clean" laboratory or electronics plant room, the probability of contamination from the air alone must be considered essentially unity per part. Aerosol contamination, even under clean room conditions, contributes 10^1 to 10^3 organisms/ft^2/hr that grow on certain common bacterial culture media,[50,60,61] and perhaps a larger number of organisms for which these media are unsuitable. (It is clear that ordinary surgical procedures do not maintain sterility but rather keep the number of pathogenic organisms introduced small enough for normal body defenses to overcome.)

If the technique is supplemented by applying liquid sterilants to mating surfaces during the assembly operation, the chance that contamination remains is estimated to be 10^{-1} to 10^{-2} per part, or essentially unity for 100 parts; thus, the situation is only insignificantly improved.

A slightly better approach would be to assemble sterile, bagged parts under a standard bacteriological hood provided with a positive pressure of filtered air. The hood, sprayed in advance with a liquid sterilant, would be furnished with ultraviolet lamps to reduce contamination further. Manipulations would be manual, with the operator's hands in previously sterilized gloves. Under such circumstances, the chances of contamination from the bags, hands, gloves, and air are estimated at 10^{-2} per part. This estimate is based upon data obtained by Food and Drug Administration inspectors, who, using this procedure in drug industry plants, detected 55 infected lots out of about 1500 sampled in simple routine operations such as bottling of sterile solutions for injection.[62] At 10^{-2} per part, the probability that contamination occurs in 100 parts would again be about unity.

If a liquid sterilant were applied to mating surfaces during the assembly operations in the hood, a further reduction in the chance of contamination of 10^{-1} to 10^{-2} per part should be attainable, resulting in an over-all chance of contamination of 10^{-3} to 10^{-4} per part. For 100 parts, this would amount to 10^{-2} or greater.

If assembly in a hood is used, but the parts brought in have been externally contaminated, the resulting assembly would certainly contain trapped contaminants. Sterility might then depend on reaching microbes in crevices with a gaseous or liquid sterilant; the probability is that contamination remains would again be close to unity for 100 parts.

Sterile assembly in a glove box. Perhaps the best technique for sterile assembly would be to assemble the parts in a glove box containing a sterilizing gas such as ethylene oxide. One difficulty here is that no available gloves are sufficiently impervious to sterilant to permit an operator to use them for very long without severe blistering of the hands. Ethylene oxide dissolves in and diffuses through rubber or plastic in a relatively short time, thus causing this regrettable situation. Present methods require a purge of the box and gloves with sterile air or inert gas for some hours after the ethylene oxide treatment before one can reinsert his hands into the gloves.[49] With such a technique, if the parts to be assembled are internally sterile and are placed in the box before the ethylene oxide treatment is initiated, the reductions in contamination should be as described previously ($< 10^{-3}$). The chance that contaminated air might leak into the system after the ethylene oxide has been removed must also be considered. If the purging air has been properly filtered or heated to remove microbes, and if the air system, the chamber itself, and the gloves have been properly pretested and monitored, the chance of having such a leak could be reduced to 10^{-3} or less. This estimate is based on the experience of the National Institutes of Health, where glove manipulations have been performed with no break in sterility several times a week for 4 years in several chambers containing germ-free mice.[63] This record, a contamination level of 10^{-3} to 10^{-4}, or even lower, per manipulation appears to be unusually good; it is based on the use of permanent, welded, stainless-steel boxes and highly trained personnel. With temporary or flexible enclosures, it would be more difficult to ensure freedom from leaks; the chance of contamination would be higher and more difficult to estimate.

A modification of the glove-box procedure would permit bringing internally sterile parts and tools into the sterilized glove box through an airlock. Leakage through the airlock closures, however, increases the chance of contaminating the box. Normal indoor air admitted usually contains 1 to 10 or more organisms/ft^3 (Ref. 145);[18,40-43,60,61,64-66] if this air were not sterilized, the chance of contamination would, of course, be near unity.

The presence of microbes on the parts brought in or on their containers means that there will be some chance that these microbes will reach supposedly sterile parts through contacts with box, gloves, and tools. The probability is estimated to be 10^{-2} per part or higher; for 100 parts, therefore, the probability of contamination is essentially unity.

Previous application of a liquid sterilant could reduce the probability of surface contamination of tools, etc., by a factor of 10^{-1} to 10^{-2} per part, as mentioned previously. If sterile, bagged parts were brought in through a U-tube containing liquid sterilant, the chance of the sterilant not reaching all organisms on the bags (especially at seals) would be perhaps 10^{-3} to 10^{-4} per bag, or 10^{-1} to 10^{-2} for 100 bags. Exposure to the liquid for some hours would be required to reach this degree of assurance of sterilization, since time for wetting and penetration by the sterilant must be allowed.

Certain plans for sterile assembly envisage the transference of sterile fluids through piping and fittings into a presterilized spacecraft or capsule. The chance of contamination of piping and fittings then becomes important. It should be noted that with techniques involving connections opened to laboratory air followed by application of a liquid sterilant to the surfaces, the chance of contamination per part is 10^{-1} to 10^{-2}.

Many other variations of the glove-box technique could be suggested. It should be remembered, however, that a spacecraft is a complicated device; *Ranger,* for example, contains over 100 electrical connectors, 500 mating flanges, 1000 screws, etc.[67] Assembly of such a spacecraft is therefore a lengthy procedure, involving many persons. In addition, the size of the spacecraft makes glove techniques more difficult to perform than the common laboratory procedures for which glove boxes are usually designed.

It should also be noted that if pieces are sterilized separately and then assembled, the probabilities of contamination must be added for each of the total number of pieces involved, thus increasing the total probability of contamination and very likely bringing it nearer to one. If the operating personnel or inspectors are not highly trained in sterilization techniques and sterile procedures, the chance of a breach in sterility is very much increased; a factor of perhaps 10^3 is a conservative estimate.

Miscellaneous Methods

This Section deals with various miscellaneous or fortuitous occurrences that might, on the one hand, be considered effects of the "natural" environment of the spacecraft or of conditions encountered in the course of performing a mission, and, on the other hand, could be modifications of previously discussed methods.

Sterilization in flight. The question has been raised whether the space environment itself might not be adequate to sterilize a spacecraft. The results of studies of ultrahigh vacuum have been mentioned previously[68,69] (see also Refs. 769, 1366). With these results in mind, it must be said that the probability of contamination will not be decreased by vacuum exposure.

The outer surface of the spacecraft is also exposed to solar ultraviolet and soft X-rays in those positions in which it faces the Sun. This radiation should sterilize the exposed outer surfaces, but we recall that there are many areas of the spacecraft that ultraviolet and soft X-radiation cannot reach. Therefore, any decrease in the probability of contamination due to ultraviolet light and X-rays must be considered insignificant.

Particle radiation is also present, and if the spacecraft flies through the Van Allen radiation belts, taking perhaps 10 hr in transit, the dose received close to the surface, within 10^{-3} g/cm^2 or less, may be as much as 10^7 rad — enough to sterilize to this shallow depth. Through the shielding thicknesses provided by many parts of the spacecraft structure (approximately 1 g/cm^2), the dose in 10 hr would be less than 10^2 rad, an insufficient amount of radiation for sterilization.

Cosmic rays produce a total dose of the order of 10^0 to 10^1 rad/year even through heavy shielding. Solar-flare particles, according to present data, provide a total dose of 10^2 to 10^4 rad/year through 10^{-3} g/cm^2 and less through heavier shielding. These doses will not eliminate microbes on exposed surfaces, much less those within.

Finally, sterilization by the low-temperature conditions encountered in space must be considered. There is a great deal of evidence that low temperatures, even in the liquid helium range, do not kill microorganisms (see Section on The Persistence of Life). High temperatures will kill, but unless a heat sterilization procedure for use during the flight is deliberately built into the spacecraft, it will not be subjected to temperatures above 100°C, which, in general, is not high enough to sterilize.

Sterilization in flight as a deliberate part of the flight sequence might be a useful technique. As we have seen, however, chemical agents will not penetrate sealed interiors of spacecraft subassemblies or components, nor, in this case, can they be applied to outside surfaces, where high vacuum conditions exist. Heat sterilization during flight could succeed if the components were kept hot enough for a long enough period. There is a probability, however, that the sterilization cycle would not operate as designed and that the mission subsequently could not be aborted. In addition, we would then be faced with additional difficult engineering problems: to heat a spacecraft evenly in space and to avoid throwing certain instruments out of calibration, assuming that other problems pertaining to heat sterilization of components had been solved. If mechanisms are needed to provide sterilization in space, the reliability of the operation would probably be no better than 10^{-2}. In special cases, for instance when solar heating could be used directly to provide the high temperatures needed, a smaller probability of contamination might be attainable. This technique has been suggested for sterilization of the last stage of a launch vehicle after it has completed its operation and been separated from the spacecraft.[69] The probability that this scheme will fail would depend primarily on the spatial relationships required with respect to the Sun and the methods of obtaining and maintaining these conditions, a difficult matter to assess, indeed.

Sterilization during and after entry. It has been suggested that adequate sterilization can be attained by ablation during passage through a planetary atmosphere or by sheer impact on a planetary surface.

If a heat shield is provided, sterilization by ablation is precluded; however, even if no heat shield were provided, very small fragments, below 0.001 in. in diameter, would not reach temperatures high enough to be sterilized. Such fragments might be blown or broken off the spacecraft during the early entry stages and would be analogous to the fine dust that enters a planetary atmosphere and reaches the surface without significant heating. Moreover, during entry, large components will not be sufficiently heated at their centers to cause sterilization. Parts equivalent to polytetrafluoroethylene spheres larger than about $\frac{1}{2}$ in. in diameter (equivalent to a flat plate about $\frac{1}{4}$-in. thick) would not be sterilized by the heat of entry even at Venus, where entry heating is expected to be very severe.[70] Planetary spacecraft will usually include at least some plastic parts of these sizes, and entry heating alone cannot therefore be counted on to sterilize them, let alone the myriad of parts that are

Consider next sterilization by impact with the planetary surface. If there is an atmosphere present, some fragments of the spacecraft will not hit the surface at high speed, as we have already indicated in part. Even if the spacecraft were deliberately designed to pass through the atmosphere very rapidly without breakup, such a design might fail, and it seems unlikely that a probability of less than 0.1 could be given for the occurrence of a failure of this type.

Suppose there were no atmosphere present, as is the case for the Moon. There is good reason to believe that hitting the Moon at the hyperbolic velocity of 2 to 3 km/sec would not sterilize a vehicle. Data exist[71] indicating that some electronic devices can withstand impact decelerations of 200,000 g with relatively little damage; this is equivalent to the impact of a spacecraft at 2 km/sec, with complete arrest of motion within only 1 m. It is almost certain that microbes aboard various pieces of equipment would likewise withstand the impact. Microbes are also known to have survived chemical high explosions (Ref. 1392), although some decrease in the microbial count could probably be observed here as in the spacecraft in question.

If microorganisms were to withstand both entry and landing, what is the probability that they would be released from the spacecraft or capsule and contaminate the planetary atmosphere or surface? From the outside of an entry vehicle or lander, the probability of contamination is high, because the organisms may escape as dust during the initial stages of entry while still high in the atmosphere. From the inside of a spacecraft or capsule not designed to remain completely intact upon entry and landing, the probability of some release is again essentially unity. The number released would be less than the total number of living organisms aboard, but the chance of contamination would not be reduced significantly unless the initial microbial population had been made very low.

From inside a container designed to withstand entry and landing completely intact, presumably no organisms would be released if the container performed exactly as intended. Nevertheless, there is always some chance of failure; the possibility that the container might break open is not likely to be less than 10^{-1} to 10^{-2}.

If only a very small number of organisms are released, a possibility of 10^{-1} to 10^{-2} might exist that these do not include the varieties suited to growth under the planetary conditions.

Problems of Maintaining Spacecraft Sterility

Recontamination. With any of the methods of sterilization that have been discussed, the possibility of recontamination by subsequent leakage of nonsterile air into the container must be considered. In a welded, leak-tested box, the chance that contamination will pass through the seals is less than 10^{-6}. If the method of sealing to keep out nonsterile air is less perfect, the chance is greater, but, again, how much greater is a difficult question to answer.

At each stage of handling, there is some chance of contamination, the probability depending upon the design. Contamination of a previously sterilized spacecraft or capsule may occur during cross-country transport or on the launching pad. It does not seem possible to assign numbers to these probabilities, since they depend so heavily upon the design of the equipment.

If a sterile assembly operation is undertaken, it is possible for contamination of one of the subassemblies or components to occur during handling prior to the sterile assembly. One method of handling items intended for subsequent sterile assembly might be to sterilize and seal them in internally sterile bags kept under the immediate control of a special group whose sole purpose is to account for sterile procedures. Thereafter the bags would not be permitted to leave the custody of this group; that is, the cognizant assembly engineer and his technicians could not have access for any adjustments, modifications, or repairs. With this system of handling, the chance of mix-up in identification, other human error, or leak, might be as low as 10^{-6} per piece handled; for 100 pieces, this would amount to a total probability of contamination from these causes of 10^{-4}. If a "double sign-out system" is used at all stages, an additional reduction of 10^{-1} should be possible.

On the other hand, if the items were handled only by the "sterility group" but allowed to be touched or otherwise externally contaminated, there is the chance that contamination might penetrate to an interior area not reached by subsequent microbicidal treatments. The probability would greatly depend upon the design and character of the individual items and the spacecraft as a whole.

Another situation for consideration is that if sterilization takes place under the supervision of the commercial builder of the spacecraft equipment or cognizant assembly engineer and the package, sealed in an internally sterile bag, then remains in the custody of either, the chances of mix-up, other human error, or leak are estimated to be 10^{-2} per piece; for 100 pieces the chance of contamination is then unity. We can estimate these figures from the fact that for a spacecraft of the *Mariner* or *Ranger* class, there are typically about 30 to 50 cognizant engineers and hundreds of commercial subassembly vendors. With a double sign-out system, the chance might be reduced by a factor of 10^{-1}.

When items are sterilized internally under supervision of a vendor or cognizant assembly engineer and are handled unsealed by him and his men, the chance of mix-up, tampering, or other human error is perhaps 10^{-1} per piece; for 100 pieces, loss of sterility is thus virtually certain.

Inadvertent contamination during or after launching. The possibility that a sterilized spacecraft becomes contaminated during the launching operation must also be considered. This might occur, for example, by leakage into a closed shroud on the launching pad. The concentration of organisms in outdoor air varies strongly with season and meteorological conditions, but at sea level it can be 10^3 organisms/ft^3 or more; these are mostly fungal spores (Ref. 145). The bacterial count is about 10 per ft^3 (Ref. 145).[72] To attain contamination probabilities of 10^{-1} or 10^{-4}, the total volume of air permitted to leak into the shroud during launching operations must be less than 10^{-4} or 10^{-7} per ft^3, respectively, during the entire period from sterilization to attainment of an altitude of 100 km. It is generally assumed that Earth organisms do not rise to greater altitudes. Since the air in the shroud must ordinarily flow out during ascent to permit pressure equalization and removal of the shroud, a difficult engineering problem in control of air flow is posed.

It is also possible for a sterile spacecraft or capsule to become contaminated during a separation malfunction; e.g., by inadvertently permitting the nonsterile materials to remain with the sterile elements or to touch them during a separation procedure. Such materials might include retrorocket gases or nozzle fragments, loose pieces or dust blown about by the gas or by the explosive separation devices that are often used, enclosure or barrier wrappings that do not separate properly, etc. The probability that this will occur depends entirely upon the design, particularly of the separation mechanism and procedure. It would appear to be very difficult to get a significantly low probability of contamination during separation; there seems to be no way around the problem, except perhaps by sterilization in flight or during entry. Failure-proof separation designs are still required for sterility but have not as yet been perfected.

The launch environment itself might be used to sterilize or even to resterilize a spacecraft contaminated by accidental leakage of air into a shroud. Aerodynamic heating during acceleration is the factor that seems applicable. Using this technique, it might be possible to achieve a very low chance of contamination because the most likely source of abnormally low heating would be a low exit velocity, and if this occurred, the spacecraft could not reach its target. To sterilize by aerodynamic heating while launching would, however, require a very special spacecraft design involving extreme constraints. It is unlikely that this would be acceptable.

Technique of Non-entry

If the avowed purpose of the unmanned space exploration program is exploration absolutely without contamination, yet sterilization is so extremely difficult and the actual results virtually impossible to assess, there remains the technique of flyby or non-entry, whereby all data about the planetary surface are gathered remotely. This is perhaps the easiest way to avoid contaminating a planet, but it probably will not suffice to make certain orbital measurements necessary for biological exploration. Hovis[73] has pointed out, for instance, that infrared emission spectra are nearly impossible to get, except under very special conditions perhaps not realizable under the extraterrestrial conditions we are concerned with in planetary exploration.

We may classify our flights into entries, orbiters, and flybys. An entry flight is intended to hit a planet or its atmosphere; the probability that it will do so is presumably somewhere near unity. In general, a rather small error or failure in the guidance or in the retropropulsion of a planetary orbiter could cause the spacecraft to enter the atmosphere of the planet. The chance of hitting the planet with an orbiter is therefore high, probably near unity. For a flyby, the chance can be reduced as much as desired by aiming away from the planet; that is, by increasing the planned distance by which the planet is missed relative to the scatter in the guidance system. This method, however, could very well reduce the value of the flight. An alternative would be to introduce one or more midcourse maneuvers that could reduce the probable scatter in trajectory near the planet without changing the planned miss distance. Because such a maneuver may not take place as intended (probability 0.5 to 10^{-2}),[74] the probability of hitting may not be sufficiently reduced unless the aiming point is initially set at some distance from the planet ("biased") and then subsequently reduced by the appropriate maneuvers.

Midcourse maneuver capabilities add relatively little to the total weight. They add appreciable complication, however, and so reduce the reliability of the mission.[75] Biasing an "injection" away from a target means that if a subsequent maneuver fails, the distance by which the planet is missed will be so great that the value of the shot will be reduced considerably compared to that following a procedure in which no bias has been used.

The probability of hitting the planet with the last stage of the launch vehicle should also be considered. It should not be forgotten that the last stage of a launch vehicle leaves the vicinity of the Earth with essentially the same trajectory as the spacecraft it is launching. Accordingly, measures must be taken to prevent this entire stage from contaminating the target planet. If no avoidance or retromaneuver has been scheduled, the probability that this stage will hit the planet depends upon the "injection errors". If a launch-vehicle avoidance or retromaneuver is scheduled, then a factor of maneuver reliability must be introduced (10^{-1} to 10^{-2}).[74] If impact probabilities are still not sufficiently small, one might consider trying to achieve a more reliable retrosystem, changing the planned injection trajectory, or even sterilizing the launch vehicle. However, retrosystems on the launch vehicle add complications and again reduce reliability.[76] Launch-vehicle sterilization seems least practical, unless it can be done in flight, after separation.[69] At the present, launch vehicles have not been designed especially for unmanned planetary or lunar missions and perhaps never will be. They are designed for other purposes; persons responsible for scientific missions currently have no influence on the design of launch vehicles and therefore cannot require that they withstand rigorous sterilization procedures.

Associated Practical Considerations

Monitoring and accounting. Making certain that no breach in sterility has occurred while carrying out a systematic program will be a major undertaking, unless such a breach is mechanically impossible. Otherwise, an organization is needed to monitor the handling of sterile components or packages and to keep records on the items that have been sterilized. Considerable manpower will be involved in this monitoring and accounting job. Sterility monitors will have to follow each component to be sure that nothing is done to destroy its sterility; this responsibility could not be turned over to cognizant assembly engineers without seriously degrading the likelihood of sterility. These engineers are already dealing with highly complex problems, and it would be impractical and unfair to divert their attention to an additional field of activity and expect to achieve the necessary results. An administrative system is also needed to make sure that the monitors themselves do not make mistakes.

Reliability of spacecraft. Sterilization treatments of whatever sort may degrade reliability of operation. Preliminary results of an experimental study of sterilization by dry heat indicate that an appreciable increase in failure rate occurs during longevity testing of those electronic components not initially destroyed by the heat.[77] There is also some evidence that increased failure rates appear during proof-testing of electronic assemblies sterilized by dry heat.[67] This is most important, since there is little point in using equipment that is likely to fail during a flight; reliability is usually the principal characteristic desired in a spacecraft. There are almost no data on the effects of sterilization techniques other than heat upon reliability. Data on reliability are not easy to obtain; many thousands of tests are probably required.

Adjustments and Repairs. The need for last-minute calibration and adjustment of equipment conflicts strongly with the sterility requirement. Current practices often involve manual access to the equipment and necessarily jeopardize sterility. The sterilization requirement suggests that equipment be designed to be self-calibrating or be capable of remote calibration, no manual access whatsoever being involved.

The need for final repairs or replacement of components or subassemblies also conflicts seriously with sterilization procedures. This conflict can be reduced by placing sterilization as late in the development sequence as possible so that repairs and replacements can be made before rather than after sterilization.

If incorrect operations are found during a countdown at the time of launching, it is often necessary to make corrections and repeat both the countdown and a good deal of the precountdown preparation of the spacecraft. The time required for such repetitions is always a problem in any of the lunar or planetary launchings. If resterilization is then involved, the additional loss of time may be very serious owing to astronomical limitations on the launch period and firing window. Any procedure that interferes by requiring periods as long as 24 hr for completion is highly undesirable. Sterilization methods requiring only a few minutes are greatly to be desired.

Safety of personnel. Many of the procedures used for sterilization include hazards to personnel involved. Beta-propiolactone is carcinogenic and is not a currently recommended chemical sterilant. Ethylenimine is also suspected of being carcinogenic. Both of these liquids are vesicants. Gaseous ethylene oxide and formaldehyde are toxic in moderate concentrations. Ethylene oxide, even as prepared and supplied commercially, is flammable when mixed with oxygen.[78] The alcoholic solvents used with formaldehyde are flammable as well. Heating may conceivably ignite squibs and propellants. Radiation sterilization obviously involves considerable personnel hazards. Thus, certain precautions must be taken and certain risks to personnel understood and accepted if effective sterilization procedures with the smallest hazards possible are to be implemented.

Training. Sterilization of such complex mechanisms as spacecraft is such a complicated and difficult undertaking that many of the problems involved do not appear until it has been tried. There is, therefore, a great need to train personnel in the procedures of sterilization to be used for spacecraft and spacecraft components; rehearsing the procedures that are to be used, so that they are carried out without errors, is of vital importance as well. Training will no doubt be easier to accomplish once the problem areas are well defined and the methods reduced to a satisfactory routine.

Costs. Sterilization costs are major when reckoned in terms of money, time, manpower, and advanced research and development required. When these are limited, sterilization is likely to be slighted or even circumvented. Important psychologically is the very serious development effort needed for many components or subassemblies to make them compatible with sterilization requirements. Engineers responsible for the equipment may object strenuously on the grounds that there are enough serious difficulties already in the way of basic engineering. Their response is likely to be an attempt to find short-cut methods of sterilization or to attempt to prove that sterilization is not really needed. Likewise, there must be an awareness that sterilization may cost a good deal in performance achieved. For example, a propulsion system capable of sterilization to the required degree of assurance may be heavier than a similar system which need not be sterilized.

Many of the techniques proposed for sterilization are themselves dependent upon the successful and timely completion of considerable research or advanced development. To be consistent with the philosophy of spacecraft design that has been successfully used in the past, such methods should be rejected for all missions already in the design or fabrication stages. Sterilization of spacecraft in these stages should be carried out by methods whose effectiveness and compatibility with the planned mission are already well established. If this is not done, completion of the mission or sterility will probably be seriously jeopardized.

NECESSARY STERILIZATION PROBABILITIES

Granting that a "degree of sterilization" can be achieved by an appropriate method, we may ask what level of assurance of spacecraft sterility is required for each of the planets to be investigated with unmanned spacecraft. Sagan and Coleman[79] have recently made calculations based upon probability theory which make possible an estimate of the probability that a number of biologically meaningful missions to a planet can be made successfully before the planet is considered to be contaminated. Although their calculations were based on a Mars model, the same kind of reasoning could be applied to any of the planets to be considered.

In the following Sections, each of the planets is discussed in turn, and values for the probability of contamination are given based upon a few simple assumptions predicated on what is hoped can be achieved in early phases of biological exploration before contamination of the planet could seriously interfere with the investigations. With these few assumptions, it will be seen that, for the number of missions planned, the assurance of sterility necessary is remarkably similar to Sagan and Coleman's deductions. Their results are, however, somewhat more mathematically detailed as well as being more optimistic than those presented here.

Mars

According to many views that have been expressed, Mars holds the best chance for discovery and observation of an indigenous biota of any of the terrestrial planets to be investigated. On the basis of experiments made under simulated Martian conditions, it would appear that the probability for growth of some terrestrial organisms transported to Mars is close to unity.[35] Accordingly, there seems to be no question that we should assiduously avoid contaminating Mars with terrestrial organisms. Arguments confirming this viewpoint have been presented in full by the Cetex[80,81] and Westex Committees, by Davies and Comuntzis (Ref. 1377), Lederberg (Ref. 1443), Phillips and Hoffman (Ref. 1342), Hobby,[42] and others.[35]

For engineering purposes, it is necessary to designate, if possible, the degree of assurance that contamination will not occur. In other words, the risk of contamination that will be taken needs to be specified;

it must be acceptably small, yet a realistic and attainable figure. One way to obtain an intuitively reasonable number is to attempt to keep the probability of contaminating Mars as small as the chance that no useful biological data will be obtained for all other reasons combined.

There are seven oppositions of Mars remaining before 1980. If it is assumed that 2 to 4 flights are attempted at each opposition, then 14 to 28 flights in all can be attempted. For each attempt, the probability of reaching the planet is perhaps 1/2. If a spacecraft reaches the planet, it may still return no data relevant to the presence of life because of failures in landing procedure, radio communication, power supply, scientific instrumentation, telemetry, unfortunate selection of landing site, etc. The probability of such failures is perhaps 3/4. Thus, the chance that no useful data concerning the presence of life will be obtained in any one attempt becomes 7/8. The corresponding probability that no useful biological data will be obtained in an entire series of 28 attempts is $(7/8)^{28}$, or approximately 10^{-2}. We then conclude that the probability of contaminating Mars during the entire program should be kept as low as 10^{-2}. Sagan and Coleman,[79] on the other hand, would require all these missions to be successful before the planet is considered to be contaminated with the above degree of confidence.

Another method of obtaining a reasonable estimate is to keep the probability of contaminating Mars in the course of unmanned exploration small compared to the chance of contaminating it the first time a manned landing occurs. During a manned landing, contamination of Mars with terrestrial microorganisms is likely because of such factors as small, outward air leaks from space suits, the difficulty of sterilizing all crevices in space suits and other equipment by chemical means, the added difficulty of sterilization within a spacecraft rather than in a terrestrial laboratory, and various human errors during surface explorations leading to accidents, crash landings, etc. Most engineers consulted on this problem place the probability of microbes being released in these ways at about 10^{-1} or even higher. With this in mind, 10^{-2} might be an adequately small number for the probability of contamination during the entire unmanned program of exploration. This figure is similar to those obtained above.

The number 10^{-2} for a program in which 14 flights actually reach Mars leads to 10^{-3}, approximately, for the maximum probability of contamination acceptable on each flight. Perhaps a value of about 10^{-4} per flight is conservative and reasonable. Hobby[42] and the Space Science Board Study[82] have also suggested this probability, and agreement at the 1964 COSPAR meeting held in Florence, Italy, reaffirms this value.

It is clear that reasons could be given for selecting widely differing values; for example, 10^{-6} has been mentioned. The engineering difficulties of attaining even 10^{-4} are great; attaining 10^{-6} might require postponing unmanned exploration for many years. If manned exploration were not postponed correspondingly, then serious difficulties for basic biological studies might result. On the other hand, if all unmanned flights failed to return relevant data concerning the possibility of Martian life, or if no unmanned flights were tried, other considerations would almost certainly force manned flights to be tried when they become feasible — perhaps by the late 1980s. It is also possible that postponement of unmanned exploration might reduce the number of unmanned attempts possible prior to manned landings and so reduce the chances of receiving meaningful biological data before contamination occurs, assuming that manned landings are nearly synonymous with contamination.

If only manned landings are attempted, provisions could be made for retrieving an uncontaminated sample of Martian soil or perhaps several samples. If these were large enough, they might keep biologists busy for many years attempting to study Martian microorganisms in their original habitat or examining the remnants of a past Martian life if this proved to be the case. These ideas also raise a host of problems on back contamination.

Venus

For Venus, the required degree of assurance against microbial contamination can be mitigated by the probability that no environment suitable for growth would be encountered there by terrestrial organisms. Measurements from Earth and from *Mariner 2*[83] indicate that the surface temperature is far too high to permit survival of terrestrial life forms. There are, however, regions in the upper atmosphere of Venus which are estimated to be suitably cool and would permit survival of Earthly organisms. Nevertheless, microorganisms apparently cannot multiply in the atmosphere of Earth,[63] and presumably would not do so in that of Venus. Accordingly, the chance that some terrestrial microorganisms will find a suitable environment for growth on Venus is estimated to be 10^{-3}. Dividing the value of 10^{-4} per flight proposed for assurance against contamination by 10^{-3}, we obtain 10^{-1} per flight as a suggested assurance against releasing viable microorganisms into the upper atmosphere of Venus. This is, indeed, not a very restrictive value with respect to practical considerations involved in spacecraft sterilization.

The Moon

For the Moon, sterility of spacecraft is probably not essential: it is probably impossible for terrestrial organisms to grow and reproduce on or near the surface of the Moon. Sagan (Ref. 281) and Imshenetsky[84] believe that there is a remote chance for growth; no one else, however, seems to share this view. Below a few centimeters, the surface of the

Moon, to a considerable depth, appears to be well below the freezing point of water. The outermost few centimeters are alternately exposed to subzero and very high temperatures as well as to high vacuum and radiation.

There have been no published descriptions of the sterilization method used on *Lunik II*; it seems probable that the spacecraft and launch vehicle that hit the Moon in fact were not sterile. Sterilization procedures were used on *Ranger 4,* which hit the Moon, but a few components probably were not sterile. Details of these procedures are discussed by Hobby.[67]

Lederberg and Cowie (Ref. 256) have pointed out that it is highly desirable not to contaminate the Moon to the extent that biologists will be unable to determine whether organic substances found on the Moon are native or were brought from Earth, assuming that organic substances are found there at all. The Moon has a surface area of 4×10^7 cm^2. The chances of picking up terrestrial organisms within this area should be low, compared to the other chances of contamination or error in a single experiment, approximately 10^{-3}. Accordingly, the probability that an Earth organism is found on the lunar surface should be held to 10^{-6} per cm^2. For the entire Moon, then, it should be undesirable to put down more than 4×10^{11} organisms from all unmanned flights. For a 40-flight, unmanned program, this would mean an average of less than 10^{10} organisms per flight. A bacterium weighs about 10^{-12} g; thus, the total weight of viable organisms should be limited to 0.01 g per flight, a very difficult thing to determine, indeed.

Lederberg and Cowie (Ref. 256), Sagan (Ref. 281), and others have pointed out that it is also undesirable to land nonviable organisms on the Moon. Unfortunately, there is no known way to remove nonviable organisms from a spacecraft completely. Decontamination procedures and great care and cleanliness during fabrication procedures could probably reduce their numbers considerably. This would hold true as well for viable organisms.

Mercury

The planet Mercury can, perhaps, be dismissed from present considerations, since one face is hotter than temperatures reached in any heat sterilization procedure we contemplate using for spacecraft, and the opposite face is perpetually cold and dark, too cold to allow any growth and metabolism of microorganisms. There remains the possibility that a narrow band or twilight zone in the region between light and dark might provide sufficiently temperate conditions. However, we are faced with other difficulties such as the very possible lack of a suitable atmosphere and water. Here, as for Mars, astronomical observations have been of some help and probably can provide further hints of possible conditions that might be encountered.

The Jovian Planets

Little is known about the surfaces of these planets beyond the estimations that abundances of methane and ammonia are likely to be present. The planetary masses are so large that these reducing substances, among others, including hydrogen, are probably available in liquid form. One author (Ref. 1178), at least, does not discount the possibility that the surfaces, particularly of Jupiter and perhaps Saturn, are warm enough to sustain chemical reactions of interest in life processes. Perhaps a kind of heterotrophic life could have arisen there that subsists on vast quantities of ready-made organic compounds, which supply energy for metabolism as well as carbon for the necessary molecular skeletons. Under such conditions, no oxygen or photosynthetic mechanisms would be needed, and hydrogen itself could provide for the required electron acceptance in a particular metabolic pathway. Metabolism might, of course, be limited to fermentative mechanisms only.

With such possibilites in mind, exploration of these planets might be started using the same assumptions we have presented for Mars. Actually, by the time instruments and spacecraft are sophisticated enough to begin exploration of the Jovian planets, a good deal more information about actual conditions there might be available from astronomical or satellite-based observations. A more informed and realistic approach to sterilization, if still considered necessary, will no doubt be possible at that time.

PROCEDURES CURRENTLY ENVISIONED FOR
PLANETARY EXPLORATION

Lunar Exploration

As we have discussed earlier, it would appear at this time that sterility is not needed for lunar flights. For lunar landers and orbiters, the mass of living material aboard should be held to about 10^{-2} g per flight, or about 10^{10} microorganisms per spacecraft. This quantity should be readily attainable with the ordinary clean techniques of spacecraft preparation and assembly that are routinely observed at the present time.

Exploration of Venus

Flybys and orbiters. It was suggested earlier that the probability of introducing a viable organism into the atmosphere of Venus should be held to 10^{-1} per flight for the present. This figure should generally be attainable on flybys without sterilization. With an intended distance for missing the planet of perhaps 30,000 km, injection-trajectory scatter typically gives an impact probability of about 10^{-2} for the spacecraft and the last stage of the launch vehicle.[75,85] A midcourse maneuver, intended to reduce trajectory scatter near the target planet and permit more accurate location of scientific instruments, will generally reduce the probability of accidental entry. This technique was in fact used with *Mariner II*. In addition, since the allowable impact probability was originally set lower when the flight was planned, a retromaneuver was used for the last launch-vehicle stage and was carried out after this stage had separated from the spacecraft.

It might also be practical to use the above technique for an orbiter of Venus. One difficulty would be that large velocity changes are required to transfer a spacecraft from an approach trajectory to the desired orbit, and a guidance or propulsion malfunction during this transfer could easily put the spacecraft into the Venusian atmosphere. The techniques are difficult, and much care would be needed to keep the possibility of atmospheric entry to below 10^{-1}. The chance of unintentionally achieving an orbit that would slowly tighten and pass into the Venusian atmosphere within a few years would also have to be held to an acceptably low figure.

Techniques for entry. Since the surface temperature of Venus is very high,[83] a lander intended for surface operation would almost certainly be designed to operate with high internal temperatures. Heat sterilization of such a lander prior to launch, or perhaps in space, should therefore be a simple matter if considered necessary at all.

An entry capsule designed to return data from within the atmosphere but not to survive at the surface might not need to be as heat-resistant. It should not be too difficult, therefore, to devise a sterilization procedure that would hold the probability of contamination to 10^{-1} and prevent release of terrestrial microbes into the upper atmosphere on the chance that Venus is not truly self-sterilizing despite current indications.

Exploration of Mars
Techniques for flybys. For Martian missions, it was suggested previously that the probability of introducing a viable organism should be held to 10^{-4} per flight. One procedure would be to sterilize the spacecraft and last stage of the launch vehicle; disadvantages of sterilization have already been pointed out. An alternative approach would again be to reduce the probability of entering the planetary atmosphere. For a Mars flyby, with an intended miss distance set at perhaps 20,000 km, injection-trajectory scatter typically gives a probability of impact of about 10^{-2}.[86] This is not small enough for Mars, as has already been pointed out. A

midcourse maneuver would generally reduce the chance of unintended entry. The probability of failure of a midcourse maneuver is, however, likely to be 10^{-1} or higher.[74,85] We are left with a probability of entry greater than 10^{-3}; this, according to present thinking, is unacceptable. To reduce the probability of entry further, the injection trajectory can be farther away from the planet and midcourse maneuvers used to reduce the miss distance to that desired for the mission. For example, biasing the injection trajectory in order to miss the planet by 50,000 km might be enough to lower the impact probability to 10^{-4}. Midcourse maneuvers could then bring the trajectory back to 20,000 km from the target. An important point is that if any of these maneuvers failed, the probability of entry would not be increased. Note also that biasing the injection trajectory would lower the probability of launch-vehicle entry just as it lowers the probability of spacecraft entry.

Techniques for orbiters. As was indicated above in the case of Venus, it seems difficult to hold to 10^{-1} the probability that a malfunction will occur that would put an intended orbiter into the planetary atmosphere. To hold the probability of such a malfunction to 10^{-4} appears beyond the state of the art. Accordingly, orbiters should be sterilized as outlined for entry spacecraft below. If the chance of entry can be held to 10^{-1}, then a probability of 10^{-3} could be allowed for a breach in sterility and the over-all probability of contamination still kept at 10^{-4}. This might allow a slight relaxation of the procedures recommended for entry craft.

Techniques for entry. For a Mars entry capsule or lander that is required to open in order to perform certain experiments, the factor of 10^{-4} becomes the permissible likelihood that a viable organism is aboard. Currently, the technique that gives the lowest probability is heating the entire capsule or lander, including its propulsion system, in a sealed container. The procedure must ensure that all parts are held at a high enough temperature for an adequate period; say, 135°C for 24 hr. Somewhat shorter times at higher temperatures can also be used. The inward leak rate of the sealed container during ground handling and launching procedures would have to be extremely low and the mechanism for separating lander from container so designed that the probability that contaminated materials touch or remain with the lander during separation is smaller than 10^{-4}. If any repairs or manual adjustments are needed on the sterilized lander, a complete resterilization will be required.

Whether sterile packages could be added to a previously sterilized lander using sterile assembly is a question akin to that already considered for sterile assembly during fabrication of a spacecraft. The assembly technique that so far provides the best chance of achieving sterility is the use of the closed glove box filled with gaseous sterilant. Sterile parts and tools, sealed in internally sterile plastic bags, would be placed inside the box and sterilized with ethylene oxide (for, say, 17 hr) then purged with sterile air or nitrogen before the assembly is resumed. In this procedure, liquid sterilants would not be necessary; but additional tests of the adequacy of the ethylene oxide treatment are needed at present.

All sterilization and sterile assembly would have to be under the direct control of a single, unified group responsible solely for the sterility of spacecraft. The cognizant assembly engineer would have no access to his sterilized equipment, components, or materials for any reason whatever except under sterile glove-box operations directly controlled by the sterility group. A rather elaborate system of accounting for and monitoring all sterile items is thus necessary. Even with all these precautions, it is not certain that glove-box assembly can provide a probability of contamination as low as 10^{-4}. Currently, the glove-box technique must be considered a poor second choice to sterilization by heating the entire, finished assembly before launching. Liquids, gases, and filters do not assure sterility to 10^{-4}, as previously discussed.

Exploration of Other Planets

As has been mentioned, only reasonable requirements of cleanliness are presently to be applied for the Moon. On the other hand, for Mercury and for the Jovian planets, decisions for or against sterilization will have to be made when the programs for their exploration are devised. In the absence of information, one might predict that the same methods need to be applied for Mercury as for Venus. For the Jovian planets, perhaps the methods required for exploration of Mars will be necessary.

By the time programs for these planets are extant, however, we might expect to have newer, more effective methods of sterilization or extremely rugged spacecraft, for which sterilization poses no problems; perhaps we will even have both.

SUMMARY AND CONCLUSIONS

Current thoughts tend toward a conservative argument. If life is assumed to have arisen independently on Mars or any other planet we wish to explore, then there is a definite obligation not to destroy forever the chance of discovering this fact and subsequently adding to man's knowledge on the subject of life in the universe.

Sterilization methods for space exploration are still under study and development, but apparently the simplest and most effective that has been found thus far is heat—dry heat applied for 24 hr at 135°C, disregarding the warming and cooling periods. Even the toughest microorganisms are not likely to survive such treatment. On the other hand, whether spacecraft technology can develop certain necessary components, sterilizable under these conditions, is a difficult question that must be left undecided at the present.

If we then set aside considerations of space exploration programs for Mercury or the Jovian planets, the necessary constraints presently envisioned are as follows:

1. An entry capsule or lander for Mars should be sterilized and handled using procedures that will assure that the probability of a single viable organism is aboard is no greater than 10^{-4}.

2. To achieve a probability of 10^{-4}, the entire spacecraft should be sterilized in space, or, alternatively, sealing and separation mechanisms must be available to provide a very high degree of assurance that leaks and malfunctions that would contaminate the previously sterilized lander cannot occur prior to or during launching nor at separation of the lander from shroud and launch vehicle.

3. Sterilization of a Mars lander should, if at all possible, be by heat, either in space or in the final sealed container, no access then being permitted for any except vital reasons, and then only if followed by complete resterilization with heat. A considerable amount of development work on spacecraft and their components is yet needed before this becomes feasible.

4. If heat sterilization of the complete lander is impossible, a second but poorer choice is that heat sterilization should be used on as large a lander assembly as possible, and sterile parts, including fluids, then added by a glove-box procedure with the use of ethylene oxide.

5. Sterilization should also be required for Mars orbiters. The probabilities of a breach in sterility and of accidental atmospheric entry (for instance, by some malfunction) should be controlled to retain the 10^{-4} figure for the over-all probability of introducing a viable terrestrial organism into the atmosphere of Mars.

6. For Mars and Venus flyby spacecraft, for Venus orbiters, and for the last stages of launch vehicles, sterilization should be used or trajectories should be controlled to ensure a probability of not greater than 10^{-4} for hitting Mars and of 10^{-1} for hitting Venus. For Venus entry craft, sterilization should continue to be required until further data are obtained.

7. Sterilization does not seem essential for lunar missions. Clean procedures should be used to assure that no more than about 10^{10} microorganisms per flight are deposited on the Moon.

REFERENCES

1. VALLENTYNE, J. R., Environmental Biophysics and Microbial Ubiquity, *Annals of the New York Academy of Sciences*, vol. 108 (1963), pp. 391–6.
2. MEYER, G. H., MORROW, M. B., and WYSS, O., Antarctica: The Microbiology of an Unfrozen Saline Pond, *Science*, vol. 138 (1962), pp. 1103–4.
3. ZOBELL, C. E., Microbiological Activities at Low Temperatures with Particular Reference to Marine Bacteria, *Quarterly Review of Biology*, vol. 9 (1934), pp. 460–6.
4. HAINES, R. B., The Influence of Temperature on the Rate of Growth of *Sporotrichum carnis*, from −10°C to +30°C, *Journal of Experimental Biology*, vol. 8 (1931), pp. 379–88.
5. ZERNOW, S. A., On Limits of Life at Negative Temperatures, *Comptes Rendus Hebdomadaires des Séances de l'Académie des Sciences*, vol. 44 (1944), pp. 76–7.
6. BORGSTROM, G., Unsolved Problems in Frozen Food Microbiology, *Proceedings of the Low Temperature Microbiology Symposium* (1961), Campbell Soup Co., pp. 197–250.
7. LENO, G. A., The Terrestrial Life of the Antarctic, *Scientific American*, vol. 207 (1962), pp. 213–30.
8. ALLEN, M. B., Utilization of Thermal Energy by Living Organisms, *Comparative Biochemistry*, ed. by M. FLORKIN and H. S. MASON, New York: Academic Press (1960), pp. 487–514.
9. ZOBELL, C. E., Ecology of Sulfate Reducing Bacteria, *Producers Monthly*, vol. 22 (1958), pp. 12–29.
10. ZOBELL, C. E., and MORITA, R. Y., Barophilic Bacteria in some Deep Sea Sediments, *Journal of Bacteriology*, vol. 73 (1956), pp. 563–8.
11. SCOTT, W. J., Available Water and Microbial Growth, *Proceedings of the Low Temperature Microbiology Symposium* (1961), Campbell Soup Co., pp. 89–105.
12. ZEUCH, L. Untersuchungen zum Wasserhaushalt von *Pleurococcus vulgaris*, *Planta*: *Archiv für wissenschaftliche Botanik*, vol. 22 (1934), pp. 614–43.
13. THIMANN, K. V., *The Life of Bacteria*, 2nd ed., New York: MacMillan Co. (1963), p. 783.
14. ANDERSON, A. W., NORDAN, H. C., CAIN, R. F., PARRISH, G., and DUGGAN, D., Studies on a Radio-Resistant Micrococcus, *Food Technology*, vol. 10 (1956), pp. 575–8.
15. AHMADJIAN, V., Lichens, *Physiology and Biochemistry of Algae*, ed. by R. LEWIN, New York: Academic Press (1962), p. 820.
16. KALINENKO, V. O., Multiplication of Heterotrophic Bacteria in Distilled Water, *Mikrobiologiya*, vol. 26 (1957), pp. 148–53.
17. WILKANSKY, B., Life in the Dead Sea, *Nature*, vol. 138 (1936), p. 467.
18. ABRAM, D., and GIBBONS, N. E., The Effect of Chlorides of Monovalent Cations, Urea, Detergents, and Heat on Morphology and the Turbidity of Suspensions of Red Halophilic Bacteria, *Canadian Journal of Microbiology*, vol. 7 (1961), pp. 741–50.
19. THIMANN, K. V., *The Life of Bacteria*, 2nd ed., New York: MacMillan Co. (1963), p. 166.
20. DOMBROWSKI, H. J., *Bacillus circulans* from Zechstein Salts, *Zentralblatt für Bakteriologie, Parasitenkunde, Infektionskrankheiten und Hygiene, Abteilung I* (a) *Referate*, vol. 178 (1961), p. 83.
21. BAAS BECKING, L. G. M., KAPLAN, I. R., and MOORE, D., Limits of the Natural Environment in Terms of pH and Oxidation–Reduction Potentials, *Journal of Geology*, vol. 68 (1960), pp. 243–84.
22. STARKY, R. L., and WAKSMAN, S. A., Fungi Tolerant to Extreme Acidity and High Concentrations of Copper Sulfate, *Journal of Bacteriology*, vol. 45 (1943), pp. 509–19.
23. ALLEN, M. B., Studies with *Cyanidrium caldarium*, an Anomalously Pigmented Chlorophyte, *Archiv für Mikrobiologie*, vol. 32 (1959), pp. 270–7.
24. THIMANN, K. V., *The Life of Bacteria*, 2nd ed., New York: MacMillan Co. (1963), p. 169.
25. HECKLY, R. J., Preservation of Bacteria by Lyophilization, *Advances in Applied*

Microbiology, vol. 3, ed. by W. W. UMBREIT, New York: Academic Press (1961), pp. 1–76.

26. SCHMIDT, B., FELDMAN, S., and DOBBERSTEIN, H., Untersuchungen zur Frage der Änderung der biologischen Eigenschaften von Bakterien nach Trocknung und Gefriertrocknung, *Zentralblatt für Bakteriologie, Parasitenkunde, Infektionskrankheiten und Hygiene, Abteilung I. Originale,* vol. 172 (1958), pp. 573–80.

27. BRUESCHKE, E. E., SUESS, R. H., and WILLARD, M., The Viability of Microorganisms in Ultra-High Vacuum, *Planetary and Space Science,* vol. 8 (1961), pp. 30–4.

28. DAVIS, N. S., SILVERMAN, G. J., and KELLER, W. H., Combined Effects of Ultra-High Vacuum and Temperature on the Viability of Some Spores and Soil Organisms, *Applied Microbiology,* vol. 11 (1963), pp. 202–10.

29. GEIGER, P. J., MORELLI, F. A., and CONROW, H. (1964), To be published.

30. BECQUEREL, P., Nouvelles possibilitées experimentales de la vie sur la planète Mars, *L'Astronomie, Bulletin de la Sociétée Astronomique, France,* vol. 64 (1950), pp. 351–5.

31. RODENBECK, H., Über die thermische Sterilisation wasserfreier Stoffe und die Resistenz einiger Bakterien bei Erhitzung in solchen Stoffen, *Archiv für Hygiene und Bakteriologie,* vol. 109 (1932), pp. 67–84.

32. SILVERMAN, G. S., DAVIS, N. S., and KELLER, W. H., Exposure of Microorganisms to Simulated Extraterrestrial Space Ecology, COSPAR Sixth Planetary Meeting and Fourth International Space Science Symposium, 3–12 June 1963, Warsaw, Poland.

33. SHIELDS, L. M., DURRELL, L. W., and SPARROW, A. H., Preliminary Observations on Radiosensitivity of Algae and Fungi from Soils of the Nevada Test Site, *Ecology,* vol. 42 (1961), pp. 440–1.

34. SCHMIDT, C. F., and NANK, W. K., Radiation Sterilization of Food. I. Procedures for the Evaluation of the Radiation Resistance of Spores of *Clostridium botulinum* in Food Products, *Food Research,* vol. 25 (1960), pp. 321–6.

35. PACKER, E., SCHER, S., and SAGAN, C., Biological Contamination of Mars. II. Cold and Aridity as Constraints on the Survival of Terrestrial Microorganisms in Simulated Martian Environment, *Icarus,* vol. 2 (1963), pp. 293–316.

36. *Antiseptics, Disinfectants, Fungicides, and Sterilization,* ed. by G. F. REDDISH, 2nd ed., Philadelphia: Lea and Febiger (1957).

37. BRUCH, C. W., Gaseous Sterilization, *Annual Review of Microbiology,* vol. 15 (1961), pp. 245–62.

38. SCHMIDT, C. F., Thermal Resistance of Microorganisms, *Antiseptics, Disinfectants, Fungicides, and Sterilization,* ed. by G. F. REDDISH, 2nd ed. Philadelphia: Lea and Febiger (1957), pp. 831–84.

39. PHILLIPS, C. R., Sterilizing Properties of Ethylene Oxide, *Sterilization of Surgical Materials,* London: Pharmaceutical Press (1961).

40. HASTRUP, R. C., *Impact Probability Values for Planetary Missions,* Internal communication, Jet Propulsion Laboratory, Pasadena, California, 1962.

41. JAFFE, L. D., Analysis of data in C. W. BRUCH, *Sterilization of Space Probe Components,* Status Reports 2 and 3, Wilmot Castle Co., Rochester, New York, September 1, 1961 and December 1, 1961; Personal communication, 1961; and in M. G. KOESTERER, *Sterilization of Space Probe Components,* Final Report, Wilmot Castle Co., Rochester, New York, April 1961–July 1962.

42. HOBBY, G. L., *Sterilization Criteria for Mariner Spacecraft Design,* Internal communication, Jet Propulsion Laboratory, Pasadena, California, 1962.

43. LOWE, H. N., JR., LACY, W. J., SURKIEWICZ, B. F., and JAEGER, R. G., Destruction of Microorganisms in Water, Sewage Sludge by Ionizing Radiations, *Journal of the American Water Works Association,* vol. 48 (1956), pp. 1363–72.

44. HUGHES, D. E., and NYBORG, W. L., Cell Disruption by Ultrasound, *Science,* vol. 138 (1962), pp. 108–14.

45. MORELLI, F. A., *Determination of Sterilizing Time for RA-3 Spacecraft Terminal Operations,* Internal communication, Jet Propulsion Laboratory, Pasadena, California, February 13, 1962.

46. HOBBY, G. L., Personal communication, Jet Propulsion Laboratory, Pasadena, California, 1962.

47. OPFELL, J. B., HOHMANN, J. P., and LATHAM, A. B., Ethylene Oxide Sterilization of Spores in Hygroscopic Environments, *Journal of the American Pharmaceutical Association, Scientific Edition,* vol. 48 (1959), pp. 617–19.

48. OPFELL, J. B., Personal communication, Dynamic Science Corp., South Pasadena, California, 1962.

49. HASTRUP, R., Personal communication, Jet Propulsion Laboratory, Pasadena, California, 1962.

50. *Surveyor Sterilization Handbook,* Dynamic Science Corp., South Pasadena, California, 1962 (in Ref. 8, vol. 2, pp. D2–D78).

51. *Effect of Encasement of Bacterial Spores on the Sterilization Effectiveness of Exposure to Gaseous Sterilant and Application of Liquid Sterilant,* Dynamic Science Corp., South Pasadena, California, 1962 (in Ref. 8, vol. 2, pp. D119–D134).

52. *Sterilization Experiments with Ethylene Oxide,* Final Report to Jet Propulsion Laboratory, Dynamic Science Corp., South Pasadena, California, 1962.

53. ERNST, R. R., and SHULL, J. J., Ethylene Oxide Gaseous Sterilization. I. Concentration and Temperature Effects, *Applied Microbiology,* vol. 10 (1962), pp. 337–41.

54. ERNST, R. R., and SHULL, J. J., Ethylene Oxide Gaseous Sterilization. II. Influence of Method of Humidification, *Applied Microbiology,* vol. 10 (1962), pp. 344–52.

55. VARGA, R. J., *Surveyor Spacecraft System,* Final Sterilization Report, vol. 1, SSD-3372R, Hughes Aircraft Co., Space Systems Division, El Segundo, California, 1962.

56. OPFELL, J. B., MILLER, C. E., and LOUDERBACK, A. L., *Evaluation of Liquid Sterilants,* Semifinal Report to Jet Propulsion Laboratory, Dynamic Science Corp., South Pasadena, California, March 16, 1962.

57. SPAULDING, E. H., Chemical Disinfection of Medical and Surgical Materials. *Antiseptics, Disinfectants, Fungicides, and Chemical and Physical Sterilization,* ed. by G. F. REDDISH, 2nd ed., Philadelphia: Lea and Febiger (1957), pp. 619–48.

58. OPFELL, J. B., MILLER, C. E., and HAMMONS, P. N., *Evaluation of Liquid Sterilants,* Final Report to Jet Propulsion Laboratory, Dynamic Science Corp., South Pasadena, California, August 28, 1961.

59. Bernard Chiego and Associates, Bloomfield, New Jersey, *Determination of the Bacteriostatic and Bactericidal Activity of Monomethylhydrazine and Nitrogen Tetroxide* (Undated); and Food and Drug Research Laboratories, New York, New York, *Bactericidal Test with Methyl Hydrazine and Nitric Acid on Specific Organisms* (1961), Reports to Thiokol Chemical Corp., Reaction Motors Division, Denville, New Jersey (in Ref. 8, vol. 2, pp. D135–D142).

60. DRUMMOND, D. W., *Contaminants Assay of Building 71 Clean Room,* Internal communication, Jet Propulsion Laboratory, Pasadena, California, July 14, 1961.

61. KUNDSIN, R. B., and WALTER, C. W., In-Use Testing of Bactericidal Agents in Hospitals, *Applied Microbiology,* vol. 9 (1961), pp. 167–70.

62. SLOCUM, G., Personal communication, U.S. Department of Health, Education, and Welfare, Food and Drug Administration, Washington, D.C., 1962.

63. NEWTON, W., Personal communication, U.S. Department of Health, Education, and Welfare, National Institutes of Health, Washington, D.C., 1962.

64. MORELLI, F. A., *Aerosol and Fallout Samples Taken at Cape Canaveral,* Internal communication, Jet Propulsion Laboratory, Pasadena, California, 1962.

65. HERMAN, L. G., and MORELLI, F. A., Air Sampling Techniques in a Hospital Environment, *Bacteriological Proceedings, 1961,* Detroit: American Society for Microbiology (Abstract), vol. 61 (1961), p. 114.

66. BOURDILLON, R. B., and COLEBROOK, L., Air Hygiene in Dressing Rooms for Burns and Major Wounds, *Lancet,* No. 1 (1946), pp. 561–5, 601–5.

67. HOBBY, G. L., Review of the NASA–JPL Spacecraft Sterilization Program, *Review of Space Research,* National Academy of Sciences–National Research Council, Publication 1079, Washington, D.C. (1962), pp. 10-25–10.35.

68. BAKANAUSKAS, S., *Resistance of Microorganisms to High Vacuums* (*July 1958–April*

1959) WADC TN 59–142, Wright Air Development Center, Wright-Patterson Air Force Base, Ohio, 1959. AD-228, 156.

69. PHILLIPS, C. R., and HOFFMAN R., Personal communication, Fort Detrick, Frederick, Maryland, 1962.

70. SPIEGEL, J., and LUCAS, J., Aerodynamic Sterilization of Missile Components, *Space Programs Summary No. 37–11,* vol. 2, Jet Propulsion Laboratory, Pasadena, California (1961), p. 176. CONFIDENTIAL.

71. LETARTE, M., and MOIR, L. E., A High Telemetry System for Gun and Rocket Firing, *Proceedings of the 1st International Electronic Circuit Packaging Symposium* (University of Colorado, Boulder, Colorado, August 18–19, 1960), Englewood, Colorado: Rogers Publishing Co. (1960), pp. 243–97; and CARDE TM-351/60, Canadian Armaments Research and Development Establishment, Valcartier, Quebec, August 1960.

72. WOLF, H. W., *et al., Sampling Microbiological Aerosols,* Monograph 60, U.S. Department of Health, Education, and Welfare, Public Health Service, Washington, D.C. 1959.

73. HOVIS, W. A., Infrared Emission Spectra of Organic Solids from 5 to 6.6 Microns, *Science,* vol. 143 (1964), pp. 587–8.

74. KOHLHASE, C., JR., *Effect of Trajectory Biasing and Midcourse Maneuver Reliability Upon Probability of Capture for 1964 Mars Flyby Mission,* Internal communication, Jet Propulsion Laboratory, Pasadena, California, 1962.

75. CUTTING, E. J., and DETLEF, J., *Mariner Retro Maneuver,* Memorandum No. 312–172, Jet Propulsion Laboratory, Pasadena, California, March 15, 1962.

76. PARKS, R., Personal communication, Jet Propulsion Laboratory, Pasadena, California 1962.

77. LOCKYEAR, W. H., *Component Sterilization Program,* Interoffice Memo, Jet Propulsion Laboratory, Pasadena, California, June 13, 1962.

78. VANGO, S. P., *Explosive Mixtures with Oxygen and the Disinfecting Mixture Containing 11% Ethylene Oxide and 89% Freon,* Interoffice Memo, Jet Propulsion Laboratory, Pasadena, California, June 7, 1960.

79. SAGAN, C., and COLEMAN, S., *Biological Contamination of Mars. III. Required Spacecraft Sterilization Levels,* Preprint (1964).

80. Development of International Efforts to Avoid Contamination by Extraterrestrial Bodies, *Science,* vol. 128 (1958), pp. 887–8.

81. Contamination by Extraterrestrial Exploration, *Nature,* vol. 183 (1959), pp. 925–8.

82. Working Subgroup on Space Probe Sterilization, Space Probe Sterilization, *Review of Space Research,* National Academy of Sciences–National Research Council, Publication 1079, Washington, D.C. (1962), pp. 10–19.

83. BARATH, F. T., BARRETT, A. H., COPELAND, J., JONES, D. E., and LILLEY, A. E., *Mariner II:* Preliminary Reports on Measurements of Venus — Microwave Radiometers, *Science,* vol. 139 (1963), pp. 908–9.

84. IMSHENETSKY, A. A., *Prospects of the Development of Exobiology,* COSPAR Third International Space Science Symposium, 1962, Washington, D.C.

85. CUTTING, E., *Probability of Venus Impact of Mariner R,* Internal communication, Jet Propulsion Laboratory, Pasadena, California, 1962.

86. KOHLHASE, C., JR., Personal communication, Jet Propulsion Laboratory, Pasadena, California, October 12, 1961.

CHAPTER IX

THE RADIO SEARCH FOR INTELLIGENT EXTRATERRESTRIAL LIFE

F. D. DRAKE

National Radio Astronomy Observatory*
Green Bank, West Virginia

INTRODUCTION

THE study of extraterrestrial intelligent organisms appears to be the *pièce de résistance* of exobiology, both figuratively and literally. Contact with another sapient species will have the most profound impact on terrestrial science and philosophy. To biologists it will offer the simple practical virtue of providing access, in all likelihood, to an already developed scientific analysis of another highly evolved ecology. It offers a difficult, yet probably the easiest, method of detecting the existence of life, and possibly planetary systems accompanying other stars.

Even fortified by the promise of these potential gains, a serious attempt to detect extraterrestrial intelligent life demands a technological undertaking of discouragingly large proportions and expense—one that at present must be extremely inefficient, because our knowledge of the universe is too scant to permit a sound judgment as to which of the many plausible ways to search will lead to success at minimum cost. Nevertheless, the significance of the goal continues to attract more scientists to the related problems—this, plus the realization that the large number of stars in the galaxy, so many similar to the Sun, makes virtually inevitable the existence of other intelligent species in space. There is probably no more tantalizing thought in contemporary science than the conclusion that manifestations of other intelligent species are within the limits of detection of present technology, if we but knew which technology to apply in what manner.

Present work in this field is almost all theoretical and directed toward finding the best approach to the search before large resources are invested in it. These studies may be divided into two categories: (1) Combined astronomical and biological analyses which lead to an estimate of the

*Operated by Associated Universities, Inc., under contract with the National Science Foundation.

distribution of communicative civilizations in space. These produce a probable distance to the nearest communicative civilizations, which serves as the prime parameter in determining what search technique is most likely to be fruitful. (2) Application of physical, technological, and game-theory principles to determine the relative desirability of the various possible search techniques. It should be remarked that the emphasis on such studies does not warrant the conclusion that there is but one method which will succeed. Probably all possible manifestations of intelligent activity occur in the universe. However, some certainly appear with much more frequency, or more detectability, than others, and we seek to determine which.

This Chapter presents the progress that has been made in these aspects of the problem.

ESTIMATE OF THE DISTRIBUTION OF COMMUNICATIVE CIVILIZATIONS

A communicative civilization is defined as a civilization of intelligent beings having and applying a technology sufficiently advanced to permit detection of the civilization over interstellar distances. The arbitrary decision as to what is "sufficiently advanced" actually matters little in the statistics of communicative civilizations, because, if we are even crudely typical, a civilization passes from no technology to much more than a "sufficiently advanced" state in a time which is an insignificant fraction of the total longevity in the communicative state. The number N of communicative civilizations may be expressed by[1]

$$N = R_* f_p n_e f_l f_i f_c L \tag{1}$$

where

R_* = the mean rate of star formation over the period in which the stars now possessing communicative civilizations were being formed. If we are typical, R_* is about the mean rate of star formation 5 billion years ago;

f_p = the fractions of stars which were formed at that epoch with planetary systems;

n_e = the mean number of planets in each planetary system with environments permitting the development of life;

f_l = the fraction of such planets on which life actually develops;

f_i = the fraction of life-bearing planets on which intelligent life evolves;

f_c = the fraction of planets bearing intelligent life which give rise to a communicative civilization;

L = the mean lifetime in the communicative state of such civilizations.

The various parameters entering this equation have been discussed by

Sagan (Ref. 1374), von Hoerner,[2] Cameron,[3] Huang (Ref. 1429), Morrison,[4] and others. Only R_* is well established observationally from stellar statistics and knowledge of nuclear processes in stellar interiors. It is of the order of one per year or slightly higher (Ref. 1374).[5] There are no observational statistics for f_p, but the present theories of the origin of the solar system, the statistics of multiple star systems, the distribution of mass and angular momentum in the solar system, and the statistics of stellar rotation all combine to give a persuasive argument that virtually all "single" stars are accompanied by planetary systems. If so, f_p is about 0.5. Again, there are no statistics on which to base an estimate of n_e except those of our own system, in which n_e is of the order of 2 to 3. We may take this, along with the theories which attempt to explain Bode's Law[3] to give a good estimate of n_e. We tend to feel relatively comfortable with this figure since it is based on a counted number at least somewhat greater than 1. This is a better statistical situation than exists in our statistics of known planetary systems.

The remaining factors, excepting L, are the province of the biologist. There seems to be near unanimity of opinion that f_l is very nearly 1 – an expression of the strong tendency for the basic constituents of life to appear abundantly in those experiments which have attempted to replicate conditions on the primitive Earth. We have an even better understanding of evolution, which shows it to be such a powerful mechanism that its effects will be strong, inevitably, in any ecology. Thus, f_i must be close to 1. Until recently, we would have believed that the evolution of an intelligent species would have assured, in time, a communicative civilization. However, the recent studies of dolphin intelligence[6] have indicated, and may soon prove, that an intelligent species may never become technical. This possibility necessitates the inclusion of a factor f_c. The results of dolphins may perhaps be interpreted in a less specific way, however: i.e. that more than one intelligent species may evolve on a planet. If this is the correct conclusion, our old picture remains valid. The combination of an inter- or intraspecies competition and the survival value contributed by technological prowess are still sufficient to conclude, from evolutionary theories, that in most cases technological development would appear. In any case, terrestrial history argues strongly for the emergence of technology and for a value of f_c of nearly 1.

From the previous discussion, we find the produce $R_* f_p n_e f_l f_i f_e$ to be about 1 yr⁻¹. This means that the number of communicative civilizations will be, by coincidence, equal to the mean longevity L. We have virtually no means of estimating L. Our own civilization, having just entered the communicative state, provides us only with what we hope is a very low lower limit on L. Attempts have been made to estimate L. These estimates range from approximately 10^3 yr (already two orders of magnitude greater than our own experience) as given by von Hoerner,[2] up to estimates of the order of 10^6 yr, as given by Morrison.[7] The factors assumed to limit L are primarily a nuclear war in which over-kill is practised, and loss of interest in technology, or at least in interstellar contacts. It has been pointed out, by von Hoerner in particular, that there are many factors which will tend to enhance L over our naive estimates, and few that tend to shorten it. Factors tending to enhance L include the probability than even an extreme nuclear war will not eliminate all life on a planet, allowing the possibility for intelligent life to re-evolve on the planet. There might then be a cyclic evolution of communicative species, if the later species did not learn from the early species' mistake. Another factor tending to enhance L is interstellar contact itself. The long time required for interstellar dialogue alone will tend to keep a species communicative for a considerable length of time.

If we are conservative, and accept L of the order of 10^3 to 10^4 yr, then perhaps one in 10^7 stars in the solar neighborhood presently possesses communicative species. The mean distance between them, and the distance any search method must then reach, is of the order of 300 parsec, or 1000 light years.

Study of Eq. (1) leads to the conclusion that there are really only three parameters which may still be greatly in error. One is f_p, for which we have no observational statistics at all. The detection of only one other planetary system in the vicinity of the Sun would greatly reinforce our estimate of f_p. Although such a detection would only increase the counted number of planetary systems to two, we would still be rather certain that planetary systems are quite abundant simply because it is highly improbable that the only two planetary systems in a galaxy would be found in the same minute fractional volume of the galaxy. It will be possible, though still very difficult, to detect in the near future other planetary systems around nearby stars. This may be done by direct photography at long wavelengths, or by measurement of gravitational perturbations of the parent stars (Ref. 1496), either method almost certainly requiring a telescope in space.

Another parameter for which we have no statistics is f_l. The data here will certainly be strengthened in the near future by probes to Mars. If living things are found on Mars, it will appear that the estimate $f_l = 1$ is accurate.

Lastly, there is the weakest parameter L, with which there appears to be no method to improve the estimates other than interstellar contacts. This is a most unfortunate situation. However, it may well be that knowledge of L is itself important enough to provide a justification for a search for extraterrestrial intelligent life. If so, perhaps we should remove L from the design parameter category and include it as a goal of our search.

The above discussion is largely a summary of the consensus of the Space Science Board–National Academy of Sciences Conference on Extraterrestrial Intelligent Life, held at Green Bank, West Virginia, in November, 1961.

It appears that we must be content with an estimate of about 1000 light years to the nearest civilizations; space research of the near future is likely merely to add weight to that estimate. Only the detection of several communicative civilizations will allow a major improvement in this value.

POSSIBLE MEANS OF COMMUNICATION

The various available means of communication, from what we now know of physics, appear to include the actual transport of solid material across space (rocketry), radiation in the form of nuclear particles, and electromagnetic radiation.

The physics of interstellar rockets has been examined by Purcell,[8] von Hoerner,[9] and Pierce,[10] with extremely discouraging conclusions. In each case, they assume that the rocket must travel at some appreciable fraction of the velocity of light; otherwise, the time for round trips over distances of the order of 1000 light years becomes unacceptable. Under such conditions, they find that the relativistic rocket equations lead to rockets of payload/initial mass ratios which are preposterous — 10^{-4} and less are typical of these calculations. This situation obtains even if the most powerful of propulsion systems are considered; for instance, those utilizing controlled nuclear fusion of hydrogen, or annihilation of matter by antimatter. Even were the payload/mass ratios reasonable, there would be apparently insuperable problems in constructing a rocket engine which would generate the required thrust, yet not consume all the payload weight, and in shielding the rocket payload from the nuclear radiation of its own engine and the onrushing interstellar medium whose particles may appear to the rocket as a powerful flux of particles of many billion electron volts of energy.

A solution to the mass ratio, or source of energy, problem has been offered by Bussard[11] and emphasized by Sagan (Ref. 1374), in which the spacecraft scoops up the interstellar medium while in flight, and uses this material as both fuel and reaction mass in a ramjet-like engine. The difficulties with this device again include the problem of shielding, but most difficult is the requirement that the dimensions of the scoop be of the order of perhaps thousands of kilometers. However, an argument against a physically feasible technique on the basis that it appears *to us* technically unfeasible is a very dangerous one indeed. Other communicative civilizations will be far more advanced technically than we, in most cases, and may accomplish with ease what is difficult to us. This is a direct consequence of our acceptance of a mean L of 10^3 yr or more. Thus, the Bussard solution cannot be ruled out. Nor can we rule out the even simpler solution that the rocket travels at much lower velocities.

The decision as to which is the most desirable means of interstellar communication should perhaps in the long run be based on arguments of economy—a concept all successful intelligent species will understand and employ. Even though a rocket of any size, for example, is within the capabilities of an extraterrestrial technology, some rockets will still be easier, or cheaper, to build than others that accomplish the same purpose, and the cheaper will be the ones employed. By the same reasoning, the cheapest interstellar messengers that accomplish their task, which is, after all, nothing more than to convey information (Ref. 1542), will be the ones usually employed (Ref. 1409). It is primarily in the realm of economy that all rockets are far inferior to the other plausible means of interstellar communication. For this reason, one rules that the use of rockets for interstellar communication is probably very rare compared to, say, electromagnetic waves. The same economic argument applies to the system of radio-equipped interstellar rockets proposed as interstellar space probes by Bracewell (Ref. 1542); here again, we would expect a relatively rare use of the technique for economic reasons.

There remains the use of radiation, which, as implied above, turns out to be the most economical means of communication now known to us. This economy is easily demonstrated. As an example, a microwave communication system consisting of two 300-ft parabolic antennas, and transmitters and receivers readily available on Earth, requires only about 1 kw-hr of radiated power, or perhaps five cents worth of gross energy, to transmit one bit of information 1000 light years. This may be done with a total capital investment much lower than that required for a single space probe, and the resultant communication system is flexible; it may be used to send enormous total numbers of bits of information to as many stars as desired, all at light velocity.

However, a simple decision that radiation is the most frequently used of interstellar communication methods does not really solve many problems. With radiation communication systems, it is our usual experience that more sensitivity or range is achieved as a narrower band of wavelengths is used. Thus, we may expect interstellar messages to arrive only in very restricted wavelength ranges. For example, it is technically feasible for us, at present, to restrict our messages to a bandwidth of 10^{-10} of the frequency used. Other communicative civilizations can certainly do as well. If this is to be the bandwidth criterion, it implies that there are roughly 10^{10} possible frequency bands on which messages may arrive. To search all these bands, with each of the many stars that are likely abodes of life, is an inconceivably difficult task. We conclude that we cannot proceed without more information which will lead us to the wavelength and type of radiation most often used in interstellar communication.

We can quickly rule out nuclear particle radiation. All useful known nuclear particles possess vastly more energy than, say, a microwave photon. In the long run, this means that single nuclear particles will be much more costly to produce than single microwave photons. Yet both particle and photon carry the same amount of information. Thus, by the economic arguments given before, the use of nuclear particles in interstellar communication appears much less probable than the use of microwave photons. This leaves electromagnetic radiation as the most likely of interstellar communication systems, but even then, many possibilities remain.

APPROACHES TO A SEARCH FOR ELECTROMAGNETIC MANIFESTATIONS OF EXTRATERRESTRIAL INTELLIGENT LIFE

The Frequency of Best Sensitivity

The prime problem now confronting us is the determination of the electromagnetic frequency most often used in interstellar communication. Perhaps the simplest approach that might yield that frequency is to invoke the economical argument used previously; that is, we seek the frequency that is easiest to use. Of course, in determining the easiest frequency, we cannot use the state of our technology as a prime criterion. The choice of frequency must be forced on us only by the laws of physics and the arrangement of the universe. It turns out, perhaps fortuitously, that these do lead to a best frequency.

The argument used to eliminate nuclear radiation can again be applied here, with modifications. The energy of a photon is directly proportional to its frequency. Thus, by our previous reasoning, we shall have a more economical system as we go to lower frequencies. This would lead us to communicate at dc frequencies, were it not for the existence of cosmic radio noise, which produces a deleterious effect that finally dominates the advantage gained by using lower-frequency photons. Cosmic noise increases as we go to lower frequencies and emanates from all points in the sky. Thus, our radio telescopes cannot avoid it, and in capturing it, they lose sensitivity. To find the consequences of these effects, we may write an equation giving the minimum detectable signal for a radio telescope, as limited only by the quantum nature of light and the cosmic radio noise, and thus independent of parameters of our own civilization.

The radio astronomer prefers to express the minimum detectable signal as proportional to a fictitious temperature T_s, the so-called system noise temperature. This is the temperature to which a resistor, properly matched electrically, would have to be heated to degrade the performance of an ideal receiver to that of an actual receiver limited in sensitivity by cosmic radio noise and quantum effects, and, in contemporary receivers, its own inherent noise.[12] The noise temperature T_q due to the quantum nature of light may be written:[13]

$$T_q = \frac{h\nu}{k} \tag{2}$$

where h is the Planck constant, k is the Boltzmann constant, and ν is the frequency. The contribution due to cosmic noise, T_c, is given by

$$T_c = T(\alpha,\delta)\,\nu^{-\gamma(\alpha,\delta)} \tag{3}$$

where $T(\alpha,\delta)$ and $\gamma(\alpha,\delta)$ are both functions of position (α,δ) in the sky, as noted, and must be determined by observation. The system noise for an optimum radiometer is simply the sum of these two contributions:

$$T_s = \frac{h\nu}{k} + T(\alpha,\delta)\nu^{-\gamma(\alpha,\delta)} \tag{4}$$

If we differentiate this, set the result equal to zero, and solve for ν, we obtain the frequency of best sensitivity, ν_0:

$$\nu_0 = \left[\frac{kT(\alpha,\delta)\,\gamma(\alpha,\delta)}{h}\right]^{\frac{1}{1+\gamma(\alpha,\delta)}} \tag{5}$$

Now ν_0 will be the frequency of maximum economy, and thus, perhaps the frequency most often used for interstellar communication, only if the laws of physics do not affect any other parameter of the link so markedly as to produce new sensitivity limitations which overwhelm the results of the effects just discussed. Hence, we must now assure ourselves that the laws of physics do not, for example, allow us to build higher-gain transmitters at light, as compared to radio, frequencies to such a degree that the sensitivity of the link as a whole is enhanced over that of the radiofrequencies despite the higher noise level. Thus, before accepting that ν_0 is defined by Eq. (5), we must examine the limitations on the entire electromagnetic communication link.

In such a link, the power P_r received by the receiving energy collector is given by

$$P_r = \frac{P_t G_t A}{4\pi R_s^2} \tag{6}$$

where

P_t = transmitter power output
G_t = gain of the transmitter antenna
A = effective collecting area of the receiving antenna
R_s = separation of the receiver and transmitter

If the power received is equal to the minimum detectable power level P_d, which is proportional to T_s, the maximum range R at which the system will function successfully will be

$$R^2 = \frac{P_t G_t A}{4\pi P_d} \tag{7}$$

We ask now: What limitations do the laws of physics place on P_t, G_t, and A as a function of frequency? This is a complex matter, although some of the relations are intuitively obvious. We know, for example, that it becomes more difficult or expensive to build a collector of a given size as the dimensional tolerances, which are set by the operating wavelength, become smaller. Thus, the construction of a 17-ft telescope for microwave wavelengths is a trivial job, but a 200-in. telescope for optical wavelengths is barely feasible.

Consider now only G_t and A, both of which are proportional to the size of the antenna we may build. The limitation on size, given a tolerance dictated by the wavelength to be used, is set by the elasticity of the structure. This is, in turn, controlled by Hooke's Law, which is a consequence of the binding forces in solid materials. Thus, in fact, the size of an antenna structure is limited by the binding forces in solid materials. We might note that this remains true even when we utilize servo-controlled structures or the surface of the Earth as a support. This is a pleasing result, because we understand it and also because it means that the limitations we encounter in antenna structures are not peculiar to ourselves but are common to all civilizations.

The limitations on P_t appear to be more complicated. In a simple transmitter, they seem to be set by the fact that (1) for efficient energy generation at one frequency, we must use a structure which has some dimensions of the order of the wavelength to be generated; and (2) we can permit only a certain maximum electric field strength within the transmitter. A higher field strength will destroy the walls of the transmitter. This means that the total energy content of the transmitter, and thus the power output, is limited by the wavelength and, again, the binding forces in materials. However, it is possible to add many transmitters together in parallel so as to enhance the total output power. Here the ultimate limitation is in keeping all the transmitter outputs in phase, or coherent. It would appear a little more difficult at one wavelength than at another to connect in parallel a given number of transmitters. This means that the over-all difficulty in constructing a compound transmitter of any size is just proportional to the difficulty in building a simple transmitter. Thus, in the end, the wavelength and solid-state binding forces limit the transmitter power we may achieve with a given effort. Again, this same situation would obtain on other planets.

We may get a good estimate of the practical effect of these limitations simply by looking at their consequences in our civilization. To do this, in Fig. 1 we have plotted, as a function of frequency, the best values presently available terrestrially for the various parameters. There is a

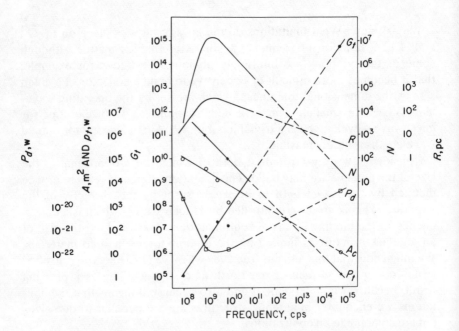

FIG. 1. Contemporary values of parameters entering into determination of range of an interstellar electromagnetic wave communication system and resultant maximum effective range R and number of stars N within R. (The points for A and G_t at an abscissa of 10^8 cps are based on a proposed telescope for Cambridge University; those at 10^9 on the Cornell 1000-ft antenna; those at $3(10^9)$ on the NRL 600-ft telescope; those at 10^{10} on the NRAO 140-ft telescope; and those at 10^{15} on the 200-in telescope. The plotted points for P_t are mean values for currently available transmitters, except at 10^{15} cps, where we have assumed that a l-w average power laser will soon be available.)

long gap in frequencies in the infrared, in which we have made no attempt to build equipment and for which there is therefore no empirical evidence. However, the run of the points on this log–log plot indicates that there is some justification for interpolating straight lines, as has been done with dotted lines. In these plots, we see clearly how the available collecting area A and transmitter power P_t decrease with increasing frequency; the value of G_t increases with frequency because of the dominance of ν^2 in the equations for antenna gain. If, now, mankind has not applied his resources to various frequencies with great inequity, these curves describe with some accuracy the effects of the physical limitations on the parameters of interest. We would expect to find curves of approximately the same slope for other civilizations. However, the vertical level of the curves would vary with the state of advancement of the civilization. Fortunately, it is only the slope of the curves that matters to us here, since the slopes alone determine any adjustments to the frequency of best sensitivity.

Specifically, do the parameters A, G_t, and P_t alone suggest a best frequency? If we add the curves for these parameters, we get a curve describing the logarithm of the product $P_t G_t A$. This curve is very nearly a horizontal line, and thus, these parameters taken together do not give a significant indication of a best frequency.

The remaining parameter, P_d, then controls the frequency of maximum R, or of best sensitivity. Since P_d is proportional to T_s, the best frequency is given by Eq. (5), without modification, which is what we set out to check.

This lengthy discussion has shown that, after all, only cosmic noise and the values of Planck and Boltzmann constants control the frequency of best sensitivity. This seems to be quite a certain result. For example, P_t, G_t, and A could reverse this situation only if there were to be an enhancement of their product by a factor of at least 10^6 at optical frequencies, with no enhancement at radio frequencies. The same conclusion has been reached by Oliver[14] and is implied in the work of Schwartz and Townes (Ref. 503). It appears very unlikely that future technical developments will create such a relative growth in optical capabilities, particularly when one remembers that development of radio technology will be continuously pursued.

As a matter of interest, a curve of P_d has been plotted in Fig. 1. This is not the curve given by Eq. (4) but is rather one based on actual contemporary radiometers. These are controlled in sensitivity at light frequencies by quantum effects and at the low radio frequencies by cosmic noise, but at the microwaves they do not yet approach the theoretical limit of Eq. (4). Nevertheless, the curve of P_d is of the same rough shape as Eq. (4). Curves of maximum range R and the number of stars N within that range, as obtained from Eq. (7), are also included. It is interesting to see that in the microwaves we already may reach to a range of about 1000 light years or $N = 10^7$ stars. Thus, we have answered in the affirmative another question that has been tacitly implied in this discussion: Can present technology reach to the estimated distance of the nearest communicative civilizations?

What are the optimum frequencies of Eq. (5)? Limiting values of $T(\alpha,\delta)$ and $\gamma(\alpha,\delta)$ have been given by Kraus and Ko.[15] From these, we obtain

$$3.7 < \nu_0 < 9.3 \text{ Gc}$$

or

$$3.2 < \lambda < 8.1 \text{ cm}$$

For any given star of interest, we could accurately compute the frequency that is appropriate for that star. There would be some uncertainty due to the observational uncertainties in $T(\alpha, \delta)$ and $\gamma(\alpha, \delta)$ and also because the other star may see a slightly different radio sky from the one we see. These effects limit the results of our calculations to a small band of frequencies in which signals might be expected.

It is perhaps encouraging that the optimum frequencies, as found from this hypothesis, are ones at which our atmosphere is transparent and at which we already have strong technical capabilities.

The Short-Pulse Approach

At the Space Science Board–NAS Conference, B. M. Oliver proposed a communication technique which circumvents the question of proper frequency. He notes that the bandwidth B of the transmission of a transmitter emitting a pulsed signal is related to the pulse duration τ by

$$B\tau \simeq 1 \qquad (8)$$

He further notes that the equation for radiometer sensitivity contains B and τ only as their product $B\tau$. If the radiometer is to be "matched" to the incoming signal, its B and τ should be the same as in the transmitted signal. If B differs from that of the incoming signal, we shall either be rejecting some of the signal power or monitoring frequencies on which there is no signal and thus accepting noise unnecessarily. Similarly, if τ is not matched to that of the signal, we shall either be rejecting some signal power or accepting noise during intervals when the signal is not present. Thus, in the radiometer, we should maintain the relation (8). However, as expression (8) shows, we are permitted a wide range of trade-offs between B and τ without loss of sensitivity. Oliver suggests an extreme situation in which a very short τ is used, so that B will become extremely wide. In fact, he suggests that τ be so short that B is equal to the width of, say, the entire radio window of the atmosphere. This case would require $\tau \simeq \frac{1}{10}$ nanosec. We would then have to make no choice of frequency, since the signal would arrive on all frequencies. Our system sensitivity with respect to mean transmitted power level would remain as good as if we were using the more conventional technique of narrowband transmission. We do not yet have the technical ability to practice this mode of transmission, but recent broadband detectors, such as the germanium bolometer, show that we are close to a solution, at least for the reception of signals.

It should be noted that this approach does not really reduce the magnitude of the search for signals. Now, rather than searching at various frequencies, we must search at various times. There will be as many time intervals to search as there were frequency intervals. What Oliver has pointed out is that, because of the conjugate nature of B and τ, any combination of B and τ fulfilling expression (8) may be an equally good candidate for interstellar communication, since the sensitivity is always equally good. At one extreme is the very slow narrow-bandwidth transmission which is the technique most often assumed, perhaps naively; at the other is the short-pulse transmission which places the signal on all frequencies. Between these extremes is a vast family of transmission formats of intermediate bandwidth and duration which has not yet been considered.

Recently, Oliver himself has criticized the short-pulse concept on two bases: (1) The interstellar electron density is sufficiently high to create a dispersion in the arrival time of the pulse energy on different frequencies. Thus, the pulse would arrive smeared out in time, leading to a great loss in sensitivity. This difficulty might be overcome by utilizing a receiver which introduces a time delay at different frequencies so as to correct for the variations in arrival time. Use of such a receiver presupposes a good knowledge of the distribution of interstellar electrons, something far beyond our grasp at present. (2) As the pulse becomes shorter, the instantaneous power level in the transmitter becomes greater. As mentioned in the discussion on the frequency of the best sensitivity, this power increase eventually encounters the physical limitation on transmitter power set by the binding forces in solid materials. Thus, there is an actual physical limitation which would indicate that the longer the pulse length, the greater the economy of operation. We already see the practical effect of this limitation in our space effort, where slow transmissions are used. If we accept this physical limitation as a sufficient criterion, we are led back to the narrowband format, which has already been most widely considered.

Naturally Significant Frequencies

Historically, the first philosophy proposed to serve as a guide to an optimum frequency was the use of a universally significant frequency. Cocconi and Morrison (Ref. 307) suggested that such a frequency was that of the 21-cm line of interstellar hydrogen, since it was the one striking natural spectral line in the radio spectrum. To this day, no other line has been found, indicating that the hydrogen line is, indeed, by far the dominant discrete feature in the natural radio spectrum.

The only lengthy search made so far for extraterrestrial intelligent radio signals was carried out at Green Bank near the 21-cm line frequency. Actually, the frequency was picked for economic reasons alone and the project started about six months before Cocconi and Morrison suggested the scientific rationale for use of the frequency. The equipment used in the search was the 85-ft parabolic reflector of the National Radio Astronomy Observatory (NRAO) and a special radiometer incorporating a room-temperature parametric amplifier for high sensitivity (graciously donated by Dana Atchley, Jr., of Microwave Associates, Inc.). The design of the radiometer is described elsewhere (Ref. 1551), and the equipment is shown in Figs. 2, 3, and 4. With this equipment, the stars Tau Ceti and

Fig. 2. 85-ft telescope of the NRAO.

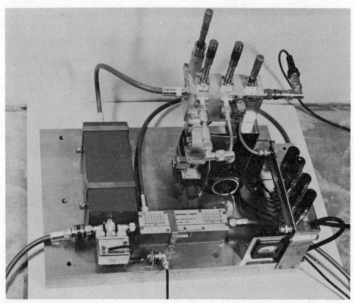

FIG. 3. First stages of radiometer used in 1960 NRAO search for extraterrestrial radio signals. (In the upper right-hand corner is the parametric amplifier used; the rest of the equipment is that of a typical superheterodyne radiometer; it was mounted at the telescope focus.)

FIG. 4. Remainder of radiometer of Fig. 3. (The equipment here principally selected the narrow bands to be studied, measured the frequency of reception, and detected and recorded the radiometer output.)

Epsilon Eridani, the nearest apparently single solar-type stars, were observed during May, June, and July 1960. Approximately 400 kc of total bandwidth, centered on the 21-cm line frequency, were explored with each star. The radiometer operating bandwidth was 100 cps and the radiometer time constant 30 sec. The radiometer was tuned continuously at a rate such that each 100 cps of bandwidth were observed for 1 min. No signals were detected. The lower limit on detectable signal strength was 10^{13} w of effective radiated power, in a bandwidth at 100 cps or less with either star. This limit is equivalent to a 1-Mw transmitter operating through a 600-ft antenna pointed at the Sun (Ref. 1554).

There is now some objection to the use of the 21-cm line itself, in that it is a noisy region of the spectrum; it has been proposed that subharmonics or harmonics of the line frequency might better be used.[16] The harmonics are probably the best choice, since they will fall nearer the frequencies of best intrinsic sensitivity derived previously.

In fact, it is possible to combine the naturally significant frequency hypothesis with the frequency of best sensitivity hypothesis by suggesting that the frequency most often used is the harmonic of the 21-cm line frequency which is closest to ν_0 of Eq. (5). Only crude observational knowledge of $T(\alpha, \delta)$ and $\gamma(\alpha, \delta)$ is necessary to pick the proper harmonic.

The Detection of the Aggregate of Signals a Civilization Uses for its Own Purposes

All the above approaches have been based on the assumption that another communicative civilization is overtly attempting to contact us. Surely this assumption is somewhat presumptuous — after all, we do nothing to contact other civilizations and are very unlikely to make such attempts until another civilization is detected. If, in fact, everyone listens and no one sends, then, for success, we must utilize a technique that will detect the signals a civilization uses for its own purposes. It is possible that such signals will not be strong enough to be detected individually. What is then needed is a system which will detect the aggregate effect of the numerous transmissions that coexist in a highly developed civilization.

Such a technique is suggested by the coded-pulse method of modern radar. In that technique, a series of pulses is sent out, and the returned echo, also in the form of a series of pulses, is cross-correlated against the waveform that was transmitted. At the limits of detectability, none of the individual pulses are discernible; the aggregate, however, is detectable because it leads to a significant positive cross-correlation coefficient when the cross-correlation is performed with correct time delay. In effect, the echoes of all the pulses are added together to give a net echo which is greater than the noise.

If we point a telescope at another communicative civilization and scan our radiometer in frequency, we will create a record in time which will contain many small signals from each of the transmitters that were transmitting in our direction in the band of frequencies scanned. Perhaps none of these signals will be individually detectable. If we knew the allocation of transmitter frequencies in the other civilization, we could simply cross-correlate this against our record to achieve the same gain as occurs in coded-pulse radar. But we do not have such data. However, we can generate a crude, noisy version of it simply by making a second frequency scan of the subject star. The signals in each of the records will be correlated, but the noise will not. By cross-correlating the two records, it is possible to detect the existence of the aggregate of signals, though no single signal is detectable in either of the records.

Quantitatively, it may be shown that the aggregate effect of a civilization's signals will be detectable to a good approximation if

$$\frac{m}{\sqrt{N}} > \frac{\sigma^2}{\epsilon^2} \tag{9}$$

where

N = the number of bands sampled;

m = the number of bands in which signals occur;

ϵ = the rms strength of signals, as measured at the radiometer input;

σ = the rms fluctuation in the radiometer noise, referred to the radiometer input.

To demonstrate how this works, we have constructed an example of what might be obtained in practice. From two sequences of 400 numbers, distributed in a gaussian manner about zero, we have made up two imitations of a radiometer output record in which only random noise is present. At the same 18 locations in each of these records, we have inserted positive signals, all of the same amplitude, which persist over four units of the record. Figure 5 shows the result if we simply take the sum of these two pseudorecords, as would be done if we used the conventional means of searching analog records for signals. One would be reluctant to conclude from Fig. 5 that there is evidence for intelligent transmissions in the composite record. Nevertheless, we have set the parameters of these records so that

$$\frac{m}{\sqrt{N}} = 2\frac{\sigma^2}{\epsilon^2}$$

meaning that condition (9) is just fulfilled. Thus, the cross-correlation function of the two records should show a significant coefficient when the records are cross-correlated with the same phase. Figure 6 shows the actual cross-correlation function obtained; the existence of the system

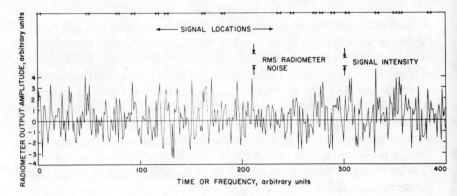

FIG. 5. Sum of two simulated radiometer records in which 18 intelligent signals of equal intensity have been inserted.

of intelligent signals is indicated, as predicted, by the peak at reference delay zero.

This technique can produce substantial advantages if very large numbers of frequencies are examined. As an example, if we examine the entire radio window, 10^{10} cps, with a 100-cps bandwidth, giving $N=10^8$, and we hypothesize a civilization that utilizes the spectrum as fully as we do, so that m is of the order of $10^8/2$ (one half of the spectrum occupied), we find that we can detect the existence of a civilization by this technique if $\epsilon/\sigma \simeq 0.01$. Thus, although we are a factor of one hundred away from detecting any signals individually, we still detect the civilization. This has the effect of increasing the range of our telescope 10 times or bringing 1000 times more stars within reach.

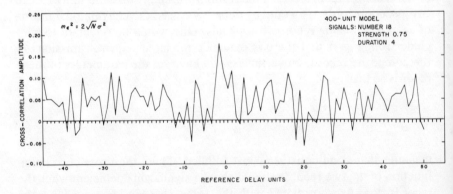

FIG. 6. Cross-correlation function of the two records of Fig. 5.

It may be shown that cross-correlating more than two records leads to no significant advance in sensitivity. One is usually better off summing the records so as to produce two net records of better sensitivity and then cross-correlating as above.

Thus, there is some hope that we might detect a civilization by eavesdropping, even though the signals will be very weak. This approach also suggests that our civilization may itself be easily detectable despite our failure to send signals for the purpose of being recognized.

Conclusions

The preceding discussion has shown that we now have the technology to detect reasonable signals over the distances we feel separate communicative civilizations. We have lines of logic which lead us, hopefully, to the frequencies most probably used in interstellar communication. On the other hand, our optimism must be tempered by the possibilities that our logic is not actually that most often used and that the majority of civilizations do not attempt to contact other communicative civilizations. To provide a chance of success in the face of these latter two difficulties, we should make any radio search for signals with equipment that may thoroughly sample the entire radio window. This conclusion, which it would be very dangerous to ignore, escalates tremendously the amount of equipment that must be employed in an efficient search. Specifically, we must provide a very high sensitivity radiometer which operates well anywhere in the radio window. If the search is to be carried on with any speed, we must provide the means to monitor many frequencies simultaneously. The data must be recorded in a way which is susceptible to the easy combining of the results from adjacent frequency bands, to the analysis of data with different integration times after the data are recorded, and tò the cross-correlation procedure. All this calls for a complicated multichannel radiometer, with tremendous data-storage capabilities.

When one studies the over-all problem quantitatively, one determines that a 300-ft or larger telescope should be used. The number of radiometer channels should be at least 1000, and the data storage that of a very large computer. With this combination, it would be possible to study enough stars in the order of 30 yr to give a high probability of success if our estimates of the number of communicative civilizations are correct. The total capital cost of such a facility might be $15,000,000. All of this is feasible. However, the scale of the undertaking, the shortage of people qualified to participate and interested in doing so, and the novel nature of the experiment all militate against early commencement of the project.

One last comment. Our experience with Project Ozma showed that the constant acquisition of nothing but negative results can be discouraging. A scientist must have some flow of positive results, or his interest flags. Thus, any project aimed at the detection of intelligent extraterrestrial life should simultaneously conduct more conventional research. Perhaps time should be divided about equally between conventional research and the intelligent signal search. From our experience, this is the arrangement most likely to produce the quickest success.

LESS PROBABLE APPROACHES TO THE DETECTION OF INTELLIGENT EXTRATERRESTRIAL LIFE

As has been emphasized above, our present knowledge can only say that radio is the most probable means of interstellar communication. There is still a good possibility that other means are used, although we would think less frequently than radio. Two other possible manifestations of intelligent extraterrestrial life are as follows.

Stellar Markers

As has become obvious above, a search for extraterrestrial life would be greatly facilitated if the stellar candidates could be reduced in number. The task would be made even easier if we could, in some economical way, mark a star in a striking manner so that it would stand out from the general run of galactic stars. This marker would be still more helpful if it took a form strongly suggesting its intelligent origin. As we have seen above, radio beacon markers do not really do the job well. A better approach would be one that actually acted on the radiation from the central star. There is such a vast supply of energy in the luminous flux from a star that any small perturbation on it will achieve the manipulation of large quantities of energy, by our usual standards.

At first glance, the most effective way to perturb the stellar radiation is to place around the star a sheath of material which absorbs a narrow band of radiation in the stellar spectrum. This will insert an artificial spectral line, which, if properly chosen, will be judged by most intelligent species to be of intelligent origin. We may consider this possibility seriously if we obtain a plausible quantitative estimate of the amount of material necessary to produce a useful spectral line. The following is a crude estimate.

Assume that we deal with an atom absorbing an optical line whose strength is nearly that of a resonant line. Then, typically, the Einstein A value may be of the order of 10^8 per sec. This means that the atom may scatter about 10^8 quanta/sec or a total power of 10^8 hv. An optical quantum has an energy of the order of 10^{-12} erg, so a single atom may scatter a power of about 10^{-4} erg/sec. Let us assume that a line width of the order of 1Å may be achieved and that a 1% absorption will constitute a detectable line. Then, we will have to scatter about $(0.01)/5000$ or $0.5(10^{-6})$ of the solar flux of $4(10^{33})$ erg/sec or about $2(10^{+27})$ erg/sec. The number of scattering atoms required is then about $2(10^{31})$. With an atomic weight of the order of 10, the mass of material required is of the order $2(10^{31})$ (10) $2(10^{-24}) = 4(10^8)$ g $= 400$ tons. Thus, a mass of several hundred tons, quite a reasonable value, may produce a detectable spectral line.

There are several serious practical problems to be overcome before such a system would be feasible, such as the attainment of the proper spatial distribution, the severe radiation pressure and solar wind to which the absorbing material would be subjected, probably resulting in its rapid loss, and the probable need for a cooling agent in the material. Nevertheless, the system is physically possible and requires plausible supplies of material and energy.

The material of the marker should be of a type that is very difficult to explain except as a result of intelligent activity. A short-lived isotope is a good example. The lines of one such element, technetium, have been found in stellar spectra. The halflife of the most stable isotope is $2(10^5)$ yr. However, technetium lines have so far been found not in solar-type stars but only in S-type stars, whose unstable structure offers a natural explanation of the lines.

Probably the greatest obstacle in searching the sky for markers is the multitude of unexpected spectral features which appear in stars. Much study will have to be given to the establishment of criteria on which to base a judgment as to whether a spectral feature is of natural or intelligent origin.

Probably the strongest criticisms of the marker technique are that (1) it conveys virtually no information except that the star possesses a civilization; and (2) it is of no benefit to its originators; thus, only the most altruistic of civilizations would employ it. Because of these various objections to its use, we guess it to be a rare activity in space.*

Evidence of Direct Contacts

As mentioned previously, the possibility of direct space flight to the Earth cannot be eliminated, although it appears a relatively infrequent means of interstellar communication. Sagan (Ref. 1374) has recently discussed this subject in detail and re-examined terrestrial history for evidence of interstellar contacts. The difficulty encountered is that, in

*The author is indebted to E. M. Purcell of NRAO for a useful discussion of the marker hypothesis.

the vast accumulated history and mythology of the Earth, there are sure to be some accounts that agree perfectly, purely by accident, with our preconceived notion of an interstellar visit. Thus, an account which agrees with preconceived notions cannot be taken seriously as evidence for an interstellar contact. Even a statistical approach will not aid us, since we do not know what the incidence of chance coincidences might be.

It appears that there is absolutely no choice in this matter but to be extremely conservative and to require material evidence of clearly non-terrestrial intelligent origin before accepting any account as even suggesting a direct interstellar contact. Thus, we establish the criterion that an undeniable artifact is a necessary and sufficient condition to prove a direct contact. No such artifact has been brought forward.

However, no strong conclusions should be drawn from this, because there are reasons why we should not expect any existing artifacts to be discovered easily. Sagan calculates that interstellar visits may be separated by thousands of years. If the last contact was made many thousands of years ago, the probability is great that, if an artifact passed into the possession of terrestrial inhabitants, it still lies buried in a yet unexcavated archæological site. Sagan suggests that, of known sites, the best opportunity appears to lie in the excavation of the ancient Sumerian city Sippara because of the striking mythology connected with that city.

Another possible reason for difficulty in locating artifacts is that visitors of many thousands of years ago probably would not have wished to leave an important artifact with the then primitive people of Earth. They would have feared that ignorance of the artifact's purpose and significance might lead to its loss, abuse, or destruction. They therefore might have hidden it purposely in such a way that it would not be found until a technical civilization had developed. A way to achieve this might be to conceal the artifact in the interior of a limestone cave, since there it would stand a good chance of avoiding burial or disturbance for many millennia, and then to mark it in such a way that only an advanced technology could find it, but could do so easily. A simple method would be to mark it with an active radioisotope. It would then remain invisible until radiation detectors were developed.

Doubtlessly, there are numerous other possibilities. In fact, there are so many as to be discouraging, since their very number means that any specific one, if any, is unlikely to be the one used. The conclusion one reaches is that any effort to search for such artifacts for this purpose alone is too unlikely to be successful to be justifiable economically. One can only, and one should, remain alert for any discovery which might produce an artifact.

SUMMARY

Our final conclusions are that microwave radio signals are the most common means of interstellar communication; that terrestrial technology is capable of carrying on a successful search for signals but that the project, if it is to cope with all the reasonable possibilities, must be one of very great expense, complexity, and duration. We also conclude that there are many other possible ways in which manifestations of intelligent life might be found, but at present few, if any, appear to offer enough hope for success to justify their active pursuit.

REFERENCES

1. DRAKE, F. D., Discussion at Space Science Board–National Academy of Sciences Conference on Extraterrestrial Intelligent Life, November 1961, Green Bank, West Virginia.
2. VON HOERNER, S., The Search for Signals from Other Civilizations, *Science*, vol. 134 (1961), pp. 1839–43.
3. CAMERON, A. G. W., Stellar Life Zones, *Interstellar Communication*, New York: W. A. Benjamin Co. (In press).
4. MORRISON, P., Interstellar Communication, *Bulletin of the Philosophical Society of Washington*, vol. 16 (1962), pp. 58–81.
5. SCHMIDT, M., The Rate of Star Formation. II: The Rate of Formation of Stars of Different Mass, *The Astrophysical Journal*, vol. 137 (1963), pp. 758–69.
6. LILLY, J. C., Vocal Behavior of the Bottlenose Dolphin, *Proceedings of the American Philosophical Society*, vol. 106 (1962), pp. 520–9.
7. MORRISON, P., Unpublished data.
8. PURCELL, E. M., Radioastronomy and Communication Through Space, BNL–658, *Brookhaven Lecture Series*, No. 1, Brookhaven National Laboratory, Upton, New York, November 16, 1960.
9. VON HOERNER, S., General Limits of Space Travel, *Science*, vol. 137 (1962), pp. 18–23.
10. PIERCE, J. R., Relativity and Space Travel, *Proceedings of the Institute of Radio Engineers*, vol. 47 (1959), pp. 1053–61.
11. BUSSARD, R. W., Galactic Matter and Interstellar Flight, *Astronautica Acta*, vol. 6 (1960), pp. 179–94.
12. DRAKE, F. D., Radio-Astronomy Radiometers and Their Calibration, *Telescopes*, ed. by G. P. KUIPER, Chicago: University of Chicago Press (1960), pp. 210–38.
13. STRANDBERG, M. W. P., Inherent Noise of Quantum-Mechanical Amplifiers, *The Physical Review*, vol. 106 (1957), pp. 617–20.
14. OLIVER, B. M., Some Potentialities of Optical Masers, *Proceedings of the Institute of Radio Engineers*, vol. 50 (1962), pp. 135–41.
15. KRAUS, J. D., and KO, H. C., *Celestial Radio Radiation*, Radio Observatory Scientific R-1, Ohio State University, Research Foundation, Electrical Engineering Department, Columbus, Ohio, May 1957.
16. GOLAY, M. J. E., Note on the Probable Character of Intelligent Radio Signals from Other Planetary Systems, *Proceedings of the Institute of Radio Engineers*, vol. 49 (1961), p. 959.

CHAPTER X

TRENDS AND PROBLEMS IN EXOBIOLOGY

M. H. Briggs* and G. Mamikunian

Jet Propulsion Laboratory
Pasadena, California

INTRODUCTION

The authors wish to suggest that exobiological problems fall into several overlapping, yet in certain ways distinct, areas. The problems which exobiologists aim to solve are as follows.

First, within our solar system:

1. On which planets does organic matter occur? What is the amount and chemical composition of this material?
2. On which planets is the organic matter organized into life forms? Has life become extinct on any planet?
3. How does organic matter originate on planets? How does organic matter spontaneously organize into life?
4. Are there natural mechanisms whereby life can be transferred in a viable state from planet to planet? To what extent is artificial transfer possible? What would be the effects of such transfers?

Secondly, within the universe as a whole:

1. How abundant are life-bearing planets?
2. How common is intelligent life in the universe? Is communication possible across interstellar distances?

We would now like to outline briefly the state of knowledge of these problems and to suggest possible avenues for future research.

PLANETARY ORGANIC MATTER

Before considering the possibility of organic matter on other planets, it is of interest to look at some estimates of the amount and types of terrestrial organic substances. According to Borchert (Ref. 125), the mass of carbon in the biosphere is about 3×10^{17} g. This includes all types of living organisms in all habitats but excludes material of presumed biological origin in geological materials (i.e. coal, petroleum, dissolved

---

*Present address, Analytical Laboratories Ltd., Corsham, Wiltshire, England.

347

organic matter in the hydrosphere, particulate organic matter in the atmosphere, trapped "biochemical fossils" in sedimentary rocks, and biological carbonate deposits). It is important to realize that in every terrestrial environment in which organic matter occurs, the vast majority is extracellular. Thus, in soils, less than 5% of the total organic matter is present in living organisms (Ref. 152). In freshwater lakes, less than 10% of the total organic matter is intracellular,[1] and a similar situation holds for the oceans (Ref. 149).

In the atmosphere, much of the organic matter occurs as droplets of volatile plant products (Ref. 186).

The compounds making up the bulk of living cells (proteins, nucleic acids, fats, and sugars) are but trace constituents of the extracellular organic matter. Thus, the major constituents of petroleum are hydrocarbons (paraffins, naphthenes, and aromatics); of coal, condensed aromatic hydrocarbons (Ref. 144); of sedimentary organic matter, humic compounds (polycondensed aromatic acids and phenols)[2] (Ref. 185); of soils, humic compounds (Ref. 152); of dissolved organic matter in lakes, hydroxylated aliphatic acids (Refs. 127, 128, 174), while the extracellular organic matter in the oceans is largely unidentified (Ref. 180); of the atmosphere, terpenes and their oxidation products (Ref. 186).

Thus, not only is most of the organic matter on our planet *not* contained within living cells, but it is composed of substances which are not major constituents of life. Admittedly, terrestrial organic matter is probably entirely of biological origin, but it is of only minor biochemical interest in that it is largely metabolic endproducts.

It is clear that considerable work remains to be done on identifying the amounts and nature of terrestrial organic matter in different environments. In particular, the nature of the organic constituents of sea water and of marine and fresh-water sediments remains to be investigated in detail.

However, having considered terrestrial organic matter and gained some idea of its amount and distribution, it becomes possible to consider the forms of organic matter that may exist on the other planets.

There would seem to be four possible types of organic matter that may occur on any planet:

1. Organic matter surviving from the solar nebula prior to the origin of planets.
2. The products of reactions in primitive planetary atmospheres.
3. The products of biological activity.
4. Organic matter added by meteoric materials.

There is now no doubt that a great variety of organic compounds can be synthesized from methane or carbon dioxide by electric discharges or radiation and that these reactions occurred in the solar nebula and in the primitive planetary atmospheres. Moreover, there are several mechanisms whereby the products of these reactions can accumulate and become concentrated. It is widely assumed that under suitable conditions and over a long period of time, these compounds would organize into living cells. However, there is no guarantee than the compounds might not simply become incorporated into the surface of the planet. Thus, there have been suggestions that the clouds of Venus may contain complex carbon compounds from nonbiological syntheses[3] (Refs. 104, 211) and that such compounds are trapped in the surface of the Moon (Refs. 187, 282).

The known composition of the atmospheres of the major planets (Jupiter, Saturn, Uranus, and Neptune), which contain large quantities of methane, immediately suggests that abiogenic organic synthesis is still occurring in the atmospheres of these planets by the action of incident solar radiation and discharges due to atmospheric turbulence (Ref. 85). It has been suggested that the color changes of Jupiter can be explained in terms of such reactions (Ref. 1032); the recent discovery of red pigments by Oró (Ref. 1295) in simulated primitive mixtures strengthens this idea.

Thus, it seems likely that organic matter of abiogenic origin occurs on all the major planets, and also possibly on Venus. It would be interesting to know how the composition of this organic matter varies from planet to planet, for while there are similarities among the conditions of the major planets, they are far from identical. It seems quite likely that these variations in chemical and physical conditions will influence the nature of the organic products of the radiation- or discharge-induced reactions.

While the occurrence of biologically synthesized organic matter on the planets cannot definitely be ruled out, it seems likely that Mars is the only other planet with a biosphere. Consequently, only there would one expect the accumulation of organic matter similar to that of the Earth. If Mars possesses a biosphere of biochemistry similar to that of Earth, then the surface of Mars should contain humic compounds of the same chemical type as terrestrial soils.

Similarly, the Martian atmosphere should possess particulate organic matter like that of Earth. It has been suggested independently by Briggs (Ref. 327) and Guerin (Ref. 409) that the "blue haze" of Mars is due to small droplets of volatile plant products such as terpenes. However, it remains to be demonstrated whether droplets of such compounds can simulate the properties of the Martian haze.

The third source of planetary organic matter, from meteoric materials, is also difficult to evaluate.

There is now no doubt that carbonaceous chondrites contain indigenous

organic matter, and it has been pointed out (Ref. 19) that if these meteorites have been falling on Earth throughout geological time with the
frequency observed over the past century, then our planet has accumulated about 10^{13} g of organic matter from these meteorites. The recent
observation that some meteor fragments possess organic attachments
(Ref. 952) suggests that the above estimate may be too low by several
orders of magnitude.

As there is no way of determining the infalls of meteorites on other
planets, there is no way at present of estimating the quantities of meteoric
organic matter added to them. Nevertheless, it seems possible that all
planets and satellites inside the asteroid belt have accumulated considerable amounts of organic matter from carbonaceous chondrites, and
perhaps from meteor fragments. On planets with biospheres, this organic
material may have been simply metabolized, but on lifeless planets,
it may still be present on the surface.

LIFE IN THE SOLAR SYSTEM

Assuming, on the grounds given above, that organic matter is common
in the solar system, it is important to know on which planets life exists.
There are three ways to investigate the incidence of life on planets other
than Earth. First, there is the use of traditional astronomical techniques
to examine the surface properties of planets to determine whether or
not their chemical and physical properties are conducive to the existence
of, or show any signs of, life.

Research of this kind has produced tentative evidence of existence
of life on the "maria" of Mars but on no other planet or satellite. The
evidence for life on Mars is as follows:

1. The chemical and physical properties of the atmosphere and surface
   are compatible with the existence of life forms based on a terrestrial-type biochemistry, and the survival of some terrestrial organisms
   under simulated, near-Martian conditions has been demonstrated
   in the laboratory[4] (Refs. 399, 411, 516).
2. The maria have rapid regenerative properties (Ref. 463).
3. The infrared absorption spectra of the Martian maria, but not the
   deserts, show absorptions at 3.5μ (Ref. 523). There is, however,
   the possibility that the absorptions are due to inorganic carbonates
   or nitrogen oxides (Ref. 1041).
4. There are certain similarities between the reflection spectra of the
   maria and those of terrestrial vegetation adapted to high, cold
   habitats (Refs. 1480, 1481).
5. The seasonal changes in the polarization of light reflected from the
   maria somewhat resemble those produced by certain types of

vegetation (Ref. 30). Alternately, the change could be due to variations in average particle size of the Martian "soil" resulting from climatic changes.

6. There is a seasonal wave of darkening of the maria that proceeds from the melting icecaps toward the equator (Ref. 534). Color changes associated with this wave have been reported, but may be illusory.

Taken together, these data are only suggestive of a Martian biosphere, and it is debatable whether or not traditional astronomical methods can ever provide conclusive evidence of extraterrestrial life. Perhaps the most promising approach would be a more detailed study of the infrared absorption spectra of the Martian maria. In particular, one would like to know whether absorptions due to aromatic groupings can be detected because of the preponderance of humic materials on Earth.

Secondly, life may be detected by the use of "soft-landed" space vehicles containing life-detector instruments. The following is a selection of some of the instruments that are either being planned or constructed for such missions:

1. *Gulliver* (Ref. 997). A device to detect the evolution of radioactive CO_2 released from C^{14}-labeled substrates by microorganisms.

2. *Mars Microscope* (Ref. 154). A device to collect, examine microscopically, and transmit via video to Earth morphological characteristics of any indigenous microorganisms.

3. *Gas Chromatograph* (Ref. 998). A device to pyrolize any indigenous organic matter and determine the pattern of pyrolysis products after separation in the gas phase by column chromatography.

4. *Mass Spectrograph*. A device to determine the occurrence of hydrocarbons and other organic compounds in extracts of the Martian surface.

5. *Multivator*. An instrument conceived by Lederberg, containing several devices to search for various biological properties (such as phosphatase activity, membrane transport phenomena, optical activity, etc.) in samples of the Martian surface.

6. *Wolf Trap* (Ref. 1000). A device to measure changes in pH or turbidity of a nutrient medium due to the growth of extraterrestrial microorganisms.

An evaluation of (1) the difficulties involved in the use and design of such instruments, and (2) the problems of interpretation is presented elsewhere (Ref. 990).

The final way of determining the presence or absence of life on the other planets is by direct examination. This can be accomplished either by the observations of an astronaut landed on the planet or by investigations on Earth of samples from other planets returned by automated devices or by an astronaut. Full details of the proposed schemes of analysis of returned extraterrestrial samples are given elsewhere. It should be stated here, however, that it is unlikely that any automated device will prove capable of detecting an extinct biosphere, such as may occur on the Moon (Ref. 233). Such investigations will have to be conducted directly on the lunar samples.

The problem of distinguishing between (1) extracellular organic matter of biological origin, (2) extracellular organic matter of nonbiological origin, (3) viable life forms, and (4) fossilized life forms is particularly acute when the origin of the organic constituents of the carbonaceous chondrites is considered. These meteorites contain on the average about 2% of organic matter which they carry in from space. It has been claimed that some of the organic compounds are of biological origin (Ref. 940). Similarly, there are reports of viable microorganisms isolated from within the meteorites (Refs. 908, 909, 961, 967), and also of indigenous microfossils (Refs. 871, 874, 876, 974, 985). However, each of these points has been interpreted differently by other workers. Thus, the organic compounds have been suggested to be nonbiological (Ref. 866), viable organisms, mere terrestrial contaminants (Refs. 863, 961), and the "microfossils" a variety of mineral, inorganic, and abiogenic organic structures[5] (Ref. 859).

It is perhaps an interesting reflection on the current state of exobiological techniques that, after study for several years by over a dozen leading scientists, several kilograms of carbonaceous chondrites have failed to yield any conclusive evidence either for or against the presence of life on the meteorite parent body.

It must also be mentioned that the nature of the parent body of the carbonaceous chondrites is still debated. Suggestions include: (1) the primitive Earth, (2) the surface of the Moon, (3) the asteroid belt, and (4) the primeval solar nebula.

Thus, at the present stage, even if conclusive evidence of past-life in meteorites were forthcoming, it would not be possible to state where in the solar system this life had existed.

SPONTANEOUS ORIGINS OF LIFE

There have now been numerous experimental demonstrations that simple gaseous mixtures, when acted upon by ultraviolet radiation or electric discharges, will react to yield a variety of organic compounds. Many of these compounds, though by no means all, are important constituents of modern living cells. Among the groups of compounds identified in the products of reactions in simple gaseous mixtures are cyanides, amino acids, amines, sugars, heterocyclic bases, simple acids, aldehydes, and aromatic derivatives (Refs. 1038, 1041, 1115, 1285).

It has been demonstrated that, under selected and rather artificial conditions, many of these discharge products can be converted to other compounds of biochemical interest. Thus, under anhydrous conditions or in the presence of strong phosphoric acid, amino acids can be polymerized to proteins of quite high molecular weight.[6] Similarly, cyanides readily yield various heterocyclic bases (Ref. 1295), while formaldehyde in the presence of lime produces a large number of simple sugars (Ref. 1308). The synthesis of polynucleotides from ribose and purines in the presence of an ester of polyphosphate has also been examined (Ref. 1316). The latter reaction has so far been demonstrated only in nonaqueous solvents.

Considerable research remains to' be conducted into mechanisms for the synthesis of biopolymers under conditions more approaching those of the primitive Earth. Thus, it would be interesting to know whether discharge-produced amino acids will polymerize thermally in the presence of the other discharge products, or whether pressure-induced polymerization could occur in the deep oceans.

It is apparent that considerable quantities of organic compounds will probably accumulate on any planet with a methane–ammonia–water–hydrogen atmosphere given sufficient time and incident solar radiation (Ref. 98).

The origination of cellular life forms from a dilute solution of organic compounds is obviously a highly complex process of organization. Its details are still largely obscure, and there has been little experimental investigation of this aspect of the origin of life.

An interesting problem in this field is whether the essential organelles (nuclei, mitochondria, flagellae, etc.) of modern cells originated independently and were gradually incorporated into living cells or whether these structures are evolutionary specializations that have appeared later in the history of life. It has been pointed out recently (Ref. 1377) that the evidence of comparative cytology is that organelles are evolutionary specializations and that the first cells lacked such structures, their functions being carried out by the undifferentiated cytoplasm. Consequently, the organization of the primeval organic solution into a relatively inefficient monocellular organism does not present the problem of intracellular organization and specialization. The latter is a problem of *cellular* and not of chemical evolution.

Perhaps the most difficult research task remaining is to explain the origin and formation of the first cell membranes. A considerable amount of work along those lines has been done by several groups, but no clear-cut results can be said to have been forthcoming. Thus, Fox (Ref. 1069) has shown that the treatment of thermally synthesized proteinoid with water yields microspheres about $2\,\mu$ in diameter. These microspheres retain their integrity on centrifugation, show volume changes in hypertonic salt solutions, and can be made in various shapes by incorporating other substances, such as lipids or nucleic acids. It seems possible that the surfaces of these protein microspheres possess some properties in common with cell membranes. Similarly the coacervates of Oparin (Ref. 1149) and of Booji and DeJong (Ref. 1330), although made from materials of biological origin (gelatin, gum arabic, etc.), are simple systems and do possess limiting membranes with osmotic properties. Moreover, the absorption of compounds by some classes of coacervates is selective. Binary fission of the coacervate droplet occurs under suitable conditions, while vacuole formation is common.

A study of coacervate formation by the polymeric products of abiogenic reactions may yield interesting and relevant findings to the origin of cells.

The origin of optical activity is similarly an unsolved problem. While there are several hypotheses to account for the phenomenon (Ref. 1206), it is not known whether optical differentiation occurred during the abiogenic synthesis of organic compounds or during the origination and evolution of the first cells. Several natural agents could have influenced the primeval system to produce an excess of one enantiomorph. Thus, a local concentration of a quartz stereoisomer is one offered explanation. It would be of interest to know whether the addition of powdered quartz of one isomer only to a simulated primitive atmosphere experiment can produce any net optical activity in the organic products.

Perhaps the most important experiment that would follow the discovery of an extraterrestrial life form would be the examination of the optical properties of the constituent compounds to determine whether or not they were the same as in terrestrial organisms.

INTERPLANETARY TRANSFER OF ORGANISMS

While there is little doubt that chemical evolution can account for the origin of life on Earth, it is impossible to be certain that terrestrial life did *in fact* originate in this manner, for there is an obvious alternative (Ref. 325). The first terrestrial organisms could have been transferred from some other planet. The hypothesis of an extraterrestrial contact for the origin of life can be considered in two parts. First, a mechanism must be suggested by which organisms could leave their native planet, and second, it must be shown that organisms can survive the conditions of outer space so as to arrive in a viable state. A foremost proponent of the hypothesis of an extraterrestrial contact was Arrhenius (Refs.

1347, 1348) who proposed that the spores of microorganisms can be carried into the upper atmosphere by currents of air. Once in the upper atmosphere, the spores would be repelled from the Earth by electrostatic forces; and once in interplanetary space, they would drift, their direction being controlled largely by the pressure of sunlight. In this way, given sufficient time, a microbial spore might cross between planets or even between stars. These hypothetical spores have been named panspermia. A recent study of interstellar panspermia has been made by Sagan (Ref. 1368).

It is apparent that many aspects of this hypothesis are open to experimental investigation, although the basic premise, that life began on the primitive Earth by the arrival of one or more panspermia, probably is not. Yet, if Arrhenius is correct, viable microbial spores occur in the upper atmosphere and in outer space. There is already evidence that microorganisms do exist in the upper atmosphere (Refs. 145, 1367); however, there is no evidence currently that any of these upper atmospheric microorganisms can leave the planet, and the electrostatic repulsion effects postulated by Arrhenius seem doubtful. Alternate mechanisms of escape include:

1. Grazing meteorite collisions.
2. Spores captured by debris flung into space by violent volcanic explosions, or explosions due to impacts of large comets, etc.
3. Violent upper atmospheric turbulence due to the solar protonic wind.

At present, there are no available data on the effectiveness of these mechanisms.

Once in space, the problem becomes one of anabiosis: the effects of extremely adverse conditions on the viability of terrestrial organisms (Ref. 1359). In space, the hazards to an organism are great, including complete lack of nutrients, considerable temperature variation, low pressure, and radiation. Bacterial spores can resist the first two hazards,[7] but it is unlikely that they could survive the ultraviolet and other radiations of space.[8] Nevertheless, there is no direct evidence to show that spores do not exist in space. Such evidence could be obtained by means of an artificial satellite, or even a specially designed high-altitude rocket. The artificial transfer of organisms by space vehicles undoubtedly has occurred, and there is a strong probability that the Moon now possesses (dead?) terrestrial bacteria. Hence, assuming that the Moon does not, and never did, have indigenous organisms, any life found on the Moon must be of extralunar origin and not the result of chemical evolution.

To lessen the chances of altering the properties of other planets considerably by introducing viable terrestrial organisms, a program of gaseous sterilization of U.S. space vehicles was undertaken (Refs. 1377,

1392). However, 100% effective sterilization is still impossible to achieve in practice.

The effects of introducing viable terrestrial organisms onto other planets are impossible to foresee, but considerable alteration of the atmospheric and surface properties might well result. It is obviously desirable to prevent this from happening before a detailed first-hand examination of the planets has been completed. Then, perhaps, the task of deliberately altering the planets with introduced organisms to attain a desired end (e.g. such as an oxygen atmosphere on Mars and Venus) might be attempted (Ref. 692).

INCIDENCE OF PLANETARY SYSTEMS

At the present stage of exobiology, it is inevitable that most research will be conducted on our solar system. Nevertheless, to gain a correct perspective of the life process, it is proper to consider the abundance and distribution of life in the universe as a whole.

The number of stars in our galaxy is of the order of 10^{11}; of these, about 14% are G-type stars similar to our Sun. About 75% of all stars are binaries.

Using traditional astronomical techniques, it is impossible to determine directly the presence or absence of planet-sized objects around other stars. The only observational evidence of other planetary systems is derived from studies of the orbital dynamics of binaries, and this work has been confined to only a few systems (Ref. 1496).

There are theoretical grounds for predicting a high incidence of planets, but these are based on hypothetical models for the origin of the solar system. Thus, if the planets arose from condensations in an equatorial nebula of the primitive Sun (Refs. 1524, 1534), then a slowing of the solar rotation would result. Consequently, from this point of view, the rate of rotation of any star could be used as a criterion of the presence of planets.[9] Approximately two-thirds of the galactic population are slow-rotating stars and may, therefore, be accompanied by planets.

While planetary systems may be abundant, there is no guarantee that life is similarly widely distributed. There is evidence that our Sun is a second-generation star in the galaxy, and only such recent stars will possess sufficient elements of high atomic weight to yield high-density planets such as Earth. First-generation stars may possess only planets of H, He, C, N, O, etc., and may be unsuitable abodes for life. Similarly, radiation variations on planets of binary stars may be too extreme to support life. There are obviously a multitude of factors to be considered, and the relevant data are almost completely unobtainable.

Nevertheless, the universe is so large that it is a statistical certainty that extraterrestrial life, even intelligent life, exists elsewhere. Attempts to detect directed radio signals from two nearby local stars have already been made (Ref. 1552), and it is probable that similar experimental programs will be conducted in the future.

If life in the universe is more abundant than we believe, it is possible that direct contacts have occurred in the past, and a careful search for possible accounts of such events through historical archives, and particularly of mythological sources, might be a profitable occupation for a qualified historian.

CONCLUSIONS

It is our belief that exobiology offers one of the most exciting and challenging fields for scientific research. In this Chapter, we have merely outlined some of the trends and achievements. In closing, we list some of the suggested experimental approaches that have been given above:

1. A determination of the amounts and chemical nature of organic compounds accumulating on the Earth in different environments.
2. A complete chemical characterization of the organic compounds formed in various "primitive atmosphere" mixtures under different conditions.
3. Experiments to determine the effect of natural asymmetric substances, such as quartz, on the reactions in primitive atmospheres.
4. Experiments to determine the mechanisms whereby the organic products of "primitive atmosphere" reactions could organize into cell-like accumulations.
5. A determination of the presence or absence of viable microorganisms in space near the Earth.
6. A complete study of the orbital dynamics of nearby binary systems to determine the presence or absence of planetary systems.

REFERENCES

1. HUTCHINSON, G., *Treatise on Limnology,* vol. 1, New York: John Wiley and Sons, Inc. (1957).
2. PONOMAREV, A. N., Composition of Ural Sapropels, *Zhurnal Prikladnoi Khimii,* USSR, vol. 20 (1940), pp. 391–401.
3. KUIPER, G. P., Planets, Satellites, and Comets, *Smithsonian Contributions to Astrophysics,* vol. 1, No. 1 (1956), pp. 89–93.
4. SIEGEL, S. M., HALPERN, L. A., GIUMARRO, C., RENWICK, G., and DAVIS, G., Martian Biology: The Experimentalist's Approach, *Nature,* vol. 197 (1963), pp. 329–31.
5. ANDERS, E., and FITCH, F., Search for Organized Elements in Carbonaceous Chondrites, *Science,* vol. 138 (1962), pp. 1392–9.
6. FOX, S. W., HARADA, K., and VEGOTSKY, A., Thermal Polymerization of Amino Acids and a Theory of Biochemical Origins, *Experientia,* vol. 15 (1959), pp. 81–5.

7. WILLIAMS, O. B., *et al.*, Symposium on the Biology of Bacterial Spores, *Bacteriological Reviews*, vol. 16 (1952), pp. 89–143.
8. LEA, D. E. *Actions of Radiations on Living Cells*, New York: Cambridge University Press (1947).
9. STRUVE, O., *Stellar Evolution*, Princeton: Princeton University Press (1950).

BIBLIOGRAPHY

I. THE SOLAR SYSTEM

A. General Reviews

1. ABELSON, P. H., Extraterrestrial Life, *Proceedings of the National Academy of Sciences of the United States of America*, vol. 47 (1961), pp. 575–81.
2. ADAMS, W. S., The Atmosphere of the Planets, *Publications of the Astronomical Society of the Pacific*, vol. 46 (1934), p. 69.
3. ADEL, A., A Determination of the Amount of Carbon Dioxide Above the Reflecting Layer in the Atmosphere of the Planet Venus, *The Astrophysical Journal*, vol. 85 (1937), pp. 345–61.
4. ADEL, A., Note on the Temperature of Venus, *The Astrophysical Journal*, vol. 86 (1937), pp. 337–9.
5. ADEL, A., Spectroscopic Studies of Planetary Atmospheres, *The Astrophysical Journal*, vol. 89 (1939), pp. 311–12.
6. ADEL, A., The Importance of Certain CO_2 Bands in the Temperature Radiation From Venus, *The Astrophysical Journal*, vol. 93 (1941), pp. 397–400.
7. ADEL, A., Near Infra-Red Spectra of the Planets, *The Physical Review*, vol. 72 (1947), p. 538.
8. ADEL, A., and LAMPLAND, C. O., Planetary Atmospheres and Water-Cell Temperatures, *The Astrophysical Journal*, vol. 93 (1941), pp. 391–6.
9. AMBARTSUMIAN, V. A., *The Scattering of Light in Planetary Atmospheres*, Report No. T-63, Rand Corporation, Santa Monica, California (1956).
10. ANTONIADI, E. M., Sur une anomalie de la phase dichotome de la planète Vénus, *Comptes Rendus Hebdomadaires des Séances de l'Académie des Sciences*, vol. 131 (1900), pp. 468–9.
11. ARRHENIUS, S., Die Atmosphären der Planeten, *Annalen der Naturphilosophie*, vol. 9 (1910), pp. 76–81.
12. ARTHUR, G. F., *Physical and Positional Properties of the Planets*, WADC TN 58–347, Wright Air Development Center, Wright-Patterson AFB, Ohio, 1958. AD-206, 671.
13. BAZYKINE, V., The New Science of Astro-Botany, *Suid-Afrikaanse Joernaal van Wetenskap*, vol. 56 (1960), pp. 229–31.
14. BERLAGE, H. P., On the Composition of the Bodies of the Solar System, *Koninklijke Nederlandse Akademie van Wetenschappen, Proceedings*, Series B, vol. 56 (1953), pp. 45–55.
15. BETHE, H. A., Energy Production in Stars, *The Physical Review*, vol. 55 (1939), pp. 434–56.
16. BIUTNER, E. K., The Dissipation of Gas from Planetary Atmospheres, *Soviet Astronomy–AJ*, vol. 2 (1958), pp. 528–38.
17. BIUTNER, E. K., Time in Which a Steady Amount of Oxygen is Established in the Atmosphere of Planets Containing Water Vapour, *Doklady Akademii Nauk SSSR*, vol. 138 (1961), pp. 1050–3.
18. BRIGGS, M. H., Life on Other Planets, *Humanist (London)*, vol. 72, No. 8 (1957), pp. 18–20.
19. BRIGGS, M. H., Meteorites and Planetary Organic Matter, *The Observatory*, vol. 82 (1962), pp. 216–18.

20. BRIGGS, M. H., The Distribution of Life in the Solar System, *Journal of the British Interplanetary Society,* vol. 18 (1963), pp. 431–7.

21. BUSCOMBE, W., Planetary Atmospheres, *Astronomical Society of the Pacific Leaflets,* vol. 6, No. 277 (1954), pp. 213–20.

22. CHANDRA, S., and SRIVASTAVA, B. P., Absorption of Microwaves in Planetary Atmospheres, *Zeitschrift für Astrophysik,* vol. 47 (1959), pp. 127–34.

23. COBLENTZ, W. W., and LAMPLAND, C. O., Measurements of Planetary Radiation, *Lowell Observatory Bulletin,* vol. 3, No. 85 (1923), pp. 91–134.

24. COBLENTZ, W. W., and LAMPLAND, C. O., Planetary Temperatures, *The Physical Review,* vol. 25 (1925), p. 255.

25. DAMON, P. E., and KULP, J. L., Inert Gases and the Evolution of the Atmosphere, *Geochimica et Cosmochimica Acta,* vol. 13 (1958), pp. 280–92.

26. DAVIDSON, M., The Atmospheres of the Earth and Planets, *Irish Astronomical Journal,* vol. 1 (1950), pp. 69–74.

27. DELSEMME, A. H., and SWINGS, P., Hydrates de gaz dans les noyaux cométaires et les grains interstellaires, *Annales d'Astrophysique,* vol. 15 (1952), pp. 1–6.

28. DE MARCUS, W. C., Planetary Interiors, *Handbuch der Physik,* ed. by S. FLÜGGE, vol. 52, Berlin: Springer-Verlag (1959), pp. 418–48.

29. DOLLFUS, A., Étude des planètes par la polarisation de leur lumière, *Annales d'Astrophysique,* Suppl. No. 4 (1957), p. 117.

30. DOLLFUS, A., Polarization Studies of Planets, *The Solar System, Vol. III: Planets and Satellites,* ed. by G. P. KUIPER and B. M. MIDDLEHURST, Chicago: University of Chicago Press (1961), pp. 343–99.

31. DRAKE, F. D., Radio Emission From the Planets, *Physics Today,* vol. 14, No. 4 (1961), pp. 30–34.

32. FESENKOV, V. G., Some Considerations About the Primaeval State of the Earth, *The Origin of Life on the Earth,* ed. by A. I. OPARIN *et al.,* New York: Pergamon Press, Inc. (1959), pp. 9–15.

33. FIRSOFF, V. A., *Our Neighbor Worlds,* London: Hutchinson and Co. (1952).

34. FIRSOFF, V. A., Dissipation of Planetary Atmospheres, *Science,* vol. 130 (1959), pp. 1337–8.

35. FIRSOFF, V. A., An Ammonia-Based Life, *Discovery,* vol. 23 (1962), pp. 36–42.

36. FOWLER, W. A., GREENSTEIN, J. L., and HOYLE, F., Nucleosynthesis During the Early History of the Solar System, *Geophysical Journal,* vol. 6 (1962), pp. 148–220.

37. GAUROY, P., *Les mondes du ciel,* Paris: Arthene Fayard (1960).

38. GAUZIT, J., La vie dans l'univers. Les atmosphères planétaires, *l'Astronomie,* vol. 53 (1939), pp. 78–82.

39. HERZBERG, G., The Atmospheres of the Planets, *The Journal of the Royal Astronomical Society of Canada,* vol. 45 (1951), pp. 100–23.

40. HESS, S. L., Atmospheres of Other Planets, *Science,* vol. 128 (1958), pp. 809–14.

41. HESS, S. L., Atmosphärische Bedingungen auf anderen Planeten, *Weltraumfahrt,* vol. 10 (1959), pp. 87–89.

42. HESS, S. L., and PANOFSKY, H. A., The Atmospheres of the Other Planets, *Compendium of Meteorology,* ed. by T. F. MALONE, Boston: American Meteorological Society (1951), pp. 391–8.

43. HORNER, F., Radio Noise from Planets, *Nature,* vol. 180 (1957), p. 1253.

44. HOYLE, F., *Frontiers of Astronomy,* New York: Harper and Bros. (1955).

45. HOYLE, F., *Nature of the Universe,* 2nd edition, New York: Harper and Bros. (1960).

46. HULBERT, E. O., Temperature of the Planets, *The Physical Review,* vol. 34 (1929), p. 1063.

47. JEANS, J., Is There Life on the Other Worlds? *Science,* vol. 95 (1942), pp. 589–92.

48. KAISER, H. K., Physical Conditions and Condition of Life on Other Planets, *Probleme aus der astronautischen Grundlagenforschung,* ed. by H. N. KÖLLE, Baden, Switzerland: International Astronautical Federation (1952), pp. 226–38.

49. KIENLE, H., Die Atmosphären der Planeten, *Die Naturwissenschaften,* vol. 23 (1935), pp. 244–6.

50. KIESS, C. C., and LASSORZSKY, K., *Known Physical Characteristics of the Moon*

and the Planets, Georgetown College Observatory, Georgetown, Kentucky (1958). AD-115, 617.

51. KING E. S., Revised Magnitudes and Color Indices of the Planets, *Annals of the Harvard College Observatory,* vol. 85, No. 4 (1923), pp. 63–71.

52. KUHN, W., Über das Alter der Sauerstoffatmosphäre der Erde, *Chemische Berichte,* vol. 89 (1956), pp. 303–8.

53. KUIPER, G. P., Infrared Spectra of Planets, *The Astrophysical Journal,* vol. 106 (1947), pp. 251–4.

54. KUIPER, G. P., *Atmospheres of the Earth and Planets,* Revised edition, Chicago: University of Chicago Press, (1952).

55. KUIPER, G. P., Infrared Observations of Planets and Satellites, *The Astronomical Journal,* vol. 62 (1957), p. 245.

56. KUIPER, G. P., The Environments of the Moon and the Planets, *Physics and Medicine of the Atmosphere and Space,* ed. by O. O. BENSON and H. STRUGHOLD, New York: John Wiley and Sons, Inc. (1960), pp. 577–83.

57. KUIPER, G. P., *Planetary Atmospheres and Lunar Surfaces,* Yerkes Observatory, Williams Bay, Wisconsin, Project 8602 Contract AF 19 (604)-3873 (1961).

58. KUIPER, G. P., *Planetary Properties,* Yerkes Observatory, Williams Bay, Wisconsin, Project 8602 Contract AF 19 (604)-5193 (1961).

59. KUZ'MIN, A. D., SALOMONOVICH, A. E., Radio Emissions From Venus in the 8-mm Wave-Length Range, *Soviet Astronomy – AJ,* vol. 4 (1960), pp. 279–82.

60. MACDONALD, G. J. F., On the Internal Constitution of the Inner Planets, *Journal of Geophysical Research,* vol. 67 (1962), pp. 2945–74.

61. MAKEMSON, M. W., BAKER, R. M. L., JR., and WESTROM, G. B., Analysis and Standardization of Astrodynamic Constants, *Journal of Astronautical Sciences,* vol. 8 (1961), pp. 1–13.

62. MAYER, C. H., Planetary Radiation at Centimeter Wave Lengths, *The Astronomical Journal,* vol. 64 (1959), pp. 43–45.

63. MAYER, C. H., Radio Emission of the Moon and Planets, *The Solar System, Vol. III: Planets and Satellites,* ed. by G. P. KUIPER and B. M. MIDDLEHURST, Chicago: University of Chicago Press (1961), pp. 442–72.

64. MAYER, C. H., Temperature of the Planets, *Scientific American,* vol. 204, No. 5 (1961), pp. 58–65.

65. MENZEL, D. H., *Planetary Atmospheres,* Harvard University Project 8602, Contract AF 19 (604)-3074, (1962).

66. MINTZ, Y., The General Circulation of Planetary Atmospheres, *Proceedings of Lunar and Planetary Exploration Colloquium,* vol. 3, No. 1, Aerospace Laboratories, North American Aviation, Inc., Downey, California (1962).

67. MINTZ, Y., The Energy Budget and Atmospheric Circulation on a Synchronously Rotating Planet, *Icarus,* vol. 1 (1962), pp. 172–3.

68. NAGY, B., and CLAUS, G., Mineralized Microstructures in Carbonaceous Meteorites, *Advances in Organic Geochemistry,* ed. by U. COLOMBO and G. D. HOBSON, New York: Pergamon Press, Inc. (1964), pp. 109–14.

69. NEWBURN, R. L., JR., The Exploration of Mercury, the Asteroids, the Major Planets and Their Satellite Systems and Pluto, *Advancements in Space Science and Technology,* vol. 3, ed. by F. I. ORDWAY, New York: Academic Press Inc. (1961), pp. 196–272.

70. OBULJEN, A., Atmospheres of the Planets, *Vasiona* (Belgrade), vol. 1 (1953), pp. 39–40.

71. ÖPIK, E. J., *Oscillating Universe,* New York: New American Library of World Literature, Inc. (1960).

72. ÖPIK, E. J., Surface Conditions on the Nearest Planets, *American Journal of Physics,* vol. 28 (1960), pp. 618–22.

73. PECKER, J. C., and ATHEY, R. C., CN Bands in the Chromosphere, *The Astrophysical Journal,* vol. 12 (1949), pp. 391–9.

74. PHILIPS, T. E. R., Planetary Atmospheres: I. Visual and Photographic Observations, *Monthly Notices of the Royal Astronomical Society,* vol. 96 (1936), pp. 376–81.

75. PHILLIPS, C. R., and WEDUM, A. G., Safety Practices Applicable to Exobiological Research, *Symposium on Extraterrestrial Biochemistry and Biology*, American Association for the Advancement of Science, 128th Annual Meeting, Denver, Colorado, December 26–30, 1961 (In press).

76. POSIN, D. Q., *Life Beyond Our Planet*, New York: McGraw-Hill Book Co., Inc. (1962).

77. RASOOL, S. I., The Structures of Planetary Atmospheres, *AIAA Journal*, vol. 1 (1963), pp. 6–19.

78. REA, D. G., Molecular Spectroscopy of Planetary Atmospheres, *Space Science Reviews*, vol. 1 (1962), pp. 159–96.

79. REYNOLDS, O. E., Space Biosciences, *American Institute of Biological Sciences, Bulletin*, vol. 12, No. 5 (1962), pp. 49–51.

80. ROSS, F. E., Photographs of Venus, *The Astrophysical Journal*, vol. 68 (1928), pp. 57–92.

81. RUSSELL, H. N., Atmospheres of the Planets, *Science*, vol. 81 (1935), pp. 1–9.

82. RUSSELL, H. N., DUGAN, R. S., and STEWARD, J. Q., *Astronomy; Vol. I, Solar System*, Boston: Ginn and Co. (1945).

83. SADIL, J., The New Science–Astrobotanics, *Říše Hvězd* (Prague), vol. 35 (1954), pp. 75–79.

84. SAGAN, C., and KELLOGG, W. W., The Terrestrial Planets, *Annual Review of Astronomy and Astrophysics* (1963), pp. 3–36.

85. SAGAN, C., and MILLER, S. L., Molecular Synthesis in Simulated Reducing Planetary Atmospheres, *The Astronomical Journal*, vol. 65 (1960), p. 499.

86. SCHOENBERG, E., Neue Beleuchtungsformeln für die grossen Planeten, *Handbuch der Astrophysik*, vol. 2, No. 1, Berlin: Julius Springer Verlag (1929), pp. 82–85.

87. SEYBOLD, P., *A Survey of Exobiology*, Research Memorandum No. RM-3178-PR, Rand Corporation, Santa Monica, California, 1963.

88. SHAPLEY, H., The Probable Environment of Other Planets and Its Suitability for Some Forms of Life. *The Biology of Space Travel*, ed. by N. W. PIRIE, New York: Hafner Publishing Co. (1961).

89. SHKLOVSKII, I. S., Is Communication Possible with Intelligent Beings on Other Planets? *Priroda*, vol. 4 (1960), pp. 21–30.

90. SINTON, W. M., Recent Radiometric Studies of the Planets and the Moon, *The Solar System, Vol. III: Planets and Satellites*, ed. by G. P. KUIPER and B. M. MIDDLEHURST, Chicago: University of Chicago Press (1961), pp. 429–41.

91. SMITH, A. G., and CARR, T. D., Radio-Frequency Observations of the Planets in 1957–8, *The Astrophysical Journal*, vol. 130 (1959), pp. 641–7.

92. SOLOMON, G., Planetary Atmospheres, *Vistas in Astronautics*, ed. by M. ALPERIN and M. STERN, New York: Pergamon Press, Inc. (1958), p. 37.

93. STRUGHOLD, H., *Comparative Ecological Study of the Chemistry of the Planetary Atmospheres*, Special Report, USAF School of Aviation Medicine, Randolph Field, Texas, December 1953. AD-25,628.

94. STRUGHOLD, H., The Ecosphere in the Solar Planetary System, *Proceedings of the 7th International Astronautical Congress* (September 17–22, 1956), Rome: Assoziazione Italiana Razzi (1956), pp. 277–88.

95. STRUGHOLD, H., The Oxygen Belt in the Planetary System, *Journal of Astronautics*, vol. 3 (1956), pp. 27–28, 52.

96. STRUGHOLD, H., The Possibilities of an Inhabitable Extraterrestrial Environment Reachable From the Earth, *The Journal of Aviation Medicine*, vol. 28 (1957), pp. 507–12.

97. STRUGHOLD, H., and RITTER, O. L., Solar Irradiance From Mercury to Pluto, *Aerospace Medicine*, vol. 31 (1960), pp. 127–30.

98. SUESS, H. E., Thermodynamic Data on the Formation of Solid Carbon and Organic Compounds in Primitive Planetary Atmospheres, *Journal of Geophysical Research*, vol. 67 (1962), pp. 2029–34.

99. SWINGS, P., Reflexions au sujet de l'astrophysique moléculaire, *Scientia*, vol. 83 (1948), pp. 10–16.

100. SWINGS, P., and ROSENFELD, L., Considerations Regarding Interstellar Molecules, *The Astrophysical Journal*, vol. 86 (1937), pp. 483–6.

101. TOCQUET, R., *La vie sur les planètes*, Paris: Éditions du Seuil (1960).

102. TREMBATH, R. E., Conditions Necessary for the Existence of Life, *Monthly Notes of the Astronomical Society of South Africa*, vol. 7(1948), pp. 13–15.

103. UREY, H. C., *Planets, Their Origin and Development*, New Haven, Connecticut: Yale University Press (1952).

104. UREY, H. C., The Atmospheres of the Planets, *Handbuch der Physik*, ed. by S. FLÜGGE, vol. 52, Berlin: Springer-Verlag (1959), pp. 363–418.

105. UREY, H. C., Planets, *Science in Space*, ed. by L. V. BERKNER and H. ODISHAW, New York: McGraw-Hill Book Co., Inc. (1961), pp. 199–217.

106. UREY, H. C., and BREWER, A. W., Fluorescence in Planetary Atmospheres, *Proceedings of the Royal Society (London)*, Series A, vol. 241 (1957), pp. 37–43.

107. WILDT, R., Ozon und Sauerstoff in den Planeten-Atmosphären, *Veröffentlichungen der Universitäts-Sternwarte zu Göttingen*, No. 38 (1934).

108. WILDT, R., Photochemistry of Planetary Atmospheres, *The Astrophysical Journal*, vol. 86 (1937), pp. 321–36.

109. WILDT, R., On the State of Matter in the Interior of the Planets, *The Astrophysical Journal*, vol. 87 (1938), pp. 508–16.

110. WILDT, R., Cosmochemistry, *Scientia* (Milan), vol. 67(1940), pp. 85–90.

111. WILDT, R., The Geochemistry of the Atmosphere and the Constitution of the Terrestrial Planets, *Reviews of Modern Physics*, vol. 14 (1942), pp. 151–9.

112. WRIGHT, W. H., On Photographs of the Brighter Planets by Light of Different Colours, *Monthly Notices of the Royal Astronomical Society*, vol. 88 (1928), pp. 709–18.

113. YOUNG, R. S., Exobiology, *Proceedings of the NASA — University Conference on the Science and Technology of Space Exploration*, (Chicago, November 1–3, 1962), vol. I, Washington, D.C.: National Aeronautics and Space Administration (1962), pp. 423–9.

B. Terrestrial Organic Matter

114. ABELSON, P. H., Paleobiochemistry, *Carnegie Institution of Washington Yearbook No. 54*, Baltimore: Lord Baltimore Press, Inc. (1954).

115. ABELSON, P. H., Geochemistry of Organic Substances, *Researches in Geochemistry*, ed. by P. H. ABELSON, New York: John Wiley and Sons, Inc. (1959).

116. ABELSON, P. H., Major Biologic Innovations and the Geologic Record, *Proceedings of the National Academy of Sciences of the United States of America*, vol. 47 (1961), pp. 1705–12.

117. ABELSON, P. H., Factors Limiting the Long Term Viability of Organisms, *Symposium on Extraterrestrial Biochemistry and Biology*, American Association for the Advancement of Science, 128th Annual Meeting, Denver, Colorado, December 26–30, 1961 (In press).

118. ABELSON, P. H., HOERING, T. C., and PARKER, P. L., Fatty Acids in Sedimentary Rocks, *Advances in Organic Geochemistry*, ed. by U. COLOMBO and G. D. HOBSON, New York: Pergamon Press, Inc. (1964), pp. 169–74.

119. ADEL, A., Note on the Spectra of Jupiter and Saturn, *The Physical Review*, vol. 48 (1935), p. 103.

120. ANFINSEN, C. B., *Molecular Basis of Evolution*, New York: John Wiley and Sons, Inc. (1959).

121. AULT, W. V., and KULP, J. L., Isotopic Geochemistry of Sulfur, *Geochimica et Cosmochimica Acta*, vol. 16 (1959), pp. 201–35.

122. BARGHOORN, E. S., Fossil Organisms From Pre-Cambrian Sediments, *Annals of the New York Academy of Sciences*, vol. 108 (1963), pp. 451–2.

123. BARGHOORN, E. S., and TYLER, S. A., Microfossils From the Middle Pre-Cambrian of Canada, (Abstract only) First International Conference on Palynology, Tucson, Arizona, April 23–27, 1962.

124. BELOZERSKII, A. N., On the Species Specificity of the Nucleic Acids of Bacteria, *The Origin of Life on the Earth*, ed. by A. I. OPARIN *et al.*, New York: Pergamon Press, Inc. (1959), pp. 322–31.

125. BORCHERT, H., Zur Geochemie des Kohlenstoffs, *Geochimica et Cosmochimica Acta*, vol. 2 (1951), pp. 62–75.

126. BRIGGS, M. H., Dating the Origin of Life on Earth, *Evolution*, vol. 13 (1959), pp. 416–18.

127. BRIGGS, M. H., Presence of Free Amino Acids, Sugars and Peptides in Filtered Lake Water, *Life Sciences*, vol. 1 (1962), pp. 377–80.

128. BRIGGS, M. H., Further Organic Constituents of Filtered Lake Water, *Life Sciences*, vol. 1 (1962), pp. 649–51.

129. BRIGGS, M. H., and SEGAL, L., Preparation and Properties of a Free Soil Enzyme, *Life Sciences*, vol. 2 (1963), pp. 69–72.

130. BRIGGS, M. H., and SPEDDING, J. D., Soil Enzymes, *Science Progress* (London), vol. 51, No. 202 (1963), pp. 217–25.

131. CAMERON, R. E., Soil Studies — Microflora of Desert Regions, *Space Programs Summary No. 37-15*, vol. 4, Jet Propulsion Laboratory, Pasadena, California, June 30, 1962, pp. 12–21.

132. CAMERON, R. E., *The Role of Soil Science in Space Exploration*, Technical Report No. 32-399, Jet Propulsion Laboratory, Pasadena, California, February 16, 1963.

133. CERNOVODEANU, P., and HENRI, V., Comparaison des actions photo-chimiques et abiotiques des rayons ultraviolets, *Comptes Rendus Hebdomadaires des Séances de l'Académie des Sciences*, vol. 150 (1910), pp. 549–51.

134. CHILINGAR, G. V., DEGENS, E.T., and PIERCE, W. D., On the Origin of Petroleum Inside Freshwater Carbonate Concretions of Miocene Age, *Advances in Organic Geochemistry*, ed. by U. COLOMBO and G. D. HOBSON, New York: Pergamon Press, Inc. (1964), pp. 149–64.

135. COSTAIN, C. H., ELSMORE, B., and WHITFIELD, G. R., Radio Observations of a Lunar Occultation of the Crab Nebula, *Monthly Notices of the Royal Astronomical Society*, vol. 116 (1957), pp. 380–5.

136. CRAIG, H., Isotopic Standards for Carbon and Oxygen and Correction Factors for Mass-Spectrometric Analysis of Carbon Dioxide, *Geochimica et Cosmochimica Acta*, vol. 12 (1957), pp. 133–49.

137. DEGENS, E. T., and REUTER, H. J., Analytical Techniques in the Field of Organic Geochemistry, *Advances in Organic Geochemistry*, ed. by U. COLOMBO and G. D. HOBSON, New York: Pergamon Press, Inc. (1964), pp. 377–402.

138. DOLE, M., The History of Oxygen, *Science*, vol. 109 (1949), pp. 77–81, 96.

139. DUFRESNE, E. R., and ANDERS, E., The Record in the Meteorites: V. A Thermometer Mineral in the Mighei Carbonaceous Chondrite, *Geochimica et Cosmochimica Acta*, vol. 23 (1961), pp. 200–8.

140. ERDTMAN, J. G., Geochemistry of the High Molecular Weight Non-hydrocarbon Fraction of Petroleum, *Advances in Organic Geochemistry*, ed. by U. COLOMBO and G. D. HOBSON, New York: Pergamon Press, Inc. (1964), pp. 215–38.

141. EVANS, E. D., KENNY, G. S., MEINSCHEIN, W. G., and BRAY, E. E., Distribution of N-Paraffins and Separation of Saturated Hydrocarbons From Recent Marine Sediments, *Analytical Chemistry*, vol. 29 (1957), pp. 1858–61.

142. EVANS, W. D., The Occurrence of Biogenic Residues in Carboniferous Coals, *Advances in Organic Geochemistry*, ed. by U. COLOMBO and G. D. HOBSON, New York: Pergamon Press, Inc. (1964), pp. 71–86.

143. EVANS, W. D., The Organic Solubilization of Minerals in Sediments, *Advances in Organic Geochemistry*, ed. by U. COLOMBO and G. D. HOBSON, New York: Pergamon Press, Inc. (1964), pp. 263–70.

144. FRANCIS, W., *Coal: Its Formation and Composition*, second edition, London: Edward Arnold, Ltd. (1961).

145. GREGORY, P. H., Microbiology of the Atmosphere, *Plant Science Monograph*, London: Leonard Hill Co. (1961).

146. HANYA, T., and OGURA, N., Application of Ultraviolet Spectroscopy to the Examina-

tion of Dissolved Organic Substances in Water, *Advances in Organic Geochemistry*, ed. by U. COLOMBO and G. D. HOBSON, New York: Pergamon Press, Inc. (1964), pp. 447–56.

147. HUTCHINSON, G. E., Biochemistry of the Terrestrial Atmosphere, *The Solar System*, *vol. II: Earth as a Planet*, ed. by G. P. KUIPER and B. M. MIDDLEHURST, Chicago: University of Chicago Press (1954), pp. 371–427.

148. HYDE, H. A., and ADAMS, K. F., *Atlas of Airborne Pollen Grains*, London: The Macmillan Co. (1958).

149. JEFFREY, L. M., and HOOD, D. W., Organic Matter in Sea Water; an Evaluation of Various Methods for Isolation, *Journal of Marine Research*, vol. 17 (1958), pp. 247–71.

150. JEFFREY, L. M., PASBY, B. F., STEVENSON, B., and HOOD, D. W., Lipids of Ocean Water, *Advances in Organic Geochemistry*, ed. by U. COLOMBO and G. D. HOBSON, New York: Pergamon Press, Inc. (1964), pp. 175–98.

151. KEILIN, D., Stability of Biological Materials and Its Bearing Upon the Problem of Anabiosis, *Science Progress* (London), vol. 41 (1953), pp. 577–92.

152. KONONOVA, M., *Soil Organic Matter*, New York: Pergamon Press, Inc. (1961).

153. KOYAMA, T., Gaseous Metabolism in Lake Sediments and Paddy Soils, *Advances in Organic Geochemistry*, ed. by U. COLOMBO and G. D. HOBSON, New York: Pergamon Press, Inc. (1964), pp. 363–76.

154. LEDERBERG, J., Exobiology: Experimental Approaches to Life Beyond the Earth, *Science in Space*, ed. by L. V. BERKNER and H. ODISHAW, New York: McGraw-Hill Book Co., Inc. (1961), pp. 407–25.

155. LOVE, L. G., Biogenic Primary Sulfide of the Permian Kupferschiefer and Marl Slate, *Economic Geology and the Bulletin of the Society of Economic Geologists*, vol. 57 (1962), pp. 350–66.

156. LOVE, L. G., Further Studies on Microorganisms and the Presence of Syngenetic Pyrite, *Palaeontology*, vol. 5 (1962), pp. 444–59.

157. LOVE, L. G., *Fossil and Recent Microorganisms Associated With the Formation of Biogenic Sulfides*, First International Conference on Palynology, Tucson, Arizona, April 23–27, 1962.

158. LOVE, L. G., Pyrite Spheres in Sediments, *Symposium on the Biogeochemistry of Sulfur Isotopes*, ed. by M. L. JENSEN (In press).

159. LOVE, L. G., The Composition of *Pyritosphaera Barbaria*, *Micropaleontology*, vol. 6 (In press).

160. LOVE, L. G., and ZIMMERMANN, D. O., Bedded Pyrite and Microorganisms From the Mount Isa Shale, *Economic Geology and the Bulletin of the Society of Economic Geologists*, vol. 56 (1961), pp. 873–96.

161. MACGREGOR, A. M., A Pre-Cambrian Algal Limestone in Southern Rhodesia, *Transactions of the Geological Society of South Africa*, vol. 43 (1941), pp. 9–16.

162. MEINSCHEIN, W. G., and KENNY, G. S., Analysis of a Chromatographic Fraction of Organic Extracts of Soils, *Analytical Chemistry*, vol. 29 (1957), pp. 1153–61.

163. NAUMOVA, S. N., *Lower Paleozoic and Pre-Cambrian Flora*, First International Conference on Palynology, Tucson, Arizona, April 23–27, 1962.

164. PALMER, M. C., Comments in Panel Discussion, The Identity of the 'Organized Elements', *Annals of the New York Academy of Sciences*, vol. 108 (1963), p. 614.

165. PIRIE, N. W., Solar Wind and Terrestrial Oxygen, *Nature*, vol. 190 (1961), p. 706.

166. PIRIE, N. W., Germanium as a Carbon Analogue, *The Scientist Speculates*, ed. by I. J. GOOD et al., New York: Basic Books, Inc. (1962), pp. 280–1.

167. PISANI, F., Étude chimique et analyse de l'aérolithe d'Orgueil, *Comptes Rendus Hebdomadaires des Séances de l'Académie des Sciences*, vol. 59 (1864), pp. 132–5.

168. RANKAMA, K., Early Precambrian Carbon of Biogenic Origin From the Canadian Shield, *Science*, vol. 119 (1954), pp. 506–7.

169. RANKAMA, K., Geologic Evidence of Chemical Composition of the Precambrian Atmosphere, *Geological Society of America, Special Papers*, No. 62 (1955), pp. 665–84.

170. ROBINSON, R., The Duplex Origins of Petroleum, *The Scientist Speculates*, ed. by I. J. GOOD *et al.*, New York: Basic Books, Inc. (1962), pp. 377–87.
171. ROBINSON, R., Theorie zur Entstehung des Erdöls, *Angewandte Chemie*, vol. 74 (1962), pp. 508–9.
172. RUBEY, W. W., Development of the Hydrosphere and Atmosphere With Special Reference to Probable Composition of the Early Atmosphere, *Geological Society of America, Special Papers*, No. 62 (1955), pp. 631–50.
173. SCHENCK, P. A., and EISMA, E., Quantitative Determination of n-Alkanes in Crude Oils and Rock Extracts by Gas Chromatography, *Advances in Organic Geochemistry*, ed. by U. COLOMBO and G. D. HOBSON, New York: Pergamon Press, Inc. (1964), pp. 403–16.
174. SHAPIRO, J., Chemical and Biological Studies on the Yellow Organic Acids of Lake Water, *Limnology and Oceanography*, vol. 2, No. 4 (1957), pp. 161–79.
175. SIEGEL, S. M., LeFEVRE, B., JR., and BORCHARDT, R., Ultraviolet-Absorbing Components of Fossil and Modern Plants in Relation to Thermal Alteration of Lignins, *American Journal of Science*, vol. 256 (1958), p. 48.
176. SOKOLOV, V. A., The Evolution of the Atmosphere of the Earth, *The Origin of Life on the Earth*, ed. by A. I. OPARIN *et al.*, New York: Pergamon Press, Inc. (1959), pp. 54–66.
177. STRUGHOLD, H., and RITTER, O. L., Oxygen Production During the Evolution of the Earth's Atmosphere, *Aerospace Medicine*, vol. 33 (1962), pp. 275–8.
178. THODE, H. G., WANLESS, R. K., and WALLOUCH, R., Origin of Native Sulfur Deposits From Isotope Fractionation Studies, *Geochimica et Cosmochimica Acta*, vol. 5 (1954), pp. 286–98.
179. UREY, H. C., Regarding the Early History of the Earth's Atmosphere, *Bulletin of the Geological Society of America*, vol. 67 (1956), pp. 1125–8.
180. VALLENTYNE, J. R., The Molecular Nature of Organic Matter in Lakes and Oceans, With Lesser Reference to Sewage and Terrestrial Soils, *Fisheries Research Board of Canada, Journal*, vol. 14 (1957) pp. 33–82.
181. VALLENTYNE, J. R., Isolation of Pyrite Spherules From Recent Sediments, *Limnology and Oceanography*, vol. 8 (1963), pp. 16–30.
182. VALLENTYNE, J. R., A Chemical Study of Pyrite Spherules Isolated From Sediments of Little Round Lake, Ontario, *Symposium on the Biogeochemistry of Sulfur Isotopes*, ed. by M. L. JENSEN (In press).
183. VEGOTSKY, A., and FOX, S. W., Protein Molecules: Intraspecific and Interspecific Variations, *Comparative Biochemistry*, ed. by M. FLORKIN and N. S. MASON, New York: Academic Press, Inc. (1962), pp. 185–244.
184. VON HARTECK, P., and JENSEN, I. H. D., Über den Sauerstoffgehalt der Atmosphäre, *Zeitschrift der Naturforschung*, Part a, vol. 3 (1948), pp. 591–5.
185. WAKSMAN, S. A., Distribution of Organic Matter in the Sea Bottom and the Chemical Nature and Origin of Marine Humus, *Soil Science*, vol. 36 (1933), pp. 125–47.
186. WENT, F. W., Organic Matter in the Atmosphere and Its Possible Relation to Petroleum Formation, *Proceedings of the National Academy of Sciences of the United States of America*, vol. 46 (1960), pp. 212–21.
187. WILSON, A. T., The Origin of Petroleum and the Composition of the Lunar Maria, *Nature*, vol. 196 (1962), pp. 11–13.
188. ZOBELL, C. E., Geochemical Aspects of the Microbial Modification of Carbon Compounds, *Advances in Organic Geochemistry*, ed. by U. COLOMBO and G. D. HOBSON, New York: Pergamon Press, Inc. (1964), pp. 339–56.

C. The Moon

189. ABINERI, K. W., and LENHAM, A. P., Lunar Banded Craters, *Journal of the British Astronomical Association*, vol. 65, No. 4 (1955), pp. 160–6.
190. ADAMS, W. S., and DUNHAM, T., JR., Absorption Bands in the Infra-Red Spectrum of Venus, *Publications of the Astronomical Society of the Pacific*, vol. 44 (1932), pp. 243–5.

191. ADAMS, W. S., and DUNHAM, T., JR., Note About the Ultraviolet Spectrum of Venus, *Carnegie Institution of Washington Yearbook No. 40*, July 1, 1940–June 30, 1941, Baltimore: Lord Baltimore Press, Inc. (1941).

192. ALFVÉN, H., The Early History of the Moon and the Earth, *Icarus*, vol. 1 (1936), pp. 357–63.

193. ALTER, D., Nature of the Lunar Rays, *Publications of the Astronomical Society of the Pacific*, vol. 67 (1955), pp. 237–45.

194. ALTER, D., Nature of the Lunar Maria, *Publications of the Astronomical Society of the Pacific*, vol. 68 (1956), pp. 38–45.

195. ALTER, D., Nature of the Typical Lunar Mountain Walled Plains, *Publications of the Astronomical Society of the Pacific*, vol. 68 (1956), pp. 437–43.

196. ALTER, D., Suspected Partial Obscuration of the Floor of Alphonsus, *Publications of the Astronomical Society of the Pacific*, vol. 69 (1957), pp. 158–61.

197. ALTER, D., Nature of the Domes and Small Craters of the Moon, *Publications of the Astronomical Society of the Pacific*, vol. 69 (1957), pp. 245–51.

198. ALTER, D., Explosion Craters of the Moon, *Publications of the Astronomical Society of the Pacific*, vol. 69 (1957), pp. 533–40.

199. ALTER, D., Scientific Aspects of the Lunar Surface, *Proceedings of Lunar and Planetary Exploration Colloquium*, vol. 1, No. 1, Aerospace Laboratories, North American Aviation, Inc., Downey, California (1958), pp. 3–10.

200. ALTER, D., The Crater Linné, *Proceedings of Lunar and Planetary Exploration Colloquium*, vol. 1, No. 3, Aerospace Laboratories, North American Aviation, Inc., Downey, California (1958), pp. 33–38.

201. ALTER, D., Peculiar Features of the Lunar Surface, *Publications of the Astronomical Society of the Pacific*, vol. 70 (1958), pp. 489–94.

202. ALTER, D., The Alphonsus Story, *Proceedings of Lunar and Planetary Exploration Colloquium*, vol. 1, No. 4, Aerospace Laboratories, North American Aviation, Inc., Downey, California (1959), pp. 19–22.

203. ANDERS, E., The Moon as a Collector of Biological Material, *Science*, vol. 133 (1961), pp. 1115–19.

204. AVIGLIANO, D. P., Lunar Colors, *Strolling Astronomer*, vol. 8 (1954), pp. 50–55.

205. BALDWIN, R. B., *Face of the Moon*, Chicago: University of Chicago Press (1949).

206. BARABASHOV, N. P., and CHEKIRDA, A. T., Reflection of Light From the Surface of the Moon and of Mars, *Astronomicheskii Zhurnal*, vol. 22 (1945), pp. 11–22.

207. BARABASHOV, N. P., and CHEKIRDA, A. T., Comparison of Colour and Coefficient of Brightness of Different Regions on the Moon's Surface with Some Terrestrial Rocks, *Astronomicheskii Zhurnal*, vol. 33 (1956), pp. 549–55.

208. BARABASHOV, N. P., and CHEKIRDA, A. T., A Study of the Rocks Most Closely Resembling the Surface Constituents of the Moon, *Soviet Astronomy—AJ*, vol. 3 (1960), pp. 827–31.

209. BARKER, R., The Harvests of Plato, *Popular Astronomy*, vol. 48 (1940), pp. 19–21.

210. BRANDT, J. C., Density of the Lunar Atmosphere, *Science*, vol. 131 (1960), p. 1606.

211. BRIGGS, M. H., The Clouds of Venus, *The Observatory*, vol. 79 (1959), pp. 20–22.

212. BRIGGS, M. H., The Chemistry of the Lunar Surface, *Journal of the British Interplanetary Society*, vol. 18 (1962), pp. 386–9.

213. COATES, R. J., Lunar Brightness Variations With Phase at 4.3-mm Wavelength, *The Astrophysical Journal*, vol. 133 (1961), pp. 723–5.

214. (See Ref. 135.)

215. DOLLFUS, A., Nouvelle recherche d'une atmosphère au voisinage de la lune, *Comptes Rendus Hebdomadaires des Séances de l'Académie des Sciences*, vol. 234 (1952), pp. 2046–9.

216. DUCKWALL, W. E., Life on the Moon, *Popular Astronomy*, vol. 47 (1939), pp. 517–18.

217. DuFRESNE, E. R., Note on the High Relief of the Lunar Maria, *The Astrophysical Journal*, vol. 124 (1956), pp. 638–41.

218. EDWARDS, W. F., and BORST, L. B., Possible Sources of a Lunar Atmosphere, *Science*, vol. 127 (1958), pp. 325–8.

219. ELSMORE, B., Radio Observations of the Lunar Atmosphere, *The Philosophical Magazine*, vol. 2, 8th Series (1957), pp. 1040–6.
220. ELSMORE, B., The Atmosphere of the Moon, *New Scientist*, vol. 2 (1957), pp. 22–23.
221. FIELDER, G., The Lunar Grid System, *Journal of the British Astronomical Association*, vol. 67 (1957), pp. 315–18.
222. FIELDER, G., The Physical Nature of the Surface of the Moon, *Journal of the British Interplanetary Society*, vol. 17 (1959), pp. 57–58.
223. FIELDER, G., *Structure of the Moon's Surface*, London: Pergamon Press, Ltd. (1961).
224. FIRSOFF, V. A., Lunar Occultations Observed in Blue Light and the Problems of the Moon's Atmosphere, *Journal of the British Astronomical Association*, vol. 66 (1956), pp. 257–61.
225. FIRSOFF, V. A., On the Structure and Origin of Lunar Surface Features, *Journal of the British Astronomical Association*, vol. 66 (1956), pp. 314–19.
226. FIRSOFF, V. A., Color on the Moon, *Sky and Telescope*, vol. 17 (1958), pp. 329–31.
227. FIRSOFF, V. A., *Strange World of the Moon*, New York: Basic Books, Inc. (1959).
228. FIRSOFF, V. A., *Surface of the Moon*, London: Hutchinson and Co. (1961).
229. FIRSOFF, V. A., *Life on Earth and Beyond, A Study in Astrobiology*, London: Hutchinson and Co. (1963).
230. GIAMBONI, L. A., Lunar Rays: Their Formation and Age, *The Astrophysical Journal*, vol. 130 (1959), pp. 324–35.
231. GIBSON, J. E., Lunar Thermal Radiation at 35 kmc, *Proceedings of the Institute of Radio Engineers*, vol. 46 (1958), pp. 280–6.
232. GIBSON, J. E., Lunar Surface Characteristics Indicated by the March 1960 Eclipse and Other Observations, *The Astrophysical Journal*, vol. 133 (1961), pp. 1072–80.
233. GILVARRY, J. J., Origin and Nature of Lunar Surface Features, *Nature*, vol. 188 (1960), pp. 886–91.
235. GODDARD, A. V., Unusual Lunar Phenomenon, *Popular Astronomy*, vol. 40 (1932), pp. 316–17.
234. GIRAUD, A., Characteristics of the Moon's Surface Layer: An Analysis of Its Radio Emission, *The Astrophysical Journal*, vol. 135 (1962), pp. 175–86.
236. GOLD, T., Dust on the Moon *Vistas in Astronautics*, vol. 2, ed. by M. ALPERIN and H. F. GREGORY, New York: Pergamon Press, Inc. (1959), pp. 261–6.
237. GREEN, J., Physical Characteristics of the Lunar Surface, *Proceedings of Lunar and Planetary Exploration Colloquium*, vol. 1, No. 1, Aerospace Laboratories, North American Aviation, Inc., Downey, California (1958), pp. 11–15.
238. GREEN, J., Geochemical Implications of Lunar Degassing, *Proceedings of Lunar and Planetary Exploration Colloquium*, vol. 1, No. 4, Aerospace Laboratories, North American Aviation, Inc., Downey, California, (1959), pp. 1–18.
239. HAAS, W. H., Color Changes on the Moon, *Popular Astronomy*, vol. 45 (1937), pp. 337–41.
240. HAAS, W. H., Lunar Changes in the Crater Aristarchus, *Popular Astronomy*, vol. 46 (1938), pp. 135–7.
241. HAAS, W. H., Does Anything Ever Happen on the Moon? *The Journal of the Royal Astronomical Society of Canada*, vol. 36 (1942), pp. 237–72, 317–28, 361–76, 397–408.
242. HAMILTON, G. H., Lunar Changes, *Popular Astronomy*, vol. 32 (1924), pp. 237–40.
243. HERRING, J. R., and LICHT, A. L., Effect of Solar Wind on the Solar Atmosphere, *Science*, vol. 130 (1959), p. 266.
244. HERSCHEL, W., Account of Three Volcanos in the Moon, *Philosophical Transactions of the Royal Society of London*, vol. 77 (1787), pp. 229–31.
245. HERZBERG, G., On a Critical Test for the Presence of a Lunar Atmosphere, *Popular Astronomy*, vol. 54 (1946), pp. 414–15.
246. HOUSDEN, C. E., *Is Venus Inhabited?* London: Longmans, Green, and Co., Ltd. (1915).
247. HOUTGAST, J., Indication of a Magnetic Field of the Planet Venus, *Nature*, vol. 175 (1955), pp. 678–9.

248. Jastrow, R., Exploration of the Moon, *Scientific American*, vol. 202, No. 5 (1960), pp. 61–69.

249. Jeffreys, H., On the Earth History of the Solar System, *Monthly Notices of the Royal Astronomical Society*, vol. 78 (1918), pp. 424–41.

250. Kopal, Z., Our Neighbor Mars, *New Scientist*, vol. 1 (November 22, 1956), pp. 41–43.

251. Kopal, Z., Essentials for Mapping the Moon, *American Scientist*, vol. 47 (1959), pp. 505–8.

252. Kozyrev, N. A., Observation of a Volcanic Process on the Moon, *Sky and Telescope*, vol. 18 (1959), pp. 184–6.

253. Kuiper, G. P., Observation of a Volcanic Process on the Moon, (Letter) *Sky and Telescope*, vol. 18 (1959), p. 307.

254. Kuiper, G. P., *Photographic Lunar Atlas*, Chicago: University of Chicago Press (1960).

255. Lear, J., Biological Activity on the Moon? *New Scientist*, vol. 7 (1960), p. 398.

256. Lederberg, J., and Cowie, D. B., Moondust, *Science*, vol. 127 (1958), pp. 1473–5.

257. Lipski, Y. N., Über das Vorhandensein einer Mondatmosphäre, *Doklady Akademii Nauk SSSR*, vol. 65 (1949), pp. 465–8.

258. Lugo, F. A., Dust on the Moon, *Strolling Astronomer*, vol. 13 (1959), pp. 23–27.

259. Macvey, J., Unchanging Moon? *Spaceflight*, vol. 3 (1961), pp. 210–12.

260. Maskelyne, N., An Account of An Appearance of Light Like a Star Seen in the Dark Part of the Moon, *Philosophical Transactions of the Royal Society of London*, vol. 84 (1794), pp. 429–40.

261. Mezger, P. G., and Strassl, H., The Thermal Radiation of the Moon at 1420 mc/s, *Planetary and Space Science*, vol. 1 (1959), pp. 213–26.

262. Moore, P. A., *Guide to the Moon*, New York: W. W. Norton and Co., Inc. (1952).

263. Moore, P. A., What We Know About the Moon, *Journal of the British Interplanetary Society*, vol. 11 (1952), pp. 19–39.

264. Nininger, H. H., Do We See a Lunar Tunnel? *Sky and Telescope*, vol. 11 (1952), pp. 192–3.

265. Ogilvy, C. S., Lights in the Moon, *Popular Astronomy*, vol. 57 (1949), pp. 229–33.

266. O'Keefe, J. A., Lunar Rays, *The Astrophysical Journal*, vol. 126 (1957), p. 466.

267. Öpik, E. J., The Density of the Lunar Atmosphere, *Irish Astronomical Journal*, vol. 4 (1957), pp. 186–9.

268. Öpik, E. J., Surface Properties of the Moon. *Progress in the Astronomical Sciences* ed. by S. F. Singer, vol. 1, Amsterdam: North-Holland Publishing Co. (1962). pp. 219–60.

269. Öpik, E. J., The Lunar Atmosphere, *Planetary and Space Science*, vol. 9 (1962), pp. 211–44.

270. Öpik, E. J., and Singer, S. F., Escape of Gases From the Moon, *Journal of Geophysical Research*, vol. 65 (1960), pp. 3065–70.

271. Öpik, E. J., and Singer, S. F., *Density of the Lunar Atmosphere*, Report from the University of Maryland, Physics Department, National Aeronautics and Space Agency Contract No. NSG-58-60 (1960).

272. Pickering, W. H., *Moon, A Summary of the Existing Knowledge of Our Satellite, With a Complete Photographic Atlas*, New York: Doubleday and Co., Inc. (1903).

273. Pickering, W. H., A Study of Eratosthenes, *Harvard College Annals*, vol. 53, No. 7 (1905), p. 75.

274. Pickering, W. H., Snow Peaks of Theophilus, *Popular Astronomy*, vol. 25 (1917), pp. 149–56.

275. Pickering, W. H., Life on the Moon, *Popular Astronomy*, vol. 45 (1937), pp. 317–19.

276. Platt, J. R., On the Nature and Colour of the Moon's Surface, *Science*, vol. 127 (1958), pp. 1502–3.

277. Rosen, H., Jastrow, R., Urey, H., Gold, T., and Brown, H., Discussing the Moon, *Spaceflight*, vol. 2 (1960), pp. 167–73.

278. Ross, H. E., New Look at the Moon, *Spaceflight*, vol. 3 (1961), pp. 78–80.

279. RUBLOWSKY, J., Is There Life on the Moon? *Space World,* vol. 1 (1961), pp. 12–15, 49–50.

280. SAGAN, C., Indigenous Organic Matter on the Moon, *Proceedings of the National Academy of Sciences of the United States of America,* vol. 46 (1960), pp. 393–6.

281. SAGAN, C., Biological Contamination of the Moon, *Proceedings of the National Academy of Sciences of the United States of America,* vol. 46 (1960), pp. 396–402.

282. SAGAN, C., Organic Matter and the Moon, *Publication 757, National Academy of Sciences—National Research Council, Washington, D.C.,* 1961. AD-261, 191.

283. SALOMONOVICH, A. E., Radio Emission of the Moon at 8 Millimeters, *Soviet Astronomy—AJ,* vol. 2 (1958), pp. 112–18.

284. SINTON, W. M., Temperatures on the Lunar Surface, *Physics and Astronomy of the Moon,* ed. by Z. KOPAL, New York: Academic Press, Inc. (1962), pp. 407–28.

285. STRUGHOLD, H., The Ecological Profile of the Moon, *Lectures in Aerospace Medicine* (January 8–12, 1962), School of Aviation Medicine, USAF Aerospace Medical Center, Brooks Air Force Base Texas, 1962.

286. UREY, H. C., Cosmic Abundance of the Elements and the Chemical Composition of the Solar System, *American Scientist,* vol. 39 (1951), pp. 590–609.

287. UREY, H. C., Origin and Development of the Earth and Other Terrestrial Planets, *Geochimica et Cosmochimica Acta,* vol. 1 (1951), pp. 209–77.

288. UREY, H. C., Zum Ursprung der Oberflächenstruktur des Mondes, *Angewandte Chemie,* vol. 68 (1956), pp. 17–18, 533–9.

289. UREY, H. C., The Origin and Nature of the Moon, *Endeavour,* vol. 19 (1960), pp. 87–99.

290. UREY, H. C., ELSASSER, W. M., and ROCHESTER, M. G., Note on the Internal Structure of the Moon, *Astrophysical Journal,* vol. 129 (1959), pp. 842–98.

291. VAN DIGGELEN, J., Photometric Properties of Lunar Crater Floors, *Recherches Astronomique de l'Observatoire d'Utrecht,* vol. 14, No. 2 (1958–9), pp. 1–114.

292. VESTINE, E. H., Evolution and Nature of the Lunar Atmosphere, *Proceedings of Lunar and Planetary Exploration Colloquium,* Aerospace Laboratories, North American Aviation, Inc., Downey, California (1958), pp. 19–23.

293. WHIPPLE, F. L., Texture of the Moon's Surface, *Sky and Telescope,* vol. 17 (1958), p. 456.

294. WHIPPLE, F. L., On the Lunar Dust Layer, *Vistas in Astronautics,* vol. 2, ed. by M. ALPERIN and M. F. GREGORY, New York: Pergamon Press, Inc. (1959), pp. 267–72.

295. WILKINS, H. P., *Our Moon,* London: Frederick Muller, Ltd. (1954).

296. (See Ref. 187.)

D. Mars

297. ADAMS, W. S., Results With the Coudé Spectrograph of the Mt. Wilson Observatory, *The Astrophysical Journal,* vol. 93 (1941), pp. 11–23.

298. ADAMS, W. S., and DUNHAM, T., JR., The B-Band of Oxygen in the Spectrum of Mars, *The Astrophysical Journal,* vol. 79 (1934), pp. 308–16.

299. ADAMS, W. S., and ST. JOHN, C., An Attempt to Detect Water Vapor and Oxygen Lines in the Spectrum of Mars With the Registering Microphotometer, *The Astrophysical Journal,* vol. 63 (1926), pp. 133–7.

300. ANTONIADI, E. M., *La planète Mars,* Paris: Hermann (1930).

301. ASHBROOK, J., A New Determination of the Rotation Period of the Planet Mars, *The Astronomical Journal,* vol. 58 (1953), pp. 145–55.

302. BAKOS, G. A., Water on Mars, *The Journal of the Royal Astronomical Society of Canada,* vol. 46 (1952), pp. 209–10.

303. BARABASHOV, N. P., On the Surface and Atmosphere of Mars, *Astronomicheskii Zhurnal,* vol. 23 (1946), pp. 321–31.

304. BARABASHOV, N. P., On the Variability of Martian Seas, *Astronomicheskii Zhurnal,* vol. 24 (1947), pp. 137–44.

305. BARABASHOV, N. P., Investigation of Various Phenomena on Mars, *Astronomicheskii Zhurnal*, vol. 29 (1952), pp. 538–55.

306. BARABASHOV, N. P., On the Possibility of Noticing the Reflection of the Sun in the Martian Seas, *Kharkov Universitet, Astronomicheskaia Observatoria, Tsirkuliar*, No. 10 (1952), pp. 3–6.

307. BARABASHOV, N. P., Basic Results of Observations of Mars During the Favorable Opposition of 1956, *Astronomicheskii Zhurnal*, vol. 35 (1958), pp. 869–80.

308. BARABASHOV, N. P., Basic Results of Observations of Mars During the Favorable Opposition of 1956, *Soviet Astronomy – AJ*, vol. 2 (1958), pp. 814–24.

309. (See Ref. 206.)

310. BARABASHOV, N. P., and CHEKIRDA, A. T., Reflection of Light from Venus, Mars, Jupiter and Saturn, *Kharkov Universitet, Astronomicheskaia Observatoria, Publikatsii*, vol. 1, No. 9 (1951), pp. 19–23.

311. BARABASHOV, N. P., and CHEKIRDA, A. T., Spectrophotometry of Mars in Red, Yellow, Green and Blue Light, *Kharkov Universitet, Astronomicheskaia Observatoria, Tsirkuliar*, No. 9 (1952), pp. 3–28.

312. BARABASHOV, N. P., and GARAZHA, V. I., Some Remarks on the Dust and Haze Formation on Mars, *Soviet Astronomy – AJ*, vol. 4 (1960), pp. 473–9.

313. BARABASHOV, N. P., and KOVAL, I. K., On the Difference of the Photographic Diameter of Mars in Red and Violet Light, *Astronomicheskii Zhurnal*, vol. 33 (1956), pp. 890–2.

314. BARABASHOV, N. P., and KOVAL, I. K., Contribution to the Study of the Structure of the South Polar Ice Cap of Mars During 1956, *Soviet Astronomy – AJ*, vol. 2 (1958), pp. 234–8.

315. BARABASHOV, N. P. and KOVAL, I. K., Results of Studies of Contrast on Mars, *Soviet Astronomy – AJ*, vol. 4 (1960), pp. 283–5.

316. BASA, K. B., and HAWRYLEWICZ, E. J., *Life in Extraterrestrial Environments*, Phase Report, Illinois Institute of Technology, Armour Research Foundation, Chicago, Illinois, February 13, 1962.

317. BERRY, C. A., Space Programs and the Future, *Aerospace Medicine*, vol. 33 (1962), pp. 464–8.

318. BINDER, O., Mars Colony, *Space World*, vol. 1, No. 8 (1961), pp. 30–31, 57–58.

319. BLACKADAR, A. K., On the Scattering of Blue Light in the Martian Atmosphere, *Study of Planetary Atmospheres*, ed. by E. C. SLIPHER *et al.*, Final Report, Contract No. AF 19(122)162, Lowell Observatory, Flagstaff, Arizona, September 30, 1952, pp. 3–18. AD-10,609.

320. BOGESS, A., III, and DUNKELMAN, L., Ultraviolet Reflectivites of Mars and Jupiter, *The Astrophysical Journal*, vol. 129(1959), pp. 236–7.

321. BOIVIN, A., Mars, la planète étrange, *The Journal of the Royal Astronomical Society of Canada*, vol. 35 (1941), pp. 421–7.

322. BORRICELLI, N. A., Prospects and Physical Conditions for Life on Venus and Mars, *Scientia*, vol. 96 (1961), pp. 337–46.

323. BOTH, E. E., Second Report on Mars, 1960–1, *Strolling Astronomer*, vol. 15 (1961) pp. 53–59.

324. BOWMAN, N. J., Mars, Planet of Mystery, *The Journal of Space Flight and the Rocket News Letter*, vol. 6, No. 1 (1954), pp. 1–7.

325. BRIGGS, M. H., The Origins of Life on the Earth: A Review of the Experimental Evidence, *Science and Culture* (Calcutta), vol. 26 (1960), pp. 160–70.

326. BRIGGS, M. H., New Evidence of Martian Life, *Spaceflight*, vol. 2 (1961), pp. 237–8.

327. BRIGGS, M. H., The Blue Haze of Mars, *The Scientist Speculates*, ed. by I. J. GOOD *et al.*, New York: Basic Books, Inc. (1962), pp. 247–52.

328. BRIGGS, M. H., and REVILL, J. P., The Chemistry of Mars: I. The Atmosphere, *Journal of the British Interplanetary Society*, vol. 17 (1960), pp. 391–3.

329. BRIGGS, M. H., and REVILL, J. P., The Chemistry of Mars: II. The Surface, *Journal of the British Interplanetary Society*, vol. 17 (1960), pp. 459–61.

330. BULLEN, K. E., On the Constitution of Mars, *Monthly Notices of the Royal Astronomical Society*, vol. 109 (1949), pp. 688–92.

331. BURRELL, B., On the Martian Yellow Cloud in 1956, *The Observatory*, vol. 79 (1959), pp. 107–9.

332. CAMICHEL, H., Mars Observations at the Pic du Midi, *Sky and Telescope*, vol. 18 (1959), pp. 600–4.

333. CAMPBELL, W. W., Spectrum of Mars as Observed by the Crocker Expedition to Mt. Whitney, *Lick Observatory Bulletin*, vol. 5 (1909), pp. 149–56.

334. CAMPBELL, W. W., A Review of the Spectroscopic Observations of Mars, *Lick Observatory Bulletin*, vol. 5 (1909), pp. 156–64.

335. CAMPBELL, W. W., Note on the Spectrum of Mars, *The Observatory*, vol. 51 (1928), pp. 322–3.

336. CAMPBELL, W. W., and ALBRECHT, S., On the Spectrum of Mars as Photographed With High Dispersion, *Lick Observatory Bulletin*, vol. 6 (1910), pp. 11–16.

337. CARPENTER, A. H., Principles of Historical Geology Applied to Neighboring Planets and Life on Mars, *Popular Astronomy*, vol. 56 (1948), pp. 233–46.

338. CARRAGAN, W. D., Visual Problems of Mars, *Sky and Telescope*, vol. 15 (1956), pp. 297–9.

339. CAVE, T. R., JR., The Canals of Mars, *The Griffith Observer*, vol. 17 (1953), pp. 14–18.

340. CAVE, T. R., JR., Some Observations of Mars in 1956, *Sky and Telescope*, vol. 16 (1957), pp. 218–21.

341. CLURMAN, M., Does Anybody Live on Mars? *Popular Science Monthly*, vol. 162 (1953), pp. 126–30, 260, 262, 264, 266.

342. COBLENTZ, W. W., Temperature Estimates of the Planet Mars, Scientific Paper No. S512, *National Bureau of Standards (U.S.), Technical News Bulletin*, vol. 20 (1924–6), pp. 371–97.

343. COBLENTZ, W. W., Climatic Conditions on Mars, *Popular Astronomy*, vol. 33 (1925), pp. 310–16, 363, 382.

344. COBLENTZ, W. W., and LAMPLAND, C. O., Radiometric Measurements on Mars, *Publications of the Astronomical Society of the Pacific*, vol. 36 (1924), pp. 274–6.

345. COBLENTZ, W. W., and LAMPLAND, C. O., Further Radiation Measurements and Temperature Estimates of the Planet Mars, Scientific Paper No. S553, *National Bureau of Standards (U.S.), Technical News Bulletin*, vol. 22 (1927–8), pp. 237–76.

346. COBLENTZ, W. W., and LAMPLAND, C. O., Radiometric Measurements on the Planet Mars, *The Physical Review*, vol. 29 (1928), p. 372.

347. COBLENTZ, W. W., LAMPLAND, C. O., and MENZEL, D. H., Temperatures of Mars, 1926, as Derived From Water-Cell Transmissions, *Publications of the Astronomical Society of the Pacific*, vol. 39 (1927), pp. 97–100.

348. COLTHUP, N. B., Identification of Aldehyde in Mars Vegetation Regions, *Science*, vol. 134 (1961), p. 529.

349. COMPTE PORTA, R., ¿Hay vida en el planeta Marte? *Urania* (Barcelona), vol. 37 (1952), pp. 56–59.

350. CROSS, C. A., Conditions on Mars, *Spaceflight*, vol. 2 (1959), pp. 25–29.

351. CYR, D. L., *Life on Mars*, El Centro, California: Desert Magazine Press (1944).

352. CYR, D. L., Life on Mars, *Popular Astronomy*, vol. 52 (1946), pp. 247–8.

353. CYR, D. L., Life on Mars – After Ten Years, *Strolling Astronomer*, vol. 8 (1954), pp. 35–38.

354. CYR, D. L., The Marsitron Hypothesis. The Appearance of Lucus Lunae and Biblis Fons as Evidence of a Mobile Species on Mars, *Strolling Astronomer*, vol. 10 (1956), pp. 110–13.

355. CYR, D. L., *Mars Revisited*, Philadelphia: Dorrance and Co. (1959).

356. DATE, E., Colour Observation on the Surface of Mars, *Astronomia*, vol. 1 (1938), pp. 139–41.

357. DAVIS, I., and FULTON, J. D., The Reactions of Terrestrial Microorganisms to Simulated Martian Conditions, *International Astronautical Congress, Proceedings, 10th Congress, London, 1959*, Vienna: Springer-Verlag (1959), pp. 778–85.

358. DAVIS, I., and FULTON, J. D., Microbiologic Studies on Ecologic Considerations

of the Martian Environment, *USAF School of Aviation Medicine Report*, Rev. 2-60 (1959), AD-235,895.

359. DE LA BAUME PLUVINEL, A., and BALDET, F., Sur la photographie de la planète Mars, *Comptes Rendus Hebdomadaires des Séances de l'Académie des Sciences*, vol. 149 (1909), pp. 838–46.

360. DEVAUCOULEURS, G., *Le problème Martien*, Paris: S. A. Elsevier (1948).

361. DEVAUCOULEURS, G., *Planet Mars*, London: Faber and Faber, Ltd. (1951).

362. DEVAUCOULEURS, G., La planète Mars, *l'Astronomie*, vol. 65 (1951), pp. 103–6.

363. DEVAUCOULEURS, G., Physics of the Planet Mars, *Astronomical Society of the Pacific Leaflets*, vol. 6, No. 276 (1952), pp. 205–12.

364. DEVAUCOULEURS, G., Mars, *Scientific American*, vol. 188, No. 5 (1953), pp. 65–73.

365. DEVAUCOULEURS, G., Photographic Observations in 1956 of the Blue Clearing on Mars, *Publications of the Astronomical Society of the Pacific*, vol. 69 (1957), pp. 530–2.

366. DEVAUCOULEURS, G., Multicolor Photometry of Mars in 1958, *Planetary and Space Science*, vol. 2 (1959), pp. 26–32.

367. DEVAUCOULEURS, G., Observations of Mars in 1958, *Sky and Telescope*, vol. 18 (1959), pp. 484–9.

368. DEVAUCOULEURS, G., Remarks on Mars and Venus. *Journal of Geophysical Research*, vol. 64 (1959), pp. 1739–44.

369. DEVAUCOULEURS, G., Physical Environment on Mars, *Physics and Medicine of the Atmosphere and Space*, ed. by O. O. BENSON, JR., and H. STRUGHOLD, New York: John Wiley and Sons, Inc. (1960), pp. 584–605.

370. DEVAUCOULEURS, G., *Photometric Observations of Mars in 1941 and 1948*, Scientific Report No. 5, Harvard University, Cambridge, Massachusetts, August 15, 1960. AD-243,029.

371. DEVAUCOULEURS, G., and MENZEL, D. H., Results of the Occultation of Regulus by Venus, July 7, 1959, *Nature*, vol. 188 (1960), pp. 28–33.

372. DOLLFUS, A., La frange sombre polaire de la planète Mars en 1943–44, *l'Astronomie*, vol. 60 (1946), pp. 132–4.

373. DOLLFUS, A., Étude polarimétrique de la lumière réfléchie par les nuages et l'atmosphère de la planète Mars, *Comptes Rendus Hebdomadaires des Séances de l'Académie des Sciences*, vol. 227 (1948), pp. 383–5.

374. DOLLFUS, A., La polarisation de la lumière renvoyée par les différentes régions de la surface de la planète Mars et son interpretation, *Comptes Rendus Hebdomadaires des Séances de l'Académie des Sciences*, vol. 233 (1951), pp. 467–9.

375. DOLLFUS, A., Recherche de la vapeur d'eau dans l'atmosphère de la planète Mars, faite en ballon libre, vers 7,000 m d'altitude, *Comptes Rendus Hebdomadaires des Séances de l'Académie des Sciences*, vol. 239 (1954), pp. 954–6.

376. DOLLFUS, A., Les conditions météorologiques sur la planète Mars, *Meteorologie*, No. 42 (1956), pp. 81–91.

377. DOLLFUS, A., The Nature of the Surface of Mars, *Publications of the Astronomical Society of the Pacific*, vol. 70 (1958), pp. 56–64.

378. DOLLFUS, A., La vie sur la planète Mars, *Comptes Rendus Hebdomadaires des Séances de l'Académie des Sciences*, vol. 250 (1960), pp. 463–5.

379. Evidence for Vegetation on Mars, *Journal of the British Astronomical Association*, vol. 68 (1958), p. 196.

380. EWING, A., Life on Mars Seen Possible, *Science News Letter*, vol. 81 (June 16, 1962), pp. 378–9.

381. FAUST, H., Welche Eigenschaften der Erdatmosphäre dürfen wir auf die Marsatmosphäre übertragen? *Weltraumfahrt* (1956), pp. 65–68.

382. FESENKOV, V. G., On the Atmosphere of Mars; Photometrical Analysis of Wright's Phenomenon, *Astronomische Nachrichten*, vol. 228 (1926), pp. 25–32.

383. FESENKOV, V. G., On the Reflecting Properties of the Soil and Atmosphere of Mars, *Astronomicheskii Zhurnal*, vol. 21 (1944), pp. 257–75.

384. FESENKOV, V. G., On the Existence of Open Bodies of Water on Mars, *Astronomicheskii Zhurnal*, vol. 26 (1949), pp. 273–7.

385. FESENKOV, V. G., Vegetation on Mars, *Doklady Akademiia Nauk SSSR*, vol. 94 (1954), pp. 197–8.
386. FESENKOV, V. G., On the Physical Properties and Problems of Life on Mars, *Voprosy Filosofii*, vol. 3 (1954), pp. 106–24.
387. FESENKOV, V. G., On the Problem of Life on Mars, *Astronomicheskii Zhurnal*, vol. 33 (1956), pp. 440–3.
388. FESENKOV, V. G., The Existence of Life on Mars, *Pokroky*, vol. 2 (1957), pp. 112–16.
389. FESENKOV, V. G., Observations of Mars With an 8-inch Refractor at the Opposition of 1956, *Izvestiya Astrofizicheskogo Instituta, Akademiya Nauk Kazakhskoi, SSSR*, vol. 7 (1958), pp. 19–27.
390. FIRSOFF, V. A., Does Water Vapour Escape From Mars? *Journal of the British Astronomical Association*, vol. 66 (1956), pp. 53–59.
391. FIRSOFF, V. A., On the Radiation Balance in the Atmospheres of the Earth, Venus and Mars, *Journal of the British Astronomical Association*, vol. 69 (1959), pp. 196–211.
392. FOURNIER, G., Recherches photométriques sur les plages de la topographie martienne, *Observations des Surfaces Planétaires*, vol. 7 (1926), p. 148.
393. FOURNIER, G., La planète Mars et la vie, *l'Astronomie*, vol. 53 (1939), pp. 348–53.
394. FRAENKEL-CONRAT, H., and SINGER, B., The Infective Nucleic Acid From Tobacco Mosaic Virus, *The Origin of Life on the Earth*, ed. by A. I. OPARIN *et al.*, New York: Pergamon Press, Inc. (1959), pp. 303–6.
395. FRANCK, J., Possibility of Photosynthesis on Mars, *Atmospheres of the Earth and Planets*, ed. by G. P. KUIPER, Chicago: Chicago University Press (1949), pp. 355–6.
396. FRENCH, H., Some Notes on the Origin of the Colour of the Martian Deserts, *Journal of the British Astronomical Association*, vol. 70 (1960), pp. 136–8.
397. FREUDENTHAL, H., *Lincos; Design of a Language for Cosmic Intercourse*, Amsterdam: North-Holland Publishing Co. (1960).
398. FRIBERG, G., Astrobotaniken Och Mars, *Urania* (Kopenhagen), vol. 14 (1957), pp. 37–38.
399. FULTON, J. D., Survival of Terrestrial Microorganisms Under Simulated Martian Conditions, *Physics and Medicine of the Atmosphere and Space*, ed. by O. O. BENSON and H. STRUGHOLD, New York: John Wiley and Sons, Inc. (1960), pp. 606–13.
400. GAUROY, P., Le mystère de la vie martienne, *l'Astronomie*, vol. 62 (1948), pp. 33–40.
401. GIFFORD, F., JR., The Surface-Temperature Climate of Mars, *The Astrophysical Journal*, vol. 123 (1956), pp. 154–61.
402. GOLDIE, A. H. R., The Martian Atmosphere, *Weather*, vol. 5 (1950), p. 329.
403. GOLOSNITSKII, L. P., Über die physikalischen Bedingungen und die Möglichkeit des Lebens auf Mars, *Bulletin der astronomisch–geodätischen Gesellschaft der UdSSR* (1958), pp. 3–13.
404. GOODY, R. M., The Atmosphere of Mars, *Journal of the British Interplanetary Society*, vol. 16 (1957), pp. 69–83.
405. GOSSNER, S., Is There Plant Life on Mars? *Nature Magazine*, vol. 49 (1956), pp. 380–1.
406. GRANDJEAN, J., and GOODY, R. M., The Concentration of Carbon Dioxide in the Atmosphere of Mars, *The Astrophysical Journal*, vol. 121 (1955), pp. 548–52.
407. GUÉRIN, P., Les indices de vie végétale sur Mars, *La Nature* (Paris), vol. 83 (1955), pp. 194–7.
408. GUÉRIN, P., Spectrophotometric Study of the Reflectivity of the Centre of the Martian Disk at Opposition and the Nature of the Violet Layer, *Planetary and Space Science*, vol. 9 (1962), pp. 81–87.
409. HAGEN, C., and HAWRYLEWICZ, E. J., *Life in Extraterrestrial Environments*, Phase Report, Illinois Institute of Technology, Armour Research Foundation, February 28, 1963.
410. HAWRYLEWICZ, E. J., and EHRLICH, R., *Studies With Microorganisms and Plants Under Simulated Martian Environments*, Symposium on Extraterrestrial Biochemis-

try and Biology, American Association for the Advancement of Science, 128th Annual Meeting, Denver, Colorado, December 26–30, 1961.

411. HAWRYLEWICZ, E. J., GOWDY, B., and EHRLICH, R., Microorganisms Under a Simulated Martian Environment, *Nature,* vol. 193 (1962), p. 497.

412. HEINTZ, W. D., Rätsel des Mars: II, Leben oder nicht? *Die Umschau in Wissenschaft und Technik,* vol. 58 (1958), pp. 289–91.

413. HEINTZ, W. D., Visual Observations of Mars in 1954 and 1956, *Astronomische Nachrichten,* vol. 285 (1959), p. 3.

414. HENNESSY, D. J., Comments in Panel Discussion, The Identity of the 'Organized Elements', *Annals of the New York Academy of Sciences,* vol. 108, Art. 2 (1963), p. 611.

415. HESS, S. L., A Meteorological Approach to the Question of Water Vapor on Mars and the Mass of the Martian Atmosphere, *Publications of the Astronomical Society of the Pacific,* vol. 60 (1948), pp. 289–302.

416. HESS, S. L., *Investigations of the Meteorology of Mars,* Lowell Observatory Report No. 2 to the U.S. Weather Bureau, Lowell Observatory, Flagstaff, Arizona, 1949.

417. HESS, S. L., Some Aspects of the Meteorology of Mars, *The Journal of Meteorology,* vol. 7 (1950), pp. 1–13.

418. HESS, S. L., Distribution of Mars' Temperature and Its Atmospheric Circulation, *Sky and Telescope,* vol. 9 (1950), pp. 155–7.

419. HESS, S. L., Color Changes on Mars, *Study of Planetary Atmospheres,* Final Report, Lowell Observatory, Flagstaff, Arizona, September 30, 1952, pp. 34–38, AD-10,609.

420. HESS, S. L., Blue Haze and the Vertical Structure of the Martian Atmosphere, *The Astrophysical Journal,* vol. 127 (1958), pp. 743–50.

421. HESS, S. L., Mars as an Astronautical Objective, *Advances in Space Science and Technology,* ed. by F. I. ORDWAY, vol. 3, New York: Academic Press, Inc. (1961), pp. 151–93.

422. JAMES, P., Martian Vegetation, *Journal of the British Interplanetary Society,* vol. 14 (1955), pp. 290–1.

423. JASTROW, R., and RASOOL, S. I., Radiative Transfer in the Atmospheres of Venus and Mars, *Space Research III,* Amsterdam: North-Holland Publishing Co. (1963).

424. JEFFERS, H. M., Mars Photographs with the 36-inch Telescope, *Publications of the Astronomical Society of the Pacific,* vol. 70 (1958), pp. 305–7.

425. KELLOGG, W. W., and SAGAN, C., *The Atmospheres of Mars and Venus,* Publication 944, National Academy of Sciences – National Research Council, Washington D.C. (1961).

426. KIESS, C. C., CORLISS, C. H., and KIESS, H. K., Evidence for Oxides of Nitrogen in the Atmosphere of Mars, *Science,* vol. 131 (1960), p. 1319.

427. KIESS, C. C., KARRER, S., and KIESS, H. K., New Explanation of Martian Phenomena *The Astronomical Journal,* vol. 65 (1960), p. 348.

428. KIESS, C. C., KIESS, H. K., and CORLISS, C. H., High Dispersion Spectra of Mars, *The Astrophysical Journal,* vol. 126 (1957), pp. 579–84.

429. KING, J. I. F., Probing the Atmospheres of Venus and Mars, *Journal of the Franklin Institute, Monograph Series,* No. 6 (1958), pp. 150–60.

430. KIRBY, D. S., *Summary of Orbital and Physical Data for the Planet Mars,* Research Memoranda No. RM 2567, Rand Corporation, Santa Monica, California, August 1960.

431. KOOISTRA, J. A., MITCHELL, R. B., and STRUGHOLD, H., The Behavior of Microorganisms Under Simulated Martian Environmental Conditions, *Publications of the Astronomical Society of the Pacific,* vol. 70 (1958), pp. 64–68.

432. KOVAL, I. K., Results of Photographic Observations of Mars at the Kharkov Astronomical Observatory During 1954, *Soviet Astronomy – AJ,* vol. 1 (1957), pp. 404–10.

433. KOZYREV, N. A., Erklärung der Farbe von Mars aus spektralen Eigenschaften seiner Atmosphäre, *Mitteilungen des astrophysikalischen Observatoriums auf der Krim,* vol. 15 (1955), pp. 147–52.

434. KUIPER, G. P., Barnard's Photographs of Mars (set of 15 taken in 1909), *The Astrophysical Journal*, vol. 105 (1947), p. 215.
435. KUIPER, G. P., Visual Observations of Mars, 1956, *The Astrophysical Journal*, vol. 125 (1957), pp. 307–17.
436. LEE, D., *Life on Mars*, El Centro, California: Desert Magazine Press (1944).
437. LEVIN, G. V., and CARRIKER, A. W., Life on Mars? *Nucleonics*, vol. 20 (1962), pp. 71–72.
438. Liv paa Mars? *Urania* (Kopenhagen), vol. 15 (1958), pp. 30–34.
439. LIVANDER, R., On the Colour of Mars, *Publications de l'Observatoire Astronomique de l'Université de Tartu (Dorpat)*, vol. 27, No. 6 (1933), pp. 1–29.
440. LLEGET, M., Volviendo sobre el enigma de Marte, *Ibérica*, vol. 7 (1948), pp. 386–9.
441. LOWELL, P., *Mars*, 3rd edition, Boston: Houghton Mifflin Co. (1897).
442. LOWELL, P., *Mars and Its Canals*, New York: The Macmillan Co. (1906).
443. LOWELL, P., *Mars as the Abode of Life*, New York: The Macmillan Co. (1910).
444. Martian Atmosphere Restudied, *National Bureau of Standards (U.S.), Technical Bulletin*, No. 42 (1958), pp. 48–52.
445. MARTZ, E. P., JR., Heterochromatic Photography and Photometry of Mars in 1937 and 1939, *The Astronomical Journal*, vol. 58 (1953), pp. 221–2.
446. MARTZ. E. P., JR., Variation in Atmospheric Transparency of Mars in 1939, *Publications of the Astronomical Society of the Pacific*, vol. 66 (1954), pp. 45–51.
447. MAUDE, A. J. P., Vegetation on Mars, *Journal of the British Astronomical Association*, vol. 52 (1942), pp. 254–5.
448. MAYER, C. H., McCULLOUGH, T. P., and SLOANAKER, R. M., Observations of Mars and Jupiter at a Wavelength of 3.15 cm, *The Astrophysical Journal*, vol. 127 (1958), pp. 11–16.
449. McLAUGHLIN, D. B., Interpretation of Some Martian Features, *Irish Astronautical Journal*, vol. 3 (1954), pp. 109–11.
450. McLAUGHLIN, D. B., Interpretation of Some Martian Features, *Publications of the Astronomical Society of the Pacific*, vol. 66 (1954), pp. 161–70.
451. McLAUGHLIN, D. B., Changes on Mars, as Evidence of Wind Deposition and Volcanism, *The Astronomical Journal*, vol. 60 (1955), pp. 261–71.
452. McLAUGHLIN, D. B., Changes on Mars, Interpreted as Evidence of Volcanism, *Publications of the Astronomical Society to the Pacific*, vol. 67 (1955), pp. 15–16.
453. McLAUGHLIN, D. B., Possible Condensation Clouds Over Martian Volcanoes, *The Astronomical Journal*, vol. 61 (1956), pp. 184–5.
454. McLAUGHLIN, D. B., The Volcanic-Aeolian Hypothesis of Martian Features, *Publications of the Astronomical Society of the Pacific*, vol. 68 (1956), pp. 211–18.
455. MENZEL, D. H., The Atmosphere of Mars, *The Astrophysical Journal*, vol. 63 (1926), pp. 48–59.
456. MOORE, P., Planet Mars, *Journal of the British Interplanetary Society*, vol. 14 (1955), pp. 65–84.
457. MOORE, P., The Alphonsus Outbreak, *Spaceflight*, vol. 2 (1959), pp. 11–12.
458. MOORE, P., Could Life Survive on Mars? *Listener*, vol. 65 (1961).
459. MOORE, P., *Guide to Mars*, Second edition, London: Frederick Muller, Ltd. (1963).
460. MOROZ, V. I., and KHARITNOV, A. V., Photoelectric Photometry of Sections of the Surface of Mars, *Soviet Astronomy—AJ*, vol. 1 (1957), pp. 874–90.
461. A New Theory of the Surface of Mars, *The Journal of the Royal Astronomical Society of Canada*, vol. 50 (1956), pp. 193–200.
462. ÖPIK, E. J., Mars and the Asteroids, *Irish Astronomical Journal*, vol. 1 (1950), pp. 22–24.
463. ÖPIK, E. J., Spectroscopic Evidence of Vegetation on Mars, *Irish Astronomical Journal*, vol. 5 (1958), pp. 12–13.
464. ÖPIK, E. J., The Composition of the Martian Atmosphere, *Irish Astronomical Journal*, vol. 5 (1959), pp. 137–9.
465. ÖPIK, E. J., The Atmosphere and Haze of Mars, *Journal of Geophysical Research*, vol. 65 (1960), pp. 3057–63.
466. ÖPIK, E. J., Atmosphere and Surface Properties of Mars and Venus, *Progress in the*

Astronautical Sciences, ed. by F. S. SINGER, Amsterdam: North-Holland Publishing Co. (1962), p. 267.

467. ORLOVA, N. S., Effect of the Dustiness of Martian Atmosphere on Brightness Distribution Over the Disk in Various Regions of the Spectrum, *Astronomichski Tsirkulyar,* No. 209 (1960), pp. 6–8.

468. PETTIT, E., Photographing the Canals of Mars, *Publications of the Astronomical Society of the Pacific,* vol. 58 (1947), pp. 125–9.

469. PETTIT, E., Canals of Mars, *Publications of the Astronomical Society of the Pacific,* vol. 59 (1947), pp. 5–11.

470. PETTIT, E., Photography of the Canals of Mars, *Publications of the Astronomical Society of the Pacific,* vol. 65 (1953), pp. 197–201.

471. PETTIT, E., Photography of the Canals of Mars, *Sky and Telescope,* vol. 13 (1953), p. 27.

472. PETTIT, E., and NICHOLSON, S. B., Measurements of the Radiation From the Planet Mars, *Publications of the Astronomical Society of the Pacific,* vol. 36 (1924), pp. 269–72.

473. PICKERING, W. H., *Mars,* Boston: The Gorham Press (1921).

474. PICKERING, W. H., Seas of Mars, *Vega* (Boughton, Chester), vol. 2, No. 34 (1956), p. 2.

475. POOLE, J. H. G., The Evolution of the Atmosphere, *The Scientific Proceedings of the Royal Dublin Society,* vol. 22 (1941), pp. 345–65.

476. PRESSMAN, R. E., Climate and Vegetation of Mars Compared With the Earth's, *Journal of the British Astronomical Association,* vol. 52 (1942), pp. 193–7.

477. PRINGLE, J. W., The Origin of Life, *Symposia of the Society for Experimental Biology,* No. 7 (1953), pp. 1–21.

478. PROELL, W., Martian Juvenation: The Effect Upon Planetary Conditions, *The Journal of Space Flight and the Rocket News Letter,* vol. 6, No. 5 (1954), pp. 1–5.

479. RANDOLPH, J. R., Are There People on Mars? *Strolling Astronomer,* vol. 5, No. 3 (1951), pp. 4–8.

480. RICHARDSON, R. S. *Exploring Mars,* New York: McGraw-Hill Book Co., Inc. (1954).

481. RICHARDSON, R. S., Preliminary Report on Observations of Mars Made at Mount Wilson in 1956, *Journal of the British Interplanetary Society,* vol. 16 (1957), pp. 1–7.

482. RICHARDSON, R. S., A Survey of Conditions on Mars and Venus, *Navigation,* vol.6 (1958), pp. 43–46.

483. RICHARDSON, R. S., Observations on Mars and Venus, *Proceedings of Lunar and Planetary Exploration Colloquium,* vol. 1, No. 3, Aerospace Laboratories, North American Aviation, Inc., Downey, California (1958).

484. RICHARDSON, R. S., and ROQUES, P. E., An Example of the Blue Clearing Observed 74 Days Before Opposition, *Publications of the Astronomical Society of the Pacific,* vol. 71 (1959), pp. 321–3.

485. ROBERTS, T. L., BALL, R. J., and WYNNE, E. S., *Studies With a Simulated Martian Environment: Bacterial Synergism—Preliminary Systems,* TDR-62-151, United States Air Force School of Aerospace Medicine, Brooks AFB, Texas, January 1963.

486. ROBERTS, T. L., and WYNNE, E. S., *Studies With a Simulated Martian Environment: Bacterial Survival and Soil Moisture Content,* TDR-62-121, United States Air Force School of Aerospace Medicine, Brooks AFB, Texas, November 1962.

487. ROSEBRUGH, D. W., How Narrow a Line Can We See on Mars? *Strolling Astronomer,* vol. 4, No. 5 (1950), pp. 4–8.

488. ROSEN, B., Origine possible de la couche violette dans l'atmosphère de Mars, *Annales d'Astrophysique,* vol. 16 (1953), pp. 288–9.

489. ROSEN, B., and SWINGS, P., Carbon Stars, Comets and Combustion Phenomena, *Annales d'Astrophysique,* vol. 16 (1953), pp. 82–95.

490. RUGIERI, G., Il pianeta Marte e i suoi enigmi, *Astronautica Acta,* vol. 6 (1959), pp. 11–16.

491. RUSSELL, H. N., Le nouveau mystère de Mars, *Hemel en Dampkring*, vol. 36 (1938), pp. 241–5.
492. SADIL, J., Today's Views on the Existence of Life on Mars, *Říše Hvězd* (Prague), vol. 35 (1954), pp. 219–25.
493. SAGAN, C., The Abundance of Water Vapor on Mars, *The Astronomical Journal*, vol. 66 (1961), p. 52.
494. SAGAN, C., Is the Martian Blue Haze Produced by Solar Protons? *Icarus*, vol. 1 (1962), pp. 70–74.
495. SAHEKI, T., Japanese Observation of a Major Change of Mars, *Sky and Telescope*, vol. 15 (1956), pp. 442–3.
496. SALISBURY, F. B., Discussion of Some Current Theories Regarding the Markings on Mars, *Publications of the Astronomical Society of the Pacific*, vol. 69 (1957), pp. 396–7.
497. SALISBURY, F. B., The Inhabitants of Mars, *Frontiers in Science*, ed. by E. HUTCHINGS, JR., New York: Basic Books, Inc. (1958), pp. 168–79.
498. SALISBURY, F. B., Martian Biology, *Science*, vol. 136 (1962), pp. 17–26.
499. SANDNER, W., Les canaux de Mars pendant l'opposition de 1956, *Gazette Astronomique*, vol. 38-39, No. 433–5 (1957), pp. 7–9.
500. SCHATZMAN, E., Sur les particules diffusantes dans l'atmosphère de Mars, *Comptes Rendus Hebdomadaires des Séances de l'Académie des Sciences*, vol. 232 (1951), pp. 692–3.
501. SCHILLING, G. F., A Note on the Atmosphere of Mars, *Journal of Geophysical Research*, vol. 67 (1962), pp. 1170–2.
502. SCHMIDT, I., Green Areas of Mars and Color Vision, *10th International Astronautical Congress* (London, 1959), ed. by F. HECHT, Vienna: Springer-Verlag (1959), pp. 170–80.
503. SCHWARTZ, R. N., and TOWNES, C. H., Interstellar and Interplanetary Communication by Optical Masers, *Nature*, vol. 190 (1961), pp. 205–8.
504. SHARONOV, V. V., On the Role of True Absorption in the Martian Atmosphere, *Soviet Astronomy—AJ*, vol. 1 (1957), pp. 547–55.
505. SHARONOV, V. V., A Lithological Interpretation of the Photometric and Colorimetric Studies of Mars, *Soviet Astronomy—AJ*, vol. 5 (1961), pp. 199–202.
506. SHARPLESS, B. P., Secular Accelerations in the Longitudes of the Satellites of Mars, *The Astronomical Journal*, vol. 51 (1945), pp. 185–6.
507. SHAW, J. H., *Natural Environment of the Planet Mars*, Report No. TN-847-1, Ohio State University, Research Foundation, Columbus, Ohio, February 1959. AD-242,176.
508. SHAW, J. H., *et al., Near Infrared Spectrum of Mars*, Report No. SR-8, Ohio State University, Research Foundation, Columbus, Ohio, November 1957. AD-58,203.
509. SIEGEL, S. M., Effects of Exposures of Seeds to Various Physical Agents: I. Effects of Brief Exposures to Heat and Cold on Germination and Light-Sensitivity, *The Botanical Gazette*, vol. 112 (1950), pp. 57–70.
510. SIEGEL, S. M., Effects of Reduced Oxygen Tension on Vascular Plants, *Physiologia Plantarum*, vol. 14 (1961), p. 554.
511. SIEGEL, S. M., Observations on Peroxide Toxicity in Seed Germination, *Physiologia Plantarum*, vol. 15 (1961), p. 21.
512. SIEGEL, S. M., The Protection of Plants Against Airborne Oxidants: Experiments with Cucumber Seedlings at Extreme Ozone Levels, *Plant Physiology*, vol. 37 (1962), pp. 261–6.
513. SIEGEL, S. M., HALPERN, L., RENWICK, G., and DAVIS, G., Martian Biology: The Experimentalist's Approach, *Nature*, vol. 197 (1962), pp. 329–31.
514. SIEGEL, S. M., RENWICK, G., and ROSEN, L. A., On the Formation of Carbon Monoxide During Seed Germination and Seedling Growth, *Science*, vol. 137 (1962), p. 683.
515. SIEGEL, S. M., and ROSEN, L. A., Effects of Reduced Oxygen Tensions on Vascular

Plants, II. Observations on Germination and Seedling Growth, *Physiologia Plantarum*, vol. 15 (1962), pp. 437–44.

516. SIEGEL, S. M., ROSEN, L. A., and GIUMARRO, C., Effects of Reduced Oxygen Tension on Vascular Plants: IV. Winter Rye Germination Under Near-Martian Conditions and in Other Nonterrestrial Environments, *Proceedings of the National Academy of Sciences of the United States of America*, vol. 48 (1962), pp. 725–8.

517. SIEGEL, S. M., ROSEN, L. A., and RENWICK, G., Effects of Reduced Oxygen Tension on Vascular Plants, III. Growth and Composition of Red Kidney Bean Plants in 5% Oxygen, *Physiologia Plantarum*, vol. 15 (1962), pp. 304–14.

518. SIEGEL, S. M., ROSEN, L. A., and RENWICK, G., Further Studies on the Composition of Seedlings Grown at Sub-atmospheric Oxygen Levels, *Physiologia Plantarum* (In press).

519. SINGER, S. F., *Some Considerations of Expected Radiation Belts of Planets Mars and Venus*, AAS Paper 60-53, American Astronautical Society, 6th Annual Meeting, New York, January 18–21, 1960.

520. SINGER, S. F., *Radiation Belts of the Planet Mars*, 41st Annual American Geophysical Union Meeting, Washington, D.C., April 27–30, 1960.

521. SINTON, W. M., New Findings About Mars, *Sky and Telescope*, vol. 14 (1955), pp. 360–3.

522. SINTON, W. M., Spectroscopic Evidence of Vegetation on Mars, *The Astrophysical Journal*, vol. 126 (1957).

523. SINTON, W. M., Further Evidence of Vegetation on Mars, *Science*, vol. 130 (1959), pp. 1234–7.

524. SINTON, W. M., An Upper Limit to the Concentration of NO_2 and N_2O_4 in the Martian Atmosphere, *Publications of the Astronomical Society of the Pacific*, vol. 73 (1961), pp. 125–8.

525. SINTON, W. M., and STRONG, J., Radiometric Observations of Mars, *The Astrophysical Journal*, vol. 131 (1960), pp. 459–69.

526. SLATER, A. E., Some Comments on Strughold's Ideas on Martian Vegetation, *Journal of the British Interplanetary Society*, vol. 13 (1954), pp. 334–6.

527. SLATER, A. E., The Volcanic Theory of Martian Green Areas, *Journal of the British Interplanetary Society*, vol. 14 (1955), pp. 319–23.

528. SLATER, A. E., The Colors of Martian Vegetation, *Spaceflight*, vol. 1 (1956), pp. 35–39.

529. SLATER, A. E., Life in the Universe, *Spaceflight*, vol. 4 (1962), p. 88.

530. SLIPHER, E. C., Great White Spot in the Martian Tropics, July 9, 1922, *Publications of the Astronomical Society of the Pacific*, vol. 34 (1922), pp. 215–18.

531. SLIPHER, E. C., Atmospheric and Surface Phenomena on Mars, *Publications of the Astronomical Society of the Pacific*, vol. 39 (1927), pp. 209–16.

532. SLIPHER, E. C., An Outstanding Atmospheric Phenomenon on Mars, *Publications of the Astronomical Society of the Pacific*, vol. 49 (1937), pp. 137–40.

533. SLIPHER, E. C., Results of Observations of Mars at Lamont-Hussey Observatory, South Africa, *Publications of the Astronomical Society of the Pacific*, vol. 52 (1940), pp. 284–6.

534. SLIPHER, E. C., *Mars: The Photographic Story*, ed. by JOHN S. HALL, Cambridge, Massachusetts: Sky Publishing Corp. (1962).

535. SLIPHER, V. M., Spectrum Observations of Mars, *Publications of the Astronomical Society of the Pacific*, vol. 36 (1924), pp. 261–2.

536. SLIPHER, V. M., On the Spectral Proof of Water and Oxygen on Mars, *The Observatory*, vol. 53 (1930), pp. 79–81.

537. STRONG, J., and SINTON, W. M., Radiometry of Mars and Venus, *Science*, vol. 123 (1956), p. 676.

538. STRUGHOLD, H., Life on Mars in View of Physiological Principles, *U.S. Central Air Document Office (N.A.F.) Technical Data Digest*, vol. 16 (1951), p. 15.

539. STRUGHOLD, H., Ecological Aspects of Planetary Atmospheres With Special Reference to Mars, *The Journal of Aviation Medicine*, vol. 23 (1952), pp. 130–40.

540. STRUGHOLD, H., Physiological Considerations on the Possibility of Life Under

Extraterrestrial Conditions, *Space Medicine*, ed. by J. P. MARBARGER, Urbana: University of Illinois Press (1952), pp. 31–48.

541. STRUGHOLD, H., *The Atmospheres of Earth and Mars in the Light of Recent Physiological Concepts*, ARS Paper 67–52, American Rocket Society, New York, 1952.

542. STRUGHOLD, H., *The Green and Red Planet: A Physiological Study of the Possibility of Life on Mars*, Albuquerque, New Mexico: University of New Mexico Press (1953).

543. STRUGHOLD, H., Das Leben auf dem Mars, *Weltraumfahrt* vol. 4 (1953), pp. 24–28.

544. STRUGHOLD, H., *Biological Profile of Mars*, Symposium on Extraterrestrial Biochemistry and Biology, American Association for the Advancement of Science, 128th Annual Meeting, Denver, Colorado, December 26–30, 1961.

545. STRUVE, H., Beobachtungen der Marstrabanten in Washington, Pulkowa und Lick Observatory, *Memoires de l'Académie Imperiale des Sciences de St. Petersbourg*, vol. 8, p. 3.

546. STRUVE, H., Bestimmung der Abplattung und des Aequators von Mars, *Astronomische Nachrichten*, vol. 138 (1895), pp. 218–27.

547. STRUVE, H., Über die Lage der Marsachse und die Konstanten im Marssystem, *Sitzungsberichte der preussischen Akademie der Wissenschaften, physikalisch-mathematische Klasse* (1911), pp. 1056–83.

548. SUWOROW, N. I., and PARSCHINU, S. S., Hypothesis on the Paleobotany of Mars, *Vestnik Akademii Nauk Kazakhskoi SSSR*, vol. 4 (1954), pp. 98–102.

549. TIKHOV, G. A., Reflection Spectra of the Green Areas With a Note on Vegetation on Mars, *Bulletin der astronomisch-geodätischen Gesellschaft der UdSSR*, vol. 1 (1947), pp. 3–13.

550. TIKHOV, G. A., Vegetation on Mars, *Priroda* (Leningrad), vol. 36, No. 2 (1947). pp. 3–6.

551. TIKHOV, G. A., *New Observations on the Problem of Vegetation on Mars*, Moscow: Pravda (1948).

552. TIKHOV, G. A., *The Planet Mars*, Alma Ata: Verlag der Akademie der Wissenschaften, Kasach (1948).

553. TIKHOV, G. A., Vegetation on Mars, *Leningrad Universitet Vestnik*, vol. 4, No. 11 (1949), pp. 29–42.

554. TIKHOV, G. A., Is There Vegetation on the Planet Mars? *Priroda* (Leningrad), vol. 38, No. 7 (1949), pp. 3–8.

555. TIKHOV, G. A., Plant Life on Mars and Venus, *Vestnik Akademii Nauk Kazakhskoi SSSR*, vol. 8, No. 4 (1951), pp. 72–86.

556. TIKHOV, G. A., Paleobotany of Mars and Venus, *Vestnik Akademii Nauk Kazakhskoi SSSR*, vol. 10, No. 1 (1953), pp. 100–4.

557. TIKHOV, G. A., Concerning N. A. Kosyrev's Article, Explanation of the Colour of Mars by Spectral Properties of Its Atmosphere, *Akademiia Nauk SSSR, Krimskaya Astrofizicheskaia Observatoriia*, vol. 16 (1956), pp. 159–61.

558. TOMBAUGH, C. W., Geological Interpretation of the Markings on Mars, *The Astronomical Journal*, vol. 55 (1950), p. 184.

559. TOMBAUGH, C. W., Mars—World for Exploration, *Astronautics*, vol. 4 (1959), pp. 30–31, 86–93.

560. TOMBAUGH, C. W., Life on Mars, *Space World*, vol. 2 (1962), pp. 36–37.

561. TROITSKAYA, O. V., *About the Possibilities of Plant Life on Mars*, Astronautics Information Translation No. 8, Jet Propulsion Laboratory, Pasadena, California, February 1960.

562. TRUMPLER, R. J., Observations of Mars at the Opposition of 1924, *Lick Observatory Bulletin*, vol. 13, No. 387 (1926), pp. 19–45.

563. UREY, H. C., The Structure and Chemical Composition of Mars, *The Physical Review*, vol. 80 (1950), p. 295.

564. UREY, H. C., On the Escape of Water from Mars, *Publications of the Astronomical Society of the Pacific*, vol. 68 (1956), pp. 220–2.

565. UREY, H. C., The Blue Haze of Mars, *The Astrophysical Journal*, vol. 128 (1958), p. 736.

566. UREY, H. C., Lines of Evidence Regarding the Composition of the Moon, *Space Research*, ed. by KALLMAN BIJL, Amsterdam: North-Holland Publishing Co. (1960), pp. 1114–22.

567. VAUGHN, F. R., The Canals of Mars, From Schiaparelli to 1956, *Strolling Astronomer*, vol. 11 (1957), pp. 86–91.

568. ¿ Vegetación en Marte ? *El Universo*, vol. 44 (1958), p. 154.

569. Vegetation on Mars? *Sky and Telescope*, vol. 16 (1957), p. 275.

570. VERPLOEGH, G., De Kanalen van Mars en het ei van Columbus, *Hemel en Dampkring*, vol. 55 (1957), pp. 36–39.

571. VERY, F. W., Measurements of the Intensification of Aqueous Bands in the Spectrum of Mars, *Lowell Observatory Bulletin*, vol. 1, No. 41 (1909), pp. 207–12.

572. VERY, F. W., Quantitative Measurements of the Intensification of Great B in the Spectrum of Mars, *Lowell Observatory Bulletin*, vol. 1, No. 41 (1909), pp. 221–9.

573. VERY, F. W., Intensification of Oxygen and Water-Vapor Bands in the Martian Spectrum, *Astronomische Nachrichten*, vol. 199 (1914), pp. 153–70.

574. ¿Vida en Marte? *El Universo*, vol. 40 (1957), p. 125.

575. VON BRAUN, W., *The Mars Project*, Urbana, Illinois: University of Illinois Press (1953).

576. VON REGEL, C., Pflanzenleben auf dem Mars? *Weltraumfahrt*, vol. 1 (1950), pp. 139–40.

577. WALLACE, A. R., *Is Mars·Habitable?* London: Macmillan and Co., Ltd. (1906).

578. WANDERS, A. J. M., The Physical Conditions on the Planet Mars, *Proceedings, 9th International Astronautical Congress, Amsterdam, August 25–30, 1958*, vol. 1, Vienna: Springer-Verlag (1959), pp. 394–404.

579. WEBB, H. B., *Observations of Mars and Its Canals*, Jamaica, New York: Privately published (1941).

580. WEBB, W. A., Analysis of the Martian Canal Network, *Publications of the Astronomical Society of the Pacific*, vol. 67 (1955), pp. 283–92.

581. WEBB, W. A., *Mars: The New Frontier*, San Francisco: Fearon Publishers, Inc. (1956).

582. WEBB, W. A., Análisis de la red de canales del planeta Marte, *Astronomía Popular* (Mexico), vol. 1, No. 4 (1958), pp. 3–7.

583. WILKINS, H. P., The Mystery of Mars, *Annual Report of Smithsonian Institute for 1956*, Publication No. 4274, Smithsonian Institute, Washington, D.C. (1956), pp. 229–44.

584. WILSON, A. G., *Spectrographic Observations of the Blue Haze in the Atmosphere of Mars*, Report No. P-1509, Rand Corporation, Santa Monica, California, 1958.

585. WILSON, A. G., Problem of the Martian Blue Haze, *Proceedings of Lunar and Planetary Exploration Colloquium*, vol. 1, No. 4, Aerospace Laboratories, North American, Aviation, Inc., Downey, California (1959), pp. 33–37,

586. WOOLLEY, R., Monochromatic Magnitudes of Mars in 1952, *Monthly Notices of the Royal Astronomical Society*, vol. 113 (1953), pp. 521–5.

587. WOOLLEY, R., GOTTLIEB, K., HEINTZ, W., and DEVAUCOULEURS, G. Monochromatic Magnitudes of Mars in 1954, *Monthly Notices of the Royal Astronomical Society*, vol. 115 (1955), pp. 57–59.

588. WRIGHT, W. H., Photographs of Mars Made With Light of Different Colors, *Publications of the Astronomical Society of the Pacific*, vol. 36 (1924), pp. 239–54.

589. WRIGHT, W. H., Photographs of Mars Made With Light of Different Colors, *Lick Observatory Bulletin*, vol. 12 (1925), pp. 48–61.

590. WRIGHT, W. H., Filter Photographs of Mars, *Publications of the Astronomical Society of the Pacific*, vol. 51 (1939), pp. 292–3.

591. WRIGHT, W. H., and KUIPER, G. P., Clouds on Mars, *Publications of the Astronomical Society of the Pacific*, vol. 47 (1935), pp. 29–93.

592. YANOW, G., *A Study of the Martian Upper Atmosphere and Ionosphere*, Preprint

No. 61-9, American Astronautical Society 7th Annual meeting, Dallas, Texas, January 16-18, 1961.

593. ZIGEL, F., Is There Intelligent Life on Mars? *Space World*, vol. 1 (1961), p. 20.

E. Venus

594. ADAMS, W., Investigations on the Moon, Comets, and Planets, *Carnegie Institution of Washington Yearbook No. 31*, Baltimore: Lord Baltimore Press, Inc. (1932), pp. 153-4.

595. ADAMS, W., What Lies Between the Stars? *Publications of the Astronomical Society of the Pacific*, vol. 53 (1942), pp. 73-83.

596. *Atmosphere of Venus — Review of the Soviet Literature*, AID Report 61-30, Library of Congress, Science and Technology Section, Air Information Division, Washington, D.C., March 21, 1961.

597. BARRETT, A. H., Microwave Absorption and Emission in the Atmosphere of Venus, *The Astrophysical Journal*, vol. 133 (1961), pp. 281-93; *Journal of Geophysical Research*, vol. 65 (1960), pp. 1835-8.

598. BARRETT, A. H., COPELAND, J., JONES, D. E., and LILLEY, A. E., *Objectives of the Mariner Venus Microwave Radiometer Experiment*, Technical Report No. 32-156, Jet Propulsion Laboratory, Pasadena, California, August 22, 1961.

599. BARTLETT, J. C., JR., Venus — Lady with a Past, *Strolling Astronomer*, vol. 15 (1961), pp. 9-14.

600. (See Ref. 322.)

601. BRIGGS, M. H., and MAMIKUNIAN, G., Venus — A Summary of Present Knowledge, *Journal of the British Interplanetary Society*, vol. 19 (1963), pp. 45-52.

602. CARR, T. D., *et al.*, Recent Decameter-Wave-Length Observations of Jupiter, Saturn, and Venus, *The Astrophysical Journal*, vol. 134 (1961), pp. 105-25.

603. CHAMBERLAIN, J. W., and KUIPER, G. P., Rotational Temperature and Phase Variation of the CO_2 Bands of Venus, *The Astrophysical Journal*, vol. 124 (1956), pp. 399-405.

604. DANJON, A., Photométrie et colorimétrie des planètes Mercure et Vénus, *Bulletin Astronomique*, vol. 14 (1949), pp. 315-45.

605. (See Ref. 368.)

606. DEVAUCOULEURS, G., The Occultation of Regulus by Venus in July, *Sky and Telescope*, vol. 18 (1959), pp. 606-9.

607. D'HALLUIN, H., Vénus en plein jour et lumière candrée de Vénus, *l'Astronomie*, vol. 74 (1960), p. 255.

608. DOLE, S. H., *The Atmosphere of Venus*, Report No. P-978, Rand Corporation, Santa Monica, California, 1956.

609. DOLE, S. H., The Venusian Atmosphere, *Proceedings of Lunar and Planetary Exploration Colloquium*, vol. 1, No. 5, Aerospace Laboratories, North American Aviation, Inc., Downey, California (1959), pp. 12-18.

610. DOLLFUS, A., Étude visuelle et photographique de l'atmosphère de Vénus, *l'Astronomie*, vol. 69 (1955), pp. 413-25.

611. DOLLFUS, A., Recherches sur l'atmosphère de Vénus, *Mémoires de la Société Royale des Sciences de Liège*, Quatrième Série, vol. 18 (1956), pp. 141-6.

612. DRAKE, F. D., 10-cm Observations of Venus in 1961, *National Radio Astronomical Observation*, vol. 1, No. 11 (1962), pp. 165-78.

613. DRAKE, F. D., 10-cm Observations of Venus Near Superior Conjunction, *Nature*, vol. 195 (1962), p. 894.

614. DUCKWALL, W. E., Venus — the Veiled Mystery, *Popular Astronomy*, vol. 48 (1940), pp. 100-3.

615. DUNHAM, T., Note on Planetary Spectra of Venus, *Carnegie Institution of Washington Yearbook No. 31*, Baltimore: Lord Baltimore Press, Inc. (1932). pp. 153-4.

616. EDSON, J. B., Measuring the Venusian Atmosphere by Russel's Method, *Proceedings of Lunar and Planetary Exploration Colloquium*, vol. 1, No. 5, Aerospace Laboratories, North American Aviation, Inc., Downey, California (1959), pp. 22-30.

617. (See Ref. 391.)

618. FIRSOFF, V. A., The Earth's Twin, *Science News*, vol. 52 (1959), p. 79.
619. FIRSOFF, V. A., On the Carbon Dioxide in the Atmosphere of Venus, *The Observatory*, vol. 81 (1961), pp. 62–64.
620. GIBSON, J. E., The Brightness Temperature of Venus at 8.6 mm, *The Astrophysical Journal* (In press).
621. GIBSON, J. E., and CORBETT, H. H., Brightness Temperature of Venus at 1.35 cm, *The Astronomical Journal*, vol. 68 (1963), p. 74.
622. GIBSON, J. E., and MCEWAN, R. J., Observations of Venus at 8.6 mm Wavelength, *Paris Symposium on Radio Astronomy*, ed. by R. N. BRACEWELL, Stanford, California: Stanford University Press (1959), pp. 50–52.
623. GOLD, T., The Lunar Surface, *Monthly Notices of the Royal Astronomical Society*, vol. 115 (1955), pp. 585–604.
624. GRANT, C. R., and CORBETT, H. H., Observations of Venus at 4.3 mm, *The Astronomical Journal*, vol. 67 (1962), pp. 115–6.
625. HERZBERG, G., and VERLEGER, H., Two New Bands of CO_2 in the Photographic Infrared, *The Physical Review*, vol. 48 (1935), p. 706.
626. HEYDEN, F. J., KIESS, C. C., and KIESS, H. K., Spectrum of Venus in the Violet and Near-Ultraviolet, *Science*, vol. 130 (1959), p. 1195.
627. HYNEK, J. A., Occultation of the Bright Star Regulus by Venus, *Science*, vol. 130 (1959), p. 707.
628. Is the Existence of Life on Venus Certain? *Heavens* (Kyoto Imperial University, Japan), vol. 41 (1960), p. 130.
629. (See Ref. 423.)
630. JONES, D. E., *A Microwave Radiometer Experiment for the Planet Venus*, Technical Release No. 34-112, Jet Propulsion Laboratory, Pasadena, California, October 10, 1960.
631. JONES, D. E., The Microwave Temperature of Venus, *Planetary and Space Science*, vol. 5 (1961), pp. 166–7.
632. JONES, H. S., The Planet Venus and Its Atmosphere, *Proceedings of the Royal Institution of Great Britain*, vol. 37, Pt. 3 (1959), pp. 241–55.
633. KAPLAN, L. D., A New Interpretation of the Structure and CO_2 Content of the Venus Atmosphere, *Planetary and Space Science*, vol. 8 (1961), pp. 23–29.
634. KAPLAN, L. D., *New Interpretation of the Structure and CO_2 Content of the Venus Atmosphere*, Report No. R2213, Rand Corporation, Santa Monica, California, May 2, 1961.
635. KAPLAN, L. D., *A Preliminary Model of the Venus Atmosphere*, Technical Report No. 32–379, Jet Propulsion Laboratory, Pasadena, California, December 12, 1962.
636. (See Ref. 425.)
637. (See Ref. 429.)
638. KING, J. I. F., *The Dynamic Stability of the Upper Atmosphere of Venus*, Report R60 SD453, General Electric Co., Missile and Space Vehicle Dept., Valley Forge Space Technology Center, Philadelphia, Pennsylvania, October 1960.
639. KOVAL, I. K., The Absolute Photometry of Venus in Ultraviolet and Infrared Light, *Soviet Astronomy—AJ*, vol. 2 (1958), pp. 739–43.
640. KOZYREV, N. A., Über das Leuchten des Nachthimmels der Venus, *Mitteilungen des astrophysikalischen Observatoriums auf der Krim*, vol. 12 (1954), pp. 169–76.
641. KOZYREV, N. A., Molecular Absorption in the Violet Region of the Spectrum of Venus, *Mitteilungen des astrophysikalischen Observatoriums auf der Krim*, vol. 12 (1954), pp. 177–81.
642. KOZYREV, N. A., The Night-Sky Spectrum of Venus, *Journal of the Royal Astronomical Society of Canada*, vol. 49 (1955), pp. 202–3.
643. KRAUS, J. D., Impulsive Radio Signals From the Planet Venus, *Nature*, vol. 178 (1956), p. 33.
644. KRAUS, J. D., Radio Observations of the Planet Venus at a Wave-Length of 11 m, *Nature*, vol. 178 (1956), pp. 103–4.
645. KRAUS, J. D., Class II Radio Signals from Venus at a Wave-Length of 11 metres, *Nature*, vol. 178 (1956), pp. 159–60.

646. KRAUS, J. D., Rotation Period of the Planet Venus as Determined by Radio Observations, *Nature*, vol. 178 (1956), pp. 687–8.

647. KUIMOV, K. W., Venus 1954, *Bulletin der astronomisch–geodätischen Gesellschaft der UdSSR*, No. 21 (1958), pp. 30–32.

648. KUIPER, G. P., The Atmosphere and the Cloud Layer of Venus, *Threshold of Space*, ed. by M. ZELIKOFF, London: Pergamon Press, Ltd. (1957).

649. LAMPLAND, C. O., On the Observable Radiation From the CO_2 in the Atmosphere of Venus, *The Astrophysical Journal*, vol. 93 (1941), pp. 401–2.

650. LILLEY, A. E., The Temperature of Venus, *The Astronomical Journal*, vol. 66 (1961), p. 290.

651. LINK, F., and NEUZIL, L., The Color of Venus and the Nature of Its Clouds, *Bulletin of the Astronomical Institutes of Czechoslovakia*, vol. 8 (1956), pp. 23–27.

652. MAKAROWA, S. P., Venus 1956, *Astronomischer Jahresbericht*, vol. 58, Item No. 7116 (1958), p. 231.

653. MANN, R. T., Chi vive sugli altri mondi, *Coelum*, vol. 28 (1960), pp. 166–73.

654. MARTYNOV, D. YA., The Radius of Venus, *Soviet Astronomy—AJ*, vol. 4 (1960), pp. 798–804.

655. MARTYNOV. D. YA., Venus—The Physical Nature of the Planet, *Vestnik Moskovskogo Universiteta, Seriya III, Fizika Astronomiia*, No. 5 (1961), pp. 23–38.

656. MARTYNOV, D. YA., and POSPERGELIS, M. M., A Note on the Photometric Analysis of the Structure of the Atmosphere of Venus, *Astronomicheskii Zhurnal*, vol. 38 (1961), pp. 558–61.

657. MARTZ, E. P., JR., Venus and Life, *Popular Astronomy*, vol. 42 (1934), pp. 165–7.

658. MATHER, S. M., The Atmosphere of Venus, *Journal of the British Interplanetary Society*, vol. 6 (1947), pp. 194–6.

659. MAYEDA, H., Attempts at Colour Drawings of Mars From Direct Visual Observation, *Astronomia* (Japan), vol. 1 (1938), pp. 172–84.

660. MAYER, C. H., *Measurements of Radiation From Venus at 3.15 cm Wavelength*, U.S. Naval Research Laboratory Report 4998, vol. 1, Washington, D.C., 1938, pp. 172-184. AD-143,375.

661. MAYER, C. H., McCULLOUGH, T. P., and SLOANAKER, R. M., Observations of Venus at 3.15 cm Wavelength, *The Astrophysical Journal*, vol. 127 (1958), pp. 1–10.

662. MAYER, C. H., McCULLOUGH, T. P., and SLOANAKER, R. M., Observations of Venus at 10.2 cm Wavelength, *The Astrophysical Journal*, vol. 65 (1960), pp. 349–50.

663. MAYER, C. H., McCULLOUGH, T. P., and SLOANAKER, R. M., 3.15 cm Observations of Venus in 1961, *Mémoires de la Société Royale des Sciences de Liège* (In press).

664. MENZEL, D. H., and deVAUCOULEURS, G., Results From the Occultation of Regulus by Venus, *The Astronomical Journal*, vol. 65 (1960), p. 351.

665. MENZEL, D. H., and WHIPPLE, F. L., The Case for H_2O Clouds on Venus, *Publications of the Astronomical Society of the Pacific*, vol. 67 (1955), pp. 161–8.

666. MOORE, P., Problems of the Moon, *The Advancement of Science*, vol. 17 (1960), pp. 33–41.

667. MOORE, P., *Planet Venus*, 3rd edition, New York: The Macmillan Co. (1961).

668. MOORE, P., and CATTERMOLE, P. J., The Markings of Venus, *Journal of the British Interplanetary Society*, vol. 70 (1960), p. 130.

669. MOORE, P., and GREENWOOD, S. W., Venus as an Astronautical Objective, *Advances in Space Science and Technology*, vol. 3, ed. by F. I. ORDWAY, New York: Academic Press, Inc. (1961), pp. 113–49.

670. MURRAY, B. C., WILDEY, R. L., and WESTPHAL, J. A., *Preliminary Results of Observations of Venus at 10 μ on the 200-inch Telescope*, 2nd Western National Meeting, American Geophysical Union, Stanford, California, December 27-29, 1962.

671. NEWKIRK, G. A., JR., Airglow of Venus, *Planetary and Space Science*, vol. 1 (1959), pp. 32–36.

672. ÖPIK, E. J., Cloud Reflection and Atmospherical Scattering: The Variation of Brightness of Venus With Phase Angle, *Publications de l'Observatoire Central Astrophysique de Russie*, vol. 1 (1922), pp. 237–65.

673. ÖPIK, E. J., The Surface Conditions on Venus, *Irish Astronomical Journal*, vol. 4 (1956), pp. 37–48.
674. ÖPIK, E. J., The Aeolosphere and Atmosphere of Venus, *Journal of Geophysical Research*, vol. 66 (1961), pp. 2807–19.
675. (See Ref. 466.)
676. PETTENGILL, G. H., Radar Measurements of Venus, *Space Research III*, New York: John Wiley and Sons, Inc. (1963), pp. 872–85.
677. PETTENGILL, G. H., *et al.*, Radar Investigation of Venus, *The Astronomical Journal*, vol. 67 (1962), pp. 181–90.
678. PETTIT, E., and NICHOLSON, S. B., Radiation From the Dark Hemisphere of Venus, *Publications of the Astronomical Society of the Pacific*, vol. 36 (1924), pp. 227–8.
679. PETTIT, E., and NICHOLSON, S. B., Temperatures on the Bright and Dark Sides of Venus, *Publications of the Astronomical Society of the Pacific*, vol. 67 (1955), pp. 293–303.
680. PRICE, R., and GREEN, P. E., JR., Radar Echoes From Venus, *Sky and Telescope*, vol. 18 (1959), pp. 384–5.
681. RAYMOND, J. L., *Thermodynamic Properties of the Atmosphere of Venus*, Research Memorandum No. RM 2292, Rand Corporation, Santa Monica, California, 1958.
682. RICE, F. O., The Chemistry of Jupiter, *Scientific American*, vol. 194, No. 6 (1956), pp. 119–28.
683. RICHARDSON, R. S., Observations of Venus Made at Mount Wilson in the Winter of 1954–1955, *Publications of the Astronomical Society of the Pacific*, vol. 67 (1955), pp. 304–14.
684. RICHARDSON, R. S., Spectroscopic Observations of Venus for Rotation Made at Mount Wilson in 1956, *Journal of the British Interplanetary Society*, vol. 16 (1958), pp. 517–24.
685. (See Ref. 482.)
686. (See Ref. 483.)
687. RICHARDSON, R. S., Some Recent Russian Observations of Venus, *Griffith Observer*, vol. 23 (1959), pp. 118–24.
688. RICHARDSON, T. H., *The Spectrum of Venus*, 104th Meeting of the American Astronomical Society, Cleveland, Ohio, December 27–30, 1959. Abstract in *The Astronomical Journal*, vol. 65 (1960), p. 56.
689. RUBASCHEW, B. M., New Findings Regarding Physical Conditions on Venus, *Priroda*, vol. 29, No. 11 (1950), pp. 37–38.
690. RUSSELL, H. N., Atmosphere on Venus, *The Astrophysical Journal*, vol. 9 (1899), pp. 284–99.
691. SAGAN, C., *The Radiation Balance of Venus*, Technical Report No. 32-34, Jet Propulsion Laboratory, Pasadena, California, September 15, 1960.
692. SAGAN, C., The Planet Venus, *Science*, vol. 133 (1961), pp. 849–58.
693. SAGAN, C., Structure of the Lower Atmosphere of Venus, *Icarus*, vol. 1 (1962), pp. 151–69.
694. SAGAN, C., The Physical Environment of Venus: Models and Prospects, *Space Age Astronomy*, ed. by A. DEUTSCH and W. B. KLEMPERER, New York: Academic Press, Inc. (1962), pp. 430–43.
695. SAGAN, C., Venus, *International Science and Technology*, No. 15 (March 1963), pp. 86–94.
696. SAGAN, C., SIEGEL, K. M., and JONES, D. E., On the Origin of the Venus Microwave Emission, *The Astronomical Journal*, vol. 66 (1961), pp. 52–53.
697. ST. JOHN, D. E., and NICHOLSON, S. B., Absence of Oxygen and Water-Vapor Lines in the Spectrum of Venus, *The Astrophysical Journal*, vol. 56 (1922), pp. 380–99.
698. ST. JOHN, D. E., and NICHOLSON, S. B., The Physical Constituents of the Atmosphere of Venus, *The Physical Review*, vol. 19 (1922), p. 444.
699. SCARF, F. L., Plasma Instability and the Microwave Radiation From Venus, *Journal of Geophysical Research*, vol. 68 (1963), pp. 141–6.
700. SCHINDLER, C. A., ROBERTS, T. L., and WYNNE, E. S., Feasibility of Laboratory Studies Concerning Life on Venus, *Aerospace Medicine*, vol. 33 (1962), pp. 859–61.

701. SCHOENBERG. E., and SANDNER, W., Die Dichotomie der Venusscheibe, *Annales d'Astrophysique*, vol. 22 (1959), pp. 839–44.
702. SHAW, J. H., and BOBROVNIKOFF, N. T., *Natural Environment of the Planet Venus*, Report No. TN-847-2, Ohio State University, Research Foundation, Columbus, Ohio, February 1959. AD-242,176.
703. (See Ref. 519.)
704. SINTON, W. M., *Distribution of Temperatures and Spectra of Venus and Other Planets*, Ph.D. Thesis, Johns Hopkins University, Baltimore, Maryland, 1953.
705. SINTON, W. M., and STRONG, J., Radiometric Observations of Venus, *The Astrophysical Journal*, vol. 131 (1960), pp. 470–90.
706. SLIPHER, E. C., and EDSON, J. B., Photographs of the Twilight Ring Around Venus and the Behavior of Her Atmosphere, *Publications of the American Astronomical Society*, vol. 9 (1939), pp. 229–31.
707. SLIPHER, V. M., Spectrographic Investigation of the Rotation Velocity of Venus, *Lowell Observatory Bulletin*, No. 3 (1903).
708. SMARONOV, V. V., Determination of Horizontal Refraction in the Atmosphere of Venus From the Observations of the Lomonosov Effect, *Doklady Akademii Nauk SSSR*, vol. 82 (1952), pp. 351–3.
709. SMITH, F. A., Venus Probe, *Journal of the British Interplanetary Society*, vol. 17 (1959), pp. 42–45.
710. SOTKIN, I. T., and SHERESHEVSKAYA, A. E., Sichelform und Details auf Venus 1951, *The Astronomical Journal*, vol. 58 (1958), p. 232.
711. SPINRAD, H., A Search for Water Vapor and Trace Constituents in the Venus Atmosphere, *Icarus*, vol. 1 (1962), pp. 266–70.
712. SPINRAD, H., Spectroscopic Temperature and Pressure Measurements in the Venus Atmosphere, *Publications of the Astronomical Society of the Pacific*, vol. 74 (1962), pp. 187–201.
713. STRAHLE, W. C., *The Thermodynamic Properties and Shock-Wave Characteristics of a Model Venus Atmosphere*, Research Memorandum No. RM 2826-PR, Rand Corporation, Santa Monica, California, November 1962.
714. STRONG, J., ROSS, M. D., and MOORE, C. B., Some Observations of the Atmosphere of Venus and Earth During the Strato Lab IV Balloon Flight, *Journal of Geophysical Research*, vol. 65 (1960), p. 2526.
715. (See Ref. 537.)
716. STRONG, J., and SINTON, W. M., Radiometric Observations of Venus, *The Astrophysical Journal*, vol. 131 (1960), pp. 470–90.
717. (See Ref. 556.)
718. TOLBERT, C. W., STRAITON, A. W., A Consideration of Microwave Radiation Associated With Particles in the Atmosphere of Venus, *Journal of Geophysical Research*, vol. 67 (1962), pp. 1741–4.
719. TOMBAUGH, C. W., Visual and Photographic Observations of Venus and Mars, *Publication 944, National Academy of Sciences—National Research Council* (1961), pp. 72–75.
720. VICTOR, W., STEVENS, R., and GOLOMB, S., *Radar Exploration of Venus*, Technical Report No. 32-132, Jet Propulsion Laboratory, Pasadena, California, August 1, 1961.
721. WARNER, B., The Emission Spectrum of the Night Side of Venus, *Monthly Notices of the Royal Astronomical Society*, vol. 121 (1960), pp. 279–83.
722. WARNER, B., The Constituents of the Atmosphere of Venus, *Strolling Astronomer*, vol. 15 (1961), pp. 8–9.
723. WILDT, R., Note on the Surface Temperature of Venus, *The Astrophysical Journal*, vol. 91 (1940), pp. 266–8.
724. WILDT, R., On the Possible Existence of Formaldehyde in the Atmosphere of Venus, *The Astrophysical Journal*, vol. 92 (1940), pp. 247–55.
725. WILDT, R., On the Chemistry of the Atmosphere of Venus, *The Astrophysical Journal*, vol. 96 (1942), pp. 312–4.
726. WRIGHT, W. H., Photographs of Mars and Jupiter Taken by Light of Different Colors During 1926, *Lick Observatory Bulletin*, vol. 13 (1927), pp. 50–67.

727. WRIGHT, W. H., Photographs of Venus Made by Infra-red and by Violet Light, *Publications of the Astronomical Society of the Pacific*, vol. 39 (1927), pp. 220–1.

F. Jupiter

728. ADEL, A., and SLIPHER, V. M., Constitution of the Atmospheres of the Giant Planets, *The Physical Review*, vol. 46 (1934), pp. 902–6.
729. BANERJI, A. C., Jupiter's Atmosphere, *Indian Journal of Physics and Proceedings of the Indian Association for the Cultivation of Science*, vol. 13 (1939), pp. 73–85.
730. BARDWELL, J. A., and HERZBERG, G., Laboratory Experiments on the Detectability of Silane (SiH_4) and Methyl Deuteride (CH_3D) in the Atmospheres of the Outer Planets, *The Astrophysical Journal*, vol. 117 (1953), pp. 462–5.
731. BARROW, C. H., Magnetic Field of Jupiter, *Nature*, vol. 188 (1960), pp. 924–5.
732. BARROW, C. H., Recent Radio Observations of Jupiter at Decameter Wavelengths, *The Astrophysical Journal*, vol. 135 (1962), pp. 847–54.
733. BARROW, C. H., and CARR, T. D., Eighteen-Megacycle Radiation From Jupiter, *Journal of the British Astronomical Association*, vol. 68 (1958), pp. 63–9.
734. BARROW, C. H., CARR, T. D., and SMITH, A. G., Sources of Radio Noise on the Planet Jupiter, *Nature*, vol. 180 (1957), p. 381.
735. BAYLEY, D. P., The Colours of Jupiter's Polar Regions, *Journal of the British Astronomical Association*, vol. 55 (1945), pp. 116–20.
736. BOBROVNIKOFF, N. T., Note on the Spectrum of Jupiter, *Publications of the Astronomical Society of the Pacific*, vol. 45 (1933), pp. 171–4.
737. BURKE, B. F., Radio Observations of Jupiter, *The Solar System, Vol. III: Planets and Satellites*, ed. by G. P. KUIPER and B. M. MIDDLEHURST, Chicago: University of Chicago Press (1961), pp. 473–99.
738. BURKE, B. F., and FRANKLIN, K. L., Observations of a Variable Radio Source Associated With the Planet Jupiter, *Journal of Geophysical Research*, vol. 60 (1955), pp. 213–17.
739. BURKE, B. F., SMITH, A. G., SMITH, H. J., and WARSICK, J. W., Report of Working Group of Commission 40 for the Definition of Radio Longitudes of Jupiter, *International Astronomical Union, Information Bulletin No. 8*, Royal Greenwich Observatory, Hailsham, Sussex, England (1962), p. 4.
740. CARR, T. D., Radio Frequency Emission From the Planet Jupiter, *The Astronomical Journal*, vol. 64 (1959), pp. 39–41.
741. CARR, T. D., et al., Eighteen-Megacycle Observations of Jupiter in 1957, *The Astrophysical Journal*, vol. 127 (1958), pp. 274–83.
742. (See Ref. 602.)
743. CARR, T. D., SMITH, A. G., and BOLLHAGEN, H., Evidence for the Solar Corpuscular Origin of the Decameter-Wave-Length Radiation From Jupiter, *Physical Review Letters*, vol. 5 (1960), pp. 418–20.
744. CHANG, D. B., *Synchrotron Radiation From the Planet Jupiter*, Scientific Research Laboratory Report D1-82-0060, Boeing Aircraft Company, Seattle, Washington, 1960.
745. CHANG, D. B., *Synchrotron Radiation as the Source of the Polarized Decimeter Radiation From Jupiter*, Ph.D. Thesis, California Institute of Technology, Pasadena, California, 1962.
746. CHANG, D. B., and DAVIS, L., JR., Synchrotron Radiation as the Source of Jupiter's Polarized Decimeter Radiation, *The Astrophysical Journal*, vol. 136 (1962), pp. 567–81.
747. CLEMENCE, G. M., Motion of Jupiter and Mass of Saturn, *The Astronomical Journal*, vol. 65 (1960), pp. 21–2.
748. DAVIS, L., and CHANG, D. B., Synchrotron Radiation as the Source of Jupiter's Polarized Decimeter Radiation, *Journal of Geophysical Research*, vol. 66 (1961), p. 2524.
749. DE MARCUS, W. C., The Constitution of Jupiter and Saturn, *The Astronomical Journal*, vol. 63 (1958), pp. 2–28.

750. DOUGLAS, J. N., and SMITH, H. J., Presence and Correlation of Fine Structure in Jovian Decametric Radiation, *Nature*, vol. 192 (1961), p. 741.

751. DRAKE, F. D., and HVATUM, S., Non-Thermal Microwave Radiation From Jupiter, *The Astronautical Journal*, vol. 64 (1959), pp. 329–30.

752. DRAKE, F. D., and HVATUM, S., Intensity of Jupiter at 440 Mc, *Publication 880, National Academy of Sciences — National Research Council*, Washington, D.C. (1961), pp. 524–5.

753. FIELD, G. B., The Source of Radiation from Jupiter at Decimeter Wavelength: 3. Time Dependence of Cyclotron Radiation, *Journal of Geophysical Research*, vol. 66 (1961), pp. 1395–1405.

754. FRANKLIN, K. L., An Account of the Discovery of Jupiter as a Radio Source, *The Astronomical Journal*, vol. 64 (1959), pp. 37–39.

755. FRANKLIN, K. L., and BURKE, B. F., Radio Observations of the Planet Jupiter, *Journal of Geophysical Research*, vol. 63 (1958), pp. 807–24.

756. GALLET, R. M., Radio Observations of Jupiter. II, *The Solar System, Vol. III: Planets and Satellites*, ed. by G. P. KUIPER and B. M. MIDDLEHURST, Chicago: University of Chicago Press (1961), pp. 500–33.

757. GARDNER, F. F., and SHAIN, C. A., Further Observations of Radio Emission From the Planet Jupiter, *Australian Journal of Physics*, vol. 11 (1958), pp. 55–69.

758. HESS, S. L., Variations in Atmospheric Absorption Over the Disks of Jupiter and Saturn, *The Astrophysical Journal*, vol. 118 (1953), pp. 151–60.

759. HIDE, R., Origin of Jupiter's Great Red Spot, *Nature*, vol. 190 (1961), pp. 895–6.

760. HIDE, R., On the Hydrodynamics of Jupiter's Atmosphere, *Mémoires de la Société Royale des Sciences de Liège* (In press).

761. JEFFREYS, H., On the Internal Constitution of Jupiter and Saturn, *Monthly Notices of the Royal Astronomical Society*, vol. 84 (1924), pp. 534–8.

762. KIESS, C. C., CORLISS, C. H., and KIESS, H. K., High-Dispersion Spectra of Jupiter, *The Astrophysical Journal*, vol. 132 (1960), pp. 221–31.

763. (See Ref. 448.)

764. McCLAIN, E. F., NICHOLS, J. H., and WAAK, J. A., An Investigation of Possible Variations in the Centimeter Wave Emission From Jupiter, *Publication 880, National Academy of Sciences — National Research Council*, Washington, D.C. (1961), p. 524.

765. McCLAIN, E. F., NICHOLS, J. H., and WAAK, J. A., Investigation of Variations in the Decimeter-Wave Emission From Jupiter, *The Astronomical Journal*, vol. 67 (1962), pp. 724–7.

766. MILLER, A. C., and GARY, B. L., Measurements of the Decimeter Radiation From Jupiter, *The Astronomical Journal*, vol. 67 (1962), pp. 727–31.

767. MINTZ, Y., On the Formation of Disturbances in the Atmosphere of Jupiter in Response to Changes in the State of the Sun, *The Study of Planetary Atmospheres*, Final Report, Contract No. AF 19(122)-162, Lowell Observatory, Flagstaff, Arizona, 1952, pp. 200–7. AD-10, 609.

768. MINTZ, Y., Temperature and Circulation of the Venus Atmosphere, *Planetary and Space Science*, vol. 5 (1961), pp. 141–52.

769. MORELLI, F. A., FEHLNER, F. P., and STEMBRIDGE, C. H., Effect of Ultra-High Vacuum on Bacillus Subtilis var. Niger, *Nature*, vol. 196 (1962), pp. 106–7.

770. MORRIS, D., and BARTLETT, J. F., *Polarization of the 2840 Mc/s Radiation From Jupiter*, Observation No. 5, California Institute of Technology, Radio Observatory, Pasadena, California, 1962.

771. MORRIS, D., and BERGE, G. L., Measurements of the Polarization and Angular Extent of the Decimeter Radiation From Jupiter, *The Astrophysical Journal*, vol. 136 (1962), pp. 276–82.

772. ÖPIK, E. J., Jupiter: Chemical Composition, Structure and Origin of a Giant Planet. *Icarus*, vol. 1 (1962), pp. 200–57.

773. PANOFSKY, H. A., and HESS, S. L., Zonal Index and the Motion of the Great Red Spot on Jupiter, *Bulletin of the American Meteorological Society*, vol. 29 (1948), pp. 426–8.

774. PAPAZIAN, H. A., The Colors of Jupiter, *Publications of the Astronomical Society of the Pacific*, vol. 71 (1959), pp. 237–9.

775. PEEK, B. M., The Physical State of Jupiter's Atmosphere, *Monthly Notices of the Royal Astronomical Society*, vol. 97 (1937), pp. 574–82.

776. PEEK, B. M., Remarkable Spot on Jupiter, *Monthly Notices of the Royal Astronomical Society*, vol. 101 (1941), pp. 70–75.

777. RADHAKRISHNAN, V., and ROBERTS, J. A., Polarization and Angular Extent of the 960-Mc/sec. Radiation From Jupiter, *Physical Review Letters*, vol. 4 (1960), pp. 493–494.

778. RICE, F. O., Colors on Jupiter, *The Journal of Chemical Physics*, vol. 24 (1956), p. 1259.

779. RISHBETH, H., The Ionosphere of Jupiter, *Australian Journal of Physics*, vol. 12 pp. 466–8.

780. ROBERTS, M. S., and HUGUENIN, G. R., The Radiation Belt of Jupiter, *Harvard Radio Astronomy Preprint*, No. 106 (1962).

781. ROSE, W. K., BOLOGNA, J. M., and SLOANAKER, R. M., Linear Polarization of Jupiter, Saturn and Weak Radio Sources Using a 9.4 cm Maser, *The Astronomical Journal*, vol. 68 (1963), p. 78.

782. SAGAN, C., On the Nature of Jovian Red Spots, *Mémoires de la Société Royale des Sciences de Liège* (In press).

783. SHAIN, C. A., Location on Jupiter of a Source of Radio Noise, *Nature*, vol. 176 (1955), pp. 836–7.

784. SHAIN, C. A., 18.3 Mc/s Radiation from Jupiter, *Australian Journal of Physics*, vol. 9 (1956), pp. 61–73.

785. SHAPIRO, R., A Quantitative Study of Bright and Dark Spots on Jupiter's Surface, *The Study of Planetary Atmospheres*, Final Report, Contract No. AF 19(122)-162, Lowell Observatory, Flagstaff, Arizona, 1951, pp. 114–15. AD-10,609.

786. SHAPIRO, R., The Distribution and Velocities of Bright and Dark Spots on Jupiter's Surface in 1928, *The Study of Planetary Atmospheres*, Final Report, Contract No. AF 19(122)-162, Lowell Observatory, Flagstaff, Arizona, 1951, pp. 116–26, AD-10,609.

787. SHAPIRO, R., The Latitudinal Distribution of the Relative Brightness of Jupiter and Its Use in the Study of Jupiter's Large Scale Atmospheric Circulations, *The Study of Planetary Atmospheres*, Final Report, Contract No. AF 19(122)-162, Lowell Observatory, Flagstaff, Arizona, 1951, pp. 175–89. AD-10,609.

788. SHAPIRO, R., On the Nature of Jovian Spots as Indicated by Their Distribution and Velocities in 1958, *Contributions to the Study of Planetary Atmospheric Circulations*, Technical Report No. AFCRD-TR-53-35, Air Force Research Center, Cambridge, Massachusetts, 1953, pp. 115–22.

789. SLOANAKER, R. M., and BOLAND, J. W., Observations of Jupiter at a Wavelength of 10 cm, *The Astrophysical Journal*, vol. 133 (1961), pp. 649–56.

790. SMITH, A. G., Radio Spectrum of Jupiter, *Science*, vol. 134 (1961), pp. 587–95.

791. SMITH, A. G., CARR, T. D., BOLLHAGEN, H., CHATTERTON, N., and SIX, F., Ionosperic Modification of the Radio Emission From Jupiter, *Nature*, vol. 187 (1960), pp. 568–70.

792. SMITH, H. J., *et al.*, Fine Structure of Jupiter's 20-Megacycle Noise Storms, *The Astronomical Journal*, vol. 65 (1960), p. 501.

793. The Spectrum of Jupiter Photographed Using High-Dispersion Gratings, *National Bureau of Standards (U.S.), Technical News Bulletin*, vol. 44 (1960), pp. 188–90.

794. SQUIRES, P., The Equatorial Clouds of Jupiter, *The Astrophysical Journal*, vol. 126 (1957), pp. 185–94.

795. STRUVE, O., The Atmospheres of Jupiter and Saturn, *Sky and Telescope*, vol. 13 (1954), pp. 336–8.

796. WILDT, R., Methan in den Atmosphären der grossen Planeten, *Die Naturwissenschaften*, vol. 20 (1932), p. 851.

797. WILDT, R., Absorptionsspektren und Atmosphären der grossen Planeten, *Veröffentlichungen der Universitäts-Sternwarte zu Göttingen*, No. 22 (1932).

390 BIBLIOGRAPHY

798. WILDT, R., On the Chemical Nature of Colouration in Jupiter's Cloud Forms, *Monthly Notices of the Royal Astronomical Society,* vol. 99 (1939), pp. 616–23.
799. WILLIAMS, A. S., On the Periodic Variation in the Colours of the Two Equatorial Belts of Jupiter, (Third Paper) *Monthly Notices of the Royal Astronomical Society,* vol. 97 (1936–7), pp. 105–8.
800. (See Ref. 726.)

G. Other Planets

801. ADAMS, W. S., and DUNHAM, T., JR., Note on the Spectrum of Mercury, *Publications of the Astronomical Society of the Pacific,* vol. 44 (1932), p. 380.
802. (See Ref. 119.)
803. (See Ref. 728.)
804. (See Ref. 730.)
805. BECKER, W., Über Helligkeitsschwankungen der Planeten Mars, Jupiter, Saturn, Uranus, Neptun und zusammenhängende Erscheinungen, *Akademie der Wissenschaften, Berlin. Physikalisch-mathematische Klasse, Sitzungsberichte,* vol. 28 (1933), pp. 839–59.
806. BOBROV, M. S., Some Remarks on Optical Properties of Saturn's Rings, *The Astronomical Journal,* vol. 65 (1960), pp. 337–8.
807. (See Ref. 602.)
808. CHINCARINI, L., Saturno, *Astronautica Acta,* vol. 6 (1958), pp. 69–72.
809. (See Ref. 747.)
810. COOK, J. J., CROSS, L. G., BAIR, M. E., and ARNOLD, C. B., Radio Detection of the Planet Saturn, *Nature,* vol. 188 (1960), pp. 393–4.
811. (See Ref. 604.)
812. (See Ref. 749.)
813. DOLLFUS, A., Observation d'une atmosphère autour de la planète Mercure, *Comptes Rendus Hebdomadaires des Séances de l'Académie des Sciences,* vol. 231 (1950), pp. 1430–2.
814. DRAKE, F. D., Microwave Spectrum of Saturn, *Nature,* vol. 195 (1962), pp. 893–4.
815. FRANKLIN, F. A., and COOK, A. F., II, Note on the Nature of Saturn's Rings, *The Astronomical Journal,* vol. 63 (1958), pp. 398–400.
816. HEATH, M. B., Saturn in 1958, *Journal of the British Astronomical Association,* vol. 70 (1960), pp. 29–32.
817. HERZBERG, G., Spectroscopic Evidence of Molecular Hydrogen in the Atmospheres of Uranus and Neptune, *The Astrophysical Journal,* vol. 115 (1952), pp. 337–40.
818. (See Ref. 758.)
819. (See Ref. 761.)
820. JOHNSON, H. M., A Map of Mercury in 1936–8, *Journal of the Royal Astronomical Society of Canada,* vol. 33 (1939), pp. 210–2.
821. KUIPER, G. P., Titan: A Satellite With an Atmosphere, *The Astrophysical Journal,* vol. 100 (1944), pp. 378–83.
822. KUIPER, G. P., New Absorptions in the Uranus Atmosphere, *The Astrophysical Journal,* vol. 109 (1949), pp. 540–1.
823. MOORE, J. H., Spectroscopic Observations of the Rotation of Saturn, *Publications of the Astronomical Society of the Pacific,* vol. 51 (1939), pp. 274–81.
824. PECKER, J. C., Variations des raies de CH sur le disque solaire, *Annales d'Astrophysique,* vol. 12 (1949), pp. 9–20.
825. PECKER, J. C., and POYTURAUX, R., Sur la repartition des bandes de CN sur le disque solaire, *Annales d'Astrophysique,* vol. 11 (1948), pp. 90–106.
826. PETTIT, E., and NICHOLSON, S. B., Radiation From the Planet Mercury, *The Astrophysical Journal,* vol. 83 (1936), pp. 269–72.
827. PROCTER, R. A., *Saturn and Its System,* London: Longmans, Green and Co., Ltd. (1865).
828. ROSE, W. K., BOLOGNA, J. M., and SLOANAKER, R. M., Linear Polarization of the 3200 Mc/sec Radiation From Saturn, *Physical Review Letters,* vol. 10 (1963), pp. 123–5.

829. (See Ref. 781.)
830. SATTERTHWAITE, G. E., The Outer Planets, *Discovery*, vol. 21 (1960), pp. 24-30.
831. (See Ref. 795.)
832. (See Ref. 796.)
833. (See Ref. 797.)

H. Meteorites

834. ALTER, G., Interstellar Dust, *Vistas in Astronomy*, vol. 2, ed. by ARTHUR BEER, New York: Pergamon Press, Inc. (1956), pp. 1074-80.
835. ANDERS, E., Meteoritic Hydrocarbons and Extraterrestrial Life, *Annals of the New York Academy of Sciences*, vol. 93 (1962), pp. 649-64.
836. ANDERS, E., Meteorite Ages, *Reviews of Modern Physics*, vol. 34 (1962), pp. 287-325.
837. ANDERS, E., On the Origin of Carbonaceous Chondrites, *Annals of the New York Academy of Sciences*, vol. 108 (1963), pp. 514-33.
838. ANDERS, E., Meteorites and the Early History of the Solar System, *Proceedings of the Conference on the Origin of the Solar System*, ed. by R. JASTROW, New York: Academic Press, Inc. (1963).
839. ANDERS, E., and FITCH, F., Search for Organized Elements in Carbonaceous Chondrites, *Science*, vol. 138 (1962), pp. 1392-9.
840. ANDERS, E., and GOLES, G. G., Theories on the Origin of Meteorites, *Journal of Chemical Education*, vol. 38 (1961), pp. 58-66.
841. BERGER, R., Evaluation of Radiation Effects in Space, *Annals of the New York Academy of Sciences*, vol. 108 (1963), pp. 482-6.
842. BERNAL, J. D., Significance of Carbonaceous Meteorites in Theories on the Origin of Life, *Nature*, vol. 190 (1961), pp. 129-31.
843. BERNAL, J. D., Life-Forms in Meteorites, *Nature*, vol. 193 (1962), pp. 1109-13.
844. BERNAL, J. D., Life-Forms in Meteorites: Comments, *Nature*, vol. 193 (1962), pp. 1127-8.
845. BERTHELOT, M. P. E., Action de la chaleur sur quelques carbures d'hydrogène, *Comptes Rendus Hebdomadaires des Séances de l'Académie des Sciences*, vol. 62 (1866), pp. 905-10.
846. BERTHELOT, M. P. E., Action de la chaleur sur la benzine et sur les carbures analogues, *Comptes Rendus Hebdomadaires des Séances de l'Académie des Sciences*, vol. 63 (1866), pp. 788-93.
847. BERTHELOT, M. P. E., Sur l'origine des carbures et des combustibles minéraux, *Annales de Chimie et de Physique*, vol. 9, Ser. 4 (1866), pp. 481-3.
848. BERTHELOT, M. P. E., Sur la matière charbonneuse des météorites, *Comptes Rendus Hebdomadaires des Séances de l'Académie des Sciences*, vol. 67 (1868), p. 849.
849. BERTHELOT, M. P. E., Matière charbonneuse des météorites, *Annales de Chimie et de Physique*, vol. 20 (1870), pp. 531-2.
850. BERTHELOT, M. P. E., Influence de divers agents sur le carbone déjà formé, *Annales de Chimie et de Physique*, vol. 19, Ser. 4 (1870), pp. 417-20.
851. BERTHELOT, M. P. E., Méthode universelle pour réduire et saturer d'hydrogène les composés organiques, *Annales de Chimie et de Physique*, vol. 20, Ser. 4 (1870), pp. 392-537.
852. BERTHELOT, M. P. E., Nouvelles contributions a l'histoire des carbones du graphite et des météorites, *Annales de Chimie et de Physique*, vol. 30 (1873), pp. 420-2.
853. BERTHELOT, D., and GAUDECHON, H., Éffets chimiques des rayons ultraviolets sur les corps gazeaux, actions de polymérisation, *Comptes Rendus Hebdomadaires des Séances de l'Académie des Sciences*, vol. 150 (1910), pp. 1169-72.
854. BERZELIUS, J., Über Meteorsteine, *Annales de Chimie et de Physique*, vol. 33 (1834), pp. 113-44.
855. BOATO, G., Isotopic Composition of Hydrogen and Carbon in the Carbonaceous Chondrites, *Geochimica et Cosmochimica Acta*, vol. 6 (1954), pp. 209-20.
856. BOATO, G., Meaning of Deuterium Abundance in Meteorites, *Nature*, vol. 177 (1956), pp. 424-5.

857. BOURRELLY, P., Loricae and Cysts in the Chrysophyceae, *Annals of the New York Academy of Sciences*, vol. 108 (1963), pp. 421–9.

858. BRIGGS, M. H., Organic Constituents of Meteorites, *Nature*, vol. 191 (1961), pp. 1137–40.

859. BRIGGS, M. H., Properties of the Organic Microstructures of Some Carbonaceous Chondrites, *Nature*, vol. 195 (1962), pp. 1076–7.

860. BRIGGS, M. H., Nature and Origin of Meteorite Organic Matter, *Science and Culture* (Calcutta), vol. 28 (1962), pp. 357–60.

861. (See Ref. 19.)

862. BRIGGS, M. H., Organic Extracts of Some Carbonaceous Meteorites, *Life Sciences*, vol. 2 (1963), pp. 63–68.

863. BRIGGS, M. H., Biological Problems of Meteorites, *Spaceflight*, vol. 5, No. 2 (1963), pp. 45–52.

864. BRIGGS, M. H., Evidence of an Extraterrestrial Origin for Some Organic Constituents of Meteorites, *Nature*, vol. 197 (1963), p. 1290.

865. BRIGGS, M. H., and KITTO, G. B., Complex Organic Microstructures in the Mokoia Meteorite, *Nature*, vol. 193 (1962), pp. 1126–7.

866. BRIGGS, M. H., and MAMIKUNIAN, G., Organic Constituents of the Carbonaceous Chondrites, *Space Science Reviews*, vol. 1 (1963), pp. 647–82.

867. BUDDHUE, J. D., Nitrogen and Its Compounds in Meteorites, *Popular Astronomy*, vol. 50 (1942), pp. 560–3.

868. CALVIN, M., and VAUGHAN, S. K., Extraterrestrial Life: Some Organic Constituents of Meteorites, *Space Research*, ed. by H. KALLMAN BIJL, Amsterdam: North-Holland Publishing Company (1960), pp. 1171–91.

869. CHOLNOKY, B. J., Cell Structure and Environment, *Annals of the New York Academy of Sciences*, vol. 108 (1963), pp. 366–74.

870. CLAUS, G., Comments in Panel Discussion, The Identity of the 'Organized Elements' in Carbonaceous Chondrites, *Annals of the New York Academy of Sciences*, vol. 108 (1963), pp. 610–2.

871. CLAUS, G., and NAGY, B., A Microbiological Examination of Some Carbonaceous Chondrites, *Nature*, vol. 192 (1961), pp. 594–6.

872. CLAUS, G., and NAGY, B., Considerations of Extraterrestrial Taxa, *Taxon*, vol. 11, No. 5 (1962), pp. 160–1.

873. CLAUS, G., and NAGY, B., *Microfossils, New to Science, Resembling Algae and Flagellates, Found in Meteorites*, First International Congress on Palynology, Tucson, Arizona, April 23–27, 1962.

874. CLAUS, G., and NAGY, B., Taxonomical Consideration of Certain Incerta Sedes, *Phycological Society of America, News Bulletin*, vol. 15 (1962), pp. 15–19.

875. CLAUS, G., and NAGY, B., Discussion des remarques critiques sur la présence supposée de microorganismes d'origine extraterrestre dans des météorites par Georges Deflandre, *Revue Algologique* (In press).

876. CLAUS, G., NAGY, B., and EUROPA, D. L., Further Observations on the Properties of the Organized Elements of Carbonaceous Chondrites, *Annals of the New York Academy of Sciences*, vol. 108 (1963), pp. 580–605.

877. CLOEZ, S., Note sur la composition chimique de la pierre météorique d'Orgueil, *Comptes Rendus Hebdomadaires des Séances de l'Académie des Sciences*, vol. 58 (1864), pp. 986–8.

878. CLOEZ, S., Analyse chimique de la pierre météorique d'Orgueil, *Comptes Rendus Hebdomadaires des Séances de l'Académie des Sciences*, vol. 59 (1864), pp. 37–40.

879. COHEN, E., *Meteoritenkunde*, vol. I, II, III, Stuttgart, Germany: E. Schweizerbart'sche Verlagshandlung (1894, 1904, 1905).

880. CRAIG, H., Geochemistry of the Stable Carbon Isotopes: Graphites, *Geochimica et Cosmochimica Acta*, vol. 3 (1953), pp. 83–85.

881. DAUBREE, M., Nouveaux renseignements sur le bolide du 14 Mai 1864, *Comptes Rendus Hebdomadaires des Séances de l'Académie des Sciences*, vol. 58 (1864), pp. 1065–72.

882. DAUVILLIER, A., Sur la nature de Pluton et de Triton, *Comptes Rendus Hebdomadaires des Séances de l'Académie des Sciences*, vol. 233'(1951), pp. 901–3.
883. DEFLANDRE, G., Micropaléontologie des météorites, *Comptes Rendus Hebdomadaires des Séances de l'Académie des Sciences*, vol. 254 (1962), pp. 3405–7.
884. DEGENS, E. T., and BAJOR, M., Amino Acids and Sugars in the Bruderheim and Murray Meteorite, *Die Naturwissenschaften*, vol. 49 (1962), pp. 605–6.
885. DOMBROWSKI, H., Comments in Panel Discussion, The Identity of the Organized Elements, *Annals of the New York Academy of Sciences*, vol. 108 (1963), p. 614.
886. DUFRESNE, E. R., and ANDERS, E., On the Chemical Evolution of the Carbonaceous Chondrites *Geochimica et Cosmochimica Acta*, vol. 26 (1962), pp. 1085–1184.
887. EDWARDS, G., Isotopic Composition of Meteoritic Hydrogen, *Nature*, vol. 176 (1955), pp. 109–11.
888. EDWARDS, G., and UREY, H. C., Determination of Alkali Metals in Meteorites by a Distillation Process, *Geochimica et Cosmochimica Acta*, vol. 7 (1955), pp. 154–68.
889. FARRINGTON, O. C., Catalogue of the Meteorites of North America, to January 1, 1909. *Memoirs of the Washington National Academy of Science*, vol. 13 (1915).
890. FISH, R. A., GOLES, G. G., and ANDERS, E., The Record in the Meteorites: III. On the Development of Meteorites in Asteroidal Bodies, *The Astrophysical Journal*, vol. 132 (1960), pp. 243–58.
891. FITCH, F., and ANDERS, E., Observations on the Nature of the Organized Elements in Carbonaceous Chondrites, *Annals of the New York Academy of Sciences*, vol. 108 (1963), pp. 495–513.
892. FITCH, F., SCHWARCZ, H. P., and ANDERS, E., Organized Elements in Carbonaceous Chondrites, *Nature*, vol. 193 (1962), pp. 1123–5.
893. FRIEDHEIM, C., Die chemische Zusammensetzung der Meteoriten von Alfinaello und Concepcion, *Akademie der Wissenschaften, Berlin: Sitzungsberichte* (1888), pp. 345–67.
894. FRIEDMAN, I., Deuterium Content of Natural Waters and Other Substances, *Geochimica et Cosmochimica Acta*, vol. 4 (1953), pp. 89–103.
895. GASKELL, T., Do Meteorites Reveal Life in Other Worlds? *New Scientist*, vol. 14 (1962), p. 458.
896. GREGORY, P. H., Identity of Organized Elements From Meteorites, *Nature*, vol. 194 (1962), p. 1065.
897. GÜMBEL, H., Über die in Bayern gefundenen Steinmeteoriten, *Sitzungsberichte der mathematisch–naturwissenschaftlichen Klasse der bayerischen Akademie der Wissenschaften zu München*, vol. 1 (1878), pp. 14–72.
898. HAHN, O., *Die Meteoriten (Chondrite) und ihre Organismen*. Tübingen: Verlag der H. Laupp'schen Buchhandlung (1880).
899. HOWARD, W. E., BARRETT, A. H., and HADDOCK, F. T., Measurement of Microwave Radiation from the Planet Mercury, *The Astrophysical Journal*, vol. 136 (1962), pp. 995–1004.
900. (See Ref. 148.)
901. KAPLAN, I. R., DEGENS, E. T., and REUTER, J. H., Organic Compounds in Stony Meteorites, *Geochimica et Cosmochimica Acta*, vol. 27 (1963), pp. 805–34.
902. KERKUT, G. A., *Implications of Evolution*, New York: Pergamon Press, Inc. (1960).
903. KREJCI-GRAF, K., Organische Substanzen in Meteoriten, *Die Umschau in Wissenschaft und Technik*, vol. 62 (1962), pp. 240–50.
904. KRINOV, E. L., *Principles of Meteoritics*, tr. by I. VIDZIUNAS, New York: Pergamon Press, Inc. (1960).
905. KVASHA, L. G., An Investigation of the Stony Meteorite Staroe-Bonskius, *Meteoritika*, vol. 4 (1948), p. 83.
906. LEYMERIE, M., Sur l'aérolithe (Tarn-et-Garonne) tombé le 14 Mai 1864, à 8 heures du soir, *Comptes Rendus Hebdomadaires des Séances de l'Académie des Sciences*, vol. 58 (1864), pp. 988–90.
907. Like Nothing on Earth, *The Lamp*, vol. 44 (Summer 1962), pp. 17–21.
908. LIPMAN, C. B., Are There Living Bacteria in Stony Meteorites? *American Museum Novitates*, No. 588 (1932).

909. LIPMAN, C. B., Bacteria in Stony Meteorites, *Popular Astronomy*, vol. 44 (1936), pp. 442–3.

910. LOVERING, J. F., Pressures and Temperatures Within a Typical Parent Meteorite Body, *Geochimica et Cosmochimica Acta*, vol. 12 (1957), pp. 253–61.

911. MAMIKUNIAN, G., and BRIGGS, M. H., Some Microstructures of Complex Morphology Observed in Preparations of Carbonaceous Chondrites Made Under Sterile Conditions, *Nature*, vol. 197 (1963), pp. 1245–8.

912. MAMIKUNIAN, G., and BRIGGS, M. H., Organized Elements in Carbonaceous Chondrites, *Science*, vol. 139 (1963), p. 873.

913. MAMIKUNIAN, G., and BRIGGS, M. H., *Catalog of Microstructures Observed in Carbonaceous Chondrites*, Technical Report No. 32-398, Jet Propulsion Laboratory, Pasadena, California, March 15, 1963.

914. MASON, B., The Origin of Meteorites, *Journal of Geophysical Research*, vol. 65 (1960), pp. 2965–70.

915. MASON, B., Origin of Chondrules and Chondritic Meteorites, *Nature*, vol. 186 (1960), pp. 230–1.

916. MASON, B., Comments in Panel Discussion, The Identity of the 'Organized Elements', *Annals of the New York Academy of Sciences*, vol. 108 (1963), pp. 614–15.

917. MASON, B., Organic Matter From Space, *Scientific American*, vol. 208, No. 3 (1963), pp. 43–50.

918. MASON, B., Carbonaceous Chondrites, *Space Science Reviews* (In press).

919. MAYNE, K. I., Natural Variations in the Nitrogen Isotope Abundance Ratio in Igneous Rocks, *Geochimica et Cosmochimica Acta*, vol. 12 (1957), pp. 185–9.

920. MEINSCHEIN, W. G., Comments in Panel Discussion. The Identity of the 'Organized Elements', *Annals of the New York Academy of Sciences*, vol. 108 (1963), p. 615.

921. MEINSCHEIN, W. G., Benzene Extracts of the Orgueil Meteorite, *Science* (In press).

922. MEINSCHEIN, W. G., NAGY, B. S., and HENNESSY, D. J., Evidence in Meteorites of Former Life, *Annals of the New York Academy of Sciences*, vol. 108 (1963), p. 553.

923. MERRILL, G. P., Composition and Structure of Meteorites, *U.S. National Museum Bulletin*, No. 149, Smithsonian Institution (1930).

924. MEUNIER, S., Analyse de la météorite de Mighei (Russie); présence d'une combinaison non signalée jusqu'ici dans les météorites, *Comptes Rendus Hebdomadaires des Séances de l'Académie des Sciences*, vol. 109 (1889), pp. 976–8.

925. MOISSAN, H., Chimie minérale – Nouvelles recherches sur la météorite de Cañon Diablo, *Comptes Rendus Hebdomadaires des Séances de l'Académie des Sciences*, vol. 139 (1904), pp. 773–80.

926. MORRISON, P., Carbonaceous 'Snowflakes' and the Origin of Life, *Science*, vol. 135 (1962), pp. 663–4.

927. MUELLER, G., The Properties and Theory of Genesis of the Carbonaceous Complex Within the Cold Bokkeveld Meteorite, *Geochimica et Cosmochimica Acta*, vol. 4 (1953), pp. 1–10.

928. MUELLER, G., The Interpretation of Microstructures in Carbonaceous Meteorites, *Advances in Organic Geochemistry*, ed. by U. COLOMBO and G. D. HOBSON, New York: Pergamon Press, Inc. (1964), pp. 119–40.

929. MUELLER, G., Interpretation of Micro-Structures in Carbonaceous Meteorites, *Nature*, vol. 196 (1962), pp. 929–32.

930. MUELLER, G., Comments in *Proceedings of the Geological Society of London*, vol. 1600 (1962), p. 127.

931. NAGY, B., International Control of Investigations of Rare Meteorites, *Nature*, vol. 189 (1961), p. 967.

932. NAGY, B., Comments in Panel Discussion, The Identity of the 'Organized Elements', *Annals of the New York Academy of Sciences*, vol. 108 (1963), p. 610.

933. NAGY, B., and BITZ, H., Long-Chain Fatty Acids From the Orgueil Meteorite, *Archives of Biochemistry and Biophysics*, vol. 101 (1963), pp. 240–8.

934. (See Ref. 68.)

935. NAGY, B., and CLAUS, G., Notes on the Petrography of the Orgueil Meteorite,

Advances in Organic Geochemistry, ed. by U. COLOMBO and G. D. HOBSON, New York: Pergamon Press, Inc. (1964), pp. 115–18.

936. NAGY, B., CLAUS, G., and HENNESSY, D. J., Organic Particles Embedded in Minerals in the Orgueil and Ivuna Carbonaceous Chondrites, *Nature*, vol. 193 (1962), pp. 1129–33.

937. NAGY, B., CLAUS, G., MEINSCHEIN, W. G., and HENNESSY, D. J., *Life-Like Forms in Carbonaceous Meteorites*, 156th Annual Convention of the Medical Society of the State of New York, New York, May 14–18, 1962.

938. NAGY, B., FREDERICKSON, K., UREY, H. C., CLAUS, G. and ANDERSON, C. A., Electron Probe Microanalysis of Organized Elements in the Orgueil Meteorite, *Science* (In press).

939. NAGY, B., MEINSCHEIN, W. G., CLAUS, G., and HENNESSY, D. J., *Analyses of Some Carbonaceous Chondrites: I. Mineralogical; II. Organic; III. Microscopic*, Symposium on Extraterrestrial Biochemistry and Biology, American Association for the Advancement of Science, Annual 128th Meeting, Denver, Colorado, December 26–30, 1961.

940. NAGY, B., MEINSCHEIN, W. G., and HENNESSY, D. J., Mass Spectroscopic Analysis of the Orgueil Meteorite Evidence for Biogenic Hydrocarbons, *Annals of the New York Academy of Sciences*, vol. 93 (1961), pp. 25–35.

941. NAGY, B., MEINSCHEIN, W. G., and HENNESSY, D. J., *Mineralogical Study of the Orgueil Meteorite*, Forty-second Annual Meeting of the Mineralogical Society of America (1961).

942. NAGY, B., MEINSCHEIN, W. G., and HENNESSY, D. J., Discussion of paper by E. ANDERS entitled 'Meteoritic Hydrocarbons and Extraterrestrial Life', *Annals of the New York Academy of Sciences*, vol. 93 (1962), pp. 658–60, 663–4.

943. NAGY, B., MEINSCHEIN, W. G., HENNESSY, D. J., Aqueous, Low Temperature Environment of the Orgueil Meteorite Parent Body, *Annals of the New York Academy of Sciences*, vol. 108 (1963), pp. 534–52.

944. NININGER, H. H., Concerning Bacteria in Meteorites, *Popular Astronomy*, vol. 41 (1933), pp. 214–15.

945. NININGER, H. H., Diamonds in Canyon Diablo, Arizona, Meteorites, *Popular Astronomy*, vol. 47 (1939), pp. 504–7.

946. NININGER, H. H., *Out of the Sky; An Introduction to Meteorites*, Denver, Colorado: University of Denver Press (1952).

947. ORÓ, J., Ultraviolet-Absorbing Compound(s) Reported Present in the Murray Meteorite, *Nature*, vol. 197 (1963), pp. 756–8.

948. PALIK, P., Further Life-Forms in the Orgueil Meteorite, *Nature*, vol. 194 (1962), p. 1065.

949. PALIK, P., Studies on Some New and Interesting Microfossils From the Orgueil Meteorite, *Micropaleontology* (In press).

950. PALLISFER, J., *Unusual Earthly Forms of Life and Extra-Terrestrial Implications*, 156th Annual Conference of the Medical Society of the State of New York, New York, May 14–18, 1962.

951. PARKIN, D. W., and HUNTER, W., Meteorites and Cosmic Dust, *Advances in Astronautics and Astrophysics*, vol. 1, ed. by Z. KOPAL, New York: Academic Press Inc. (1962), pp. 105–63.

952. PARKIN, D. W., HUNTER, W., and BROWNLOW, A. E., Metallic Cosmic Dust With Amorphous Attachments, *Nature*, vol. 193 (1962), pp. 639–42.

953. PEARSON, R., Life-Forms in Carbonaceous Chondrites, *Nature*, vol. 194 (1962), pp. 1064–5.

954. PEEK, B. M., *Planet Jupiter*, New York: The Macmillan Co. (1958).

955. PETTERSSON, H., Cosmic Spherules and Meteoritic Dust, *Scientific American*, vol. 202, No. 2 (1960), pp. 123–6, 128, 130, 132.

956. PONS, W., Leben – ein irdisches oder ein kosmisches Prinzip? *Weltraumfahrt*, vol. 11 (1960), pp. 109–10.

957. PORTER, W. S., The Constitutions of Uranus and Neptune, *The Astronomical Journal*, vol. 66 (1961), pp. 243–5.

958. *Researches on Meteorites*, ed. by C. B. MOORE, New York: John Wiley and Sons, Inc. (1962).

959. ROSCOE, H., On the Existence of a Crystallizable Carbon Compound and Free Sulfur in the Alais Meteorite, *The Philosophical Magazine*, vol. 25 (1863), pp. 319–20.

960. ROSS, R., Comments in Panel Discussion, The Identity of the 'Organized Elements', *Annals of the New York Academy of Sciences*, vol. 108 (1963), p. 612.

961. ROY, S. K., The Question of Living Bacteria in Stony Meteorites, *Field Museum of Natural History, Geology Series*, vol. 4, No. 14 (1935), pp. 179–98.

962. ROY, S. K., Additional Notes on the Question of Living Bacteria in Stony Meteorites, *Popular Astronomy*, vol. 45 (1937), pp. 499–504.

963. SCHULLER, H., On a New Spectrum Attributed to the C_2H_x Molecule ($x = 1, 2$, or 3), *Mémoires de la Société Royale des Sciences de Liège*, Quatrième Série, vol. 12, Nos. I and II (1953), pp. 191–5.

964. SINGER, S. F., Meteorites and Cosmic Rays, *Nature*, vol. 170 (1952), pp. 728–9.

965. SINGER, S. F., Meteorites and Cosmic Rays, *Mémoires de la Société Royale des Sciences de Liège*, vol. 13, Nos. I and II (1953), pp. 339–49.

966. SISLER, F., *Concerning the Entry and Survival of Microorganisms in Meteorites*, Symposium on Extraterrestrial Biochemistry and Biology, American Association for the Advancement of Science, 128th Annual Meeting, Denver, Colorado, December 26–30, 1961.

967. SISLER, F., Organic Matter and Life in Meteorites; Comments, *Proceedings of Lunar and Planetary Colloquium*, vol. 2, No. 4, Aerospace Laboratories, North American Aviation, Inc., Downey, California (1961), pp. 66–73.

968. SMITH, L., Sulfhydrocarbure cristallisé, venant de l'intérieur d'une masse de fer météorique, *Comptes Rendus Hebdomadaires des Séances de l'Académie des Sciences*, vol. 81 (1875), pp. 1055–6.

969. SMITH, L., Researches on the Solid Carbon Compounds in Meteorites, *American Journal of Science*, vol. 11 (1876), pp. 388–95, 433–42.

970. SMITH, L., Recherches sur les composés du carbone dans les météorites, *Comptes Rendus Hebdomadaires des Séances de l'Académie des Sciences*, vol. 82 (1876), pp. 1042–3.

971. SMITH, L., Sur des cristaux extraits de la fonte de fer par l'éther ou le pétrole, *Comptes Rendus Hebdomadaires des Séances de l'Académie des Sciences*, vol. 88 (1879), pp. 888–90.

972. SPIELMAN, P. E., Bitumen in Meteorites, *Nature*, vol. 114 (1924), p. 276.

973. STAPLIN, F. L., Organic Remains in Meteorites – A Review of the Problem, *Journal of the Alberta Society of Petroleum Geologists*, vol. 10 (1962), pp. 575–80.

974. STAPLIN, F. L., Microfossils From the Orgueil Meteorite, *Micropaleontology*, vol. 8 (1962), pp. 343–8.

975. SWINGS, P., Considerations Regarding Cometary and Interstellar Molecules, *The Astrophysical Journal*, vol. 95 (1942), pp. 270–80.

976. SWINGS, P., Reports on the Progress of Astronomy: Cometary Spectra, *Monthly Notices of the Royal Astronomical Society*, vol. 103 (1943), pp. 86–111.

977. SWINGS, P., Spectra of the Comets, *Vistas in Astronomy*, vol. 2, ed. by A. BEER, New York: Pergamon Press, Inc. (1956), pp. 958–81.

978. SZTROTKAY, K. I., TOLNAY, V., and FOLVARI-VOGL, M., Mineralogical and Chemical Properties of the Carbonaceous Meteorite From Kaba, Hungary, *Acta Geologica* (Hungary), vol. 7 (1961), pp. 57–103.

979. TASCH, P., Paleoecological Considerations of Growth and Form of Fossil Protists, *Annals of the New York Academy of Sciences*, vol. 108 (1963), pp. 437–50.

980. TIMOFEEV, B. V., On the Occurrence of Organic Remains in Chondritic Meteorites, *Geological Society of the USSR; Abstracts of Papers Presented at the 4th Astronautics Meeting, May 1962* (1962).

981. TIMOFEEV, B. V., Vestiges of Life in Celestial Stores, *Ogoniok*, No. 42 (October 14, 1962), pp. 20–21.

982. TROFIMOV, A. V., Die isotope Zusammensetzung des Schwefels in Meteoriten und in irdischen Objekten, *Doklady Akademii Nauk SSSR*, vol. 66 (1949), p. 181.
983. TROFIMOV, A. V., Die Häufigkeit der Kohlenstoffisotopen in Meteoriten, *Meteoritika*, vol. 8 (1950), pp. 127–33.
984. UREY, H. C., Origin of Life-Like Forms in Carbonaceous Chondrites, *Nature*, vol. 193 (1962), pp. 1119–23.
985. UREY, H. C., Life-Like Forms in Meteorites, *Science*, vol. 137 (1962), pp. 623–6.
986. UREY, H. C., Comments in Panel Discussion, The Identity of the 'Organized Elements', *Annals of the New York Academy of Sciences*, vol. 108 (1963), p. 606.
987. UREY, H. C., and CRAIG, H., Composition of the Stone Meteorites and the Origin of the Meteorites, *Geochimica et Cosmochimica Acta*, vol. 4 (1953), pp. 36–82.
988. WATSON, F. G., *Between the Planets*, Cambridge, Massachusetts: Harvard University Press (1956).
989. WIIK, H. B., Chemical Composition of Some Stony Meteorites, *Geochimica et Cosmochimica Acta*, vol. 9 (1956), pp. 279–89.

II. LIFE-DETECTION SYSTEMS

A. Reviews

990. BRIGGS, M. H., Automated Life-Detection Devices, *Spaceflight* (In press).
991. CLAMMANN, H. C., How to Adapt Bio-Experiments to Space Probes, *Space Aeronautics*, vol. 35, No. 4 (1961), pp. 73, 76–77.
992. LEVIN, G. V., *et al.*, Radioisotopic Biochemical Probe for Extraterrestrial Life Detection, Quarterly Progress Report No. 1, Report Research, Inc., Washington, D.C., May 15, 1961.
993. LEVIN, G. V., HEIM, A. H., CLENDENNING, J. R., and THOMPSON, M. F., Radioisotopic Metabolic Detection, *Proceedings of Lunar and Planetary Exploration Colloquium*, Aerospace Laboratories, North American Aviation, Inc., Downey, California (In press).

B. Accounts of Specific Devices

994. BLEI, I., *Detection of Extraterrestrial Life. Method II: Optical Rotatory Dispersion*, Final Report, Melpar, Inc., Falls Church, Virginia, August 1962.
995. ELLIS, C. B., Use of Optical Frequencies for Space Communications, *IRE Transactions on Communications Systems*, vol. CS-8, No. 3 (September 1960), pp. 164–8.
996. LEDERBERG, J., and SAGAN, C., Microenvironments for Life on Mars, *Proceedings of the National Academy of Sciences of the United States of America*, vol. 48 (1962), pp. 1473–5.
997. LEVIN, G. V., HEIM, A. H., CLENDENNING, J. R., and THOMPSON, M. F., Gulliver – A Quest for Life on Mars, *Science*, vol. 138 (1962), pp. 114–21.
998. OYAMA, V., Mars Biological Detection by Gas Chromatography, *Proceedings of Lunar and Planetary Exploration Colloquium*, vol. 3, No. 2, Aerospace Laboratories, North American Aviation, Inc., Downey, California (1962), pp. 29–36.
999. PERTI, A. N., and PATHAK, H. D., Origin of Life, *Agra University Journal of Research*, vol. 10, Part 2 (1962), p. 265.
1000. VISHNIAC, W., Extraterrestrial Microbiology, *Aerospace Medicine*, vol. 31 (1960), pp. 678–80.

III. ORIGINS OF LIFE

A. Reviews

1001. ALEXANDER, J., Theories as to the Origin and Nature of Life, *Science*, vol. 96 (1942), pp. 252–3.
1002. ALEXANDER, J., *Life, Its Nature and Origin*, New York: Reinhold Publishing Corp. (1948).

1003. ALLEN, G., Reflective Catalysis, a Possible Mechanism of Molecular Duplication in Prebiological Evolution, *The American Naturalist*, vol. 91 (1957), pp. 65–78.
1004. ANKER, H. S., On the Geogenous Evolution of Self-Reproducing Systems and Macromolecules, *Perspectives in Biology and Medicine*, vol. 5 (1961), pp. 86–88.
1005. ARCOS, M., and ARCOS, J. C., Sur le rôle possible du graphite dans la biogénèse, *Bulletin de l'Association Française pour l'Avancement des Sciences*, vol. 63 (1956), pp. 89–100.
1006. *Aspects of the Origin of Life*, ed. by M. FLORKIN, Oxford: Pergamon Press, Inc. (1960).
1007. AUBEL, E., Au sujet du passage de la vie anaérobie à la vie aérobie, *The Origin of Life on the Earth*, ed. by A. I. OPARIN *et al.*, New York: Pergamon Press, Inc. (1959), pp. 585–92.
1008. BARGHOORN, E. S., Origin of Life, *Treatise on Marine Ecology and Paleoecology*, Geological Society of America, Memoir 67, vol. 2 (1957), pp. 76–86.
1009. BASTIAN, H. C., *The Beginnings of Life*, New York: D. Appleton (1872).
1010. BASTIAN, H. C., *Nature and Origin of Living Matter*, London: J. B. Lippincott Co. (1905).
1011. BELOT, M. E., L'évolution comparée continue et discontinue dans les règnes cosmique et organique, *Annales de la Société Scientifique de Bruxelles*, vol. 45 (1926), pp. 196–203.
1012. BERG, R. L., Some Conditions for the Appearance of Life on the Earth, *The Origin of Life on the Earth*, ed. by A. I. OPARIN *et al.*, New York: Pergamon Press, Inc. (1959), pp. 169–71.
1013. BERNAL, J. D., *The Physical Basis of Life*, London: Routledge and Kegan Paul (1951).
1014. BERNAL, J. D., Evolution of Life in the Universe, *Journal of the British Interplanetary Society*, vol. 12 (1953), pp. 114–8.
1015. BERNAL, J. D., The Origin of Life, *New Biology*, vol. 16 (1953), pp. 28–40.
1016. BERNAL, J. D., Evolution of Life, *Science and Culture (Calcutta)*, vol. 19, No. 5 (1953), pp. 228–34.
1017. BERNAL, J. D., The Problem of Stages in Biopoesis, *The Origin of Life on the Earth*, ed. by A. I. OPARIN *et al.*, New York: Pergamon Press, Inc. (1959), pp. 38–53.
1018. BEUTNER, R., *Life's Beginning on the Earth*, Baltimore, Maryland: The Williams and Wilkins Co. (1938).
1019. BEUTNER, R., The Independent Nature of Morphogenesis and Self-Reproduction and Its Significance for the Cosmic Development of Life, *Biodynamica*, vol. 38 (1938), pp. 1–7.
1020. BLUM, H. F., A Consideration of Evolution from a Thermodynamic View-Point, *The American Naturalist*, vol. 49 (1935), pp. 354–69.
1021. BLUM, H. F., *Time's Arrow and Evolution*, Princeton, New Jersey: Princeton University Press (1951).
1022. BLUM, H. F., Perspectives in Evolution, *American Scientist*, vol. 43 (1955), pp. 595–610.
1023. BLUM, H. F., On the Origin of Self-Replicating Systems, *Rhythmic and Synthetic Processes in Growth*, ed. by D. RUDNICK, Princeton, New Jersey: Princeton University Press (1957), pp. 155–70.
1024. BLUM, H. F., On the Origin and Evolution of Living Machines, *American Scientist*, vol. 49 (1961), pp. 474–501.
1025. BLUM, H. F., Negentropy and Living Systems (Book review), *Science*, vol. 139 (1963), p. 398.
1026. BRACHET, J., Les acides nucléiques et l'origine des protéines, *The Origin of Life on the Earth*, ed. by A. I. OPARIN *et al.*, New York: Pergamon Press, Inc. (1959), pp. 361–7.
1027. BRANFIELD, W., *Continuous Creation*, London: Routledge and Kegan Paul (1950).
1028. BRAUNSHTEÏN, A. E., The Pathways of Biological Assimilation and Dissimilation of Nitrogen and Some Aspects of Their Evolution, *The Origin of Life on the Earth*,

ed. by A. I. OPARIN *et al.,* New York: Pergamon Press, Inc. (1959), pp. 527–43.

1029. BREDER, C. M., A Consideration of an Evolutionary Hypothesis in Reference to the Origin of Life, *Zoologica,* vol. 27 (1942), pp. 131–4.

1030. BREHMER, W. G. H., Origin of the Living Organism in the Light of the New Physics, *Medical Times,* vol. 55, No. 11 (1927), pp. 247–50, 258.

1031. BRIGGS, M. H., The Chemical Origins of Life, *Spaceflight,* vol. 2 (1959), pp. 69–73.

1032. BRIGGS, M. H., The Coloring Matter and Radio Emissions of Jupiter, *The Observatory,* vol. 80 (1960), pp. 159–61.

1033. BRODA, E., Die Entstehung des dynamischen Zustandes, *The Origin of Life on the Earth,* ed. by A. I. OPARIN *et al.,* New York: Pergamon Press, Inc. (1959), pp. 334–43.

1034. CALVIN, M., Round Trip From Space, *Evolution,* vol. 13 (1959), pp. 362–77.

1035. CALVIN, M., Evolution of Enzymes and the Photosynthetic Apparatus, *Science,* vol. 130 (1959), pp. 1170–4.

1036. CALVIN, M., Origin of Life on Earth and Elsewhere, *Proceedings of Lunar and Planetary Exploration Colloquium,* vol. 1, No. 6, Aerospace Laboratories, North American Aviation, Inc., Downey, California (1959), pp. 8–18.

1037. CALVIN, M., *From Microstructure to Macrostructure and Function in the Photosynthetic Apparatus,* Report No. BNL 512, U.S. Atomic Energy Commission, 1959, pp. 160–80.

1038. CALVIN, M., *Chemical Evolution (Condon Lectures),* vol. I, From Molecule to Microbe, vol. II, Origin of Life on Earth and Elsewhere, Eugene, Oregon: Oregon State System (1961).

1039. CALVIN, M., The Chemistry of Life: III. How Life Originated on Earth and in the World Beyond, *Chemical and Engineering News,* vol. 39, No. 21 (1961), pp. 96–104.

1040. CALVIN, M., Evolution of Photosynthetic Mechanisms, *Perspectives in Biology and Medicine,* vol. 5 (1961–2), pp. 147–72.

1041. CALVIN, M., Communication: From Molecules to Mars, The *American Institute of Biological Sciences Bulletin,* vol. 12, No. 5 (1962), pp. 29–44.

1042. CARRACIDO, J. R., Physical Chemistry and Vitalism, *Scientia,* vol. 46 (1926), pp. 231–8.

1043. CHARGAFF, E., Nucleic Acids as Carriers of Biological Information, *The Origin of Life on the Earth,* ed. by A. I. OPARIN *et al.,* New York: Pergamon Press, Inc. (1959), pp. 297–302.

1044. CUADRADO, G. A., La evolución de la materia y el origen de la vida orgánica sobre nuestra planeta, *Academia de Ciencias Médicas Físicas y Naturales de la Habaña, Anales,* vol. 61 (1924–5), pp. 169–239.

1045. DARWIN, C., and WALLACE, A. R., On the Tendency of the Species to Form Varieties and on the Perpetuation of Varieties and Species by Natural Means of Selection, *The Journal of the Linnean Society of London,* vol. 3–4 (1858), pp. 45–62.

1046. DASTUR, R. H., Origin and Nature of Life, Concept of the Living Matter, *The Journal of Indian Botanical Society,* vol. 5, No. 2 (1926), pp. 81–91.

1047. DAUVILLIER, A., *Cosmologie et Chimie,* Paris: Presses Universitaires de France (1955).

1048. DAUVILLIER, A., and DESTUIN, E., *La genèse de la vie,* Paris: Hermann and Co. (1942).

1049. DEBORIN, G. A., International Life – International Symposium on the Origin of Life on the Earth, *Biochemistry,* vol. 22 (1957), pp. 1009–16.

1050. DEBORIN, G. A., Protein Complexes as Biochemically Active Systems, *The Origin of Life on the Earth,* ed. by A. I. OPARIN *et al.,* New York: Pergamon Press, Inc. (1959), pp. 470–9.

1051. DENGLER, F., Wie kam das Leben auf die Erde? *Universum: Welt, Wissen, Fortschritt* (Vienna), vol. 7, No. 7 (1946), pp. 187–8.

1052. DERCUM, F. X., Non-Living and Living Matter, *Proceedings of the American Philosophical Society,* vol. 70 (1931), pp. 1–13.

1053. DILLON, L. S., Comparative Cytology and the Evolution of Life, *Evolution,* vol. 16 (1962), pp. 102–17.

1054. Ducrocq, A., *Origins of Life*, London: Elek Books, Ltd. (1958).
1055. Ebersole, F. B., and Shrewburg, M. M., Origin Explanations and the Origin of Life, *British Journal for the Philosophy of Science*, vol. 10 (1959), pp. 103–19.
1056. Editors of Scientific American, *Physics and Chemistry of Life*, New York: Simon and Schuster, Inc. (1956).
1057. Ehrensvärd, G., *Life: Origin and Development*, Chicago: University of Chicago Press (1962).
1058. Evans, A. T., A New Concept of Origin and Evolution, *Proceedings of the Indiana Academy of Science*, vol. 51 (1942), pp. 22–29.
1059. Eyring, H., and Johnson, F. H., The Critical Complex Theory of Biogenesis, *Influence of Temperature on Biological Systems*, Washington: American Physiological Society (1957).
1060. Felix, K., Die Kontinuität des Eiweisses, *The Origin of Life on the Earth*, ed. by A. I. Oparin et al., New York: Pergamon Press, Inc. (1959). pp. 241–55.
1061. Florkin, M., L'extension de la biosphère et l'évolution biochimique, *The Origin of Life on the Earth*, ed. by A. I. Oparin et al., New York: Pergamon Press, Inc. (1959), pp. 503–15.
1062. Fox, S. W., A Correlation of Observations Suggesting a Familiar Mode of Molecular Evolution as a Concomitant of Biological Evolution, *The American Naturalist*, vol. 87 (1953), pp. 253–6.
1063. Fox, S. W., The Chemical Problem of Spontaneous Generation, *Journal of Chemical Education*, vol. 34 (1957), pp. 472–9.
1064. Fox, S. W., Origin of Life, *Science*, vol. 127 (1958), pp. 346–7.·
1065. Fox, S. W., A Chemical Theory of Spontaneous Generation, *The Origin of Life on the Earth*, ed. by A. I. Oparin et al., New York: Pergamon Press, Inc. (1959), pp. 256–62.
1066. Fox, S. W., Biological Overtones of the Thermal Theory of Biochemical Origins, *American Institute of Biological Sciences, Bulletin*, vol. 9, No. 1 (1959), pp. 20–23.
1067. Fox, S. W., Origin of Life, *Science*, vol. 130 (1959), p. 1622.
1068. Fox, S. W., Self-Organizing Phenomena and the First Life, *General Systems Yearbook*, vol. 5 (1960), pp. 57–60.
1069. Fox, S. W., How Did Life Begin? *Science*, vol. 132 (1960), pp. 200–8.
1070. Fox, S. W., *The Borders of Biochemical Evolution*, Symposium on Extraterrestrial Biochemistry and Biology, American Association for the Advancement of Science, 128th Annual Meeting, Denver, Colorado, December 26–30, 1961.
1071. Fox, S. W., *An Integrated Model of Abiogenesis*, American Association for the Advancement of Science, Symposium on Space Biology and Life Support Problems of Manned Space Missions, 129th Annual Meeting, Philadelphia, Pennsylvania, December 26–30, 1962.
1072. Fox, S. W., et al., Spontaneous Generation of Anabolic Pathways, Protein and Nucleic Acid, *Annals of the New York Academy of Sciences*, vol. 69 (1957), pp. 328–37.
1073. Fox, S. W., and Harada, K., Thermal Copolymerization of Amino Acids to a Product Resembling Protein, *Science*, vol. 128 (1958), p. 1214.
1074. Fox, S. W., and Harada, K., Thermal Copolymerization of Amino Acids in the Presence of Phosphoric Acid, *Archives of Biochemistry and Biophysics*, vol. 86 (1960), pp. 281–5.
1075. Fox, S. W., and Harada, K., The Thermal Copolymerization of Amino Acids Common to Protein, *The Journal of the American Chemical Society*, vol. 82 (1960), pp. 3745–51.
1076. Fox, S. W., Harada, K., and Rohlfing, D. L., The Thermal Copolymerization of α-Amino Acids, *Polyamino Acids, Polypeptides and Proteins*, ed. by M. A. Stahmann, Madison, Wisconsin: University of Wisconsin Press (1962), pp. 47–53.
1077. Fox, S. W., Harada, K., and Vegotsky, A., Thermal Polymerization of Amino Acids and a Theory of Biochemical Origins, *Experientia*, vol. 15 (1959), pp. 81–85.
1078. Fox, S. W., and Homeyer, P. G., A Statistical Evaluation of the Kinship of Protein Molecules, *The American Naturalist*, vol. 89 (1955), pp. 163–8.

1079. Fox, S. W., Johnson, J. E., and Vegotsky, A., On Biochemical Origins and Optical Activity, *Science*, vol. 124 (1956), pp. 923–5.
1080. Fox, S. W., and Maier, G. D., A Theory of Formation of Carbon Compounds in the Primitive Earth, *World Petroleum Congress, Proceedings, 5th Congress, New York, June 1–5, 1959*, New York (1960).
1081. Fox, S. W., Vegotsky, A., Harada, K., and Hoagland, P. D., Spontaneous Generation of Anabolic Pathways, Protein, and Nucleic Acid, *Annals of the New York Academy of Sciences*, vol. 69 (1957), pp. 328–37.
1082. Francis, W. D., The Function of Iron in the Origin of Life, *Transactions of the Royal Society of Canada, Section IV: Geological Sciences Including Mineralogy*, vol. 41 (1941), pp. 19–28.
1083. Frank, F. C., On Spontaneous Asymmetric Synthesis, *Biochimica et Biophysica Acta*, vol. II (1953), pp. 459–63.
1084. Gaffron, H., Photosynthesis and the Origin of Life, *Rhythmic and Synthetic Processes in Growth*, ed. by D. Rudrick, Princeton: Princeton University Press (1957), pp. 127–54.
1085. Gaffron, H., The Origin of Life, *Perspectives in Biology and Medicine*, vol. 3, No. 2 (1960), pp. 163–212.
1086. Gaskell, A., *What is Life?* Springfield, Illinois: Charles C. Thomas (1928).
1087. Gatland, K. W., and Dempster, D. D., *Inhabited Universe*, New York: David McKay Co., Inc. (1958).
1088. Goldacre, R. J., Surface Films, Their Collapse on Compression, the Shapes and Sizes of Cells, and the Origin of Life, *Surface Phenomena in Chemistry and Biology*, ed. by J. F. Danielli *et al.*, London: Pergamon Press, Ltd. (1958), pp. 278–98.
1089. Goldschmidt, R., *The Material Basis of Evolution*, New Haven, Connecticut: Yale University Press (1940).
1090. Goldschmidt, V. M., Geochemical Aspects of the Origin of Complex Organic Molecules on the Earth as Precursors to Organic Life, *New Biology*, vol. 12 (1952), p. 97.
1091. Gray, H. A., and Bligh, N. M., *Origin of Living Matter*, Cambridge: W. Heffer and Sons, Ltd. (1933).
1092. Gulick, A., Phosphorus as a Factor in the Origin of Life, *American Scientist*, vol. 43 (1955), pp. 479–89.
1093. Gulick, A., Phosphorus and the Origin of Life, *Annals of the New York Academy of Sciences*, vol. 69 (1957), pp. 309–13.
1094. Guy, E., Les frontières de la physique et de la biologie, *Archives des Sciences Physiques et Naturelles*, vol. 17 (1935), pp. 5–33.
1095. Haldane, J. B. S., The Origin of Life, *Rationalist Annual* (1929), pp. 148–53.
1096. Haldane, J. B. S., The Origins of Life, *New Biology*, vol. 16 (1954), pp. 12–17.
1097. Haldane, J. B. S., Genesis of Life, *Planet Earth*, ed. by D. R. Bates, New York: Basic Books, Inc. (1957).
1098. Haldane, J. B. S., Pasteur and Cosmic Asymmetry, *Nature*, vol. 185 (1959), p. 87.
1099. Harada, K., Thermal Homopolymerization of Lysine and Copolymerization With Neutral and Acidic Amino Acids, *Bulletin of the Chemical Society of Japan*, vol. 32 (1959), pp. 1007–8.
1100. Harada, K., Polycondensation of Thermal Precursors of Aspartic Acid, *The Journal of Organic Chemistry*, vol. 24 (1959), pp. 1662–6.
1101. Harada, K., On the Formation of Primitive Protein and Heat Energy: Thermal Polymerization and Condensation of Free Amino Acids, *Tampakushitsu Kakusan Koso* (Protein, Nucleic Acid, Enzyme), vol. 6 (1961), pp. 65–75.
1102. Harada, K., and Fox, S. W., The Thermal Condensation of Glutamic Acid and Glycine to Linear Peptides, *The Journal of the American Chemical Society*, vol. 80 (1958), pp. 2694–7.
1103. Harada, K., and Fox, S. W., The Thermal Copolymerization of Aspartic Acid and Glutamic Acid, *Archives of Biochemistry and Biophysics*, vol. 86 (1960), pp. 274–80.

1104. HARADA, K., and FOX, S. W., A Total Resolution of Aspartic Acid Copper Complex by Innoculation, *Nature*, vol. 194 (1962), p. 768.

1105. HARDIN, G., Darwin and the Heterotroph Hypothesis, *Scientific Monthly*, vol. 70 (1950), pp. 178–9.

1106. HENDERSON, L. J., *Fitness of the Environment; An Inquiry Into the Biological Significance of the Properties of Matter*, Introduction by George Wald, New York: Beacon Press (1958), pp. 17–24.

1107. HINSHELWOOD, C. N., On the Chemical Kinetics of Autosynthetic Systems, *Journal of the Chemical Society* (London), (1952), pp. 745–55.

1108. HINSHELWOOD, C. N., Alternative Reaction Patterns in Autosynthetic Systems, *Journal of the Chemical Society* (London), (1953), pp. 1304–10.

1109. HOBBY, G. L., Extraterrestrial Life, *McGraw-Hill Yearbook of Science and Technology, 1962*, New York: McGraw-Hill Book Co., Inc. (1963), pp. 247–9.

1110. HOFFMANN-OSTENHOF, O., Der Ursprung der Enzyme, *The Origin of Life on the Earth*, ed. by A. I. OPARIN *et al.*, New York: Pergamon Press, Inc. (1959), pp. 197–206.

1111. HOROWITZ, N. H., On the Evolution of Biochemical Synthesis, *Proceedings of the National Academy of Sciences of the United States of America*, vol. 31 (1945), pp. 153–7.

1112. HOROWITZ, N. H., On Defining 'Life', *The Origin of Life on the Earth*, ed. by A. I. OPARIN *et al.*, New York: Pergamon Press, Inc. (1957), pp. 106–7.

1113. HOROWITZ, N. H., The Origin of Life, *Frontiers in Science*, ed. by E. HUTCHINGS, New York: Basic Books, Inc. (1958), pp. 19–27.

1114. HOROWITZ, N. H., Biology in Space, *Federation Proceedings*, vol. 21 (1962), pp. 687–91.

1115. HOROWITZ, N. H., and MILLER, S. L., Current Theories on the Origin of Life, *Fortschritte der Chemie organischer Naturstoffe*, vol. 20 (1962), pp. 423–59.

1116. HULL, D. E., and BERNAL, J. D., Thermodynamics and Kinetics of Spontaneous Generation, *Nature*, vol. 186 (1960), pp. 693–5.

1117. HURST, C. T., In the Beginning, *British Intelligence Objectives Subcommittee, Published Translations*, vol. 15 (1944), pp. 157–72.

1118. HUXLEY, J., *Evolution in Action*, New York: Harper and Row (1953).

1119. HYNDMAN, O. R., *Origin of Life and the Evolution of Living Things*, New York: Philosophical Library, Inc. (1952).

1120. ISHIMOTO, M., and EGAMI, F., Meaning of Nitrate and Sulphate Reduction in the Process of Metabolic Evolution, *The Origin of Life on the Earth*, ed. by A. I. OPARIN *et al.*, New York: Pergamon Press, Inc. (1959), pp. 555–61.

1121. JACOBSON, H., Information, Reproduction and the Origin of Life, *American Scientist*, vol. 43 (1955), pp. 119–27.

1122. KAVANAU, J. L., Some Physico-Chemical Aspects of Life and Evolution in Relation to the Living State, *The American Naturalist*, vol. 81 (1947), pp. 161–84.

1123. KEOSIAN, J., On the Origin of Life, *Science*, vol. 131 (1960), pp. 479–82.

1124. KLABUNOVSKIĬ, E. I., Absolute Asymmetric Synthesis and Asymmetric Catalysis, *The Origin of Life on the Earth*, ed. by A. I. OPARIN *et al.*, New York: Pergamon Press, Inc. (1959), pp. 158–68.

1125. KOMAROV, V. L., *Origin of Planets*, Moscow and Leningrad: Izdatelstis Akademii Nauk (1943), p. 179.

1126. KRAMPITZ, G., and KNAPPEN, F., Thermal Copolymerization of Protein Hydrolysates Containing 35 S Amino-Acids and Distribution of Radioactive Sulphur after Application of 35 S-Labelled Amino-Acid Copolymers in the Rat, *Nature*, vol. 195 (1962), pp. 385–7.

1127. KRETOVICH, V. L., Le rôle de l'ammoniaque dans l'assimilation autotrophe de l'azote, *The Origin of Life on the Earth*, ed. by A. I. OPARIN *et al.*, New York: Pergamon Press, Inc. (1959), pp. 544–54.

1128. KROPOTKIN, P. N., The Geological Conditions for the Appearance of Life on the Earth, and the Problems of Petroleum Genesis, *The Origin of Life on the Earth*, ed. by A. I. OPARIN *et al.*, New York: Pergamon Press, Inc. (1959), pp. 84–94.

1129. LANHAM, U. N., Oparin's Hypothesis and the Evolution of Nucleoproteins, *The American Naturalist*, vol. 86 (1952), pp. 213–18.
1130. LEDERBERG, J., A View of Genetics, *Science*, vol. 131 (1960), pp. 269–76.
1131. LEVIN, B. Yu., The Formation of the Earth From Cold Material and the Problem of the Formation of the Simplest Organic Substances, *The Origin of Life on the Earth*, ed. by A. I. OPARIN *et al.*, New York: Pergamon Press, Inc. (1959), pp. 67–75.
1132. LOTKA, A. J., *Elements of Physical Biology*, Baltimore, Maryland: The Williams and Wilkins Co. (1925).
1133. (See Ref. 161.)
1134. MADISON, K. M., The Organism and Its Origin, *Evolution*, vol. 7 (1953), pp. 211–27.
1135. MATHER, K. F., 40 Years of Scientific Thought Concerning the Origin of Life, *Bulletin of Denison University*, vol. 27 (1927), pp. 147–57.
1136. MIRSKY, A. E., A Note on the Evolution of Nucleic Acids, *The Origin of Life on the Earth*, ed. by A. I. OPARIN *et al.*, New York: Pergamon Press, Inc. (1959), pp. 358–60.
1137. MOORE, B., Origin and Nature of Life, *Home University of Modern Knowledge*, New York: Holt, Rinehart and Winston, Inc. (1913).
1138. MOTT, A. M., *The Origin of Living Matter*, Milan: Bolla (1930).
1139. MULLER, H. J., Issues in Evolution, *Evolution After Darwin*, vol. 3, ed. by S. TAX, Chicago: University of Chicago Press (1960).
1140. NEEDHAM, A. E., The Origination of Life, *The Quarterly Review of Biology*, vol. 34, No. 3 (1959), pp. 189–209.
1141. NORTHRUP, J., Optically Active Compounds From Racemic Mixtures by Means of Random Distribution, *Proceedings of the National Academy of Sciences of the United States of America*, vol. 43 (1957), pp. 304–5.
1142. NURSALL, J. R., Oxygen as a Prerequisite to the Origin of the Metazoa, *Nature*, vol. 183 (1959), pp. 1170–2.
1143. NUTTING, P. G., The Physical Chemistry of a Cooling Planet, *Journal of the Washington Academy of Sciences*, vol. 33 (1943), pp. 121–5.
1144. ODA, Y., Significance of Molecular Hydrogen Metabolism in the Transitionary Stage From Anaerobiosis to Aerobiosis, *The Origin of Life on the Earth*, ed. by A. I. OPARIN *et al.*, New York: Pergamon Press, Inc. (1959), pp. 593–605.
1145. OPARIN, A. I., *Proischogdenie Zjisni*, Moscow: Moscovsky Robotchii (1924).
1146. OPARIN, A. I., *Origin of Life*, New York: The Macmillan Co. (1938).
1147. OPARIN, A. I., The Mendelists and Morganists Criticized in Regard to the Problems of the Origin of Life, *Urania* (Leningrad), vol. 13 (1950), pp. 96–102.
1148. OPARIN, A. I., The Problem of the Origin of Life, *The Modern Quarterly* (London), vol. 6 (1951), p. 2.
1149. OPARIN, A. I., *Origin of Life on the Earth*, tr. from the Russian by ANN SYNGE, Academic Press; New York: Oliver and Boyd, Ltd. (1957).
1150. OPARIN, A. I., *Life, Its Nature, Origin and Development*, New York: Academic Press, Inc. (1961).
1151. OPARIN, A. I., Origin of Life, *Priroda* (Sofia), vol. 7 (1961), pp. 5–12.
1152. ÖPIK, E. J., Life and Its Evolution From an Astronomical Viewpoint, *Irish Astronomical Journal*, vol. 2 (1952), pp. 9–20.
1153. ÖPIK, E. J., Destiny of Life, *Irish Astronomical Journal*, vol. 2 (1952), pp. 65–70.
1154. PANTIN, C. F. A., The Origin of Life, *Nature*, vol. 148 (1941), pp. 40–42.
1155. PASCHKE, R., CHANG, R. W. H., and YOUNG, D., Probable Role of Gamma Irradiation in Origin of Life, *Science*, vol. 125 (1957), pp. 881.
1156. PAULING, L., The Nature of the Forces Operating in the Process of the Duplication of Molecules in Living Organisms, *The Origin of Life on the Earth*, ed. by A. I. OPARIN *et al.*, New York: Pergamon Press, Inc. (1959), pp. 215–23.
1157. PIKE, F. H., The Driving Force in Organic Evolution and a Theory of the Origin of Life, *Ecology*, vol. 10 (1929), pp. 167–76.
1158. PIRIE, N. W., The Meaninglessness of the Terms Life and Living, *Perspectives in*

Biochemistry, ed. by D. E. GREEN and J. NEEDMAN, New York: The Macmillan Co. (1937), pp. 11–22.

1159. PIRIE, N. W., The Nature and Development of Life and of Our Ideas About It, *The Modern Quarterly* (London), vol. 3 (1948), pp. 82–93.

1160. PIRIE, N. W., Vital Blarney, etc., *New Biology*, vol. 12 (1952), pp. 97–105, 106–12.

1161. PIRIE, N. W., Ideas and Assumptions About the Origin of Life, *Discovery*, vol. 14 (1953), pp. 238–42.

1162. PIRIE, N. W., On Making and Recognizing Life, *New Biology*, vol. 16 (1954), pp. 41–49.

1163. PIRIE, N. W., Facts and Fancy in Discussions About the Origin of Life, *Science and Culture* (Calcutta), vol. 20 (1954), pp. 261–5.

1164. PIRIE, N. W., Some Assumptions Underlying Discussion on the Origins of Life, *Annals of the New York Academy of Sciences*, vol. 69 (1957), pp. 369–76.

1165. PIRIE, N. W., The Origins of Life: Moscow Symposium, *Nature*, vol. 180 (1957), pp. 886–8.

1166. PIRIE, N. W., Chemical Diversity and the Origins of Life, *The Origin of Life on the Earth*, ed. by A. I. OPARIN *et al.*, New York: Pergamon Press, Inc. (1959), pp. 76–83.

1167. PIRIE, N. W., The Position of Stereoisomerism in Argument About the Origins of Life, *Transactions of the Bose Research Institute* (Calcutta), vol. 22 (1959), pp. 111–20.

1168. PRIGOGINE, I., Problèmes d'évolution dans la thermodynamique des phénomènes irréversibles, *The Origin of Life on the Earth*, ed. by A. I. OPARIN *et al.*, New York: Pergamon Press, Inc. (1959), pp. 418–27.

1169. PRINGLE, J. W., The Evolution of Living Matter, *New Biology* (London), vol. 16 (1954), pp. 54–67.

1170. RAPOPORT, E. H., Problemas acerca del origen de la vida, *Holmbergia* (Buenos Aires), vol. 4 (1958), pp. 3–18.

1171. RASHEVSKY, N., On the Origin of Life, *Bulletin of Mathematical Biophysics*, vol. 5, No. 4 (1943), pp. 165–9.

1172. REID, C., The Relation Between Primitive and Present-Day Photobiological Processes, *The Origin of Life on the Earth*, ed. by A. I. OPARIN *et al.*, New York: Pergamon Press, Inc. (1959), pp. 619–25.

1173. RIGANO, E., *What Sort of Thing is Life?* Bologna: Nicolá Zanichelli (1927), p. 206.

1174. RUBIN, B. A., The Comparative Characters of the Oxidative Systems of Various Groups of Organisms in Relation to Their Evolution, *The Origin of Life on the Earth*, ed. by A. I. OPARIN *et al.*, New York: Pergamon Press, Inc. (1959), pp. 562–71.

1175. RUSH, J. H., *Dawn of Life*, New York: Doubleday and Co., Inc. (1958).

1176. RUTTEN, M. G., Origin of Life on Earth: Its Evolution and Actualism, *Evolution*, vol. 11 (1957), pp. 56–59.

1177. RUTTEN, M. G., *Geological Aspects of the Origin of Life on Earth*, New York: Elsevier Publishing Co., Inc. (1962).

1178. SAGAN, C., Radiation and the Origin of the Gene, *Evolution*, vol. 11 (1957), pp. 40–55.

1179. SAGAN, C., On the Origin and Planetary Distribution of Life, *Radiation Research*, vol. 15 (1961), pp. 174–92.

1180. SAPOZHNIKOW, D. J., Entstehung und Evolution der Phototrophen ernährungsweise, *The Origin of Life on the Earth*, ed. by A. I. OPARIN *et al.*, New York: Pergamon Press, Inc. (1959), pp. 635–41.

1181. SCHAFER, E. A., Life, Its Maintenance, Origin and Nature, *Report of the Eighty-Second Meeting of the British Association for the Advancement of Science*, Dundee, September 4–11, 1912 (1912), pp. 3–36.

1182. SCHER, S., Thermal Factors in Archaeometabolism, *The Origin of Life on the Earth*, ed. by A. I. OPARIN *et al.*, New York: Pergamon Press, Inc. (1959), pp. 650–1.

1183. SCHRAMM, G., Die Bedeutung der Virusforschung für die Erkenntnis biologischer Vermehrungsvorgänge, *The Origin of Life on the Earth*, ed. by A. I. OPARIN *et al.*, New York: Pergamon Press, Inc. (1959), pp. 307–12.

1184. SCHRODINGER, E., *What Is Life?* New York: The Macmillan Co. (1945).

1185. SHAPOSHNIKOV, V. N., Über einige wahrscheinliche Wege der Evolution des Stoffwechsels bei den Mikroorganismen, *The Origin of Life on the Earth*, ed. by A. I. OPARIN *et al.*, New York: Pergamon Press, Inc. (1959), pp. 516–26.

1186. SMALL, J., The Time Scale of Organic Evolution, *Irish Astronomical Journal*, vol. 2 (1952), pp. 21–26.

1187. ŠORM, F., Ähnlichkeit der Struktur bei Eiweissstoffen, *The Origin of Life on the Earth*, ed. by A. I. OPARIN *et al.*, New York: Pergamon Press, Inc. (1959), pp. 231–40.

1188. SOROKIN, YU. I., The Evolution of Chemosynthesis, *The Origin of Life on the Earth*, ed. by A. I. OPARIN *et al.*, New York: Pergamon Press, Inc. (1959), pp. 626–34.

1189. SPENCER, H., *First Principles*, London: Williams and Norgate, Ltd. (1862).

1190. STANLEY, W. M., On the Nature of Viruses, Genes and Life, *The Origin of Life on the Earth*, ed. by A. I. OPARIN *et al.*, New York: Pergamon Press, Inc. (1959), pp. 313–21.

1191. STRAUB, F. B., Biosynthesis of Enzymes and Their Origin, *The Origin of Life on the Earth*, ed. by A. I. OPARIN *et al.*, New York: Pergamon Press, Inc. (1959), pp. 455–9.

1192. SYNGE, R. L. M., The Occurrence of Amino Acids in Nature, *The Origin of Life on the Earth*, ed. by A. I. OPARIN *et al.*, New York: Pergamon Press, Inc. (1959), pp. 224–30.

1193. TERENT'EV, A. P., and KLABUNOVSKIĬ, E. I., The Role of Dissymmetry in the Origin of Living Material, *The Origin of Life on the Earth*, ed. by A. I. OPARIN *et al.*, New York: Pergamon Press, Inc. (1959), pp. 95–105.

1194. THODE, H. G., MACNAMARA, J., and FLEMING, H. W., Sulfur Isotope Fractionation in Nature and Geological and Biological Time Scales, *Geochimica et Cosmochimica Acta*, vol. 3 (1953), pp. 235–43.

1195. THOM, B. P., *Dust to Life; Scientific Story of Creation*, New York: E. P. Dutton and Co., Inc. (1929).

1196. THYSSEN-BORNEMISZA, S., *The Explanation of Life*, Zurich: Rascher et Cie., Ag. (1949).

1197. TIKHOV, G. A., Les atmosphères moléculaires et les possibilitées de vie dans l'univers, *Bulletin de la Classe des Sciences, Académie Royale de Belgique*, vol. 42 (1956), pp. 1184–91.

1198. UREY, H. C., On the Early Chemical History of the Earth and the Origin of Life, *Proceedings of the National Academy of Sciences of the United States of America*, vol. 38 (1952), pp. 351–63.

1199. UREY, H. C., Primitive Planetary Atmospheres and the Origin of Life, *The Origin of Life on the Earth*, ed. by A. I. OPARIN *et al.*, New York: Pergamon Press, Inc. pp. 16–22.

1200. VAUGHAN, V. C., A Chemical Concept of the Origin and Development of Life, *Chemical Reviews*, vol. 4 (1927), pp. 167–88.

1201. VERNADSKI, V. I., Conditions for the Appearance of Life on Earth, *Bulletin of the Academy of Sciences of the USSR* (1940), pp. 633–53.

1202. VINOGRADOV, A. P., The Origin of the Biosphere, *The Origin of Life on the Earth*, ed. by A. I. OPARIN *et al.*, New York: Pergamon Press, Inc. (1959), pp. 23–37.

1203. WACKER, A., Zur Entstehung des Lebens auf der Erde, *Angewandte Chemie*, vol. 70 (1958), pp. 519–26.

1204. WACKER, A., Die Spezifiziät der Desoxyribonukleinsäure, *The Origin of Life on the Earth*, ed. by A. I. OPARIN *et al.*, New York: Pergamon Press, Inc. (1959), pp. 332–3.

1205. WALD, G., Origin of Life, *Scientific American*, vol. 191, No. 2 (1954), pp. 44–53.

1206. WALD, G., The Origin of Optical Activity, *Annals of the New York Academy of Sciences*, vol. 69 (1957), pp. 352–68.

1207. WALD, G., Life in the Second and Third Periods, *Horizons in Biochemistry*, ed. by M. KASHA and B. PULLMAN, New York: Academic Press, Inc. (1962), pp. 127–42.

1208. WINCHELL, A., *Sketches of Creation*, New York: Harper (1870).

1209. WOODRING, W. P., Conference on Biochemistry, Paleoecology and Evolution, *Proceedings of the National Academy of Sciences of the United States of America*, vol. 40 (1954), pp. 219–24.

1210. YCAS, M., A Note on the Origin of Life, *Proceedings of the National Academy of Sciences of the United States of America*, vol. 41 (1955), pp. 714–16.

B. Synthesis of Organic Compounds From Simple Precursors

1211. ABELSON, P. H., Amino Acids Formed in 'Primitive Atmospheres', *Science*, vol. 124 (1956), p. 935.

1212. AKABORI, S., On the Origin of the Fore-Protein, *The Origin of Life on the Earth*, ed. by A. I. OPARIN, *et al.*, New York: Pergamon Press, Inc. (1959), pp. 189–96.

1213. AKABORI, S., OKAWA, K., and SATA, M., Introductions of Side Chains into Polyglycine Dispersed on Solid Surface, *Bulletin of the Chemical Society of Japan*, vol. 29 (1956), pp. 608–11.

1214. BAHADUR, K., Photosynthesis of Amino Acids From Paraformaldehyde and Potassium Nitrate, *Nature*, vol. 173 (1954), p. 1141.

1215. BAHADUR, K., The Reactions Involved in the Formation of Compounds Preliminary to the Synthesis of Protoplasm and other Materials of Biological Importance, *The Origin of Life on the Earth*, ed. by A. I. OPARIN *et al.*, New York: Pergamon Press, Inc. (1959), pp. 140–50.

1216. BAHADUR, K., and AGRAWAL, K. M. L., Influence of the Source of Carbon on Photochemical Fixation of Nitrogen in Aqueous Mixtures Containing Molybdic Acid as the Catalyst, *Proceedings of the National Academy of Sciences, India*, Section A, vol. 32 (1962), pp. 83–87.

1217. BAHADUR, K., and AGRAWAL, K. M. L., Photochemical Fixation of Nitrogen in Solutions Containing Paraformaldehyde as a Source of Carbon in the Presence of Catalysts, *Journal of Scientific and Industrial Research (India)*, Section B, vol. 21 (1962), pp. 336–7.

1218. BAHADUR, K., PERTI, O. N., and PATHAK, H. D., Photosynthesis of Peptides in Aqueous Solutions of Glycine, Glutamic Acid and Tyrosine, *Proceedings of the National Academy of Sciences, India*, Section A, vol. 30 (1961), pp. 206–20.

1219. BAHADUR, K., and RANGANAYAKI, S., A Study of the Influence of Hydrogen Ion Concentration on the Photosynthesis of Amino Acids from Paraformaldehyde and Potassium Nitrate, *Proceedings of the National Academy of Sciences, India*, Section A, vol. 23 (1954), pp. 21–24.

1220. BAHADUR, K., and RANGANAYAKI, S., Réactions probables concernant la photosynthèse du glycolle de la sérine et de la proline dans les mélanges de paraformaldéhyde et de nitrate de potassium, *Comptes Rendus Hebdomadaires des Séances de l'Académie des Sciences*, vol. 240 (1955), pp. 246–8.

1221. BAHADUR, K., and RANGANAYAKI, S., Formation of Amino Acids in Water Containing Dissolved Carbon Dioxide and Colloidal Molybdenum Oxide Under Action of Artificial Light, *Izvestiya Akademii Nauk SSSR, Otdelenie Khimicheskikh Nauk*, vol. 6 (1957), pp. 754–5.

1222. BAHADUR, K., and RANGANAYAKI, S., Aqueous Line of Molecular Evolution, *Izvestiya Akademii Nauk SSSR*, vol. 11 (1958), p. 1361.

1223. BAHADUR, K., and RANGANAYAKI, S., Formation of Peptide Bonds in Aqueous Solution and Aqueous Line of Molecular Evolution, *Proceedings of the National Academy of Sciences, India*, Section A, vol. 27 (1958), pp. 292–5.

1224. BAHADUR, K., RANGANAYAKI, S., and SANTAMARIA, L., Photosynthesis of Amino Acids from Paraformaldehyde Involving the Fixation of Nitrogen in the Presence of Colloidal Molybdenum Oxide as a Catalyst, *Nature*, vol. 182 (1959), p. 1168.

1225. BAHADUR, K., and SRIVASTAVA, R. B., Photosynthesis of Peptides in the Aqueous Solutions of Aspartic Acid and Glycine, *Indian Journal of Applied Chemistry*, vol. 23 (1960), pp. 131–4.

1226. BAHADUR, K., and SRIVASTAVA, R. B., The Influence of Catalysts and Period of

Irradiation on the Photosynthesis of Amino Acids in a Mixture of Paraformaldehyde and Potassium Nitrate, *Zhurnal Obshchei Khimii*, vol. 31 (1961), p. 317.

1227. BAHADUR, K., and SRIVASTAVA, R. B., Photodecomposition of Alanine in Different Types of Glass Flasks, *Vijnana Parishad Anusandhan Patrika* (India), vol. 5 (1962), pp. 57–59.

1228. BALY, E. C. C., HEILBRON, I. M., and HUDSON, D. P., Photocatalysis: II Photosynthesis of Nitrogen Compounds from Nitrates and CO_2, *Journal of the Chemical Society*, vol. 121 (1922), pp. 1078–88.

1229. BAVDEKAR, P. R., Photoreduction of Ferric Chloride in Aqueous Solution in Presence of Organic Acids and Sugars, *Journal of the University of Bombay*, vol. 12-A, Part 3 (1943), pp. 47–56.

1230. BERGER, R., Proton Irradiation of Methane, Ammonia and Water at 77°K, *Proceedings of the National Academy of Sciences of the United States of America*, vol. 47 (1961), pp. 1434–6.

1231. BEVINGTON, J. C., Use of Irradiated Polymers as Initiators of Polymerizations, *Nature*, vol. 178 (1956), pp. 1112–13.

1232. (See Ref. 1035.)

1233. CALVIN, M., *et al.*, Reduction of Carbon Dioxide in Aqueous Solutions by Ionizing Radiation, *Science*, vol. 114 (1951), pp. 416–18.

1234. CEDRANGOLO, F., The Problem of the Origin of the Proteins, *The Origin of Life on the Earth*, ed. by A. I. OPARIN *et al.*, New York: Pergamon Press, Inc. (1959), pp. 281–8.

1235. DOSE, K., and RAJEWSKY, B., Strahlenchemische Bildung von Aminen und Aminocarbonsäuren, *Biochimica et Biophysica Acta*, vol. 25 (1957), pp. 225–6.

1236. FERRARI, G., and CULTRERA, R., Photochemical Synthesis of Amino-Acids and a New Transamination Process by Transfer of Free Amino-Radicals, *Nature*, vol. 190 (1961), pp. 326–8.

1237. FOX, S. W., Evolution of Protein Molecules and Thermal Synthesis of Biochemical Substances, *American Scientist*, vol. 44 (1956), pp. 347–59.

1238. (See Ref. 1063.)

1239. FOX, S. W., Experiments Related to the Chemical Origins of Protein, *Bahamas Conference*, ed. by G. BOURNE (In press).

1240. FOX, S. W., DE FONTAINE, D., and HOMEYER, P. G., Protein Genealogy, *Federation Proceedings*, vol. 14 (1955), p. 213.

1241. (See Ref. 1073.)

1242. (See Ref. 1074.)

1243. (See Ref. 1075.)

1244. FOX, S. W., and HARADA, K., Synthesis of Uracil Under Conditions of a Thermal Model of Prebiological Chemistry, *Science*, vol. 133 (1961), pp. 1923–4.

1245. (See Ref. 1076.)

1246. (See Ref. 1077.)

1247. FOX, S. W., and MIDDLEBROOK, M. M., Anhydrocopolymerization of Amino Acids Under the Influence of Hypothetically Primitive Terrestrial Conditions, *Federation Proceedings*, vol. 13 (1954), p. 211.

1248. FOX, S. W., and VEGOTSKY, A., Pyropolymerization of Amino Acids to Proteinoids With Phosphoric Acid or Polyphosphoric Acid, *Federation Proceedings*, vol. 18 (1959), p. 343.

1249. GETOFF, N. G., The Synthesis of Organic Products From an Aqueous Solution of CO_2 Under the Influence of CO^{60} Gamma Radiation, *International Journal of Applied Radiation and Isotopes*, vol. 13 (1962), pp. 205–13.

1250. GETOFF, N. G., Reduktion der Kohlensäure in wässriger Lösung unter Einwirkung von UV-Licht, *Zeitschrift für Naturforschung, B: Chemie, Biochemie, Biophysik, Biologie und verwandte Gebiete*, vol. 17 (1962), pp. 87–90.

1251. GILBERT, D. L., Speculation on the Relationship Between Organic and Atmospheric Evolution, *Perspectives in Biology and Medicine*, vol. 4 (1960), pp. 58–71.

1252. GILVARRY, J. J., and HOCHSTIM, A. R., Possible Role of Meteorites in the Origin of Life, *Nature*, vol. 197 (1963), pp. 624–5.

1253. GODNEV, T. N., Die Grundetappen der Biogenese des Chlorophylls, *The Origin of Life on the Earth*, ed. by A. I. OPARIN *et al.*, New York: Pergamon Press, Inc. (1959), pp. 642–9.

1254. GOLDFINGER, P., Sur l'évaporation du carbone, *Mémoires de la Société Royale des Sciences de Liège*, vol. 15 (1955), pp. 378–85.

1255. GOODMAN, J., The Formation of Thin Polymer Films in the Gas Discharge, *Journal of Polymer Science*, vol. 44 (1960), pp. 551–2.

1256. GREENSTEIN, J. L., RICHARDSON, R. S., and SCHWARZSCHILD, M., On the Abundance of C^{13} in the Atmosphere, *Publications of the Astronomical Society of the Pacific*, vol. 62 (1950), pp. 15–18.

1257. GROTH, W., and SUESS, H., Bemerkungen zur Photochemie der Erdatmosphäre: Über die Entstehung des freien Sauerstoffs und die photochemische Bildung organischer Stoffe, *Die Naturwissenschaften*, vol. 26 (1938), p. 77.

1258. GROTH, W., and VON WEYSSENHOFF, H., Photochemische Bildung von Aminosäuren aus Mischungen einfacher Gase, *Die Naturwissenschaften*, vol. 44 (1957), pp. 510–11.

1259. GROTH, W., and VON WEYSSENHOFF, H., Photochemical Formation of Organic Compounds From Mixtures of Simple Gases, *Planetary and Space Science*, vol. 2 (1960), pp. 79–85.

1260. GRUDZINSKA, S., L'abondance des molécules CN, C_2 et CO^+ et des particules solides dans les comètes, *Ciel et Terre*, vol. 76 (1960), pp. 173–6.

1261. GRUNBERG-MANAGO, M., Synthèse enzymatique des ribopolynucléotides, *The Origin of Life on the Earth*, ed. by A. I. OPARIN *et al.*, New York: Pergamon Press, Inc. (1959), pp. 344–57.

1262. GRUNDLAND, I., Origines de la vie, *Experientia*, vol. 15 (1945), pp. 239–44.

1263. (See Ref. 1099.)

1264. (See Ref. 1100.)

1265. (See Ref. 1101.)

1266. (See Ref. 1102.)

1267. (See Ref. 1103.)

1268. (See Ref. 1104.)

1269. HASSELSTROM, T., HENRY, M. C., and MURR, B., Synthesis of Amino Acids by Beta Radiation, *Science*, vol. 125 (1957), pp. 350–1.

1270. HERRERA, A. L., The Origin of Life, *Science*, vol. 96 (1942), p. 14.

1271. HEYNS, K., WALTER, W., and MEYER, E., Modelluntersuchungen zur Bildung organischer Verbindungen in Atmosphären einfacher Gase durch elektrische Entladungen, *Die Naturwissenschaften*, vol. 44 (1957), pp. 385–9.

1272. (See Ref. 1114.)

1273. KNAPPEN, F., and KRAMPITZ, G., Distribution of Radioactive Sulphur After Oral Administration to the Rate of a Water-Insoluble Fraction of S^{35}-Labeled Thermal Amino Acid Copolymer, *Nature*, vol. 197 (1963), p. 289.

1274. KOVÁCS, J., *Polyglutamic and Polyaspartic Acids: Emphasizing Hungarian Research*, Wisconsin: University of Wisconsin Press (1962), pp. 37–45.

1275. KOVÁCS, J., and KÖNYVES, I., Über DL-α-β-Polyasparaginsäure, *Die Naturwissenschaften*, vol. 41 (1954), p. 333.

1276. KOVÁCS, J., KÖNYVES, I., and PUSZTAI, A., Darstellung von Polyasparaginsäuren (Polyspartsäuren) aus dem thermischen Autokondensationsprodukt der Asparaginsäure, *Experientia*, vol. 9 (1953), pp. 459–60.

1277. KOVÁCS, J., and NAGY, H., Polypeptide Formation From Asparagine Under Hypothetically Primitive Conditions, *Nature*, vol. 190 (1961), pp. 531–2.

1278. KRAMPITZ, G., Untersuchungen an Aminosäure-Kopolymerisaten, *Die Naturwissenschaften*, vol. 46 (1959), p. 558.

1279. (See Ref. 1126.)

1280. MILLER, S. L., A Production of Amino Acids Under Possible Primitive Earth Conditions, *Science*, vol. 117 (1953), pp. 528–9.

1281. MILLER, S. L., Production of Some Organic Compounds Under Possible Primitive

Earth Conditions, *The Journal of the American Chemical Society*, vol. 77 (1955), pp. 2351–61.

1282. MILLER, S. L., Mechanism of Synthesis of Amino Acids by Electric Discharge, *Biochimica et Biophysica Acta*, vol. 23, (1957), pp. 480–9.

1283. MILLER, S. L., Formation of Organic Compounds on the Primitive Earth, *The Origin of Life on the Earth*, ed. by A. I. OPARIN *et al.*, New York: Pergamon Press, Inc. (1959), pp. 123–35.

1284. MILLER, S. L., Occurrence of Gas Hydrates in the Solar System, *Proceedings of the National Academy of Sciences of the United States of America*, vol. 47 (1961), pp. 1798–1808.

1285. MILLER, S. L., and UREY, H. C., Organic Compound Synthesis on the Primitive Earth, *Science*, vol. 130 (1959), pp. 245–51.

1286. NIKOLAEV, L. A., Complex Compounds and Models of Enzymes, *The Origin of Life on the Earth*, ed. by A. I. OPARIN *et al.*, New York: Pergamon Press, Inc. (1959), pp. 263–74.

1287. (See Ref. 1151.)

1288. ORÓ, J., Synthesis of Adenine From Ammonium Cyanide, *Biochemical and Biophysical Research Communications*, vol. 2 (1960), pp. 407–12.

1289. ORÓ, J., Formation of Purines Under Possible Primitive Earth Conditions, *Federation Proceedings*, vol. 20 (1961), p. 352.

1290. ORÓ, J., Comets and the Formation of Biochemical Compounds on the Primitive Earth, *Nature*, vol. 190 (1961), pp. 389–90.

1291. ORÓ, J., The Mechanism of Synthesis of Adenine From Hydrogen Cyanide Under Possible Primitive Earth Conditions, *Nature*, vol. 191 (1961), pp. 1193–4.

1292. ORÓ, J., Non-Enzymatic Formation of Purines and Pyrimidines, *Federation Proceedings*, vol. 22, No. 2, Pt. 1 (March and April 1963), p. 681.

1293. ORÓ, J., Synthesis of Organic Compounds by Electric Discharges, *Nature*, vol. 197 (1963), pp. 862–7.

1294. ORÓ, J., Synthesis of Organic Compounds by High-Energy Electrons, *Nature*, vol. 197 (1963), pp. 971–4.

1295. ORÓ, J., Studies in Experimental Organic Cosmo-Chemistry, *Annals of the New York Academy of Sciences*, vol. 108 (1963), pp. 464–81.

1296. ORÓ, J., Experimental Organic Cosmochemistry. Formation of Biochemical Compounds, *Proceedings of Lunar and Planetary Exploration Colloquium*, Aerospace Laboratories, North American Aviation, Inc., Downey, California (In press).

1297. ORÓ, J., and COX, A. C., Non-Enzymic Synthesis of Deoxyribose, *Federation Proceedings*, vol. 21 (1962), p. 80.

1298. ORÓ, J., and GUIDRY, C. L., A Novel Synthesis of Polypeptides, *Nature*, vol. 186 (1960), pp. 156–7.

1299. ORÓ, J., and GUIDRY, C. L., Direct Synthesis of Polypeptides: I. Polycondensation of Glycine in Aqueous Ammonia, *Archives of Biochemistry and Biophysics*, vol. 93 (1961), pp. 166–71.

1300. ORÓ, J., and KAMAT, S. S., Amino-Acid Synthesis From Hydrogen Cyanide Under Possible Primitive Earth Conditions, *Nature*, vol. 190 (1961), pp. 442–3.

1301. ORÓ, J., and KIMBALL, A. P., Direct Synthesis of Purines From Amino Acids, *Federation Proceedings*, vol. 19 (1960), p. 314.

1302. ORÓ, J., and KIMBALL, A. P., Synthesis of Purines Under Possible Primitive Earth Conditions: I. Adenine From Hydrogen Cyanide, *Archives of Biochemistry and Biophysics*, vol. 94 (1961), pp. 217–27.

1303. ORÓ, J., and KIMBALL, A. P., Synthesis of Purines Under Possible Primitive Earth Conditions: II. Purine Intermediates From Hydrogen Cyanide, *Archives of Biochemistry and Biophysics*, vol. 96 (1962), pp. 293–313.

1304. ORÓ, J., KIMBALL, A. P., FRITZ, R., and MASTER, F., Amino Acid Synthesis From Formaldehyde and Hydroxylamine, *Archives of Biochemistry and Biophysics*, vol. 85 (1959), pp. 115–30.

1305. PALM, C., and CALVIN, M., Primordial Organic Chemistry: I. Compounds Resulting

From Electron Irradiation of C^{14}H$_4$, *The Journal of the American Chemical Society*, vol. 84 (1961), pp. 2115–21.

1306. PALM, C. and CALVIN, M., *Irradiation of Methane, Ammonia, Hydrogen and Water*, UCRL-9159, University of California, Radiation Laboratory, Berkeley, California, January 31, 1961.

1307. PAVLOVSKAYA, T. E., and PASYNSKIĬ, A. G., The Original Formation of Amino Acids Under the Action of Ultraviolet Rays and Electric Discharges, *The Origin of Life on the Earth*, ed. by A. I. OPARIN *et al.*, New York: Pergamon Press, Inc. (1959), pp. 151–7.

1308. PFEIL, E., and RUCKERT, H., Über die Formaldehydkondensation: Die Bildung von Zuckern aus Formaldehyd unter der Einwirkung von Laugen, *Annalen der Chemie*, vol. 641, (1961), pp. 121–31.

1309. PONNAMPERUMA, C., A Possible Prebiotic Synthesis of Purines, *Abstracts of the International Union of Pure and Applied Chemistry, 21st Congress*, London, July 10–17, 1963, p. 288.

1310. PONNAMPERUMA, C., LEMMON, R. M., MARINER, R., and CALVIN, M., Formation of Adenine by Electron Irradiation of Methane, Ammonia and Water, *Proceedings of the National Academy of Sciences of the United States of America* (In press).

1311. PONNAMPERUMA, C., and MARINER, R., *The Formation of Ribose and Deoxyribose by Ultraviolet Irradiation of Formaldehyde in Water*, 11th Annual Meeting of the Radiation Research Society, Milwaukee, Wisconsin, May 27–29, 1963.

1312. PONNAMPERUMA, C., MARINER, R., and SAGAN, C., Formation of Adenosine by Ultraviolet Irradiation of a Solution of Adenine and Ribose, *Nature* (In press).

1313. PONNAMPERUMA, C., YOUNG, S., and MUNOZ, E., The Formation of Guanine During the Thermal Polymerization of Amino Acids, *Federation Proceedings* (In press).

1314. RYAN, J. A., and YOUNG, G. E., The Alleged Synthesis of Protein From an Inorganic Medium in the Presence of Iron, *Revue Canadienne de Biologie*, vol. 9 (1933), pp. 323–31.

1315. (See Ref. 85.)

1316. SCHRAM, G., GROTSCH, H., and POLLMANN, W., Non-Enzymatic Synthesis of Polysaccharides, Nucleosides, Nucleic Acids and the Origin of Self-Reproducing Systems, *Angewandte Chemie*, International Edition, vol. 1 (1962), pp. 1–7.

1317. SHEMIN, D., Biosynthesis of Porphyrins, *The Harvey Lectures*, vol. 50 (1954–5), pp. 258–84.

1318. SIEGEL, S. M., Catalytic and Polymerization-Directing Properties of Mineral Surfaces, *Proceedings of the National Academy of Sciences of the United States of America*, vol. 43 (1957), p. 811.

1319. SIEGEL, S. M., Non-enzymic Macromolecules as Matrices in Biological Synthesis: The Role of Polysaccharides in Peroxidase-Catalyzed Lignin Polymer Formation from Eugenol, *The Journal of the American Chemical Society*, vol. 79 (1957), p. 1628.

1320. SIEGEL, S. M., The Macromolecular Environment as a Factor in the Control of Chemical Reactions, *Annales d'Histochimie*, vol. 5 (1960), p. 44.

1321. SIEGEL, S. M., Phenol-Mineral Interactions: The Oxidation of Pyrogallol and Other O-Diphenols on Silica Gel, *Experientia*, vol. 16 (1960), p. 358.

1322. SIEGEL, S. M., and GOODMAN, N. C., Reaction-Directing Properties of Non-enzymatic Macromolecules: Pyrogallol Oxidation in the System Iron (III)–Cellulose, *Nature*, vol. 184 (1959), p. 53.

1323. SIEGEL, S. M., and SIEGEL, B. Z., Enhancement by Deoxyribonucleic Acid of the Catalytic Peroxidation of Pyrogallol, *Nature*, vol. 179 (1957), p. 421.

1324. SWALLOW, A. J., *Radiation Chemistry of Organic Compounds*, New York: Pergamon Press, Inc. (1960).

1325. TERENIN, A. N., Photosynthesis in the Shortest Ultraviolet, *The Origin of Life on the Earth*, ed. by A. I. OPARIN *et al.*, New York: Pergamon Press, Inc. (1959), pp. 136–9.

1326. VEGOTSKY, A., HARADA, K., and FOX, S. W., The Characterization of Polyaspartic

Acid and Some Related Compounds, *The Journal of the American Chemical Society*, vol. 80 (1958), pp. 3361-6.

1327. WILSON, A. T., The Synthesis of Macromolecules Under Possible Primeval Earth Conditions, *Nature*, vol. 188 (1960), pp. 1007-9.

C. Origins of Cells

1328. (See Ref. 1017.)

1329. BERNAL, J. D., The Scale of Structural Units in Biopoesis, *The Origin of Life on the Earth*, ed. by A. I. OPARIN *et al.*, New York: Pergamon Press, Inc. (1959), pp. 385-99.

1330. BOOIJ, H. L., and DEJONG, H. G. B., Biocolloids and Their Interactions, *Handbuch der Protoplasmaforschung*, vol. 2, Vienna: Springer-Verlag (1956).

1331. FOX, S. W., Abiotic Production of Primitive Protein and Formed Microparticles, *Annals of the New York Academy of Sciences*, vol. 108 (1963), pp. 487-94.

1332. FOX, S. W., HARADA, K., and KENDRICK, J., Production of Spherules From Synthetic Proteinoid and Hot Water, *Science*, vol. 129 (1959), pp. 1221-3.

1333. HERRERA, A. L., Artificial Cells Containing Albumin, *Atti della Accademia Nazionale dei Lincei, Rendiconti, Classe di Scienze Fisiche Matematiche e Naturali*, vol. 7 (1928), pp. 32-35.

1334. HERRERA, A. L., Imitation of Organisms by Albumin αHF, *Atti della Accademia Nazionale dei Lincei, Rendiconti, Classe di Scienze Fisiche, Matematiche e Naturali*, vol. 8 (1928), pp. 15-19.

1335. HERRERA, A. L., Plasmogeny, *Bulletin du Laboratoire et de la Société Internationale de Plasmogénie*, vol. 1 (1934), p. 49.

1336. (See Ref. 1270.)

1337. KHESIN, R., Cell Structure and Protein Synthesis, *The Origin of Life on the Earth*, ed. by A. I. OPARIN *et al.*, New York: Pergamon Press, Inc. (1959), pp. 460-5.

1338. KRASNOVSKIĬ, A. A., Development of the Mode of Action of the Photocatalytic System in Organisms, *The Origin of Life on the Earth*, ed. by A. I. OPARIN *et al.*, New York: Pergamon Press, Inc. (1959), pp. 606-18.

1339. KRITSMAN, M. G., and KONIKOVA, A. S., Experimental Demonstration of the Occurrence of Metabolic Processes in Simple Proteins, *The Origin of Life on the Earth*, ed. by A. I. OPARIN *et al.*, New York: Pergamon Press, Inc. (1959), pp. 275-80.

1340. MACOVSCHI, E., Some Relationships Between Coacervates and Enzymes, *The Origin of Life on the Earth*, ed. by A. I. OPARIN *et al.*, New York: Pergamon Press, Inc. (1959), pp. 466-9.

1341. MILLICH, F., and CALVIN, M., *Coacervation of Salts of Polyvinylsulfonic Acid Induced by Heavy Metal Ions*, Report UCRL-9519, University of California, Radiation Laboratory, Berkeley, California, 1961.

1342. OPARIN, A. I., Biochemical Processes in the Simplest Structures, *The Origin of Life on the Earth*, ed. by A. I. OPARIN *et al.*, New York: Pergamon Press, Inc. (1959), pp. 428-36.

1343. PASYNSKIĬ, A. G., Enzymic Reactions in Stationary Open Systems, *The Origin of Life on the Earth*, ed. by A. I. OPARIN *et al.*, New York: Pergamon Press, Inc. (1959), pp. 444-54.

1344. SISAKYAN, art Played by Structural Elements in the Biochemical Functions of Cells, *The Origin of Life on the Earth*, ed. by A. I. OPARIN *et al.*, New York: Pergamon Press, Inc. (1959), pp. 400-17.

D. Natural Interplanetary Transfer of Organisms

1345. (See Ref. 117.)

1346. (See Ref. 203.)

1347. ARRHENIUS, S., *Evolution of the Universe*, London: Harper Brothers (1908).

1348. ARRHENIUS, S., *Das Schicksal der Planeten*, Leipzig: Akademische Verlagsgesellschaft (1911).

1349. AVRUNINA, G. A., KARAMZINA, N. M., FEDOROVA, V. I., and YANOVSKAYA, B. I., The Biological Action of High Energy Radiation, *Bulletin of Experimental Biology and Medicine*, vol. 52 (1962), pp. 912–5.

1350. BECQUERREL, P., La vie terrestre provient-elle d'un autre monde? *l'Astronomie*, vol. 38 (1924), pp. 393–417.

1351. BERGER, R., An Evaluation of Radiation Effects in Space, *Annals of the New York Academy of Sciences*, vol. 108 (1963), pp. 482–6.

1352. BOEHM, G. A. W., Life (and Death) in Space, *Fortune*, vol. 65, No. 6 (1963), pp. 161–2, 243–50.

1353. BRIGGS, M. H., Meteorites and the Origin of Life, *Spaceflight*, vol. 2 (1959), pp. 39–43.

1354. CALDER, N., Hazards to Life in Space, *New Scientist*, vol. 2, No. 51 (1957); pp. 19–20.

1355. Contamination by Extraterrestrial Exploration, *Nature*, vol. 183 (1959), p. 925.

1356. GALIPPE, V., and SOUFFLAND, G., Recherches sur la présence dans les météorites, les pierres dures, les minerais, le quartz, le granite, le basalte, les cendres et les laves volcaniques, d'organites susceptibles de reviviscence et sur leur résistance aux hautes températures, *Comptes Rendus Hebdomadaires des Séances de l'Académie des Sciences*, vol. 172 (1921), pp. 1252–4.

1357. JAMES, P. F., Limits of Life, *Journal of the British Interplanetary Society*, vol. 14 (1955), pp. 265–6.

1358. (See Ref. 151.)

1359. KEILIN, D., The Problem of Anabiosis or Latent Life, *Proceedings of the Royal Society (London)*, Series B, vol. 150 (1959), pp. 149–91.

1360. MICKEY, G. H., *Electromagnetism and Its Effect on the Organism*, 156th Annual Convention of the Medical Society of the State of New York, New York, May 14–18, 1962.

1361. OSBORNE, J. F., *The Origin and Evolution of Life*, New York: C. Scribner's Sons (1917).

1362. PARKES, A. S., Biological Effects of Low Temperature, *New Scientist*, vol. 7 (1960), pp. 1057–9.

1363. PARKES, A. S., and SMITH, A. U., Transport of Life in the Frozen or Dried State, *The British Medical Journal*, Supplement No. 1 (1959), pp. 1295–7.

1364. PARKES, A. S., and SMITH, A. U., Space Transport of Life in the Dried or Frozen State, *Journal of the British Interplanetary Society*, vol. 17 (1960), pp. 319–20.

1365. PEARMAN, E., Sustaining Life in the Space Environment, *Environmental Quarterly*, vol. 8, No. 2 (1962), pp. 24–26.

1366. PORTNER, D. M., SPINER, D. R., HOFFMAN, R. K., and PHILLIPS, C. R., Effect of Ultrahigh Vacuum on Viability of Microorganisms, *Science*, vol. 134 (1961), p. 2047.

1367. PROCTER, B. E., and PARKER, B. W., Microorganisms in the Upper Atmosphere, *Aerobiology*, ed. by F. R. MOULTON, Washington: American Association for the Advancement of Science (1942).

1368. SAGAN, C., *Interstellar Panspermia*, Symposium on Extraterrestrial Biochemistry and Biology, American Association for the Advancement of Science, 128th Annual Meeting, Denver, Colorado, December 26–30, 1961.

1369. SCHLICHTING, H. E., Viable Species of Algae and Protozoa in the Atmosphere, *American Journal of Botany*, vol. 48, No. 6, Part 2 (1961), pp. 543–4.

1370. SHAPLEY, H., Photosynthesis and Life on Other Planets: A Summary, *Rhythmic and Synthetic Processes in Growth*, ed. by D. RUDNICK, Princeton, New Jersey: Princeton University Press (1957), pp. 201–5.

1371. ZHUKOV-VEREZHNIKOV, N. N., MAYSKIY, I. N., PEKHOV, A. P., and NEFEDYEVA, N. P., Space Microbiology, *Mikrobiologiya*, vol. 30, No. 5 (1961).

E. Artificial Transfer of Organisms

1372. BRIGGS, M. H., Terrestrial and Extraterrestrial Life, *Spaceflight Today*, ed. by K. W. GATLAND, London: Illife (1963).
1373. GOLD, T., Cosmic Garbage, *Space Digest*, vol. 3, No. 5 (1960).
1374. SAGAN, C., Direct Contact Among Galactic Civilizations by Relativistic Interstellar Spaceflight, *Planetary and Space Sciences* (In press).

F. Sterilization of Space Vehicles

1375. CORDARO, J. T., *Studies on the Prevention of Contamination of Extraterrestrial Bodies. Bacteriologic Examination of Hermetically Sealed Electronic Components*, Report No. 62–18, United States Air Force School of Aerospace Medicine, Brooks AFB, Texas, November 1961.
1376. CORDARO, J. T., and WYNNE, W. S., Sterilization of Electronic Components of Spacecraft, *Transactions of the 7th Symposium of Ballistic Missile and Space Technology* (Air Force Academy, Colorado, August 13–16, 1962), vol. 1 (1962), pp. 73–82.
1377. DAVIES, R. W., and COMUNTZIS, M. G., The Sterilization of Space Vehicles to Prevent Extraterrestrial Biological Contamination, *International Astronautical Congress, Proceedings, 10th Congress, London, 1959*, Vienna: Springer-Verlag (1959), pp. 495–504.
1378. DAWSON, F. W., HEARN, H. J., and HOFFMAN, R. K., Virucidal Activity of the Beta-Propiolactone Vapor: I. Effect of Beta-Propiolactone Vapor on Venezuelan Equine Encephalomyelitis Virus, *Applied Microbiology*, vol. 7 (1959), pp. 199–201.
1379. DAWSON, F. W., JANSSEN, R. J., and HOFFMAN, R. K., Virucidal Activity of Beta-Propiolactone Vapor: II. Effect on the Etiological Agents of Smallpox, Yellow Fever, Psittacosis and Q Fever, *Applied Microbiology*, vol. 8 (1960), pp. 39–41.
1380. FEAZEL, C. E., and LANG, E. W., New Vapor Phase Disinfectant, *Soap and Chemical Specialties*, vol. 35 (1959), pp. 113–21.
1381. HAENNI, E. O., *et al.*, New Nonflammable Formulations for Sterilizing Sensitive Materials, *Industrial and Engineering Chemistry*, vol. 51 (1959), pp. 685–8.
1382. HOFFMAN, R. K., and WARSHOWSKY, B., Beta-Propiolactone Vapor as a Disinfectant, *Applied Microbiology*, vol. 6 (1958), pp. 358–62.
1383. KAYE, S., The Sterilizing Action of Gaseous Ethylene Oxide: III, *American Journal of Hygiene*, vol. 50 (1949), pp. 289–5.
1384. KAYE, S., The Use of Ethylene Oxide for the Sterilization of Hospital Equipment, *The Journal of Laboratory and Clinical Medicine*, vol. 35 (1950), pp. 823–8.
1385. KAYE, S., IRMINGER, H., and PHILLIPS, C. R., The Sterilization of Penicillin and Streptomycin by Ethylene Oxide, *The Journal of Laboratory and Clinical Medicine*, vol. 40 (1952), pp. 67–72.
1386. KAYE, S., and PHILLIPS, C. R., The Sterilizing Action of Gaseous Ethylene Oxide. IV, *American Journal of Hygiene*, vol. 50 (1949), pp. 296–306.
1387. PHILLIPS, C. R., The Sterilizing Action of Gaseous Ethylene Oxide: II, *American Journal of Hygiene*, vol. 50 (1949), pp. 280–8.
1388. PHILLIPS, C. R., Relative Resistance of Bacterial Spores and Vegetative Bacteria to Disinfectants, *Bacteriological Reviews*, vol. 16 (1952), pp. 135–43.
1389. PHILLIPS, C. R., Gaseous Sterilization, *Antiseptics, Disinfectants, Fungicides and Chemical and Physical Sterilization*, ed. by G. F. REDDISH, 2nd edition, Philadelphia: Lea and Febiger (1957), pp. 746–65.
1390. PHILLIPS, C. R., Gaseous Sterilization, *The Becton, Dickinson Lectures on Sterilization*, South Orange, New Jersey: Seton Hall University, College of Medicine and Dentistry (1959).
1391. PHILLIPS, C. R., Limitations of Standard Methods for Testing Disinfectants, *Sixth International Congress of Microbiological Standardization, Wiesbaden, Germany*, Berlin: H. Hoffman Verlag (1960), pp. 378–85.

1392. PHILLIPS, C. R., and HOFFMAN, R. K., Sterilization of Interplanetary Vehicles, *Science*, vol. 132 (1950), pp. 991–5.
1393. PHILLIPS, C. R., and KAYE, S., The Sterilizing Action of Gaseous Ethylene Oxide: I, *American Journal of Hygiene*, vol. 50 (1949), pp. 270–9.
1394. PHILLIPS, C. R., and WARSHOWSKY, B., Chemical Disinfectants, *Annual Review of Microbiology*, vol. 12 (1949), pp. 525–50.
1395. (See Ref. 75.)
1396. *Proceedings of Conference on Spacecraft Sterilization* (July 9, 1962, Washington, D.C.), TN D-1357, ed. by F. H. QUIMBY, National Aeronautics and Space Administration, Washington, D.C., 1962.
1397. REED, L. L., GIDNER, R. S., and DINGER, H. S., *Apparatus for Sterilizing Components of Interplanetary Craft*, Research and Development Division, American Sterilizer Co., Erie, Pennsylvania, 1962.
1398. SCHLEY, D. G., HOFFMAN, R. K., and PHILLIPS, C. R., Simple Improvised Chambers for Gas Sterilization With Ethylene Oxide, *Applied Microbiology*, vol. 8 (1960), pp. 15–19.
1399. SPINER, D. R., and HOFFMAN, R. K., Methods for Disinfecting Large Enclosures With β-Propiolactone Vapor, *Applied Microbiology*, vol. 8 (1960), pp. 152–5.
1400. Sterilization Study, *Aviation Week*, vol. 73, No. 25 (1960), p. 61.
1401. WOODWARD, M. F., and CLARK, A. B., Hospital Decontamination With Beta-Propiolactone, *United States Armed Forces Medical Journal*, vol. 11 (1960), pp. 459–63.

IV. LIFE IN THE UNIVERSE

A. Reviews

1402. AUSTIN, R. R., Extraterrestrial Life, *Spaceflight*, vol. 4 (1962), p. 176.
1403. BRIGGS, M. H., The Detection of Planets at Interstellar Distances, *Journal of the British Interplanetary Society*, vol. 17 (1959), pp. 59–60.
1404. CHAIKIN, G. L., A Transitional Hypothesis Concerning Life on Interstellar Bodies, *Popular Astronomy*, vol. 59 (1951), pp. 50–51.
1405. CHINCARINI, L., Studio sulle ecosfere delle stelle variabili, *Astronautica Acta*, vol. 8 (1959), pp. 81–86.
1406. CLARKE, A. C., Trouble in Aguila and Other Astronomical Brainstorms, *The Scientist Speculates*, ed. by I. J., GOOD et al., New York: Basic Books Inc. (1962), p. 235.
1407. CLEATOR, P. E., Extraterrestrial Life, *Journal of the British Interplanetary Society*, vol. 2 (1935), pp. 3–4.
1408. DOLLFUS, A., Recherches concernant la vie sur les planètes, *Space Research*, ed. by H. KALLMAN BIJL, Amsterdam: North-Holland Publishing Company (1960), pp. 1146–52.
1409. DRAKE, F. D., *Intelligent Life in Space*, New York: The Macmillan Company (1962)
1410. DRAWERT, F., Extraterrestrisches Leben, *Naturwissenschaftliche Rundschau*, vol. 14 (1961), pp. 68–70.
1411. EISELEY, L. C., Is Man Alone in Space? *Scientific American*, vol. 189, No. 1 (1953), pp. 80–82, 84–86.
1412. ENGLANDS, J., On the Possible Nature of Extra-Terrestrial Life, *Journal of Space Flight and the Rocket News Letter*, vol. 4, No. 2 (1952), pp. 1–3.
1413. FAUST, H., Zur Frage ausserirdischen Lebens, *Weltraumfahrt* (1958), pp. 23–24.
1414. FEAST, M. W., Spectra of AM Cen and GP Ori, and the Opacity in the Violet Region of N^2 Type Stars, *Mémoires de la Société Royale des Sciences de Liège*, vol. 15 (1955), pp. 280–6.
1415. FORNI, G., La coltivazione di vegetali in ambienti extra-terrestri, *Astronáutica*, vol. 6 (1958), pp. 84–86.
1416. GADOMSKI, J., Ekosfery, *Postepy Astronomii Krakow, Panstwowe Wydawnictwo Naukowe*, vol. 7 (1959), pp. 272–7.
1417. GADOMSKI, J., Koniec Swiata, *Urania, Organ Polskiego Towarzystwa Milosników Astronomii* (Krakow), vol. 30 (1959), pp. 409–18.

1418. GADOMSKI, J., W Poszukiwaniu Ozywionych Planet (IV), *Urania, Organ Polskiego Towarzystwa Milosników Astronomii* (Krakow), vol. 31 (1960), pp. 166–71.

1419. (See Ref. 1087.)

1420. HEUER, K., *Men of Other Planets*, New York: Pelligrini and Cudahy (1951).

1421. HOROWITZ, N. H., Is There Life on Other Planets, *Engineering and Science*, vol. 24 (March 1961), pp. 11–15.

1422. HOWELLS, W., The Evolution of 'Humans' on Other Planets, *Discovery*, vol. 22 (1961), pp. 237–41.

1423. HOYLE, F., and DARLINGTON, C. D. Is There Life Elsewhere in the Universe? *The Listener*, vol. 42 (1949), pp. 103–5.

1424. HUANG, S.-S., Occurrence of Life in the Universe, *American Scientist*, vol. 47 (1959), pp. 397–402.

1425. HUANG, S.-S., Problem of Life in the Universe and the Mode of Star Formation, *Publications of the Astronomical Society of the Pacific*, vol. 71 (1959), pp. 421–4.

1426. HUANG, S.-S., Life-Supporting Regions in the Vicinity of Binary Systems, *Publications of the Astronomical Society of the Pacific*, vol. 72 (1960), pp. 106–14.

1427. HUANG, S.-S., Sizes of Habitable Planets, *Publications of the Astronomical Society of the Pacific*, vol. 72 (1960), pp. 489–93.

1428. HUANG, S.-S., Life Outside the Solar System, *Scientific American*, vol. 202, No. 4 (1960), pp. 63–65.

1429. HUANG, S.-S., Some Astronomical Aspects of Life in the Universe, *Sky and Telescope*, vol. 21 (1961), pp. 312–16.

1430. HUANG, S.-S., and WILSON, R. H., *Astronomical Aspects of the Emergence of Intelligence*, Paper No. 63–48, Annual Meeting, New York City, New York, Institute of the Aerospace Sciences, January 21–23, 1963.

1431. IDLIS, G. M., Physikalische Bedingungen der Existenz des Lebens im Weltall, *Pokroky Matematiki, Fysiki a Astronomie* (Prague), (1959), pp. 594–606.

1432. IMSHENETSKII, A. A., Exobiology: A New Field of Scientific Research, *Vestnik Akademii Nauk SSSR*, vol. 32 (1962), pp. 58–63.

1433. JACKSON, F., and MOORE, P., *Life in the Universe*, New York: W. W. Norton and Co., Inc. (1962).

1434. JONES, H. S., *Life on Other Worlds*, London: English University Press, Ltd. (1952).

1435. KIND, S. S., Energy Fixation and Intelligent Life, *Journal of the British Interplanetary Society*, vol. 11 (1952), pp. 168–72.

1436. KIND, S. S., Speculations on Extraterrestrial Life, *Spaceflight*, vol. 1 (1958), pp. 288–90.

1437. KOURGANOFF, V., Astrobotanique, *l'Astronomie*, vol. 68 (1954), pp. 433–6.

1438. KUIPER, G. P., On the Origin of the Solar System, *Astrophysics*, 1st edition, ed. by J. A. HYNEK, New York: McGraw-Hill Book Co., Inc. (1951), pp. 357–424.

1439. LAFLEUR, L. J., Astrobiology, *Publications of the Astronomical Society of the Pacific*, vol. 143 (1946), pp. 1–8.

1440. La vie dans l'univers, *Ciel et Terre*, vol. 55 (1939), pp. 155–7.

1441. LEDERBERG, J., Exobiology, Experimental Approaches to Life Beyond the Earth, *Space Research*, ed. by H. KALLMAN BIJL, Amsterdam: North-Holland Publishing Company (1960), pp. 1153–70.

1442. LEDERBERG, J., The Search for Life Beyond the Earth, *New Scientist*, vol. 7 (1960), pp. 386–8.

1443. LEDERBERG, J., Exobiology: Approaches to Life Beyond the Earth, *Science*, vol. 132 (1960), pp. 393–400.

1444. LEONARD, F. C., Life on Other Worlds, *Popular Astronomy*, vol. 41 (1933), pp. 260–3.

1445. MARGARIA, R., On the Possible Existence of Intelligent Living Beings on Other Planets, *Rivista di Medicina Aeronáutica e Spaziale*, vol. 25 (1962), pp. 24–35.

1446. MAUDE, A. D., Life in the Sun, *The Scientist Speculates*, ed. by I. J. GOOD *et al.*, New York: Basic Books, Inc. (1962), pp. 240–7.

1447. MAXIM, H. P., *Life's Place in the Cosmos*, London: Appleton Century (1933).

1448. MCKELLAR, A., and RICHARDSON, E. H., Relative Spectral Gradients of Several

Cool Carbon Stars in the Blue and Violet Regions, *Mémoires de la Société Royale des Sciences de Liège*, vol. 15 (1955), pp. 256–75.

1449. MICZAIKA, C. R., Vergleich der Spektren von KO-Riesen kleiner und grosser Geschwindigkeit im Violetten, *Zeitschrift für Astrophysik*, vol. 27 (1950), pp. 1–14.

1450. MILLER, S. S., Extraterrestrial Life, *Lectures in Aerospace Medicine*, Brooks Air Force Base, Texas, USAF School of Aerospace Medicine (1962), pp. 277–98.

1451. MOTZ, L., *Extraterrestrial Intelligence and Stellar Evolution*, Paper No. 63–49, Thirty-first Annual Meeting of the Institute of the Aerospace Sciences, New York City, New York, January 21–23, 1963.

1452. NELSON. A. F., *Life and the Universe*, London: Staples Press, Ltd. (1953).

1453. NOVICK, A., Astrobiology Session, *Proceedings of Lunar and Planetary Exploration Colloquium*, vol. 2, No. 1, Aerospace Laboratories, North American Aviation, Inc., Downey, California (1959), pp. 2–14.

1454. NYE, E. R., The Possibility of Potentially Pathogenic Organisms Occurring on Another Planet, *Journal of the British Interplanetary Society*, vol. 9 (1950), pp. 62–63.

1455. (See Ref. 1152.)

1456. (See Ref. 1153.)

1457. (See Ref. 71.)

1458. (See Ref. 76.)

1459. RINGWOOD, A. E., On the Chemical Evolution and Densities of the Planets, *Geochimica et Cosmochimica Acta*, vol. 15 (1959), pp. 257–83.

1460. (See Ref. 1368.)

1461. SAVIC, P., The Origin of Rotation of a System and of Cellestial Bodies, *Bulletin de l'Académie Serbe des Sciences et des Arts*, vol. 8 (1960).

1462. SCHOPP, J. D., Determination of Upper Limits to the Abundance of Carbon 13 in Normal Red Giant Stars, *The Astronomical Journal*, vol. 59 (1954), pp. 192–3.

1463. SCHWARTZ, M., Ethics and Extraterrestrial Life, *Spaceflight*, vol. 5 (1963), p. 36.

1464. SEARLE, G. M., Are the Planets Habitable? *Publications of the Astronomical Society of the Pacific*, vol. 2 (1890), pp. 165–77.

1465. (See Ref. 87.)

1466. SHAPLEY, H., *Of Stars and Men*, Boston: Beacon Press (1958).

1467. SHAPLEY, H., Extraterrestrial Life, *Astronautics*, vol. 5, No. 4 (1960), pp. 32–33, 50–52.

1468. SHAPLEY, H., Concerning Life on Stellar Surfaces, *The Scientist Speculates*, ed. by I. J. GOOD *et al.*, New York: Basic Books, Inc. (1962), pp. 225–33.

1469. SHKLOVSKII, I. S., *Intelligent Life in the Universe*, San Francisco: Holden-Day, Inc. (1963).

1470. (See Ref. 529.)

1471. SLATER, A. E., Extraterrestrial Life, *Spaceflight*, vol. 5 (1963), p. 36.

1472. (See Ref. 1186.)

1473. STAPLEDON, O., Interplanetary Man? *Journal of the British Interplanetary Society*, vol. 7 (1948), pp. 213–33.

1474. STRUGHOLD, H., Advances in Astrobiology, *Proceedings of Lunar and Planetary Exploration Colloquium*, vol. 1, No. 6, Aerospace Laboratories, North American Aviation, Inc., Downey, California (1959), pp. 1–7.

1475. STRUGHOLD, H., An Introduction to Astrobiology, *Astronautics*, vol. 5, No. 12 (1960), pp. 20–21, 86–91.

1476. STRUGHOLD, H., Planetary Ecology (Astrobiology), *Lectures in Aerospace Medicine*, No. 5 (January 11–15, 1960), School of Aviation Medicine, USAF Aerospace Medical Center, Brooks Air Force Base, Texas (1960).

1477. STRUVE, O., Life on Other Worlds, *Sky and Telescope*, vol. 14 (1955), pp. 137–40, 146.

1478. SUSWOROW, N. I., Fragen der Astrobiologie auf dem internationalen Symposium über das Problem der Entstehung des Lebens auf der Erde, *Akademiia Nauk Kazakhskoi SSSR*, vol. 8 (1960), pp. 258–62.

1479. THORSON, W. R., Life on Other Worlds, *Griffith Observer*, vol. 17 (1953), pp. 116–19.

1480. TIKHOV, G. A., *Astrobotany*, Alma Ata: Verlag der Akademie der Wissenschaften, Kasach (1949).

1481. TIKHOV, G. A., Is Life Possible on Other Planets, *Journal of the British Interplanetary Society*, vol. 65 (1955), pp. 193–204.

1482. (See Ref. 1197.)

1483. UPHOF, J. C., Dynamics of the Distribution of Life in the Universe, *Scientia*, vol. 58 (1935), pp. 30–38.

1484. VALE, W. H., The Existence of Life in the Universe, *Journal of the Astronomical Society of Victoria, Melbourne*, vol. 13 (1960), pp. 39–43.

1485. WILLIAMSON, A. A., Speculations on the Cosmic Function of Life, *Journal of the Washington Academy of Sciences*, vol. 43 (1953), pp. 305–11.

1486. WILSKA, A. P., Factors to be Considered Before Entering Biospheres of Other Celestial Bodies, *International Biophysics Congress, Stockholm, July 31–August 4, 1961* (1961), p. 142.

1487. YOUNG, R. S., Basic Research in Astrobiology, *Advances in the Astronautical Sciences*, vol. 6 (1961), pp. 317–27.

1488. YOUNGHUSBAND, F. E., *Life in the Stars*, New York: Dutton and Co., Inc. (1928).

1489. YOUNGHUSBAND, F. E., *The Living Universe*, New York: Dutton and Co., Inc. (1933).

B. Incidence of Planets

1490. ALFVÉN, H., Non-Solar Planets and the Origin of the Solar System, *Nature*, vol. 152 (1943), p. 721.

1491. ALPHER, R. A., and HERMAN, C., Theory of the Origin and Relative Abundance Distribution of the Elements, *Reviews of Modern Physics*, vol. 22 (1950), pp. 153–212.

1492. BANERJI, A. C., Non-Solar Planetary Systems, *Nature*, vol. 153 (1944), p. 779.

1493. (See Ref. 1403.)

1494. BRIGGS, M. H., Origin of the Solar System, *Nature*, vol. 187 (1960), pp. 1102–3.

1495. DEYCH, A. N., 61 Lebyedya kak troinaya systema, *Priroda*, vol. 5–6 (1944), p. 99.

1496. DRAKE, F. D., A New Approach to Differential Astrometry, *The Astronautical Journal* (In press).

1497. DUNHAM, T., JR., Knowledge of the Planets in 1938, *Publications of the Astronomical Society of the Pacific*, vol. 51 (1939), pp. 253–73.

1498. GADOMSKI, J., Die Sternokosphären im Radius von 17 Lichtjahren um die Sonne, *Report of the Polish Amateur Astronomical Society*, No. 1 (1958), p. 10.

1499. GADOMSKI, J., W Poszukiwaniu Ozywionych Planet, *Urania, Organ Polskiego Towarzystwa Milosników Astronomii* (Krakow), vol. 30 (1959), pp. 41–45, 125–30, 316–19.

1500. GADOMSKI, J., Fünf Arten von okosphärischen Planeten, *Report of the Polish Amateur Astronomical Society*, No. 2 (1959).

1501. GOLDBERG, L., and MULLER, E. A., Carbon Monoxide in the Sun, *The Astrophysical Journal*, vol. 118 (1953), pp. 397–411.

1502. HOLMBERG, E., Invisible Companions of Parallax Stars Revealed by Means of Modern Trigonometric Parallax Observations, *Lund, Universitet Observatoriet Meddelanden*, Series 2, No. 92 (1938).

1503. HUANG, S.-S., Star Formation, *Astronomical Society of the Pacific Leaflets*, vol. 7, No. 340 (1957).

1504. HUNTER, A., Non-Solar Planets, *Nature*, vol. 152 (1943), pp. 66–67.

1505. JEANS, J., Non-Solar Planetary Systems, *Nature*, vol. 152 (1943), p. 721.

1506. PARIISKII, N. W., Neue Versuche zur Erklärung der Entstehung des Sonnen-Systems, *Astronomicheskii Zhurnal*, vol. 16 (1939), pp. 77–83.

1507. REUYL, D., and HOLMBERG, E., On the Existence of a Third Component in the System 70 Ophiuchi, *The Astrophysical Journal*, vol. 97 (1943), pp. 41–45.

1508. REYN, N., and PARIISKII, N. N., Katastroficheskiye gipotezy proiskhodzheniya solenechony sistemy, *Uspekhi Astronomicheskikh Nauk*, vol. 2, (1941), p. 137.

1509. SEN, H. K., More Planetary Systems in the Universe, *Science and Culture (Calcutta)*, vol. 9 (1943), p. 131.
1510. STRAND, K. A., 61 Cygni as a Triple System, *Publications of the Astronomical Society of the Pacific*, vol. 55 (1943), pp. 29–32.
1511. STRAND, K. A., The Orbital Motion of 61 Cygni, *Proceedings of the American Philosophical Society*, vol. 86 (1943), pp. 364–7.
1512. TRANSEAU, E. N., The Accumulation of Energy by Planets, *The Ohio Journal of Science*, vol. 26 (1926), pp. 1–10.

                                C.   Origin of Planets

1513. ALFVÉN, H., *On the Origin of the Solar System*, Oxford: Clarendon Press (1954).
1514. ALFVÉN, H., On the Mass Distribution in the Solar System, *The Astrophysical Journal*, vol. 136 (1962), pp. 1005–15.
1515. ALFVÉN, H., On the Early History of the Sun and the Formation of the Solar System, *The Astrophysical Journal* (In press).
1516. ALFVÉN, H., and WILCOX, J. M., On the Origin of the Satellites and Planets, *The Astrophysical Journal*, vol. 136 (1962), pp. 1016–22.
1517. CAMERON, A. G. W., Origin of Anomalous Abundances of the Elements in Giant Stars, *The Astrophysical Journal*, vol. 121 (1955), pp. 144–60.
1518. CAMERON, A. G. W., The Formation of the Sun and Planets, *Icarus*, vol. 1 (1962), pp. 13–69.
1519. (See Ref. 25.)
1520. DAUVILLIER, A., *L'Origine des Planètes, Essai de Cosmogonie*, Paris: Presses Universitaires de France (1956).
1521. DAVIS, D. N., SiH in the Sun and Late-Type Stars, *Proceedings of the Astronomical Society of the Pacific*, vol. 52 (1940), p. 280.
1522. DOUGLAS, A. V., Origin of the Planets, *The Journal of the Royal Astronomical Society of Canada*, vol. 46 (1952), pp. 105–9.
1523. (See Ref. 44.)
1524. HOYLE, F., On the Origin of the Solar Nebula, *Quarterly Journal of the Royal Astronomical Society*, vol. 1 (1960), pp. 28–55.
1525. KUIPER, G. P., Need for Accurate Data on Cosmic Abundance of the Elements Cited, *Chemical and Engineering News*, vol. 30 (1952), pp. 4949–50.
1526. LEVIN, B. J., Origin of the Solar System, *New Scientist* (February 8, 1962), pp. 323–5.
1527. LYTTLETON, R. A., The Origin of the Solar System, *Monthly Notices of the Royal Astronomical Society*, vol. 96 (1936), pp. 559–68.
1528. MCCREA, W. H., The Origin of the Solar System, *Proceedings of the Royal Society (London)*, vol. 256 (1960), pp. 245–66.
1529. MOULTON, F. R., On the Evolution of the Solar System, *The Astrophysical Journal*, vol. 22 (1905), pp. 165–81.
1530. RUSSELL, H. N., *Solar System and Its Origin*, New York: The Macmillan Co. (1935).
1531. SMART, W. M., *Origin of the Earth*, Baltimore, Maryland: Penguin Books, Inc. (1959).
1532. SPITZER, L., JR., The Dissipation of Planetary Filaments, *The Astrophysical Journal*, vol. 90 (1939), pp. 675–88.
1533. STRUVE, O., McCrea's Theory of the Solar System's Origin, *Sky and Telescope*, vol. 19 (1960), pp. 154–6.
1534. UREY, H. C., Evidence Regarding the Origin of the Earth, *Geochimica et Cosmochimica Acta*, vol. 26 (1962), pp. 1–13.
1535. UREY, H. C., The Origin and Evolution of the Solar System, *Space Science*, New York: John Wiley and Sons, Inc. (1963), pp. 123–68.
1536. VON WEIZACKER, C. F., Über die Entstehung des Planetensystems, *Astronomicheskii Zhurnal*, vol. 22 (1944), pp. 319–55.
1537. WEIZSACKER, C., Über Elementum, *Physikalische Zeitschrift*, vol. 39 (1938), pp. 633–46.
1538. WOOLFSON, M. M., Origin of the Solar System, *Nature*, vol. 187 (1960), pp. 47–48.

D.   Communication Across Interstellar Distances

1539. ASCHER, R., and ASCHER, M., Interstellar Communication and Human Evolution, *Nature*, vol. 193 (1962), pp. 940–1.

1540. BAR-HILLEL, Y., The Present Status of Automatic Translation of Languages, *Advances in Computers*, vol. 1, New York: Academic Press, Inc. (1960), pp. 92–163.

1541. BOEHM, G. A. W., Are We Being Hailed From Interstellar Space? *Fortune*, vol. 63, No. 3 (1961), pp. 144–9, 193–4.

1542. BRACEWELL, R. N., Communications from Superior Galactic Communities, *Nature*, vol. 186 (1960), pp. 670–1.

1543. BRACEWELL, R. N., Radio Signals From Other Planets, *Proceedings of the IRE*, vol. 50 (1962), p. 214.

1544. BRIGGS, M. H., Other Astronomers in the Universe? *Southern Stars* (New Zealand), vol. 18 (1960), pp. 147–51.

1545. BRIGGS, M. H., Superior Galactic Communities, *Spaceflight*, vol. 3 (1961), pp. 109–10.

1546. BUDDEN, K. G., and YATES, G. G., A Search for Radio Echoes of Long Delay, *Journal of Atmospheric and Terrestrial Physics*, vol. 2 (1952), pp. 272–81.

1547. BUTLER, C. P., The Light of the Atom Bomb, *Science*, vol. 138 (1962), pp. 483–9.

1548. COCCONI, G., and MORRISON, P., Searching for Interstellar Communication, *Nature*, vol. 184 (1959), pp. 844–6.

1549. DRAKE, F. D., Radio Astronomy Receivers – I, *Sky and Telescope*, vol. 19 (1959), 26–28.

1550. DRAKE, F. D., Radio Astronomy Receivers – II, *Sky and Telescope*, vol. 19 (1959), pp. 87–89.

1551. DRAKE, F. D., How Can We Detect Radio Transmissions From Distant Planetary Systems? *Sky and Telescope*, vol. 19 (1960), pp. 140–3.

1552. DRAKE, F. D., Project Ozma, *Physics Today*, vol. 14, No. 4 (1961), pp. 40–46.

1553. (See Ref. 1409.)

1554. DRAKE, F. D., Project Ozma, *McGraw-Hill Yearbook of Science and Technology*, 1961, New York: McGraw-Hill Book Co., Inc. (1962), p. 384.

1555. DYSON, F. J., Search for Artificial Stellar Sources of Infrared Radiation, *Science*, vol. 131 (1960), pp. 1667–8.

1556. DYSON, F. J., MADDOX, J., ANDERSON, P., and SLOANE, E. A., Artificial Biosphere (Letters), *Science*, vol. 132 (1960), pp. 250–3.

1557. GOLOMB, S. W., Extraterrestrial Linguistics, *Astronautics*, vol. 6, No. 5 (1961), pp. 46–47, 96.

1558. HANDELSMAN, M., *Considerations on Communications with Intelligent Life in Outer Space*, IRE Paper 06-05/003-62, 1962 Western Electronic Show and Convention, Los Angeles, California, August 21–24, 1962.

1559. HOGBEN, L., Astraglossa or First Steps in Celestial Syntax, *Journal of the British Interplanetary Society*, vol. 11 (1952), pp. 258–74.

1560. *Interstellar Communication*, ed. by A. G. W. CAMERON, New York: W. A. Benjamin, Inc. (1963).

1561. JACKSON, C. D., and HOHMANN, R. E., *An Historic Report on Life in Space: Tesla, Marconi, Todd*, ARS Paper No. P-2730-62, American Rocket Society 17th Annual Meeting, Los Angeles, California, November 13–18, 1962.

1562. MACGOWAN, R. A., On the Possibilities of the Existence of Extraterrestrial Intelligence, *Advances in Space Science and Technology*, vol. 4, ed. by F. I. ORDWAY, New York: Academic Press, Inc. (1962), pp. 39–110.

1563. MACVEY, J., Alone in the Universe? *Spaceflight*, vol. 4 (1962), pp. 125–7.

1564. McKELLAR, A., The C^{12} to C^{13} Abundance Ratio in Stellar Atmospheres, *Publications of the Astronomical Society of the Pacific*, vol. 62 (1950), pp. 110–2.

1565. MILLER, E. C., Ethics and Space Travel, (Letter) *Spaceflight*, vol. 4 (1962), p. 139.

1566. MINSKY, M., Steps Toward Artificial Intelligence, *Proceedings of the Institute of Radio Engineers*, vol. 49 (1961), pp. 8–30.

1567. (See Ref. 1451.)

1568. OLIVER, B. M., Radio Search for Distant Races, *International Science and Technology,* vol. 1, No. 10 (1962), pp. 55–60, 96.
1569. (See Ref. 1374.)
1570. (See Ref. 89.)
1571. SLATER, A. E., The Probability of Intelligent Life Evolving on a Planet, *Proceedings of the 8th International Astronautical Congress, Barcelona, 1957,* Vienna: Springer-Verlag (1958), pp. 395–402.
1572. SWEITZER, D. I., *Biological and Artificial Intelligence,* Literature Search No. 254, Jet Propulsion Laboratory, Pasadena, California, 1960.
1573. VON HOERNER, S., The Search for Signals From Other Civilizations, *Science,* vol. 134 (1961), pp. 1839–43.
1574. UREY, H. C., Origin of the Earth, *Planet Earth,* New York: Simon and Schuster, Inc. (1950).